795 AD

S0-BYR-685

WITHDRAWN

# A GENTLEMAN
## OF THE PRESS

John Bayne Maclean in his middle years. Portrait by Moffett

# A GENTLEMAN
## OF THE PRESS

BY FLOYD S. CHALMERS

DOUBLEDAY CANADA LIMITED, TORONTO
DOUBLEDAY & COMPANY, INC.
GARDEN CITY, NEW YORK
1969

226203

PN
4913
m25
C5
1969

*Library of Congress Catalog Card Number 69–12204*
*Copyright © 1969 by Floyd S. Chalmers*
  *All Rights Reserved*
*Printed in the United States of America*
  *First Edition*

# CONTENTS

|  |  |  |
|---|---|---|
| | List of Illustrations | v |
| | Foreword | vii |
| I. | Son of the Manse | 1 |
| II. | Busy Young Reporter | 18 |
| III. | The First Publication | 29 |
| IV. | Man of Many Jobs | 42 |
| V. | My Friend, Sir John A. | 55 |
| VI. | On the Move | 63 |
| VII. | Officer Commanding | 79 |
| VIII. | Dear Hugh, Dear J.B. | 91 |
| IX. | The Girl He Stole from Munsey | 100 |
| X. | Life Begins at Forty | 110 |
| XI. | Collector of People | 119 |
| XII. | New Faces | 131 |
| XIII. | A Magazine Is Born | 144 |
| XIV. | Enter, the Financial Post | 154 |
| XV. | No Sausage Factory | 165 |
| XVI. | The Colonel Builds | 175 |
| XVII. | A Brilliant New Editor | 186 |
| XVIII. | The War That Jumped the Gun | 196 |
| XIX. | Tragedy in the Family | 214 |
| XX. | The Joys of Battle | 222 |
| XXI. | Battling the Bolshevists | 230 |
| XXII. | The Colonel and His Editors | 242 |
| XXIII. | Friends, Regal and Otherwise | 255 |
| XXIV. | Sundry Prime Ministers | 265 |
| XXV. | More Fights with Ottawa | 279 |

XXVI. Another Fighting Colonel          292
XXVII. Pioneer Village                   303
XXVIII. Sharing the Wealth               311
XXIX. The Social Niceties                324
XXX. A Kindly Man                        336
XXXI. Lovable Giant                      342
      Acknowledgments                    347
      Appendix                           350
      Index                              354

# LIST OF ILLUSTRATIONS

Frontispiece—John Bayne Maclean

1. Reverend Andrew Maclean
2. Reverend John Bayne
3. Mrs. Andrew Maclean and sons
4. Toronto in the 1880s
5. The *Canadian Grocer*
6. "We Never Sleep"
7. Letter accepting post of commercial editor of the *Empire*
8. *Hardware*
9. As a lieutenant in the 10th Royal Grenadiers
10. In Highland regalia
11. Officers of the Duke of York's Royal Canadian Hussars
12. In full-dress uniform of the Duke of York's Hussars
13. First mailing room at the Maclean Company
14. The first pressroom
15. Forerunner of *Maclean's Magazine*
16. *Busy Man's Magazine*
17. Table of Contents—*Busy Man's Magazine*
18. *Maclean's,* August 1916
19. "Why We Are Losing the War"
20. Maclean Company's first banquet, 1904
21. University Avenue and Dundas Street
22. Original cottage
23. Executive and editorial headquarters
24. Colonel's office
25. Anna Slade Maclean
26. At home
27. No. 13 Queen's Park Crescent
28. 3 Austin Terrace
29. John Bayne Maclean, Alex P. Moore, Frank A. Munsey
30. The Colonel's Carlsbad
31. Connie Mack, April 1916
32. Lady Williams-Taylor
33. "El Mirasol"
34. Horace T. Hunter, John Bayne Maclean, H. Victor Tyrrell
35. "That beautiful hat"
36. Sod-turning ceremony

37. John Bayne Maclean's birth-
    place
38. After renovation
39. In grateful appreciation
40. "King or Chaos"

41. Annual Christmas party
42. Company picnic
43. Maclean-Hunter building
44. Printing plant in Willowdale
45. John Bayne Maclean

# FOREWORD

JOHN BAYNE MACLEAN was one of the world's great publisher-journalists of his generation. He laid the foundations of a widely spread publishing empire. He was very individualistic, although his eccentricities were mild compared to those of some of his contemporaries—Northcliffe, Hearst, McCormick, for example. News was his main passion but he also enjoyed a ding-dong editorial battle. He knew little about corporate management and never understood a balance sheet or a profit and loss statement.

He ventured boldly into new journalistic fields where failure seemed certain—at least in Canada—and yet he achieved dramatic success.

This is the sort of man this book is about.

I was introduced to him in 1920, a year after joining his payroll as a very junior reporter on *The Financial Post*. It wasn't until a staff picnic the next spring that I met him. The theme of his conversation at our first meeting stays vividly in mind—not surprisingly, as it was to be repeated to the point of monotony on dozens of occasions later on.

"You must be related to Chalmers, the great churchman of Scotland," he declared hopefully. I said no, I didn't think so. He went on, "I was brought up among his books; my father was a protégé of his and admired him very much."

I have been extremely dilatory about tracing my relationship to Dr. Chalmers, but that casual first encounter did reveal certain Maclean characteristics which were constantly confirmed over the years. He had an immediate interest in people—all kinds, conditions, ages. Instead of the mechanical "How d'you do," he quite unconsciously adopted his own style of greetings with a comment or question individually pertinent—and usually genealogical in character—even if, as in my case, often farfetched. He believed in bloodlines—whether in humans or animals. And he believed that everyone had something unique in his experience that would make a good conversational gambit. He always sought for it. Thus he learned about people—and picked up news or gossip.

The questing spirit, supported by hard work, could achieve success for any man, according to John Bayne Maclean—and, indeed, his own record proved it. In 1887, at the age of twenty-five, he stepped forth from Toronto's newspaper reporting field and, with an initial investment of $3000, founded a business paper and magazine publishing house that would eventually add new dimensions to Canadian and world journalism. Although the present value of the company, now active in six countries, is roughly $65,000,000, Maclean's own share of the profits was modest. Long before his death in 1950 he sold the business to employees at a fraction of its potential worth, and his will disposed of an estate of slightly more than a million dollars. It was as though, with the death of his son, he adopted two or three dozen young men as his "children." He often called them just that.

He would be pleased with his organization's growth, but I doubt if he would be surprised. He had set the pattern of prudent expenditure and bold investment, which he valued principally because it enabled expansion of services and at the same time protected editorial independence. Constant growth in a setting of complete freedom from outside pressures were the goals he pursued; the matter of a private fortune was incidental and quite secondary.

He practiced and preached responsibility and self-discipline. This explained his devotion to the militia, Canada's volunteer peacetime army operating in small local units. He survived twenty years of parades, drills and patient dedication before he achieved the cherished dream of a top regimental command. From that moment John Bayne Maclean would be known to all friends and associates, at home or abroad, as the "Colonel."

He thrived on work, especially in the only career he ever aspired to—that of reporter. In his newspaper days he had discovered the importance of sources; for the rest of his life he made it a rule to seek out "the people who made the news"—and that involved travel routines—notably Palm Beach and Europe—which were to become as fixed as the seasons.

Thus his circle of acquaintance constantly widened and he developed amazing expertise in the art of people-collecting. Occasionally, on the basis of what he considered bad manners, incivility or worse, a new name on his roster would be fated for a black mark against it, and of the almost indelible kind. That unfortunate distinction awaited a brash young reporter named Churchill who visited Canada in 1900 to give firsthand accounts of the South African War. It took more than twenty years of world history, plus personal contact with the Churchill family, before Maclean was willing to modify his opinion.

Personal interests and distinguished friendships expanded, notably with the Colonel's marriage to a handsome Bostonian of impeccable ancestry, Anna Denison Slade. Their romance came swiftly into bloom following an introduction by a mutual friend, Frank A. Munsey, the well-known American publisher, who had actually hoped to marry her himself as soon as he found the time to propose. Munsey accepted the defeat, remained a lonely bachelor, continued to make a vast fortune and many enemies, yet never lost his status as the Colonel's dearest comrade.

That paradoxical situation was one of many in the record of John Bayne Maclean. He successfully launched periodicals and enlarged the organization to produce them, despite being a lifelong innocent where finance, administration and bookkeeping were concerned. Such boring matters could be left to his associates—and he had early demonstrated an aptitude for picking the right men, such as Horace T. Hunter, a brilliant executive. Thus freed from management problems, the Colonel could be the complete journalist. He turned out millions of words, yet never achieved true skill, let alone literary distinction. He tried hard, sometimes doing twenty revisions on a single feature, but once in print the result could strike the average reader as a veritable "mystery story," with no clues, no denouement, sometimes with no apparent reason for being. Most of these self-assignments he took on from a sense of public duty; he was convinced he had a vocation to expose any weakness, dishonesty or injustice threatening the world, the nation or his fellow citizens. Plotting racketeers were a constant menace; the Colonel saw them behind every bush, but seldom in sufficiently strong light for full identification; anyway, as any informed person must realize, international intriguers always operated as a "group."

Many times his exposés and campaigns resulted in abrupt changes of policy by governmental leaders. He loved a good fight in print and was never concerned as to whether it was a popular one or not.

The Colonel gave much warm support to party chiefs, only to reverse his stand when he saw evidence of evil influences in the background. Three of Canada's Prime Ministers in turn—Meighen, Bennett, King—were to suffer his rapid change of heart. At one point a wrathy, frustrated Bennett threatened to "lock Maclean up if necessary."

But violent reaction of that kind was quite incomprehensible to most of the Colonel's acquaintances. To them he was a kindly person, calm in manner and quiet in speech, delighted to stop and chat, ready with questions and eagerly attentive to the answers. Even his frequent pin-pricking criticism of the members of his staff was done with a certain gentle urbanity. He did, of course, exasperate his editors, as I can testify. Yet in that area he was merely pursuing another avowed goal, i.e. the constant training of his young men and improvement of their publications. All else became subservient to this objective, or, more precisely, was made to serve it. Instead of dismissing the rigors of his early life, he kept them in full view as important experiences, believing they formed the essential discipline for success. And perhaps he was right.

John Bayne Maclean was no ordinary man, and the attempt to recreate him through the medium of printer's ink has been formidable. Indeed, I confess I have almost heard that familiar voice expressing certain objections . . . "Chalmers, you have been most unfair to Munsey" . . . or, still more unsettling, "All it needs is complete rewriting after Chapter IV."

Toronto                                                          F.S.C.
1968

# A GENTLEMAN
## OF THE PRESS

# CHAPTER I

## *SON OF THE MANSE*

"In men and women the first essential is good
breeding, good stock."
*J. B. Maclean,* 1934

HE WAS BORN in a manse, son of a clergyman, and all his life he
thanked the Good Lord for this initial benefaction. The place was
tucked away in the remote backwoods, and the house, square, two-
storied under a steeply sloping roof, and built of sawn boards
bereft of any finish except weathering, had an appearance more forbidding than inviting. The domestic amenities numbered just the three
essentials, viz. the pump a few yards from the doorway, the tiny
outhouse striving for modesty among a clump of shrubbery around
toward the other side, and the vast kitchen stove demanding ceaseless
stoking for its delivery of food and warmth and nose-crinkling wood
smoke. The only mental diversion ready to hand was represented
in two bookshelves of ecclesiastical works. But such circumstances
bothered him not at all, especially when he viewed the scene from
an ampler atmosphere fifty years later.

That little manse in the Canadian forest, he was always to declare,
had predetermined the whole course of his life. As one exposed early
to the stern doctrine of Presbyterian predestination, he would probably
have accepted with perfect calmness the famous discovery of Nietzsche:
"Our destiny exercises its influence over us even when, as yet, we
have not learned its nature; it is our future that lays down the law
of our today."

One might almost say that John Bayne Maclean's future was shaped
by a certain incident in the Orkneys off the northerly tip of Scotland
about thirty years before his birth. It happened that a very personable
and able minister, poor yet a descendant of an old Ross-shire family
and a close relative of a belted earl, had hoped to be installed as

assistant and successor to the aging incumbent of the pulpit of Shapinsay, one of the outer islands. As a substitute preacher on several occasions, he had sensed an immediate rapport between himself and the congregation; now, with the news that all leading families in the church had signed a petition for his appointment, the Reverend John Bayne had full confidence in the outcome. But Lord Dundas, parish patron and thus final arbiter, showed his dour, unyielding character by replying to the members' appeal with a tersely worded note, ending . . . "Mr. Bayne is a very worthy young minister. I have, however, a rule in these matters from which I cannot depart. Your obedient servant, Dundas." Whatever the "rule" was it did not permit his approval of the congregation's choice.

Dejected, and longing to feel a fresher, happier climate around him, Bayne left on a visit to Canada West (now the Province of Ontario), fully intending to return to Scotland within a few months. Somehow his sailing date kept being postponed as he went the rounds of Presbyterian groups, discovering old friends and making new ones, and in general savoring the confident atmosphere of a New Land. It was not surprising, therefore, that eventually, as his biographer expressed it years later, "God gave him to Canada," and more precisely to Knox Church in Galt, where he was inducted in 1835.

Through the years of devoted leadership that followed, the Reverend Bayne was to win the unswerving love and loyalty of his "Free Kirk" supporters, plus the respect of the whole community of Waterloo and Wellington Counties. People took naturally to the handsome bachelor. They admired his capacity to judge and handle a horse and his pipe-smoking put them at ease—though they agreed, often over their own nips of an evening, that it was "a guid thing" for a minister to be "teetotal" (the queer new word, recently imported from England).

Bayne's inbuilt sense of humor needed no alcoholic stimulant. Once at a synod meeting that went on endlessly, with no move by the Chair to call for a vote on the two resolutions presented, the man from Galt finally rose. "Moderator," he said, relaxed and smiling, "I like neither of the motions now before the house, and hardly know which to vote for. Indeed, I feel like an ass between two bundles of hay, or rather, and to save my own reputation, like a bundle of hay between two asses."

In 1856 Dr. Bayne decided to make a leisurely visit to Scotland—

and in this too, there is evidence of the hand of destiny on an unborn Maclean. Before leaving, he received a delegation of settlers from West Puslinch, eight or ten miles east of Galt, who asked if he would be so kind as to try to find a young, dedicated minister "with the Gaelic" who could take charge of their new church at the crossroads. Previously West Puslinch farmers and storekeepers had gone to services at East Puslinch, several miles away. But with the spread of settlement and burgeoning of families, it had been necessary for the West to organize its own place of worship. Everything had been in readiness for several years, except for the disheartening fact that no minister fluent in the ancient tongue of the Highlands (still in daily use in the Puslinches) had yet been found.

Dr. Bayne accepted the commission with alacrity. On arrival in Edinburgh he wrote to his friend, the Reverend John Bonar, D.D., distinguished theological professor and at that time Convener of the Colonial Committee of the Free Church, requesting any suggestions on behalf of those good souls, leaderless and languishing, in Canada West. Bonar took immediate action with a letter to one of his most promising former students, the Reverend Andrew Maclean, a native of Moy, Inverness, born and brought up with the Gaelic, sound as to doctrine, now thirty-six and still unmarried.

There must have been a quick and enthusiastic reply, for, on August 26, 1856, Bayne dispatched to the unseen candidate's address in the Hebrides a long, explanatory description of the vacant pastoral post, "having heard from Mr. Bonar of your willingness to go out to Canada." In his barely decipherable hand he gives information concerning the geography and church history of the Puslinches, mentions that several worthy men in the West congregation would help a new minister get settled, and "the stipend offered is £150 yearly, equal to £120 sterling and I believe might be depended upon." As to "outfit" (special expenses of the trip), he is sure that the usual allowance accorded to missionaries would be forthcoming. Material prosperity in Canada is very great, he declares. Poverty is almost unknown, the church has obtained a firm footing and will increase in her numbers and service, "and no faithful minister need think he is going from a higher to an inferior field of usefulness—but very much the reverse—in going from Scotland to Canada."

Two months later Dr. Bayne and the Reverend Andrew Maclean were to be traveling companions on the long journey, via New York, to that missionary goal: an empty pulpit in a quiet corner of a sparsely settled land.

Everywhere the eye turned in Canada West, it encountered something new and different. Instead of the somber majesty of the Highlands wreathed in low clouds or mist, this was a world of well-defined color; a smiting blue arc of sky to contrast with the whiteness of the snow, or in Maytime with the sudden, sharp greens as the thick forests of maple, oak, beech leafed out, or, come October, to form a backdrop for the riotous crimsons and golds interspersed with the black-green of cedar. The landscape had an intimacy that could put a man at ease: the pleasant dips and swells of the earth's surface were close by, a wooded mound rising gently behind a new barn, or a pretty gully falling away within a stone's throw of a farmer's front door. Plenty of pure water filled the creeks and ponds or awaited the well-digger. Indeed, here, at the remote little hamlet marking "the corners," it seemed as if God had specially prepared a new environment, clean, ready, companionable—ideal for a stranger in a strange land.

But the term "stranger" could hardly apply to a Scotsman however recently arrived, when he found himself in a parish numbering one hundred and eleven ex-Highlanders with their families—McBeans, Stewarts, Gilchrists and others from the ancient clans. He had even discovered that on one of Puslinch Township's longest roads every farmhouse on either side belonged to people of his own name. It didn't matter how the spelling changed, as change it did—Maclean, M'Lean, MacLean, McLean, plus Maclane and Maclain in similar variations; what warmed his heart toward them and the others was the immediate sense of fellowship springing from a common heritage. The old ways of the glens and hills of home had not been lost, and when the young minister ended an afternoon visit with *"Beannachd leat!"*—the Gaelic farewell that carried an overtone of blessing—there were often tears and smiles simultaneously on the faces of the group clustered in the doorway. Another link with the past, small but significant, had been established with the renaming of the village (known as Fraserville in its early days) after Crieff, that picturesque town in the Highlands, situated midway between the city of Perth on the east and Loch Earn to the west.

The eager missionary had much to be thankful for. God had been kind in sending him to serve among people of his own breed. And

God had placed him near two dear friends and fellow toilers in the vineyard: Galt's John Bayne, for whom affection and respect deepened every day; and, about twenty miles to the north, in the church at Elora, the Reverend James Middlemiss, a constant companion during student years in Edinburgh.

Maclean and Middlemiss had indeed seen much together. They had first met in 1842 at the Edinburgh Normal School. Like a number of his classmates, Andrew had been selected, and sponsored as to tuition fees, etc., by the educational committee of the Presbyterian General Assembly; his good character and sound though modest upbringing as the son of Evan and Katharine (Fraser) Maclean had been vouched for by the local minister at Moy.

Under the guidance of his new fellow student, Middlemiss, a few years older and with some university work behind him, a broader world began to open. In place of his former teen-aged dreaming of an Army career, Andrew found himself sharing his friend's hope for a future in the pulpit, to which end he diligently pursued the essential subjects of Latin and Greek under the other man's tutoring. Day and night they were together, talking, arguing, exchanging doctrinal interpretations, analyzing their intimate revelations of God and His mysterious ways. Every Saturday evening they attended the Normal School's meeting for Bible discussion and prayer; another night was given over to the students' Mutual Improvement Society which engaged in debates on such exciting topics as church patronage or total abstinence. When the latter subject had its airing, all present were volubly "in favor"; but what happened at one annual supper of the Society had to be pardoned on the grounds of local custom.

The hotelkeeper in charge of the menu included, quite naturally in the manner of a Scottish banquet, a well-laced cup; the members, thrifty Scots to a man, partook of everything set before them, and very soon the atmosphere became remarkably relaxed, with jests and recitations spontaneously erupting around the table. Some days afterward a certain unfortunate unable to attend reported he had heard on good authority that Andrew Maclean had been guilty of "impropriety" with his contribution of a song. Unfortunately from the standpoint of posterity—there was no clue as to Andrew's choice! Was the song about lad and lass in the mountain pass . . . or a boy from Moy contriving a ploy . . . or just another rousing to-arms against the "damned Campbells"—the clan that made deals with the English? We'll never know.

But in the main, life for these young men was a serious, dedicated business. In 1843, when the Presbyterians went through their great "Disruption," splitting into two groups—one willing to accept the new State Church concept with its over-all power, the other stoutly devoted to Free Church principles—Maclean, Middlemiss and most of the Normal students and staff moved out of their school and thus away from the control of the official Kirk Session of the city. With old-time Celtic determination they organized their own Free Church Normal School which was to function successfully for many years.

After graduation Maclean took up his role as teacher, serving in several Highland communities; by careful saving over these years he was able to fulfill his dream of returning to Edinburgh—first to take his Arts course at the university, and next to move on to Free Church College for his Theology. Then in swift succession came ordination and appointment to the church in the Hebrides, where after less than a year's tenure he was to receive and act upon the "call" to Canada.

Now, here in Ontario's Wellington County, he found he was seldom without bookings ahead as a visitor to two or three other pulpits, due to his facility in both Gaelic and English. Neither Middlemiss to the north nor Bayne closer by in Galt could speak the ancient tongue, and though they visited Crieff frequently and participated in the service, it remained for the church's own minister to deliver the regular Sunday sermons. When Andrew was able to accept their pressing invitations to join with or substitute for them, they quickly learned to have full confidence in his capacity with their larger congregations.

Maclean had been early marked as one of the dependables for duties at synods, Presbyterials or other special occasions—even willing to meet the expenses out of his own pocket, since no official fund for travel existed at that time. And such assignments could be arduous. "Those were the days when there was no railway nearer than Galt," Middlemiss wrote later in his reminiscences, "and many a weary corduroy road" had to be covered on or behind a horse, whether to reach the Great Western's station in that town or to attend meetings at points farther still without benefit of train service.

A year afer his arrival in Canada Maclean was one of several clergy chosen to officiate at the ordination and induction of a new minister in Owen Sound. The group had to assemble first in Toronto, there board the train for Collingwood, then transfer to a boat for the slow passage across Nottawasaga Bay, around the point of land and into the Sound; and of course at the conclusion of the solemn ceremony the visitors faced the same travel plan in reverse. By the time Maclean saw his backwoods manse again, more than three days had elapsed—yet the actual distance between Crieff crossroads and Owen Sound is just about ninety miles.

On Thanksgiving Day in 1859 the much beloved John Bayne collapsed, and his last concern, while his assistant and the doctor were persuading him to undress, drink some essence of peppermint and lie down, was that someone must be found to go in his place to preach for his friend Maclean, at the Crieff church that morning. Within a few hours the Reverend Dr. John Bayne was dead. Galt and its environs, and many communities roundabout were to mourn his passing, and Andrew Maclean was never to forget this friend and mentor who had sought him out in the Old Land and introduced him to the New. When within a short time an official announcement proclaimed him Moderator of the Session, succeeding Bayne, he was deeply moved by this acknowledgment within the Church of the love and confidence which had bound the two together.

How Maclean, nearing his forties and still a bachelor, "did" for himself in the Crieff manse has never been revealed. The house was of fair size, obviously planned for family living: a big country kitchen complete with pantry across the rear; a small dining room with fireplace just forward; then, opening off the staircase hall at the front, the minister's study on one side, the small parlor on the other. Upstairs the wide center hall, equipped with storage closets, led to the uniformly small bedrooms, two on either side, each with a sharply descending ceiling under the roof slope.

Perhaps a women's committee of the church took over some of the housekeeping, or he may have had a servant—indeed, he needed one if only to prepare meals and see to the supply of sheets and blankets for his frequent clerical guests. These included from time to time the Roman Catholic priest from Guelph or Galt, who would drop in after visiting the three or four families of his faith nearby; our Andrew had not a vestige of prejudice, and he and the Reverend Father would settle down for an evening of lively talk and reminiscences befitting two ex-Highlanders. Perhaps they competed for the best blow on Andrew's bagpipes, or, again, deliberately retired early in order to be fresh for a fishing or hunting expedition in the woods next morning. Could be that they even enjoyed a drop or so of Scotland's bottled nectar—for some comments on Andrew's career in-

dicate this as a probability, even though one member of his family
line in later years went to some pains to mark such references as
*"not true."*

But Andrew's bachelor days were soon to end. In 1861, when he
was forty-one, he married Catherine Cameron, a spinster three years
his junior. Her address at the time was her family's newly settled
farm in Simcoe County, but, like her husband, she was a native of
Inverness, having been born in the village of Belmachree where the
Camerons of Lochiel had been residents in an unbroken line, or so the
legend ran, for seven hundred years. Certain strains of Mackillican
and Macintosh-of-Raigmore blood also contributed to her solid Highland background—and just as undoubtedly to Andrew's new state of
domestic pride and bliss. Whether he had known her in the Old
Country cannot be established with certainty, but there is strong likelihood that the Church itself brought them together by way of Andrew's
acquaintance with her brother and brother-in-law, both of whom had
been in the theology course in Edinburgh and were now ministers of
rising prominence in Ontario's Grey County.

What a happy change for the lonely middle-aged pastor! A wife at
the manse—to see to the housekeeping, the vegetable garden, the
coal-oil for the lamps, the Monday ritual of the washtub, and the
meals day in, day out; a wife to take her place in a forward pew at
every service, a worshiper who knew all the hymns by heart, one who
counted it a privilege to lead and teach the Ladies' Bible Class in the
Sunday school! The minister felt that he was a lucky man indeed—
and especially as the months advanced and there were unmistakable
signs that a new Maclean was imminent.

On September 26, 1862, the great event occurred with the birth of
a son. And as that day was Friday, the new father—probably pacing
up and down beside his desk with its tumble of sermon notes—
had ample time to prepare a prayer of reverent joy and thanks to
deliver from the pulpit, come Sunday. It was perhaps not inadvertent
that he should mention the child's name in advance of the christening.
He was happy to embrace the Heaven-sent opportunity to honor his
late friend and mentor, and the combination of names had an honest,
forthright ring: John Bayne Maclean.

The child grew and flourished, and with each passing season evinced
as expanding interest in the life around him. West Puslinch might be
dismissed as an unexciting backwater by some but not by this youngster

with the inquisitive mind. All those Macdonalds, Munros, Stewarts, *et al,* in the neighborhood were learning to be ready for his questions. "What made your cow have twins?" "Doesn't your father wear a coat for dinner?" (Shirtsleeves at mealtime were definitely taboo in the minister's house.) "Why is the barn empty?" (But the farmer's answer, no matter how honest, didn't matter, for John Bayne Maclean was never to admit at any point in his eighty-eight years the sad truth that the soil in the Crieff area was poor, stony and unpromising.)

In all such conversations the boy's face would have an intent, listening look, the piercing blue eyes wide open under the arched brows. That steady impersonal gaze was to remain a fixed feature in all the years ahead—much as would the high cheekbones with their shining rosy skin. His hair was brown, neatly parted in the center in the manner of the times. His physique had an agile wiriness that exactly matched his restless, eager mind.

People didn't scare him; he was never shy. Once, when still of pre-school age, he accompanied his father to Acton where the Reverend Andrew was to conduct the Sunday morning service. As the church had no vestry, the minister deposited his silk hat and cane beside his son whom he settled in a pew toward the front. Everything remained in decorous order during the hymns and the collection rounds but midway through the sermon little Johnnie became restless (those hour-long nineteenth-century sermons!) and decided, first, to try on the topper, then get the stick firmly in hand, and finally stride up and down the aisle. The performance lasted some minutes until one of the congregation persuaded him to stop trying to steal the limelight and subside quietly on the seat beside her.

A second son, Hugh Cameron, joined the Macleans some four years after the first. Now the family was complete, and in a modest, careful way, able to enjoy activities as a close-knit group. For the children there would be dramatic stories of families and clans from the far past —and neither of the boys would ever forget the blood-and-thunder heritage from their father's line. The Macleans were descended from Gilleain na Tuaigh, the "Youth of the Axe," who made his reputation as a fighter in the thirteenth century and played a gallant part at the Battle of Largs against the Norsemen. Fighting for James IV at Flodden (1513) they were led by the Maclean known as Hector of Duart, who was to give his life in order to save the King's. The Macleans were always ready to take up swords for the Stuart kings, and in Montrose's famous victory at Inverlochy (1645) another Hector, chief of the clan, died on the field. From that moment in history arose the Macleans' famous battle cry *"Fear eil' air son Eachuinn,"* which translates to "Another for Hector." Small wonder there has almost always been a Hector among the Christian names of each generation of clan Maclean families.

There were ancestors too at the Battle of Culloden (1746), scene of tragic disappointment for Bonnie Prince Charlie and his thousands of Scots. Catherine Cameron Maclean's grandfather had been there, a lad in his teens, and as he lived to well over the hundred mark she had often heard the story of that long-ago day from his own lips. (Years later John Bayne Maclean would recall, "My mother used to repeat stories my great-grandfather told her of his capture by the English Dragoons in the retreat from the Culloden battlefield, the last stand of the Stuarts.")

And of course the manse's firstborn had early learned the special significance of his own name, for the late Dr. Bayne continued as a powerful influence in his friend's home and life. On certain occasions, the Reverend Andrew would bring forward one of his treasured possessions: a seal inscribed with the motto, "Fear Not When Doing Right," which, accompanied by solemn blessings, had been presented to Bayne many years ago by a famous Moderator of the church of Scotland, the Reverend Thomas Chalmers. When Bayne brought Andrew to Canada he passed the seal on to him. (Ninety years later its message, still potent, still sound, was to be adopted as John Bayne Maclean's company motto, and for years the words appeared in a decorative line on the certificates for editorial achievement given to winners in the firm's various annual awards.)

John Bayne Maclean's first taste of education from blackboard, slate and textbooks was in the one-room school at Crieff where he spent two years. On completion of those early grades a student had to transfer to the establishment at Killean for the rest of the course. That meant a walk of almost five miles each morning and the same with back to sun each afternoon. So it came about that during the long winter stretches, when the snowdrifts were taller than a boy, young Johnnie stayed as a boarder with the teacher, Hugh Macpherson, whose house was just west of the school.

The sole community gathering-place at Crieff, the church itself, contributed special events to the local calendar. A week-night soirée, as reported in the Guelph paper in February 1869, filled the building "to its utmost capacity," and there were "provisions . . . of a dainty yet substantial character, provided by the people of the congregation and others of the neighborhood." The choir "discoursed some excellent music . . . with a taste and skill which surprised every one present." The Reverend Andrew was chairman, there were no fewer than four visiting speakers, and the net proceeds amounted to $68.

It was also from that same frame church, sedate with its typical Victorian-Gothic windows down each of its two long sides, that a certain congregational scandal developed—of a kind to enliven local gossip for many a month. It seems the Crieff blacksmith, one Christopher Moffat, was at heart a frustrated revivalist, always the first and longest contributor to spontaneous prayers at mid-week meeting, given to argument with the minister on any private or public occasion short of the regular Sunday services, and, in general, as one church member put it, "a man with tongue trouble."

The Reverend Andrew tried to keep him under control but nothing availed, and finally Moffat determined to transfer to a Galt church and to that end requested his certificate of church membership from Maclean—an appalling thought, especially as the minister knew the people who would soon have to suffer. Andrew refused; a few days later when he heard Moffat was forwarding his request to the district Presbytery, the minister sat himself down and drew up a document listing eighteen charges against the man. Weeks of bickerings back and forth, meetings, committee hearings, etc., ensued, but Andrew would not budge. Eventually, perhaps for the first time in Ontario history, the Presbytery, rather than an individual church over the signature of its minister, issued a membership certificate on behalf of Moffat. The Crieff minister did not appeal the decision, but it is extremely likely that he did not approve and did not forget. The Reverend Andrew Maclean, though gentle in manner, was, as a friend of his once wrote, "not wanting in Celtic fire, which could, on occasion, burst into flame."

In the pulpit he was a calm, convincing speaker, a man who used reason and sound deduction for his message rather than oratorical flourishes. Many years later, in a letter to a friend, John Bayne Maclean described his father in these words: "He possessed a fine clear mind. He was acute in discrimination and logical in his discourses. He was unassuming, pious and substantial. He was to the last a hard student of the Bible, deeply attached to his flock, and very solicitous for the eternal welfare of each of them. He had an intense abhorrence of everything dishonest, false and hypocritical."

And again in his mature years, that same son enjoyed detailing the standard of discipline which the Reverend Andrew practiced in his home life. The boys were brought up to obey, to learn the importance of keeping their promises. Any repeated infraction deserved the rod— as when young John Bayne for the *second* time in a month lingered at the creek with his schoolmates until well past the manse's regular teatime. "I deserved the whipping," the son confessed later, "and my real misery was caused by hearing my mother cry out, 'Oh, Andrew don't—please don't.'"

Aside from these strictly domestic episodes, it was long ago established that the Reverend Andrew Maclean did indeed have a strong Christian influence on young people. There was a certain occasion when he almost succeeded in diverting one of Canada's great railway builders in the direction of the ministry.

Sir Donald Mann, co-promoter with Sir William Mackenzie of the Canadian Northern Railway, as well as numerous public utilities in other countries, had been brought up in his father's manse at Acton. The two ministers were close friends and exchanged pulpits from time to time. The Reverend Hugh Mann had hopes that Donald (then in his teens, about ten years older than little John Bayne) would follow his father's career, but there was obvious resistance on the part of the lad. "In his despair," as John Bayne Maclean was to phrase it in a contribution to the *Presbyterian Record* in 1911, Mr. Mann took his son to Crieff for a heart-to-heart conference with a man they both respected. The interview was conducted in Gaelic. The Reverend Andrew strongly advised young Donald to follow his father's wishes, assuring him that "a boy as conscientious as he was would certainly make a good minister." Andrew recalled how in his own youth in Scotland his family had intended him for the Army, and then when he abandoned that idea and chose the Church, people had laughed and hinted there was too much of the devil in him to make a minister!

Donald took the advice gratefully and seriously—to the extent that within the next few weeks he made plans to enter the University of Toronto. "His trunks were packed and at the station," John Bayne Maclean continued in his article, "when he suddenly announced a change of mind. Gathering a few more belongings in a small satchel, he told his father that he would not go to the university, but would go out and make his own way in the world. He put on his hat and started across the fields. His father found him at the station and said that if he insisted he could go with his blessings, and a Bible. The trunks were taken home, and Donald went away on the train with the satchel. That Bible he carried for many years and still has. It went with him in the lumber woods, on the plains, through the Rockies, in South America, in China and wherever else his varied career has taken him."

Maclean and Mann remained good friends throughout their lives, and as old friends do, exchanged memories of their early days. They no doubt remarked on the fact that the good pastor at Crieff was never to know the outcome of Donald Mann's sudden reversal of decision. For some time the Reverend Andrew Maclean's health had been failing; he suffered from dropsy, a condition resulting from excess fluid in the body's tissues or cavities. Perhaps as a result of the increasing physical weakness, he was the victim of melancholia. Even his fellow Presbyters were aware of the change, as indicated in a few lines of the long, moving tribute which appeared in the church's *Home & Foreign Record* of July 1873. "He became nervous and despondent and looked at the dark side of things," wrote the anonymous contributor. "This often led him to shrink from fellowship with those whom he suspected, although in many instances there was no ground for his suspicion." In the spring of that year his illness took a fatal turn, and he died on April 20, 1873, in his fifty-third year. The little church at Crieff was taxed beyond its capacity by the throng of mourners from the county roundabout and the many ministers from near and far who came to participate in the last rites and watch him laid to rest in the graveyard just a few steps away from the pulpit which he had served so faithfully for sixteen years.

The scene changes, swiftly, inevitably, now that the family's sole support had been withdrawn and there was no longer a rent-free house. Mrs. Maclean and her two sons, then ten and six years old, were taken under the wing of her brother, the Reverend James Cameron, D.D., in Chatsworth near Owen Sound.

At that time Chatsworth was a village of some seven hundred souls and adequately equipped for proper functioning, having four churches and, as was normal in those days, four "hotels," wagon and black-smith shops, a shingle mill and a schoolhouse served by two teachers. For some reason the Maclean boys did not attend school; instead, they received private tuition from Uncle James. In all likelihood Dr. Cameron himself suggested the arrangement and followed it through with his usual inexhaustible energy.

In that day of community "characters" he was indeed one such in

Grey County. He enjoyed the study of politics and the men who gave them force. During Sir John A. Macdonald's platform tour in 1876, the great Conservative leader, "maker of Confederation," planned his itinerary in Canada West to include a pleasant visit with his friends, the Camerons. And while the rugged old-timer, relaxing in one of the parlor's best plush chairs, explained to his host the *real* reason why the Government Grits had delayed completing the western section of the new Pacific Railroad, and why their dangerous playing about with free trade had necessitated his current campaign for a national policy with protection of native industries, and so on, somewhere in the room young John Bayne Maclean looked and listened with eyes and ears wide open. Even as a youngster just entered on his teen years he sensed the importance of this hour or two in the presence of a great man; all the details of the meeting were to stay vividly in mind for the rest of his days.

There is evidence too that young Maclean was exposed to Macdonald's arch political foe and personal enemy, Honorable George Brown, brilliant Liberal leader, founder-publisher of the Toronto *Globe,* and also a Father of Confederation. Brown's sister had been a close friend of the Camerons for many years, and both she and her brother had visited the Chatsworth home from time to time, as did Alexander Mackenzie, another avowed opponent of Macdonald, and the man who achieved the Prime Ministership that was denied to George Brown.

Already Crieff and its intimate crossroads life and the cozy quiet of the little manse must have seemed a long time ago. But John Bayne Maclean had an inborn capacity to adjust to new places and people— and that was especially fortunate for a fourteen-year-old about to enter the special world of high school in a town where he knew few people.

Up to that point, most of his time had been spent over his uncle's carefully chosen textbooks at the manse. One volume (still in existence, though tattered) is titled, *Elementary Arithmetic for Canadian Schools,* by Smith (Cambridge) and McMurchy (Toronto), and even a casual glance through its pages reveals a no-nonsense approach to basic mathematics. In the section, "Miscellaneous Examples," there's a good test question: "How many miles in 178006 inches?"—plus its own period-style answer farther back: "2 mls., 6 fur., 18 per., 5 yds., 1 ft., 10 in." (The "per" is an abbreviation for "perch," an old-time measurement meaning "pole.") Another poser, with its special illumination on prices of the 1870s, runs this way: "If the 16 cts. loaf weighs 3.35 lbs. when wheat is $1.14 a bus., what ought to be the price of wheat per bus. when 25 lbs. of bread cost 37½ cents?"

But young Johnnie Maclean mastered these circumlocutory equations—at least sufficiently to pass his entrance examination. The record of the results still exists. He wrote his papers on December 19 and 20, 1876, in Owen Sound. Out of an obtainable maximum total of 444 marks, Maclean captured 238, or a little over 50 percent—an adequate "pass" in those days. His poorest showing occurred in geography— 29 marks out of a possible 72; his best turned up in composition—54 out of 72.

So, in 1877 he said goodbye to his mother and brother and the Camerons and made for Owen Sound, which boasted the only high school in Grey County—a building recently completed, "a model of architectural beauty and convenience throughout," no doubt well worth the $20,000 it had cost. He settled in as a boarder at the home of the headmaster, a Mr. DeLamatter—and the fact that he remained there for the duration of his course must surely attest to good behavior.

Owen Sound, then boasting a population of 4500, was a totally different experience from anything so far. One could walk for hours and never see a familiar face! But one could also find new stimulation in the atmosphere of a lively port town, with Great Lakes ships making a skyline of masts and funnels down by the docks. Life itself had begun to broaden in horizons, and surely this was the time for a fatherless teen-ager to make the right decision for his future.

Two possibilities were ever in mind. Like the Reverend Andrew in his young days, John Bayne Maclean had visions of himself as a full-time soldier of the Empire. He would enter the recently opened Royal Military College, Kingston, as a cadet; on completion of the course he would serve wherever Her Majesty Queen Victoria might command, whether in his homeland or on a jungle frontier. But such dreams, he regretfully discovered, were beyond the reach of a poor country lad even if he could get into R.M.C. In fact, there was a formidable waiting list of applicants, many with that mysterious asset called "special influence," hoping to be chosen for the strictly limited commissions—never more than five at a time—then open to Canadians in the British Army.

A military career was out. Yet here in Owen Sound, with the rousing sound of bugles and drums on every parade night of the 31st Grey Battalion, he could at least have a taste of militia life! So, at the age of fifteen, he joined the 31st as "boy" private. For a good many years and through various promotions in rank, Maclean was to become one of the regiment's solid dependables, regularly reporting for duty even when it meant traveling miles there and back, and always eager to participate in special courses, such as that presented by the Royal School of Gunnery on the grounds of R.M.C., Kingston. (Fifty years later he listed that three months' training as an essential part of his educational background.)

The other future that continued to beckon was, of course, the teaching profession. Here too, and simultaneously with his military activities, he went through all the preliminary steps with dogged determination. After obtaining his three-year matriculation certificate, he moved from Owen Sound to Durham, farther south, to spend a final year in that community's model school. In 1880, he accepted his first appointment as a teacher in a newly settled area in Glenelg Township nearby; apparently he was the entire staff in a typical "little red schoolhouse" of School Section No. 9. Fifty years later he was to attend the 67th anniversary of the school and shake hands with local people whom he had first met during that teaching year. He recalled that he had applied at three schools for a teacher's job. At Hutton Hill he was regarded as too much of a "Grit." At Orchardville he was not enough of an Orangeman. At Glenelg the key trustee was a Presbyterian which ensured his appointment. Where he resided and how he looked after his creature comforts are details now hard to come by.

Nevertheless it is apparent that he was wholly committed to a career at the blackboard, for by the end of 1881 he decided he must equip himself with the proper Normal School certificate—and that meant a move to Toronto. Glenelg students regretted their loss, as evidenced in a yellowed clipping from the Durham weekly paper which reported a presentation of "a large and handsome photograph album, pen knife and pencil" to Mr. J. B. McLean, S.S. No. 9's teacher. In the long address of thanks and good wishes, the class expressed appreciation for his "indefatigable labor for our instruction, not as a hired pedagogue for love of pay, but as a tender and affectionate brother, leading us by love and affection, step by step, in our education." They rejoiced that the separation was not caused by any "disunion between you and us . . . but your own ardent and laudable desire to further your own education . . . May you succeed in your present prospect, and may your future life be as harmonious as it has been amongst us." The message ended with a bit of poetry.

"Farewell dear teacher, fare you well
Though we in body part
Your memory shall be cherished still
In every pupil's heart."

The signatures of Andrew Matthews and James Smith appear at the bottom as the group's valedictorians.

So, immediately after New Year's, young Maclean went to Toronto and entered the Normal School course—a fairly intensive one, yet with certain compensations: the school's cadet unit received him with a warm welcome. In recognition of his four years in the Owen Sound Militia he was quickly appointed drill sergeant, and when the squad participated in the ceremonial funeral for Egerton Ryerson, founder of Ontario's school system, Maclean marched in command.

But another event of far-reaching personal significance was on the books for that year, and out of the experience would emerge one of his favorite stories. "A few days before the final examinations," he would start off, "I was called in by the principal, Reverend Dr. Davies. He said they had been asked by Port Hope to recommend a principal for the public school there. Dr. Davies and his two assistants had agreed upon me. I suggested that they should wait for the result of the examinations. I *might* be plucked in English. I was." Thus the school-mastership fell through, but Maclean's story never ended there. "Within three years," he would declare, "I was earning more with my pen than the examiners had ever received. In addition to my own paper, I had become a regular contributor to a number of Canadian, British and United States publications. I never had an article refused."

Yet that long-ago failure in English did irk him, to the point that some thirty years later he wrote to Ontario's Deputy Minister of Education, Dr. A. H. U. Colquhoun, a good friend. Could the original examination paper be found? Colquhoun sent a reassuring reply: "I have found the record of your examination in 1882. The marks obtained are creditable to you. The system today is so different from that which appears to have been in force in 1882 that we find it hard to understand why you did not receive your certificate."

From such small detours on the highway of life are careers determined. John Bayne Maclean was a very disappointed young man in that summer of 1882. But within a few weeks a new, clear route to a future quite undreamed of suddenly opened up. He was on his way.

# CHAPTER II

## BUSY YOUNG REPORTER

"Much may be made of a Scotchman, if
he be caught young."
*Samuel Johnson*

WHY JOHN BAYNE MACLEAN determined to become a newspaper reporter remains unexplained. None of his carefully saved files of notes,
memoranda and letters, ready to overflow from half-a-dozen tall
cabinets, has provided a firm answer. Nor can his remaining associates
after years of listening to his reminiscences recall any specific reason
proffered.

But in looking back to his early teens, one encounters a few rather
significant clues. The influence of the *Globe* throughout rural Ontario
was inescapable, even to a boy soon to be confronted with entrance
examinations; and he had met the fighting editorialist, the Honorable
George Brown, the paper's powerful editor and founder. Perhaps even
more important, because continuously part of the atmosphere in the
Chatsworth parsonage, was the fact that the Reverend James Cameron,
D.D., served for some years during the 1870s as editor of the *Canada
Christian Monthly,* a Presbyterian magazine printed in Toronto.

We may make the natural assumption that the lad who wrote such
a clear, neat hand should be asked to help from time to time, especially
as press day rolled around. He could be depended upon for a quick
and tidy job of copying out the missionary's contribution from far
Basutoland and then turn to the checking of galley proofs on that
mixed-up piece concerning the Society for Promoting Female Education, thus releasing Uncle James for the final polishing of his special
signed article, "The Lord a Strong Tower." (All three appeared in
Vol. VII, 1877.)

When selections for the regular department headed "Children's
Treasury" were in short supply, it is quite possible that editor Cameron
could switch quickly to tutor Cameron and assign John to deliver a

300-word composition on a suitable subject. Such tactics may have been responsible for various little story-pieces, always with a moral message, simply told, which were presented unsigned, under the titles of "How Quarrels Begin," "A Mother's Influence," etc. Today they read very much like the multitudes of penciled homilies, written in free moments the middle-aged Maclean did not wish to waste, and still spilling from his files.

We know, therefore, that he spent a good part of his growing-up period within range of the rattle of manuscript paper and the pressure of deadlines, plus the lively mealtime analysis of every day's newspaper. It has been established, too, that he contributed occasional items to the weekly Owen Sound *Times,* on certain segments of county history-in-the-making as he observed it during his Glenelg teaching period, and probably also on newsy developments within the 31st Greys.

So the contagion "took." He would be a reporter.

He found the job in Toronto. It was in the autumn of 1882, and he had just passed his twentieth birthday. The setting was, as one historian writing in the period declared, "the brilliant capital of English-speaking Canada."

The place was booming. There were citizens, still living, who remembered the town that had been known for years as "Muddy York." Now there were 120 miles of streets, most of them with cedar-block "paving" margined with long-board sidewalks. Up-to-date transport was provided by horse-drawn streetcars. The population had grown to more than 86,000, or with the swelling suburbs included, to 103,000. Everyone old enough talked about the same exciting new things: the "bi-cycle," now to be seen weaving through the mêlée of coaches, cabs, carts, drays and over the steaming heaps of horse droppings on every busy street; the phonograph, invented by a certain Mr. Edison in the United States, and occasionally encountered here in a fashionable front parlor; the elegant Grand Opera House, just opened, able to seat 1200 but ready with campstools and standing space for an additional 500; and, on a more sober note, that recent school introduction with the foreign name, "kindergarten," which most people were sure really wouldn't last. Torontonians were proud of their annual "fair" or Exhibition, now three years old.

Here was a city in the vigor of the first big stretch of youth. Its forerunner, York, founded by Lieutenant-Governor John Graves Simcoe in 1792–93 as Upper Canada's capital, with a garrison to defend it against the menace of the Americans from the south shore

of Lake Ontario, had grown up. The staid British name had been
set aside in 1834 when the place was officially incorporated; henceforth it would be known as Toronto, the Indian word meaning "place
of meeting," and thus from time immemorial aptly descriptive of this
handy junction point for canoe traffic from or to upcountry and the
big lake.

Now, in the '80s, Toronto was indeed living up to its name.
Waves of immigrants, the majority from the British Isles, were regularly
arriving, some to move farther west toward the wheat plains, but
many others to stay put. "How English is Toronto!" remarked a visitor.
Lively small communities had sprung up roundabout, as southern
Ontario farmland became settled and prosperous. A potent factor in
these and countless other developments had been the railways, virtually
all of which converged on the ancient "place of meeting." Almost
with the sensational speed of their own steam power (coal-fired engines having superseded the wood-burners by 1880), the trains had
transformed Toronto into a bustling industrial and commercial center.
Every downtown vista challenged the eye with new buildings—home
offices of insurance companies and banks. The Board of Trade and
the Stock Exchange were in action every business day. Factory chimneys disgorged black smudges on the skyline, as workers turned
out a variety of nineteenth-century necessities, whether women's but-
toned boots or hay rakes or kitchen ranges. There was a well-equipped
fire brigade operating from ten stations. The police force had grown
to well over a hundred, "a fine body of men"; and these "ulstered
and helmeted constables, making nocturnal notes by the glare of an
electric light," as an evening stroller along King Street in 1882 described
them, provided one more proof of Toronto's metropolitan status—
along with such unmistakable signs as the theatre crowds and the
"great newspaper offices ablaze with the flame of fevered journalism."

On October 19 of that year John Bayne Maclean became a reporter
on the Toronto *World*, youngest (founded 1880), smallest (two
double sheets, to make eight pages), editorially boldest (sometimes
Grit, other times Tory, but frequently and outspokenly neither), and,
as to money in the till, poorest of the city's three morning newspapers. His salary was $5 weekly—when available—for there was a
gay, happenstance tradition throughout the forty years' life of the
*World* that only the first employees to approach the cashier on Friday
night got their pay; latecomers went away emptyhanded. In fact, any
reporter who ever worked for that paper and received his full salary

every week felt somewhat *déclassé*, cheated of a memory to which he was entitled. Among them was the present writer; when he had a job there for a few months before going overseas in World War I, the pay was regular.

Maclean's newspaper career might have opened on a higher prestige level had the family friend, Brown, been still a part of the local scene, but the *Globe*'s owner had died two years before, slain by the drunken shot of a discharged employee. Thus, our Maclean found himself working for another Maclean, unrelated, and seldom visible to his staff because of various outside interests, especially politics which eventually would give him an unchallenged seat in the House of Commons.

W. F. Maclean, or "Billy" as most of Toronto knew him, left the daily routines of the paper to his brothers, Jimmie and John; nevertheless it was Billy who laid down the line for the uninhibited approach of the news columns and the editorial page. He was probably the originator of that now well-worn nickname for his country "Miss Canada"; one of his opinion pieces in 1882 describes "her" as young, inexperienced but trying hard, though facing nasty threats from both London and Washington, and winds up: "She may seek a divorce from John Bull, but never for a mésalliance with Uncle Sam."

Another editorial of the period makes a passing jab at the Governor-General whose term in office had ended just a couple of years earlier: "Lord Dufferin . . . now esteemed by the people of Canada as one of the most eloquent, plausible and successful humbugs that ever put this country to unnecessary expense." The *World*'s headings, half-a-century in advance of their time and their competition, used verbs, slang and sly winks, as in these random selections from 1882: "A Big Swindle Nipped," "Sir W. Scott Immoral" (announcing the banning of *Marmion* from high schools because of the poem's not-nice implications here and there), and "How Stiffs Are Secured," which was the only lively line in a tedious step-by-step report concerning the supply of corpses for dissecting rooms.

John Bayne Maclean's regular assignments were lodge meetings, with special attention to the numerous Orange Order groups, local ward politics from time to time, and the police court virtually every day. The magistrate was Colonel George Taylor Denison. Thirty-five years later, when this writer covered the police court for the paper, the magistrate was still the same Colonel Denison.

Within a week or two of joining the *World,* Maclean discovered there was a market for contributions to other publications, and happily their pay was dependable. For an article delivered to the *Monetary Times* or the *Merchant,* he could be sure of a cheque for $2 or $3. Since these papers were not competitive with the *World,* his regular employer raised no objection. Thus began a free-lance enterprise which over the next decade would snowball into an important source of income, at the same time broadening Maclean's knowledge on many subjects and constantly adding to his contacts with leaders in business and other fields.

The *World* period ended abruptly after just six or seven weeks, when the Toronto *Daily Mail* offered him a job at the impressive salary of $9 a week, payable on the dot. The *Mail,* of course, could afford it, having been carefully established, with ample financing, in the early 1870s as the mouthpiece of Sir John A. Macdonald and his Conservative Party. It occupied its own handsome new building, red brick in five stories surmounted by a cone-topped square tower that was already a Toronto landmark and remained such until the 1940s.

Almost from its inception, the paper had prospered, and now, for the price of 3 cents, its readers knew they could count on eight pages of soberly edited, solidly packed news each weekday, with the added attraction of a twelve- or sixteen-page issue every Saturday. Ladies found special interest in the weekend's "Woman's Kingdom," a department offering household tips ("sprinkle damp bran upon a carpet before sweeping"), menus for debutante receptions ("bouillon first, followed by tea and cakes"), and a torrent of fashion news ("black toilets are again in high vogue"—for street costumes, that is).

Advertising had continued to show a steady increase. In 1883 the CPR ran a series offering prairie lands, readily accessible to its line, for $2.50 per acre and upwards; large space was frequently used by the local "outfitters" for men or women; dignified small cards by business firms appeared regularly—notably that of stockbrokers Pellatt & Pellatt, the junior partner of that team to be famous a half-century later as the builder of Toronto's feudal pile, Casa Loma. Patent medicines bulked high in advertising linage, and the *Mail,* like other Canadian newspapers, accepted without a qualm the campaign with the beguilingly frank promise in its heading: "Use our Famous Cough Mixture! You Can Get No Better!"

For the first year or so Maclean's *Mail* assignments kept him in the same rounds, as during the *World* period, with the additional chore of covering schoolboard meetings. He particularly enjoyed the police beat—so many members of the force were old soldiers! Often in the back room of No. 1 station our young man—recently promoted to adjutant of his Owen Sound regiment, commuting back and forth for all important parades, would provide a delighted audience for personal anecdotes of the Crimea, the Indian Mutiny or those other brush fires in which some of Toronto's finest had done their duty as soldiers for Queen and Empire. One veteran even harked back to Waterloo: the old soldier would hobble in for a visit with his former police cronies and to the reporter who had set aside dreams of an Army career, the trooper "who knew Wellington" became a haloed figure indeed.

The police news as reported by Maclean seems like much of the police news of today. Speeding, for example: "Wm. Dixon, charged with fast driving on Queen Street, was fined $1 and costs or ten days." (Horses had to be kept under tight rein.) Parking: two cabmen absented themselves from their vehicles at the Union Station and were hauled in to pay $1 and costs each. Down-and-outers: "Annie Sellers, a vagrant, was sent to the Mercer (reformatory) for six months." Boisterous college undergrads: Two students arrested at 2 A.M. for alleged disorderly conduct, "singing at the top of their voices and referring to the constables as Peelers and cops."

Maclean's big effort each week was represented in a Saturday feature under the heading, "The Brotherhoods . . . Items of Interest to Members of the Secret Societies." Sometimes his news of Masons, Oddfellows, Sons of Temperance, Ancient Foresters, etc., occupied as much as three full columns, bristling with names and events from many parts of the province and beyond. Locally Maclean went the rounds faithfully and dispassionately; he made himself acquainted with Catholic groups and their church dignitaries, enjoyed contacts with the Jewish organizations (one of them received $5 from him—or half his weekly salary—toward its synagogue building fund) and of course he kept constantly in touch with the Loyal Orange Lodge, then approaching its zenith as a powerful influence in Toronto.

Fifty years later, Colonel Maclean would recall an incident that in its build-up demonstrated the then current atmosphere of strong anti-Catholic prejudice, yet in the outcome was to have a calming effect between the two major religious groups. For some time the Orangemen had sought to prevent the Roman Catholics from holding street demonstrations similar to the Loyal Orange Lodge's great July

12 parade. When the next Catholic procession took place the local militia was on duty to protect the peace and prevent possible clashes. But whoever among the civic authorities had issued the order must have had a sense of humor, for most of the men in regimental uniforms were Protestant. So, marching alongside the banner-carrying groups, the militiamen kept smartly in step by either whistling "The Protestant Boys" or singing those catchy lines, "They sprinkled the Dogans every one, and planted them under the Protestant blue." The Catholics took it in good spirit, and one gathered from the Colonel's reminiscent account that the occasion featured less elbowing and high-sticking than any normal National Hockey League game today.

The year 1884 marked a significant milestone for Maclean. The *Mail* promoted him to the post of assistant commercial-financial-marine editor—a job which the other fourteen reporters on the staff, all senior to him, had turned down as just too dull. Maclean, the neat, careful twenty-two-year-old who enjoyed figures and facts, found the work interesting from the outset; soon he discovered it was a direct route to acquaintance with the top businessmen of the community. Ultimately it would lead him into his own commercial publishing project.

One daily job on the new beat was to secure the livestock prices —information avidly awaited by farmers, drovers, etc., throughout the province. At first he followed along in his predecessor's footsteps by consulting the bank manager at Toronto's St. Lawrence Market. But soon he realized the banker was merely relaying at secondhand quotations supplied by the retail butchers at the market—and they, of course, were interested in keeping wholesale or on-the-hoof prices down! From that moment Maclean made a drastic change in his news-gathering, going direct to the only dependable source: the stockyards, situated a couple of miles west of the *Mail* office yet well worth the walk several times a week. Now he could present the correct statistics of types, weights, prices. That this constantly changing picture contained information of value even far afield was proved, probably to his surprise, when newspapers in Chicago, New York, Buffalo, Montreal sought him out for regular livestock dispatches from Toronto.

He pursued these outside connections from a legitimate profit motive, yet his missionary zeal for improved conditions for the Canadian breeder-shippers was constantly in evidence in his local coverage. In the "Live Stock Trade" column of a January 1886 issue of the

*Mail,* he chastised the City Council for knowing and caring little about the "lack of accommodation" at the cattle yards—now worse than ever because of the Garrison Creek sewer in the center of the area. "More than half the pens cannot be used," he declared, "and this means that recent heavy shipments of cattle and hogs are deteriorating rapidly in quality and value during the days and nights they stand about, awaiting purchase and slaughter." It was up to the dealers, he said, to bring the whole matter to the attention of Council, with a proper petition and a large deputation.

Although typewriters had begun to appear in editorial departments, Maclean, like most of his associates, wrote copy by hand, but, unlike the others, he produced perfectly legible results. The typesetters on the next floor up competed for his sheaf of pages each night—it represented quick production for them, and at that time they were paid on a piecework basis, by the "stick." All his work was done standing at a high desk. Far along toward the end of his life, when he sent birthday congratulations to P. D. Ross, nonagenarian publisher of the Ottawa *Journal,* Maclean recalled that he had borrowed the standing-writing habit from Ross who was sports editor of the *Mail* during the '80s. And in a typical but charming rationalization long after the event, he winds up: "There was something symbolic about your habit, I think. It is reflected in the way you have stood up for your convictions and in the interests of this nation throughout your long career."

The commercial coverage and contacts continued to grow in depth and scope. Each noon Maclean turned up at the Board of Trade to make his careful jottings of the day's grain prices. (A few years later he was to join the Board and begin a half-century's association with that important group.) To brief himself on livestock activities abroad, he traveled to Chicago, Buffalo and other centers; each trip gave a yield in friendships as well as background information. He undertook the first of these sorties at his own expense, but when W. J. Douglas, secretary-treasurer of the *Mail,* found out about them there was a firm announcement that the paper would pay for all such travel in the future. Maclean was staggered as well as pleased, for Douglas had a reputation as a hard man with the pennies. Reminiscing in 1939, the Colonel wrote: "There were 12 or 15 of us, and when the city editor sent for lead pencils, the supply was usually limited to three or four for the whole staff."

In the '80s, and indeed for some decades following, reporters frequently put in a sixteen-hour day and a seven-day working week. For the commercial reporter on a morning paper the starting-time might be 9 or 10 A.M., and by the end of the afternoon, when all the bits and pieces of market news had been written and sent to the printers, he might often be confronted with another five or six hours on other assignments. Maclean continued to cover daytime and evening political meetings, and several of these were lifted from routine jobs-of-work to special events because of the presence of his hero, Sir John A. Macdonald.

Greatest occasion of all was the Ontario Tory rally held on December 17, 1884, to honor the Chief. More than 4000 people crammed into Toronto's Grand Opera House, swarming over aisles and platform. Every constituency in the province sent an official delegation, complete with its individual formal address and pledge of unswerving loyalty ("Many were beautiful works of art," the *Mail* commented, "more particularly those of Algoma and Cornwall.") and when the adored leader stepped onto the stage at 2 P.M., "the vast audience cheered itself hoarse, hats were thrown up, delegates rose in their seats, the banners from the dress circle fluttered, while, to add to the interest of the occasion, the fair ladies in the boxes waved their handkerchiefs as demonstratively as any in the audience."

Sir John's speech, after opening with confessions of "feelings of deepest emotion . . . no moment of my life can approach the gratification with which I receive this greeting," moved suavely through all the national problems and, more particularly, his government's success in solving them, whether in the matter of cheese exports or freight rates or the recent ticklish negotiations with the Americans concerning offshore fisheries. It added up to a brilliant review of his own forty years in politics, and his every word—plus the sound effects elicited, from "Hear, Hear!" or "Cheers" or "Prolonged Laughter"— was reverently recorded in eighteen full columns of coverage in next morning's *Mail*. Maclean could not have covered it alone and must have had the assistance of several other reporters. But financial-commercial news in the December 18 issue suffered; anyway, nothing much seemed to be happening—"The horse market this week is exceedingly dull" . . . "Wheat inactive, barley quiet" . . . "Scarcely any demand heard for anything" on the produce market. It had, indeed, been Sir John A.'s day and in its special way the young reporter's too.

Another occasion with the Chief was to stay vividly in Maclean's memory for the rest of his life—perhaps because of the small, intimate group involved and the fact that the most interesting developments were certainly unrehearsed, and probably unreported. In 1947 Maclean dictated a few paragraphs recalling how Sir John A. and a party of six, accommodated in a three-doubleseated democrat, set out from Hamilton. "I was detailed by the *Mail* to accompany him," he said, and, no doubt with a touch of pride, added: "It is possible that he asked that I should be selected." On approaching a beautiful orchard they "got out to steal apples. The owner of the place came up as we were escaping and threatened to shoot us." Nevertheless they reached their destination, Chatham, where the statesman was to speak. "He had a great reception, primarily from the children who came up. He kissed them, one after another. But gradually his line-up of girls grew taller. A tall colored girl appeared in the distance. Sir John saw her; everybody watched. But the old politician knew exactly what to do. "Oh, I must stop or I shall be getting into trouble with the jealous young men," he said, and he kissed the colored girl and then stopped. On the return trip to Toronto, the party paused for a time in Hamilton, and Maclean mentions that he took the Chief to meet William Southam, founder of the Hamilton *Spectator,* the first of the great Southam chain of newspapers.

Although a reporter's life could be arduous, the plain truth is that these men with open eyes and ears and with pencils at the ready, were a happy, carefree lot. When there was an evening or a Saturday without assignment—which occasionally happened!—they would relax, each in his own way. For Maclean with his neatly compartmented timetable, there were generally several diverting projects awaiting. He seldom lacked for spare time paper work of a different kind, on behalf of the 31st Greys. For physical recreation he joined the Toronto Fencing Club and pursued that highly precise, aristocratic sport with foil, *epée* or saber. His medium height, lean and wiry frame, and exceptional agility of hands and feet showed their capacity "on the strip" right from the start; the club's experts were not surprised when, after not more than two years' study and practice, squeezed in at odd hours between assignments, he entered the annual amateur Canadian fencing competitions and captured the junior championship.

He was a dog-lover too, and, in spite of the fact that his place of residence consisted of just one room in a quiet boardinghouse on Church Street, he had an Irish terrier bitch for a constant companion. Often the dog trotted along with him to the office, then stayed put by the high desk while the master went off on the day's business. W. J. Hambly, a printer on the *Mail,* recalled the scene when he prepared a reminiscent essay concerning the old days. That animal, he wrote, was "ready at a moment's notice to start an Irish Republic with any dog, large or small." She showed her fine points of ancestry, according to Hambly, by winning the North American championship for her class.

There was, it seems, an ample, pleasant, urban life waiting to be enjoyed in Toronto and environs. Growth and development still comprised the *leitmotif:* Timothy Eaton had moved into his palatial new store at 190 Yonge Street in 1883, and the following year saw another moneymaking milestone triumphantly passed with the distribution of the company's first catalogue to visitors at Toronto's Industrial Exhibition. Eaton's would bring a lot of new dollars to the city in those twelve months, not to mention the long future.

Maclean's life, too, was on the threshold of daring expansion. In July 1887 he resigned from the *Mail,* for the purpose of starting a special paper of his own. He had been putting aside regular savings for the past few years; some weeks his earnings from commercial correspondence for out-of-town publications totaled as much as $40 (no income tax in those days) and for the past year the *Mail* had been paying him a salary of $14. On the advice of several businessmen, chief officers of reliable companies, he had made a few successful investments, first from his modest bank account, and later from the incoming dividends. The possibility of organizing his own publishing venture was opening up—and he had dreamed of this for some time, even to the point of declining a tempting offer by Joseph Medill, publisher of the Chicago *Tribune,* one of the papers which featured Maclean's business reports.

He would stay in Toronto and give his plan a full, fair trial. The time to start was now.

## CHAPTER III

# *THE FIRST PUBLICATION*

"Hardly anything will bring a man's mind
into full activity if ambition be wanting."
*Sir Henry Taylor*

DURING THE YEARS on the *Mail* Maclean had made an important discovery: namely, that full, accurate information was in itself a very valuable commodity in the commercial world. But a daily newspaper, confronted with demands on its space by politics, tragedy, sports and global happenings, could never hope to give coverage to all the news emanating, say, from the local cattle market and other business activities. The terse instructions to "Keep it brief" were the monotonous but essential rule of the copy desk.

His original plan was to start a livestock trade paper. However, when he discussed this scheme with his good friends, W. J. Douglas, the *Mail's* business manager, and T. W. Dyas, the advertising manager, they said, practically in unison, "Too limited! Why not cover the whole business of food?" The more they talked it over, the better all three liked the idea—to the point where each of the older men promised $1000 of personal backing for the $3000 capital agreed upon as necessary for the launching. This neatly shared arrangement never got further than conversation, for Douglas eventually decided against participating and Dyas could at the time find no more than $300 which he handed over to Maclean in September.

Blackett Robinson, the local printer engaged to produce the publication, put in $200 and there were a couple of smaller investments. Maclean underwrote his own venture with a good round contribution of $2000. (Forty years later he was to write to Arthur Hewitt, president of Consumers' Gas Company, "I invested in Consumers' Gas about 1885, made a nice profit on it and put that money into founding this business." But he had, as well, certain other resources

ready to dip into. In the month of July 1887 he was able to
deposit an $11 check from the London *Advertiser,* a total of $18
for two reports contributed to the *Merchant,* and four weekly payments of $2 each from the *Monetary Times*—aside from a couple
of incoming dividends, $2.50 from the Toronto Land and Investment
Corporation, and $3.50 from the British American Assurance Com-
pany. That sort of monthly return on both commercial correspondence
and small shareholdings had been going on for several years.)

The new paper would be called the *Canadian Grocer.* The name
had actually appeared the year before on a primitive type of dealers'
house organ put out by the Toronto pickle company of Bryant &
Gibson but had been allowed to die after the third issue. Maclean
asked if he might use the title, and the firm readily turned over all
rights and wished him good luck.

In Canadian periodical publishing of the nineteenth century, luck
and success had been scarce elements indeed. By the time Maclean
started up, scores of journals, hopefully created for scores of purposes,
had quietly succumbed after living their little day. There were chiefly
three publishing centers: Halifax, N.S., where a succession of magazines, such as the *Acadian* (1826–28), had made an earnest effort
with essays and comment; Montreal, which brought forth vehicles
for both English and French *litterateurs;* and Toronto, which had
received its first important stimulus from the driving leadership of
the Reverend Egerton Ryerson and his Methodist Bookroom back in
the '30s. Ryerson's *Christian Guardian* magazine began in 1829 and
lived to a ripe old age in the twentieth century. Indeed, religious
publications, especially those officially supported by their denomina-
tional groups, had the greatest total output of copies during the
nineteenth century. A few agricultural papers appeared in Ontario
from the 1840s on, but a comparison of their small circulations with
the constantly expanding rural population of the period indicates that
they barely scratched the surface. Not until the *Farmer's Advocate*
entered the field in 1866 did the man behind the plow show any
enthusiastic response. Most of the pioneer settlers had an aversion
to "farming out of books," and when there was a point to be settled
about next week's weather and the haying—well, why not have a
look at the almanacs distributed freely by Dr. Chase and other vendors
of pills and potions?

Even in the urban market few specialized periodicals were able to survive, although eager new editor-publishers seemed constantly ready to prove the trend could be changed. The *Merchantman* was born in 1874 and died the same year. The *Ladies' Journal,* too, had a short life after its introduction in 1884. The *Dramatic World and Sporting Record* made a bold effort in 1877 by printing the first number on pink paper, but even that innovation couldn't save it. The list of starts and stops for periodicals in the nineteenth century, with explanations of the reasons why in each case, would provide the basis for a lengthy Ph.D. thesis by a candidate equipped with a digital computer.

There were a few exceptions, of course: *Saturday Night,* the weekly of political analysis and witty comment, was to continue from its inception in 1887; the *Monetary Times (and Insurance Chronicle)* carved its niche in the business world in 1867 and stayed solidly put.

Quite outside normal classification were the publications sponsored, edited or regularly contributed to by Professor Goldwin Smith. This group was unique because of two powerful factors: (1) Smith was an erudite, restless editorialist and (2) he had access to plenty of funds. Following his famous career at Oxford and Cornell Universities, he was now a leading local light by virtue of his marriage to Mrs. William H. (Harriet) Boulton, widow of one of Toronto's aristocrats, and herself a rich heiress of proper Bostonian background. Her great house in its park, The Grange, represented the acme of quietly elegant living. (Eventually the property would become Toronto's twentieth-century art gallery, gift of the Goldwin Smiths.)

During his three decades in the city, Smith was the force behind several periodicals, one succeeding the other according to his need for a public platform from which he could air his changing political views. The "Canada First" surge of the '70s had captured his enthusiasm. Its leaders, of whom Edward Blake, the handsome and magnetic Liberal, was the most prominent, wanted Canada to declare its final independence and to be bound to Britain only by ties of affection. When the movement subsided, partially through lack of public interest but mainly because Blake went to Ottawa to sit in the Cabinet where he quickly abandoned his far-out notions, Smith decided Canada's destiny must lie in total free trade with the United States. He campaigned in print on all the complex angles involved, and still had time to discuss other questions of the day, such as Irish Home Rule (against!) or reforms in current electoral and legislative methods (Canadian divorce applications, he insisted, should be removed from the Senate's hands and placed before a court of justice); temperance (he was against hard liquor but for beer and wine in moderation).

Probably the most distinguished of the Smith-sponsored journals was *The Week,* founded in 1884, for which he sought out special contributions from Canada's rising writers: Bliss Carman, Pauline Johnson, Archibald Lampman and Charles G. D. Roberts, the last-named also serving for a time as editor. *The Week,* in readable, well-presented format, published and printed by Blackett Robinson, continued until 1896, although in its last years deprived of Goldwin Smith's leadership, he having switched his interest to the *Farmer's Sun,* a paper constantly fighting-mad in the interests of rural Ontario. Smith not only wrote for the *Sun* but picked up the otherwise unpayable bills.

Goldwin Smith was a man far in advance of his time: a world-famous intellectual, rich and a radical. No wonder Toronto, inhabited almost exclusively by English, Scotch and North of Ireland families, could neither understand him nor support his anti-Imperialist, anti-Tory, anti-Orange publications. Yet a certain young reporter-turned-publisher was to value his acquaintance, and took delight in recalling in later years their chats about journalism and politics and the evils of the time, even though they never agreed on the solutions.

During the summer of 1887, Maclean moved into a nine-by-twelve-foot office in his printer's building at 9 Jordan Street and there, as the sole member of his staff, he proceeded to plan the *Canadian Grocer.* Many details confronted him: general design, size and format; features deserving regular coverage in each issue; special reports and articles; master-list of prospective advertisers; advertising rates; how to build up a subscription list among Ontario's retail grocers; how much to charge per year or per issue; how to watch expenses during this all-outgo and no-income stage of planning before the publication was ready to roll.

A tall order for a twenty-five-year-old whose experience had been confined to a reporter's rounds of listening and writing! Some well-wisher among his business friends must have advised him to keep careful records. For the first year he maintained a tiny diary. This minuscule vest-pocket notebook is still in existence—the only de-

tailed record of the kind to be found in the Maclean papers. It is
a revealing day-by-day history.

Lunch cost him 10 to 20 cents; apples 5 cents; "drink" 5 cents; about
once a month there was a package of cigarettes, 10 cents. Every two
or three days he had a shave, 10 cents (Maclean stood out against the
fancy beards of the time); every few weeks "haircut and shave"
are recorded at 30 cents. Streetcar fare was 5 cents, but he also
walked a lot—and had to pay 20 cents for resoling for his boots. A new
white shirt was recorded at $1.50, a pair of pants $6.50.

And only from the little notebook do we learn that there was the
occasional interruption of fun. Maclean liked outdoor life, so with
brother Hugh, now in town and earning his living as a printer, he staked
out a tent on Toronto Island, duly recording the purchase of "a tent
rope at 25 cents and tent pins at 60 cents." The campers, of course,
commuted by ferry to their jobs, but made the most of their evenings
and Sundays to discover the complete Island life—and that always
included their neighbor Ned Hanlan, then thirty-two years old, 150
pounds in weight, and recognized the world around as the greatest
oarsman ever. Toronto-born Ned, in the years 1876–84 had won
three hundred consecutive races, breaking all previous records at
various distances, sometimes up to five miles, and with seeming effort-
lessness, defeating U.S., British and other established champions. In
1879 the grateful city of Toronto had given Hanlan a free lease to
an island property for life, and the citizens had raised $20,000 to build
him a house there. The area, named Hanlan's Point, was to become
long-remembered by generations of Torontonians as their favorite
picnic- and pleasure-grounds.

Perhaps it was the inspiration of Ned Hanlan that encouraged the
brothers to make the impressive investment, set down in the little book,
of a canoe at $35, and then to add air tanks for another $3. Next
came the logical step of joining the Toronto Canoe Club where they
rented a rack, $7, and a $1 locker, for the rest of the season.

During all these weeks Maclean's diary, in tiny, precise entries, indicates busy schedules in many voluntary activities. He collected
entry fees, $4.85 apiece, for the Ontario Rifle Association's matches
on the ranges; for their big *finale* he hired a band at $75. To the
Fencing Club he paid his annual fee of $5 gladly, no doubt, remember-
ing his championship win three years before, and the Club's subsequent
presentation to him of a silver medal with crossed foils.

Then from the little notebook arises an interesting question: was it while fencing or canoeing that he "split a rib"? Anyway, his entry shows a doctor's bill of $2, another outlay of $2 for medicine and 80 cents for a plaster. This mishap, however, didn't deter him from taking over the Canoe Club's books, sorting the details of incoming fees and outgoing checks, or helping with some special mailings on behalf of the Press Club, of which he had been a member for some time.

The summer of 1887 must have been warm, sunny and in all ways perfect for holidays. Only by some such explanation of natural causes can one imagine this young man, supposedly with the weight of a major capital investment on his mind, deciding to take a two-week vacation. Yet it happened! He and Hugh packed up their Island equipment of tent and blankets, etc., and loaded everything, including the canoe, on the train for the north. The little daily diary is virtually blank for the next fortnight as they paddled and camped through Muskoka.

In September the record resumes busily again, as Maclean rounded up news and advertisements for his first issue and accepted a few annual subscriptions. On September 19, he paid the $10 fee for the registration of the Grocer Publishing Company; he also joined the Canadian Press Association for $4. Next day, there's a jotting, "Canvassing for Canadian Grocer"—no doubt justifying the recorded expenditure of 20 cents for ale (but how many glasses?). To add to his cash resources he sold a couple of shares of his British American Assurance stock, bringing in $112.75, and five shares of Toronto Land, netting $104.50. Mr. Dyas paid in his $300. All in all, a big day.

And, finally, on September 23, 1887, the first issue of the *Canadian Grocer* came forth: sixteen pages in all, and declaring its mission under the decorative cover title in these words: "Published weekly in the interests of the grocery, produce, provision, liquor and confectionery trades." The promise of "weekly" publication could not be fulfilled for three months or so, and an announcement to that effect appeared on the opening editorial page; nevertheless this was the great moment when Canada's first weekly trade paper in any field made its bow. The subscription price was $2 per year; single copies sold for 10 cents.

For the next few issues John Bayne Maclean was the sole editor and contributor, and his writing style, which did not change much over the next sixty years, is apparent to the researcher of those back volumes. The second (October) issue did some vigorous airing of controversial subjects. "The advocates of Commercial Union" (with the U.S.) "claim that this country is rapidly going to the dogs and that our only hope lies in the adoption of their policy. We venture to assert that not one in a hundred of them has taken the trouble to study the question . . . things never so prosperous . . . trade increasing in volume . . . new manufacturies springing up . . . How do Commercial Unionists explain this?" Another editorial gives a newsy rundown on the past season's crop production: "partial failure in Ontario" due to weather . . . thus growers holding back for much higher prices . . . retailers cautious in their buying . . . and now a scarcity of railway rolling stock in the East, simply because of the huge crop in Manitoba where the CPR sent all available freight cars early-on, but out there, too, the farmers were waiting for better bids.

The same issue includes many bits and pieces of news which only a man diligently on the beat could assemble. "Mr. Jno. Morgan of Ailsa Craig (north of London, Ontario) has bought about 15,000 barrels of apples in that section this fall, the most of which have been shipped to the Western States, Eastern Provinces and the Old Country." "Tomato catsup in tins is becoming very popular . . . and costs about one-third less than the bottles." "The Canadian Pacific continues to reduce the time between here and China. Messrs. W. S. Goodhugh & Co., Montreal, cabled an order to Foochow on August 31, and the teas were delivered in Montreal on October 15. As the CP steamers do not go to Foochow, the teas had to be carried by a local steamer to Hong Kong and there transshipped."

A feature which would be avidly studied by *Grocer* readers over the years was the long list of current commodity prices to the retail trade. Under such headings as "Canned Goods," "Blacking," "Spices," etc., competitive lines were grouped, often identified with producer's name, and complete with the necessary statistics of size, weight, style of pack. In that fall of 1887 a retail grocer could get one dozen 3-pound cans of processed apples for 90 cents; "Patent" (the highest quality) flour at $3.80 per barrel; Guinness' Stout at $2.50 per dozen quarts, or domestic beers at 90 cents per dozen quarts. He could order "family proof" whiskey at 53 cents per Imperial gallon in bond, or $1.64 duty paid.

That Maclean knew the risks involved in this type of service is indicated by the statement constantly appearing over the price list, issue by issue. "All quotations in this department are under the direct control of the Editor, and are not paid for or doctored by any manufacturer or jobbing house; the right being reserved to exclude such firms as do not furnish reliable quotations."

Advertisers in the first few *Grocers* included Johnston's Fluid Beef, "the great strength giver" . . . Demerara sugar in hogsheads and barrels, ready at Davidson & Hay, Wholesale Grocers, Toronto . . . Glory Chewing Tobacco, "the best in the market" . . . and "The Food of the Future—Edwards' Desiccated Soups." Few of the original advertisers have survived under their nineteenth-century names, although it is interesting to note that the Fluid Beef, introduced in 1884 by John Lawson Johnston of Montreal and produced there, was to become the well-known Bovril after its originator returned to his native England and went into large-scale production. Johnston's eldest son, one of thirteen children, would become the "Bovril peer" as Lord Luke of Pavenham.

All illustrations in the publication were woodcuts, as photoengraving was still several years off. The masthead reflected correct Victorian taste in its ornate scrolls, which had been hand-carved by Fred Brigden, father of George and Fred H. Brigden, A.R.C.A., who were later to develop that fine family institution, the Brigden engraving house. The press run of the first few *Grocers* was 11,000 per month. Copies were mailed to "every grocer in Canada," to quote the owner's good round statement many years later, and they were asked to subscribe. Only a dozen or so responded to the first mailing, but by the time the paper became a weekly the subscriptions were pouring in.

The important matter of advertising solicitation took the young publisher on many business trips, as revealed in the little notebook. On October 3 he put on his new $17 suit and caught the train to Hamilton to call on food manufacturers, brokers and some of the leading grocers. His hotel bill for three nights came to $6.25, not counting the tip of 5 cents to the bellboy. Then on to Brantford, Preston and Galt— and that last stop apparently involved customer's entertainment for he recorded "drinks $1." Windsor and Detroit were next; they must have yielded solid results, for he treated himself to a $2 Pullman for the return to Toronto, and the porter got 25 cents. After a couple of days at headquarters he was on the road again, this time to visit the wholesale grocers and food packers in Kingston, Montreal and Ottawa.

That this introductory campaign, in person, was worthwhile is indicated by the notation dated November 29, concerning the hiring of an advertising salesman at $10 per week, plus 10 percent commission. Already there were several men engaged in selling subscriptions on commission. In the two months since *Grocer*'s first issue appeared, the paper had become a success and was paying its way.

Regardless of the pressure of operating his own business, John Bayne Maclean continued true to form by adding to his outside activities. He had become a member of the Swiss Club, the Imperial Federation League and the Gaelic Society. The last-named featured classes in Highland dancing—and he displayed some of his newly acquired prowess at the St. Andrew's Ball which was an important date on his 1887 schedule. Relieved of night assignments for a newspaper he could step out as a gay blade. Undoubtedly it was to brighten his style that he invested in a book, *The Art of Conversation*. An evening at the theatre cost him $1.50. (Did that mean one ticket or two?) A sleighing party set him back $2. That could hardly have been an affair for men only—yet it is a fact that nowhere in his notes or during conversational reminiscences in later times did he ever mention the name of a female companion during those first years in Toronto. Perhaps he deliberately held off from any romantic attachment until he felt sure of a dependable income for the future; that was an old cautious tradition from the Highlands—one certainly exemplified in his father's history. Or could it merely be that our young man's interest had not yet been engaged?

At any rate, for those first few months as a publisher, Maclean had managed an agreeable balance between business and recreation; but by the time *Grocer* was ready to appear regularly as a weekly he suddenly found himself caught up in a highly accelerated work schedule with little time for the pleasant avocations.

It happened this way.

For at least a year the Prime Minister, Sir John A. Macdonald, had realized he was without dependable newspaper support in Canada's English-language "metropolis." The *Mail,* formerly his dedicated mouthpiece, had declared itself politically independent, and even in the national election of February 1887 had shown a lukewarm attitude. The *Globe,* true to its Grit tradition, took up battle position on every move he made. Without effective journalistic backing in Ontario's capital, how could the Conservative leader hope to achieve his grand design for Canada; to unite East and West, to calm the suspicions of both the French-Canadian Catholics and the Orange-dominated citizenry of Toronto; to keep the country's assets, human and material, within the Dominion's boundaries and halt the drain southward, and to the same end establish a tariff system to ensure full growth and development from Atlantic to Pacific? True, he had, with pain and political suffering, guided the long-drawn-out project of the building of the CPR, but so much more remained to be done.

Gloom was prevalent. Numerous political commentators openly predicted the early break-up of the new nation. Even the Montreal *Gazette* raised some doubts. "It is not improbable," said a leading editorial in 1887, "that the people will, sooner than many now imagine, be called on to determine whether the work accomplished in 1867 is to be undone, whether Confederation is to be preserved or allowed to lapse into its original fragments, preparatory to absorption into the United States."

The Prime Minister believed the answer to this whole sorry situation was obvious: create a vigorous Tory organ in the Queen City. So, during that summer when young John Bayne Maclean was planning his new publication, secret meetings of a powerful Toronto group, hand-picked by the Chief, were deciding the newspaper's organization. W. R. Brock, a leading wholesale dry goods merchant, became the President; D'Alton McCarthy, brilliant lawyer and Sir John A.'s close confidant, worked at fever pitch (at one point he memoed the Prime Minister "We must start the *Empire* or prepare for defeat at the next general election, if not before that"); David Creighton, Conservative M.P.P. and Grey County organizer, formerly in the printing business in Owen Sound, was appointed manager and initial fund-raiser.

Finding the capital had its worrying complexities and disappointments. Macdonald promised to raise $50,000 from Montreal well-wishers, but whether this eventually came through remains a moot point. He personally subscribed for $4000 worth of *Empire* stock, putting up $100 in cash at the outset. Creighton's whirlwind tour of devout Tory groups, however, yielded $150,000 in stock subscriptions—and perhaps there were other participants as well, for in the "puff" notice sent to all newspapers across Canada in December 1887, it was stated, "The new paper starts under the most promising auspices. The capital of $250,000 is ample and guarantees financial soundness."

"The staff has been selected with the greatest care," the announcement continued—a fair claim, as Creighton had hand-picked what at least one outsider called "one of the most capable staffs ever assembled under one roof in Canada." There were such men as A. H. U. Colquhoun, a first-class journalist who would later become Ontario's Deputy Minister of Education: H. J. P. Good, virtually the father of sports editors in Canada, and the man who had managed Ned Hanlan; and J. Castell Hopkins, eventually to become founder-editor of the famous *Canadian Annual Review.*

A major difficulty in staffing the *Empire* had involved the post of commercial-financial editor. Creighton had known young John Bayne Maclean in Owen Sound and had watched his work on the *Mail* but now that he was launched on a career of trade-paper publishing an *Empire* offer could hardly interest him. On second thought, Creighton decided it might be worked with special strategy. The *Empire*'s manager spoke to the Prime Minister, and the Chief agreed to have a chat with the young publisher, hoping to win him back to the daily field.

As Maclean recalled the story in a letter written half-a-century later: "Early in November 1887, Sir John A. Macdonald asked me to see him and said he wanted to make the business and financial part of the *Empire* its most important section, as practically all the subscriptions came from manufacturers. He asked me first to go on as Financial Editor, but I declined, saying I had started a business and could not do so, but that I would do what I could to find him a man. Creighton had quite a collection of applications, none of them any good. He probably told Sir John, and again Sir John saw me and I agreed to go on for six months to get them started, but that I was to carry on my work on the *Grocer* at the same time." The arrangement was readily accepted and a deal concluded. Maclean was to edit the *Empire*'s commercial-financial news for six months only, with salary at the $1200 per annum rate; he would be supplied with an assistant, and— of course!—would be allowed to continue to edit and manage his own *Canadian Grocer.*

Where they met was not mentioned—whether in Toronto, on the P.M.'s private car during a train trip, or in a hotel room, in Ottawa, in the office on Parliament Hill, or at Earnscliffe, Sir John's residence. And when? In 1887 the Prime Minister, seventy-two years old, had been confronted with a succession of crises: in October came the sudden sagging of CPR stock values plus urgent requests from Baring's of London for quick monetary bolstering by Ottawa; then, a week or so later, from the interprovincial conference issued round after round of defiant demands on Ottawa—another proof of the rebellious spirit and rising power of sectional government; and for an anxious month at the end of the year there was the almost total failure of the Joint High Commission meeting in Washington, to which Britain had sent the powerful Joseph Chamberlain, in an effort to smooth out the

strained relations between Canada and the U.S. It seems most unusual
that in the midst of all such grave troubles the Chief could have
found time to talk up the *Empire*'s commercial page appointment with
twenty-five-year-old John Bayne Maclean.

How it was arranged is perhaps less important than the fact that
another of those tools which would help shape the final architecture
of a spacious life had been unexpectedly pressed upon Maclean.
No wonder he blithely drew $20 from his bank account, and on De-
cember 24 did his Christmas shopping. He bought napkin rings, $1.80;
a book, $4; tie and gloves, $2; a cake knife, $1.25—presumably all
for Aunt Bella and Uncle John with whom his mother resided; and
then shared with brother Hugh the selection of an unspecified "present
for Ma, $5.50." That same day, in anticipation of his visit with the
family, he treated himself to a Turkish bath and bought a tie, a
shirt and a bottle of hair restorer. It must have been a jubilant
Christmas.

Now, facing the challenge of two jobs, the *Empire*'s financial page
every day, and his own weekly paper, Maclean realized he needed
extra help. A second advertising man was hired for *Grocer;* he
promptly fell ill, and his new boss footed both hospital and doctor's
bills.

Then on January 1, 1888, Hugh gave up his job in a printshop and
came to work for his brother at 9 Jordan Street. For the next sixty
years there would be both co-operation and competition between two
brothers who could seldom agree on any subject, who at times would
quarrel bitterly but who would always in their own Maclean style
remain fond of each other. (In 1941, Hugh C. wrote to John B. a long,
complaining letter, one of a series of outspoken exchanges in which
they tried to establish just what had happened in the early days. "I
left a $10 a week job to go to you for $6—a half-starved printer twenty
years of age," the younger man declared. But John's little leather
notebook shows that Hugh was paid $10 per week regularly.)

The weekly edition of *Grocer* brought in a flood of subscriptions,
and the staff—Hugh, plus a girl and the advertising salesman—worked
hard. On January 6, Hugh wrote to his mother, "You will no doubt
be wondering why I haven't written but if you could see me going
through the streets of Toronto, always running, my overcoat untied,
and without gloves, and sweat pouring off my face, you would remain
without a letter. We got out the first weekly edition today, of which
you will get a copy tomorrow, and if I am kept as busy in the future

as I have been this week, you will get few letters. Jack is in a bigger hurry than I am. He wears no overcoat and hires the fire engine to carry him when he is in a hurry." The letter is written on the *Canadian Grocer* letterhead which featured the address and the name of "J. B. McLean" as general manager.

In spite of his *Empire* duties and "bigger hurry," Jack calmly accepted yet a third job early in 1888 when the Canadian Packers' Association invited him to be secretary. Here the chief responsibility was to gather figures of the pack of vegetables and fruits at various times through the seasons and then distribute the information quickly to the trade. It added up to concentrated sessions, demanding both speed and care, and there was no remuneration. Maclean remained secretary for five years, only relinquishing the post when he moved out of Canada to undertake a special business project. That the Packers appreciated his "faithful and efficient services" is still evident today in the words of the glowing resolution which the Association passed unanimously and forwarded—to become a lifetime treasure in the Maclean files.

# CHAPTER IV

# MAN OF MANY JOBS

"Seest thou a man diligent in his business,
he shall stand before kings."
*Proverbs* (Penciled note in J.B.M.'s files)

THE PATTERN of a life had been set. Already John Bayne Maclean, just past his twenty-fifth birthday, had blithely accepted diversification of work and interests, an overload in fact, not as a burden but as an opportunity to be grasped. Diversity of activity was to be the rule for the long future. For Maclean, variety was not merely the spice of life; rather, it was the essential challenge of living each day to the full. As to the cumulative results, whether in constantly widening contacts or solid cash-in-the-bank, they were already in evidence at the close of the year 1887.

In the third issue of the new *Empire,* under date of December 29, there appeared an innocent-seeming report of the Dominion Live Stock Association Executive Committee meeting, called to discuss the threat of the railways to cancel reduced-fare arrangements for the member-shippers. Nothing much was decided on this matter, but the second paragraph provides a clue as to another significant reason for the gathering: "A vote of thanks was tendered to Mr. J. B. McLean, commercial editor of the *Empire,* for the attention he had always given to the livestock trade." Proposer of the vote declared that Mr. McLean had furnished the only correct and reliable reports of the trade, and he (the speaker) had no doubt he (McLean) would more than keep his reputation in the future.

The busy young reporter must have been happy when he returned to his corner in the *Empire* offices and wrote the little piece, and happier still when he saw it on page 2 of next morning's paper. The words of praise, which no false modesty led him to suppress, gave him as much satisfaction as the substantial salary. Moreover, he could imagine the Chief in Ottawa noting the report and congratulating himself on having so able a young man on the staff of his new organ in Toronto.

The *Empire*'s career began promisingly. There was good news coverage from points around the world. From Paris: "Sarah Bernhardt is wearing mourning for her lately deceased panther kitten, Tigrette." And from London, where it was announced that Lord and Lady Randolph Churchill had arrived in St. Petersburg, Russia, and, although the Czar gave the gentleman an audience, it was emphasized that the visitors were on a private trip, specifically to escape the cold and chills of Western Europe and "try the studiously heated houses of St. Petersburg." As to local events, the hand-picked *Empire* staff appeared to be doing a good job. The big snowfall had opened the tobogganing and snowshoeing season in Toronto. The first font of type ever made in the city was manufactured at the Toronto Type Foundry, and became a part of the equipment of the *Empire*. A great WCTU campaign of speeches had a strong over-all theme: "Purity in the Home, and God in the Government." Toronto music-lovers could take their choice of *Faust, Lohengrin,* and *Queen of Sheba* during a forthcoming week of opera. And on Maclean's commercial page there was a special report concerning the brisk business at the Horse Repository where "they are paying $100 to $150 for heavy horses (1350 to 1450 lbs.) for use in the woods."

Maclean's journalistic double life moved ahead smoothly. (Perhaps one should call it a triple life for his correspondence work for out-of-town papers continued. As an example, an article on "Toronto Bucket Shops" in the Montreal *Star* of February 17, 1888, for which he was paid $4 for a single column.) Prospects for the weekly *Canadian Grocer* were encouraging. Brother Hugh reported a good reception during his first advertising sales trip which took him to the canning plants and wholesalers in the Niagara Peninsula. And even when both men had to be away from the Jordan Street office, there was no cause for concern. Miss Priscilla Forbes would keep shop for them.

Nobody ever gave more devotion to a job or an employer than John Bayne Maclean's first woman employee, a girl who had previously been working for *Grocer*'s printers. In January 1888, she accepted his offer of $4 a week and moved into the tiny office, where she quietly assumed responsibility for "everything": keeping the books, handling the correspondence, rushing down the hall to accept calls on the building's single telephone ("Just ask Central for number 630"), organizing the flow of copy to the typesetters and checking the proofs sent back, adjusting the subscription lists and, as soon as each issue came hot from the press, mailing the paper. From the first day, Priscilla Forbes efficiently served as a combination office boy and office manager, deft at all the routines including the gracious welcoming of unexpected visitors who dropped in to discuss an article in the last issue or a full-page advertisement for the next. And no matter how crowded the day's schedule, her appearance at 6 P.M. was precisely the same as at the early morning start, i.e. immaculate from the tips of her laced boots to the shining pompadour of golden-red hair.

Miss Forbes was to remain with Maclean for more than half-a-century. When this writer joined the company in 1919 she was herself an institution within the larger one; ostensibly her job was then cashier, in a brass-barred cage. She had become friend and adviser to all the women employees—or at least to those she approved of—and the guardian of all the Colonel's business secrets. Later on, when she was no longer capable of exacting work, she moved as a dignified Presence through the offices and corridors, and her chief activity at that point was to water the pots of geraniums which the Colonel had ordered placed on every window sill. (His neat soldierly soul disapproved of the cluttered newspapers, blue books and souvenir ashtrays which, from time immemorial, have been the accepted window decoration in editorial offices.)

The respect and affection between the two was mutual. To the Colonel she remained the epitome and symbol of the loyalty he demanded from his staff. Once during a conversation about his early days in publishing he declared, "There were times when, without my knowledge, Miss Forbes put her own savings into our cash box, so that we could meet urgent expenses."

In spite of the pressure of each day's work, Maclean still found time for his voluntary pursuits and one of the most important of these was the newly established Red Cross. Indeed, he had been among the little group of founders. During the Northwest Rebellion of 1885, when troops under General Middleton were sent to the South Saskatchewan River country to halt Louis Riel's second Métis uprising, Maclean had helped to organize a small committee for the collecting and dispatching of medical supplies and other comforts for Her Majesty's Forces.

From this Toronto group, consisting chiefly of militia officers, emerged the nucleus of Canada's first Red Cross Society—later to be officially associated with the British organization, and eventually to merge with other Canadian groups in the first National Council of the Canadian Red Cross. Maclean became the national secretary and rose to more senior offices over the years. In 1949, when he was the last surviving charter member of Canada's great Red Cross establishment, he received the honorary title of National Counsellor of the Society.

Another venerable service body could claim John Bayne Maclean as one of its founders, and that was the St. John's Ambulance Brigade. Far back, when he was a twenty-year-old taking his gunnery course in Kingston, he had been witness to a tragic accident. An artilleryman was thrown from a gun carriage and lay on the ground seriously injured, yet neither Maclean nor any other bystander knew how to assist him, and the man was to die shortly. Within the next year or so Maclean's efforts with the 31st Greys to train soldiers in first aid had started a similar movement in other regiments.

The formal organization of the St. John's Ambulance Brigade had to wait until 1895, when Maclean's close friend and associate in the work (and formerly the Medical Officer with the expedition to Saskatchewan) General G. Sterling Ryerson, M.D., led the way—first with the Ontario Centre, and a few weeks later with the Montreal branch which Maclean brought into being. His active interest in St. John's Ambulance over the years was to win various promotions and honors such as Honorary Associate and later Officer Brother, but when, in 1948, he was offered the rank of Commander Brother, he turned it down. No doubt what he had expected was the top-ranking Knight of Grace. At the turn of the century two of his associates in the founding of the order in Canada had been granted such knighthoods; indeed, the Colonel's files of correspondence recall at several points that he was also offered the honor then, but had suggested that it be given instead to his friend, Sir Frederick W. Borden, M.D., Laurier's Minister of Militia. There is little question that he spent the rest of his lifetime awaiting another opportunity to step into the select circle of Knights, but the offer never came.

All through the '80s and for many years after, Maclean's interest and responsibilities in the militia were to continue and expand. True, he had found it difficult to carry on with the Owen Sound Greys, but a transfer, with the rank of Lieutenant, to the Toronto unit of the 10th Royal Grenadiers in the spring of 1887 meant that he could resume regular participation in parade nights, training courses and summer camps. A happy man in uniform once again! The Grenadiers recognized their good luck by promoting him to Captain and Adjutant in double-quick time.

"You were my ideal soldier," one of the Grenadier sergeants wrote to the Colonel on his seventy-fifth birthday. The letter went on to give at least one sound reason for the statement, and as follows:

The battalion had been under canvas at Niagara-on-the-Lake, and, come Saturday, the men were granted a day's leave to visit the Falls, fifteen miles upriver. They had marched jubilantly out of camp toward the railway station when Captain Maclean, busy in the tent marked "Orderly Room," received a sudden message from the Officer Commanding. All men, said the order, were to be on parade that afternoon, smartly turned out, with buttons and boots shining. The reason? General Otter (later Sir William Otter), District Officer Commanding in the Toronto area, was in the Niagara neighborhood and had decided to drop in at the camp and review the troops. Maclean immediately dispatched Sergeant Martin to the station. By that time the men were already on the train, and the merry talk and singing turned to muttering when they were ordered out of the cars and made to fall-in on the platform.

At that moment Sergeant Martin, standing by the station window, heard a message clicking over the telegraph wires—in Morse code, of course, but the same as plain English to him. It was addressed to the O.C. of the camp and announced that Otter had been forced to postpone his visit to a later day.

What to do? After an agonizing moment of indecision, Martin marched the men back into the railway cars and waved to the train crew to take off.

He waited for a quarter-of-an-hour—time enough for delivery of the telegram—before returning to the Adjutant in the Orderly Room. "Sir," he began, hand at the salute, and launched into a full confession.

Captain Maclean listened, his face set, expressionless. When the story ended, there was a prolonged silence, broken only by the buzzing of horseflies.

"Sergeant, you disobeyed an order."

"Yes, sir."

"And in military law, disobedience by a sergeant deserves a stern reprimand."

"I know, sir, but—"

The calm voice interrupted. "But in this case there will be no reprimand. In fact, I want to congratulate you for showing initiative and acting promptly. The men will have a good day."

Meanwhile, back at 9 Jordan Street, Toronto, business had been moving ahead nicely. *Canadian Grocer* in weekly form had brought in enough money to justify the acquisition, in 1888, of a certain faltering trade paper called *Books and Notions*. It had been founded in 1884 to serve the book, stationery, fancy goods, music and wallpaper trades, and was for some years both before and after Maclean's purchase "The official organ of the Booksellers and Stationers' Association of Ontario."

The first couple of issues under new ownership appeared thin and anemic, yet there was a reason, as set forth in December's first editorial: "We enclose in this number an envelope and blank order. We ask subscribers to send their remittances upon receipt of their paper. The amount that each one owes *Books and Notions* is but small, but when you consider that we have over two thousand dollars due to us in these small amounts, you will see the necessity there is for pressing for them. To those who owe us nothing, and who have already paid for the coming year, we owe our thanks, and ask them to use the envelope to enclose information from their districts which may be interesting to the trade . . ."

Following this paragraph came a happier one, announcing an exciting new format in the next issue. Sad to relate, though, the January 1889 issue looked just like its predecessors, the reason being, as explained on the opening editorial page, that "our new type and general outfit did not arrive in time."

So the February issue acted as the proper opening gun under the Maclean ownership. The page size expanded, paper quality was better and there was eye appeal in the new typography. The general health of the publication was improving, according to the opening paragraph: "*Books and Notions* has now on its list of subscribers 1206 Canadian booksellers, stationers and newsdealers, several hundred more than any wholesale dealer or jobber thought were in the country, and within 2 percent of the total number . . . Can any other trade publication in the world show as good a record?"

In no time at all, and exactly as any contemporary of Maclean by then had learned to expect, the publisher of *Books and Notions* was wielding editorial cudgels on behalf of the trade served. In May 1889 began a long (and losing) fight against the supplying of schoolbooks free to pupils. A Toronto school trustee, "anxious of fame at the expense of the taxpayer," had introduced the plan. "Why did not he at the same time suggest supplying to each child a suit of clothes and a dinner every day, and make the general rate payer foot the bill?" the editorial raged. Surely if the taxpaying public provided schools and teaching, it was not too much to ask that the parties benefited (the parents) pay for the necessary books? Naturally the Toronto trustee would hardly get far with his wildly radical idea; still it *might* be wise for booksellers in the area to interview *their* respective trustees "and have a quietus put upon the affair at the earliest possible moment."

It was easy to take a firm stand against an unimportant local School Board member—much, much easier than to cross swords with the Dominion Government, and thus, inevitably, with the grand Old Chief. Yet this is what happened in another issue of the publication that spring. Ottawa's "National Policy" had "so far worked entirely to the disadvantage of booksellers and newsdealers," and actual discrimination against the trade was being practised by the customs and postal authorities. The editorial went on to explain that the dealer must order his foreign-published periodicals in bulk and pay a heavy duty on them; thus his over-the-counter price must be higher than the retail price printed on the cover. But it seemed that now, after educating his public to this situation, he was up against a threatening new problem, in that a big foreign publisher had announced that he was ready to mail all his publications direct to Canadian readers at the regular foreign price. And "our paternal Government is actually letting these papers come through FREE OF DUTY!"

Bold, forthright speaking—especially for the young man who venerated the paternal figure presiding over the Government. And perhaps the sudden realization of the enormity of his act inspired the last sentence of the editorial, which read, "We are not seeking a quarrel with the Government, nor using these facts for the purpose of hostile criticism; all we seek is fair play for our trade."

Eventually the name of the publication would be changed to *Bookseller and Stationer*. The paper survives today in several Maclean-Hunter journals which it "seeded" over the years, as greater specialization became desirable. The same process was to be repeated with other publications; indeed, most of the Company's trade papers have grown from sprigs whittled from existing trees and planted out in new soil.

*Hardware Merchandising* is the up-to-date descendant of *Hardware and Metal Merchant* which first saw the light of day around the end of 1888, a monthly at the outset, then geared up to weekly presentation. It was a success from the start, and the trade it served had a special fondness for the representative cover design, used for several years, consisting of a montage of overlapped drawings showing a washbasin above curlicues of pipes, a big kitchen stove complete with hot water cistern, metal pots and pans in close-up, an overwhelming basement furnace, new-fangled radiator, and a typical hardware store front. The logo was exactly right too—massive, masculine, readable—and J. W. Bengough, the most famous political cartoonist of the day, had been paid $5 for designing it.

The editorial contents of *H & M* followed much the same pattern as successfully utilized in *Grocer,* with several pages in each issue devoted to current market quotations for the numerous varieties and sizes of a store's essential items. All the news affecting the trade, plus comments thereon, found a place in its columns. In the January 1890 issue there was a survey of heating developments: Toronto's furnace trade had zoomed ahead, with at least fifteen firms in the business, compared with four or five just three years before; "gasoline" stoves were proving popular across Canada—probably 130,000 of these would be sold in 1890. Under the title "How to Use a Coal Cook Stove," there was a helpful little piece with detailed directions for the salesclerk trying to answer his lady customer's questions. "Users of wood as a fuel for cook stoves," it starts off, "often find great difficulty in managing a coal burner for the first time."

In the same issue we suddenly stumble on proof that Maclean occasionally made one story serve two purposes. Almost a full page is given over to a report, reprinted with credit line from the Toronto *Empire,* summarizing Canada's year-end situation in metals. More business was being done with American manufacturers rather than English sources, he noted . . . copper was making a good come-back after its recent low prices because of the huge stocks on hand . . . England's geared-up needs for iron and steel resulted recently in the sale of a big shipment of Alabama pig iron for export to Britain . . . Canadian iron manufacturers had been running full blast for months back, and there were still orders booked for far ahead.

With the opening of the last decade of the nineteenth century, Maclean, the publisher, could look around him and find ample signs of success. He had three trade papers, and business had developed to the point where it was necessary to open an office in Montreal. Brother Hugh C. was sent down to take charge at 115 St. François Xavier Street, and, as noted in each journal's masthead, he "will be pleased to have subscribers and advertisers call upon him there. He will also pay special attention to gathering business items and attending regularly to the interests of this paper."

There had been expansion at home base as well. The Maclean group had left the cramped quarters in the printshop and moved just around the corner to 6 Wellington St. West. Here was established the first Maclean "plant," consisting of a couple of typesetting machines, etc., plus a staff of two or three compositors under a foreman. The final printing of each issue was handled by an outside firm.

A joint stock company had been formed, with nominal capital of $25,000. J. B. Maclean was president; Hugh C. MacLean became secretary-treasurer. (Note that while both men changed the spelling of the name, they did not agree on what that spelling should be.) The brothers bought out the T. W. Dyas interest for $3000 in the year 1890—giving him a nice profit on his original investment of $300, plus another $400 that he invested a little later.

It is impossible now to determine the relative stake of the two brothers in the business at that time. No share certificates were ever issued.

Nevertheless, a firmer, businesslike foundation was in evidence by 1890. The record from the past had been good; the promise for the future was still better, and more developments could be planned.

*Dry Goods Review* made its bow in January 1891, and, as announced by the publisher, the trade to be served "is the only one in Canada which has hitherto not had a journal of its own." For the next half century and more, good old *D.G.R.* would serve the countless retailers in the business of piece goods, stockings, ready-to-wear and all the thousand oddments companioning such "dry goods." The publication had a personality of its own right from the first—special care being given to richly ornamental initial letters at the opening of each article, fancy hand-drawn headings with atmospheric backgrounds, and other up-to-date touches. Indeed, the avowed aim, as set forth in the first issue's house advertisement, was "to make the *Review* as superior to other trades' journals as fine silk is to plain homespun."

Fashion news held a good part of the spotlight, naturally. Women's dress goods for early 1891 would, it was predicted, stress "black, heliotrope, silver and iron grey, myrtle green, mordore and blue royale." ("Mordore," now a long-forgotten term, was an Anglicization of *"mordoré,"* or bronzed.) The "Gents' Furnishings" column in the first issue noted "black underwear" as a season's feature. Black silk handkerchiefs continued smart for men's evening use; but at the same time, retail buyers were asked to note "more white kid gloves with plain backs are in demand than those with stitched backs."

It goes without saying that the special economics of the dry goods field received thorough analysis, issue by issue. Even in Vol. 1, No. 1, there was an outspoken discussion concerning the involved matter of credit arrangements with a store's customers. *Dry Goods Review* was all for shorter credit periods as a protection for the retailer. "We strongly advise that all should insist on quarterly, or at the very most, half-yearly settlements. If the latter, then divide the year at 1st April and 1st October, while there is money circulating from eggs and butter or early harvest, and before the interest on mortgage and agricultural implement notes have absorbed it all." Canada, it appears, was still one big farming community.

Nevertheless the journal regularly dug into manufacturing developments. In 1891 the glove company at Acton, Ontario, had two hundred employees compared with half-a-dozen a few years previous, while down in Coaticook, Quebec, the Cascade Narrow Fabric Co. "now produces sufficient braid to bind about ten thousand dresses each day."

Success was in the air, not merely for the dry goods business but also for the publisher of its first trade paper.

One basic reason had to do with the quality of his own products and insistence on good service to both advertisers and readers. Maclean and his printer-brother produced their publications on good stock, as opposed to the cheap newsprint generally used by trade papers of the day. They had complete advertising rate cards for each paper and no private deals to cut those rates were permitted at any time. Each advertiser had the privilege of providing new "copy" for any issue as desired; there was no charge for new typesetting. (Hugh C. always claimed he and his brother were the first trade paper publishers on the continent to establish this arrangement.) Each journal stayed carefully within its own trade boundaries for subject matter. In short, the Macleans specialized. And they paid their bills promptly. All these factors contributed to the company's rapid success.

Such well-demonstrated performances undoubtedly encouraged the debut of the fifth Maclean journal, the *Canadian Printer and Publisher,* which, as the name indicates, was to serve his own industry. In May

1892's Vol. 1, No. 1, a long opening article explained that the Canadian Press Association at the recent annual meeting decided that publication of a journal devoted to printing and publishing was long overdue; subsequently the J. B. Maclean Co. was urged to establish such an organ, backed by the hearty support of the CPA. That was one reason "Why We Are Here" (the plain, no-nonsense heading on the piece) but there were others. "Is it not a fact that we are all too busy looking after the interests of everyone but the printer to think of ourselves?" To illustrate, the writer noted how the recent increase in the duty on baking powders had practically shut out U.S. manufacturers, yet "for years these people had been worth $10 to $1500 annually to nearly every paper in Canada." Now, the one or two Canadian manufacturers had the field to themselves *"and do not need to advertise."*

Or consider this other vexing situation: the duty on imported printing equipment. In the year previous, $11,375 duty was collected on presses brought into the country, "yet not one of such presses can be made in Canada, nor are they likely to be for some time. There is therefore no Canadian industry to protect . . . Surely the 3000 and odd Employing Printers in the Dominion have sufficient influence to secure the free admission of printing presses and machinery." Echoes and extensions of this legitimate complaint were to enliven John Bayne Maclean's remarks, in public, in private, or in print, for the rest of his days.

By the time *Printer and Publisher* was born, photoengraving had mastered the process of halftone illustrations; thus the printing industry's own journal had a quality appearance right from the start. Frequently a painting, such as *Spring,* with shepherdess, lambs, birds, daisies, was presented in fine halftone greys and black on a full page insert on special stock; underneath, credit was given not only to the artist but to the engraver as well, for instance "Half-tone by the Canada Photo-Engraving Bureau." No doubt the engraver supplied the block free in exchange for the credit line.

It was a publication for publishers. Each of the early issues bristled with names and happenings within the Fourth Estate and its allied groups. Vol. 1, No. 1, noted: "J. E. Atkinson and Miss Elliott (Madge Merton) of the Toronto *Globe,* joined their fortunes matrimonially some days ago, being the first event of the kind in the history of Canadian journalism. May all good fortune attend them." Atkinson, then the *Globe*'s political reporter, twenty-seven years old, was to reach his multi-millionaire zenith as publisher-owner of the Toronto *Daily Star* from 1899 to 1948.

Naturally with the surge of expansion in the Maclean group, it was necessary to increase the staff. JBM hired some promising young men who were to achieve fame and/or notoriety in various ways.

One of these was John A. Cooper, son of a Clinton, Ontario, book-seller (and avid reader of *B. & S.*). The lad had done some part-time work for the Company during his years at college. On the day of his graduation in 1892 he received word from Maclean that the editor of *Dry Goods Review* had "thrown in the sponge" and gone off to California. (Although definite identification is not possible at this distance, the departing editor may have been one Charles Morison, an older man who had been long-time city editor of the *Mail* before becoming first editor of *Dry Goods*.) The vacant chair was offered to Cooper who promptly accepted. Later he would edit *Bookseller and Stationer* and *Printer and Publisher* as well. Cooper was to serve his country in many ways. He became a distinguished editor of the *Canadian Courier,* an important magazine in the 1900s; he raised a battalion for overseas service in World War I, and his title of "Colonel" was to remain with him until death took him in his late eighties. He was active at the national level in the Red Cross. And for many years "between wars," as he would describe it, he was happily engaged as the permanent, salaried "czar" chosen by the motion picture exhibitors to overlord their industry.

His younger brother, Ernest Cooper, joined the Maclean group later on—John having asked Maclean to give the boy some training following graduation from university. After a couple of years in the Montreal office, Ernest moved on to become one of Maclean's alumni, in whom the Colonel always took pride. In 1918 he settled in London, England, where he became in time managing director of Gillette. In January 1944 he was knighted for his work in aiding Lord Beaver-brook in the Ministry of Aircraft production and also for his service as industrial adviser to the Government of Northern Ireland.

At one point the Maclean group was joined by genial, able Joseph Clark who concentrated chiefly on *Printer and Publisher*. He left to take charge at *Saturday Night,* and then to settle in for the remainder of his life as editor of Atkinson's *Star*. His son, Gregory Clark, grew up to become a popular by-liner with readers of the *Star* and various other publications.

A quite bizarre character of the long-ago group was Arthur P.

Choate, first hired—as were all the early staff members—to be a combined salesman, editor, and when necessary, bookkeeper. Choate's early career had paralleled Maclean's, in that the former had been financial reporter on both the *World* and the *Mail*. After a few years in the Maclean establishment Choate, with a good deal of money from stock market speculation, moved to New York to extend his opportunities. For the next twenty-five years he gambled in the market, or promoted such industrial ventures as streamlined fruit-raising in Central America. More than a millionaire, he returned to his native town of Peterborough, Ontario, and all might have gone well had he stayed. But Wall Street beckoned again. By this time he had lost his ability to read and interpret the tale the ticker tape was telling. His fortune dwindled, and in 1930 he died of senility and starvation in an East Side boardinghouse in New York.

As for A. H. U. Colquhoun, there was to be an interesting musical-chairs rearrangement between him and our man over the next decade or so. Colquhoun had been Maclean's boss on the *Empire,* but when this paper folded (as described in the next chapter) he was delighted to accept Maclean's invitation to join the trade paper group. He edited three papers at one time, *Dry Goods, Bookseller* and *Printer and Publisher,* did a thorough job on each and made those journals "respected, feared and trusted," as Maclean declared many years later.

Colquhoun left to join Sir John Willison on the *News,* when a wealthy businessman established it with a neat budget of $450,000, representing the profit he had made on Dominion Steel shares. But there may have been another reason for parting from Maclean. According to an interesting story the Colonel once recounted, Colquhoun wanted to invest $8000, just inherited from his mother's estate, in the Maclean Company. "I refused to accept that or any other outside money at the time," the Colonel said, "While I had perfect confidence in the future, I did not feel I should allow anyone to risk money with me."

Nevertheless the friendship between the two continued, and, when Colquhoun was appointed Ontario's Deputy Minister of Education, Maclean—along with many others—felt a new stage of confidence in the provincial school system.

## CHAPTER V

# *MY FRIEND, SIR JOHN A.*

"A great editor who never ceased to be
a good reporter."
*Said of Arthur Ford, editor, the London Free Press*

JOHN BAYNE MACLEAN'S connection with the *Empire* expanded from
the originally specified six-month period into a stretch of some three
years—proof not only of his capacity to handle several demanding
jobs simultaneously but of the newspaper's satisfaction with his service.
Occasionally there had been a flare-up, due partly to the jittery nerves
of the *Empire*'s directors as they watched their monthly financial losses
mount, and also in some degree to certain stubborn, inborn characteristics of Maclean himself.

In September 1890 the *Empire*'s prime mover, D'Alton McCarthy,
Q.C., had received a letter from a Port Hope, Ontario, man named
Beatty—probably a shareholder—criticizing the paper's change in
format from eight to six columns per page, and also remarking that, as
any reader could see, it was doing a lamentable job in the matter of
advertising solicitation. The latter comment cut close to the bone. Both
McCarthy and Creighton had struggled long and hard to make Sir
John A.'s publishing project profitable; at one point their indignation
at being omitted from the federal government's lists for departmental
advertisements had boiled up into a complaint direct to the Prime
Minister. The shrewd Old Chief had dealt with that situation nicely:
don't communicate with the individual Ministers, he said, ("the letters
are certain to get on file and be at the mercy of every government
and junior clerk in the Departments") but just choose the most
important advertisements and advise him, and then "I will personally
ask each Minister to approve them." The plan worked fairly well for
a time, although occasionally the accounts were slow pay, necessitating
private reminders to Sir John A.

To him, too, went the Beatty letter, accompanied by an angry note from McCarthy. The enclosure, he said, had undoubtedly been inspired by J. B. Maclean. "The latter, in addition to his own business, has, ever since the *Empire* started, found time to advise us as to how it should be run. Generally his suggestions are worthless but occasionally they are fair and are utilized. He has evidently been discussing the change in size with Mr. Beatty and hence the letter."

Perhaps McCarthy's suspicions were groundless, perhaps not; at any rate, if Maclean received a reprimand it is likely that his native coolness under fire would have won the final argument with a calm explanation. Already, at the age of twenty-eight, he was a man amply fortified with a reason for every move made. When one of the *Empire* directors objected to the condensation of reports of U.S. stock exchanges—and that at a time when other Canadian financial pages were dominated by New York and Chicago activities—Maclean replied curtly that he had little space for American markets; in fact, there was more news in Canada every day than he could hope to present. And hadn't Sir John A. Macdonald founded the paper to emphasize Canadian and Empire news?

This emphasis on Canadian news was to remain with him for life, and to continue as a guideline for the publications he founded. (Until 1968 *The Financial Post* was probably the only paper of its kind in the world outside of the Iron Curtain that did not publish any quotations from the New York Stock Exchange. Now it publishes weekly closing prices.)

Maclean's activities in the field of daily journalism were necessarily drawing to a close in 1890–91, because of the growing responsibilities in his own company, but the theory on which he based his success as a reporter, editor and publisher had already been thoroughly proved. It was simply this: get the news directly from the men who make it. Whether engaged in covering the Toronto livestock market, or pursuing a national or international intrigue, the Colonel sought out the newsmakers themselves, wherever they were. He had a talent for gaining their confidence, persuading them to interpret their policies, clarify inconsistencies and explain the motivation behind their decisions. He was never content just to settle for a story; always he would press on for "the story behind the story." At a time when many reporters were shabby, underpaid, occasionally underfed and frequently disdained, Maclean was an exception. He dressed well, ate well and made certain that his list of contacts constantly expanded, whether among upper-crust political and business figures or the ward aldermen and firemen.

He enjoyed extra work, particularly a political feature outside the normal day's routine of financial-commercial news. When a project of that kind brought him close to his hero, Sir John A., it would stay in his mind as an unforgettable experience. Here is one such episode:

Back in the year 1885 when Macdonald was on a visit to Britain, he had been interviewed by a journalist who discussed with him the possibilities of a federation, commercial and possibly political, of all the Empire countries. Apparently the report never saw the light of day during the '80s, perhaps because Sir John felt that the timing was wrong. Nevertheless it had been typeset and a complete sheaf of printer's proofs stayed in the Prime Minister's files in Ottawa.

According to Maclean's reminiscences thirty years later, the same subject of British federation happened to arise during a casual meeting and chat he had with the Chief in 1890. Sir John A. mentioned the unpublished interview, and immediately Maclean suggested that it be unearthed, studied and brought up to date with fresh or expanded angles—and he, of course, would be delighted to do any necessary rewriting. Macdonald agreed and the plan went ahead. As soon as all the material, old and new, was in his hands, Maclean did a complete rewriting job, which, however, was still not quite final, as the Prime Minister added a few more ideas on receipt of the manuscript.

The piece, still in the form of an interview, with short, searching questions and leisurely, discursive answers, was published in full in the *Empire*. To read it today is to be reminded once again of old Sir John A.'s unique combination of vision and common sense.

Empire Federation was, he said, practical—at least as practical as the "political connection between Canadian settlements on the Atlantic and Canadian settlements on the distant Pacific, in advance of all railway and even telegraphic connections."

The first step would have to be an experimental council of Empire in London, and, if it had a happy issue, a permanent council. The basis of the union would be not military but commercial. Britain would have to surrender her adherence to the doctrine of free trade; although theoretically correct, free trade would become a luxury— something to be enjoyed in private contemplation by professorial readers of *The Wealth of Nations*. It should not be forgotten that his "National Policy" had led to great expansion of the cotton and woollen industries in Canada, once American dumping had been stopped.

"You must remember," said Sir John A., "that across our southern boundary is a mighty nation which fosters its industries by a most jealous system of protection; they offer to our people all the attractions of a common language, a common history and an immense free market area; if, then, we are to keep our population from flowing away from Canada, it can only be done by protecting our industries. The statement that exports are the result of imports is one that sounds well in an after-dinner speech, but it is not true. As a matter of fact, our exports from Canada are stimulated by the loans we have raised in England for railway construction and other purposes, and the interest on which we pay by exports of produce. The obverse of this is true of England; her imports do not largely depend on her exports, but upon the amount of money she has loaned to foreign nations, the interest on which is paid largely by imports of foreign produce."

In a Federation scheme, Britain's departure from her largely free trade system would, or should, be simultaneous with her encouragement to the growth of her colonies by giving tariff preferences on food from the Empire. This would mean that Britain's surplus population would move to the prospering colonies rather than to the United States. And the colonies for their part, he forecast, would give preferences to British goods.

John Bayne Maclean's own views on Empire trade as the logical pathway to Imperial greatness were profoundly stimulated by Macdonald's reasoning. Many other Canadians were similarly impressed; in fact, as one looks back in history, one can see in the interview published in 1890 a foreshadowing of the Imperial preference scheme as presented seven years later by Sir Wilfrid Laurier and his Finance Minister, William S. Fielding. The Old Chief's ideas, revolutionary in their way, were to have currency for a long, long time. Well on into the twentieth century they became the subject for animated discussion between Maclean, the instigator and scriptwriter, and many of his friends, such as Presidents Calvin Coolidge and Herbert Hoover, the British Cabinet's Colonel Leopold S. Amery and others. In 1926 Canadians had an opportunity to study the proposal when Colonel Maclean republished the complete interview in the *Financial Post* under the title, "Macdonald's Vision of Empire." (Afterthought: What other publisher would think there was any news value in a 41-year-old interview, republished after thirty-six years?)

The actual kind of degree of friendship existing between Sir John A. and Maclean is difficult to assess. A search through the Macdonald

papers (a vast mass) has yielded just one reference to John Bayne
Maclean, and that of a routinely formal nature. On February 5,
1891, the young man, in his capacity of secretary-treasurer of the
Canadian Press Association, wrote to the Prime Minister, inviting him
to speak at the next dinner meeting. Joseph Pope, secretary to Sir
John, sent back "regrets"—understandably, as Parliament had been
suddenly dissolved, and the Chief, now old and tired out, was launched
on his last election campaign.

On the other hand, Maclean's bulky files of correspondence indicate that he seldom missed an opportunity, especially in later life, to
refer to his "old friend" and in countless conversations as well, Maclean
left the firm impression with his listeners that he and the great Prime
Minister had been on intimate terms. In one letter, written in 1941, he
said, "I was always loyal to Sir John and he was always dear to me.
We had first met when I was fifteen. In my newspaper years on the
*Mail* and on the *Empire* he occasionally entrusted me with confidential
missions." Was it poetic license? A young man's dream emerging by
degrees into a cherished fact? The great disparity in age—Macdonald
was forty-seven years his senior—would seem to rule out close friendship. It is quite possible that Macdonald had a genuine interest in
Maclean; after all, the young man was related to the fine Cameron
family of Chatsworth, he had established a business of his own, he was
doing a useful job on *The Empire,* and his wholehearted support for
the Conservative cause and its leader could never be doubted. Even
so, one must assume that the closeness of the friendship grew with the
telling, and the mental picture of the grizzled old-timer splitting a bottle
of his favorite restorative with a devoted young man in the chair
opposite belongs in the category of the unlikely.

The year 1891 held several important landmarks in the Maclean
career. Early in June Sir John A. Macdonald died—and probably
Maclean was one of the *Empire* team sent to Ottawa to fill the paper
for a solid week with coverage of the event, the mourners, the tributes,
the crowds, the obsequies, the memories. All columns of each successive issue were bordered with heavy black rules. Even Eaton's and
Simpson's advertisements, with their merry chat about the new ging-
hams, wore the funeral bands.

Within days of the Chief's passing, Maclean made his final farewell
to daily journalism. The President, W. R. Brock, asked him to stay,
hinting that Creighton was not making a success of his job, and
Maclean might become general manager at any time. But the young

publisher had too much else on his mind to be interested. In the *Empire's* offices there were rounds of goodbyes and mutual exchanges of good wishes, and perhaps also some good-natured envy on the part of his *confrères*. After all, Maclean had a nice little business of his own to turn to! The rest of the staff would stay on, even though they sensed that the paper's days were numbered. The *Empire* managed to continue as a separate paper only until 1895, when it was merged with the *Mail*. Its failure was due partially to its direction by politicians rather than by businessmen, and also because the board of directors split along the lines of the Tory factionalism which troubled the party for years after Macdonald's death.

Third important milestone in the year 1891 was John Bayne Maclean's first trip overseas. No pleasure jaunt, this, but a plan with a specific goal: he had decided he must visit Macdonald's birthplace in Scotland. He would write a complete report of his findings for exclusive use in the *Empire,* and to that end the paper had gladly agreed to pay his travel expenses.

The result was a 10,000-word article headed "The Chieftain's Birthplace," signed with the initials, "J. B. McL.," and presented in the *Empire's* special Saturday section of December 26, 1891.

He meticulously described his every move and encounter. On arrival in Glasgow, he talked to newspapermen who had been assigned, on Sir John's death, to find the house of his birth. "They found authorities to prove that he had been born on as many different streets as there are enterprising newspapers there." But the Glasgow *Herald,* quoting the Duke of Argyll, who had paid tribute to Macdonald in a speech in the House of Lords, insisted that the birthplace was in the Highlands. Such a statement, declared Maclean, was only "to be expected from the head of the Campbells. The history of Scotland shows that they have always claimed anything and everything in sight and out of sight, whether rightly or wrongly."

Maclean launched forth on his own careful researches. In the Records Office at Edinburgh he found the original entry of Sir John A.'s birth in Glasgow. Under the January 1815 heading the following entry appeared: "Hugh McDonald, agent, and Helen Shaw, a son, John Alexander, born 10th. Witnesses, Donald and James McDonald."

I have included an official registration certificate that I obtained from the General Register Office in Scotland. Note the date. All Macdonald biographies, including Pope's of long ago and Creighton's published in

**EXTRACT OF AN ENTRY**
**IN A REGISTER KEPT AT THE GENERAL REGISTER OFFICE, EDINBURGH**
*under the Registration of Births, Deaths and Marriages (Scotland) Act 1965*

---

January 1815

Hugh McDonald, Agent & Helen Shaw a Law: son

John Alexander born 10th    Witn: Donald & James

McDonald.

**EXTRACTED** from the REGISTER OF ....Births & Baptisms................

for the Parish of..............Glasgow..............................................

1952, have given January 11 as the date, and even Sir John himself believed that was his birthday.

Note the spelling of Macdonald as "McDonald." The casual attitude of Scottish people toward the apparently interchangeable "Mc" and "Mac" was to puzzle J.B.M. himself in his own lifetime as he went through the sequence of McLean, MacLean and finally Maclean.

Note also the lack of street address in the official registry. It was up to the young reporter to investigate all possible angles in Glasgow, and, with camera in hand, he began. The street directory for 1815 was missing from the thirty or more sets he tracked down in private collections, but eventually he located a copy in the Royal Exchange. Eureka! It showed one "Hugh Macdonald, agent," as living at 18 Brunswick Place—and this was obviously Sir John's father. Another of the same name, but described as "mechanic," caught his eye—and from that duplication may have arisen the usually accepted address of "George Street," which appears in Macdonald biographies.

The next move was a pilgrimage to the house itself. There it stood, at the corner of Irongate and Brunswick Place, and was now marked as 115 Irongate. Here indeed was the house "where Canada's late

Premier first saw light," as Maclean reported. He photographed the old place, perhaps with unsatisfactory results as no picture appeared with the published article.

But the eager journalist hadn't finished his quest. To learn more of Macdonald's ancestry Maclean visited Inverness, Rogart, Dornoch and other crofter villages, and every stop, each encounter, is carefully recorded. At Dalmore "three generations and a dog came to meet me, as I climbed the railway fence that bounded one side of their yard. Not wishing to intrude on the dog I interviewed them from the top rail." Everywhere he seemed to meet people who positively "knew" Sir John or his parents or even grandparents, and who frequently took him to see the actual graves of the older generations. Maclean, though, had his careful doubts. The name of John Macdonald (Sir John's grandfather) was a common one; also, many of the graves contained the bones of collateral relatives who could not be properly included as among the Old Chief's ancestors. Again, after careful examination of town records, he proved that reference in the many recent obituaries to "the provost of Dornoch" as one of Sir John A.'s grandparents was an understandable mistake due to the confusion of names.

Three years after the trip to Scotland, Maclean proffered his carefully kept notes to Sir Joseph Pope, then at work on his biography of Sir John. It appears that Pope had only a casual interest, for there is still on file his return letter, enclosing the notes, with the comment, "They are interesting but relate to matter treated of in my first chapter, the form of which I have long ago determined."

Later biographers have taken their dates, etc., from Pope, and, perhaps it is of little consequence if Macdonald was born on the 10th or the 11th, in Brunswick Place or on George Street. Birthdays of Washington and Lincoln are observed as holidays in most states of the U.S.A., and a discovery of an error in either date would create a national sensation. But Canada likes to celebrate birthdays of queens and saints.

Aside from his final discoveries, Maclean's quest provides us with a lively picture of a diligent young journalist pursuing a story. Occasionally he could not resist a few observations quite extraneous to the purpose of his pilgrimage, as when he wrote: "It" (Dornoch) "is famous for its golf links. Golf is the favorite game in Scotland. It is played everywhere. It is too slow a game, however, for Canada. We would go to sleep over it."

# CHAPTER VI

# ON THE MOVE

"No bird soars too high, if he soars
with his own wings."
*William Blake*

―――――――――――――――――――――――――――――――――

THE YEARS between 1893 and 1901 were to leave an indelible stamp
on John Bayne Maclean's career, interests and private life. From that
period and its series of events would emerge international contacts and
friendships, the solid beginnings of personal wealth, the happy involvement of love and marriage, and an ampler existence which
would continue to expand, though always under careful discipline,
for the next half-century.

Looking back from this distance, it is plain to see that the developments of those eight years took on something of the inevitable nature
of a chain reaction. Yet the first, the essential one destined to trigger
the others, began innocently enough as the offer of a new job.

Maclean's old friend, T. W. Dyas, then in charge of circulation for
the *Mail,* was in the throes of an idea. He needed a premium to
stimulate subscriptions and street sales and he decided to capitalize
upon the current craze for art. The new technique of photoengraving
on metal made old wood blocks or hand-done lithographs old-
fashioned; now it was possible to reproduce, quickly and cheaply, (in
one ink color, of course) any painting, wash drawing or photograph
and keep its various tonal values intact. Suppose a newspaper could
offer special supplements of famous paintings, photoengraved and well
presented, enabling people to enjoy the world's greatest masterpieces
in their own homes—why such art supplements might even share
the ultimate place of honor with the family Bible on the parlor
table!

Young Maclean was a good choice to make the plan work. His five
trade papers were established and appearing regularly; he had recently

moved his headquarters to 10 Front Street East, where the old ware-
house building (formerly occupied by a wholesale dry goods firm, in
which Timothy Eaton had been a partner briefly, before opening his
retail store in 1869) had enough space for the editorial staff, business
office, composing room with its typesetting equipment, and in the basement two or three secondhand presses which, after most cautious inspection, had been a recent major investment. Maclean had successfully initiated and developed his own project; could he be persuaded
to join in the new venture?

Yes—and to the point that he contributed some of the necessary
capital, although Dyas and his colleague, W. J. Douglas, put up more
than two-thirds of the amount required. It was decided that New York
must be the center of operation, not only because of access to the
artwork, the "raw material" of their business, and to up-to-date en-
gravers, but also because from that location they could cultivate sales
of the finished product to the much larger market. As Dyas often
said, "This thing has a lot of ramifications and potential," and the
others could only agree. Brother Hugh C. was summoned from Montreal to take over at the Front Street offices, and Maclean set off for
New York.

The time was summer, 1893, the year of the American silver "panic."
In rapid succession there had been investment house failures, call
money at 40 percent, a collapsed stock market, and swarming crowds
in front of every bank awaiting their turn at the withdrawal wicket.
The panic marked the end of the thirty-year decline in prices that
followed the Civil War and was touched off by a sharp decline in the
price of silver as a result of overproduction. Silver was important because the United States Treasury was a heavy buyer and had authority
to redeem currency in silver as well as gold. By the end of 1893 some
six hundred banks had failed, and in place of money people were
using various handy substitutes such as jewelry or farm products.
William Jennings Bryan, upcoming candidate for President, tried his
best to save the nation and the silver market as well—"You shall not
crucify mankind upon a cross of gold"—but his theories of bi-metallism
were unattractive to knowledgeable economists. Coxey led his rag-tag
army all the way to Washington to demand action for the hungry
unemployed. Yet no public figure, no party, no policy was capable of
stemming the initial disaster or averting the long depression which
followed.

There were to be many paradoxical moments in John Bayne

Maclean's career but the New York interlude must surely be acknowledged the strangest of them all. Here was a young man assigned to the creation and production of an untried luxury at a time
when the people to which it might normally appeal were hard put to
finance their basic daily needs. And here, from his vantage-point in the
small $15-per-month office engaged in the New York Times Building,
he imperturbably set about proving it could be done. His confidence is
best indicated by the fact that right from the start he paid himself a
monthly salary of $600, a sum about the equivalent of $2500 of
today's dollars. Thus was Maclean catapulted, almost overnight, into
the bracket of the well-to-do.

The new publication, christened the *Art Weekly,* consisted generally of sixteen pages, sometimes twelve, measuring 13" width by
10½" depth, the white paper of good weight and finish. Each illustrated page presented a sizable reproduction of a painting (always
in black and white, no color) with neatly printed line underneath, giving the title, artist's name and a courtesy credit to the engraver. The
booklet's final page, headed "Masterpieces from the Art Galleries of
the World," provided two wide columns of text, describing each featured picture and offering biographical facts about its creator. Many
of the "masterpieces" were the work of contemporary American artists
who were willing to sign off reproduction rights for a few dollars. Others
hailed from German sources, with which Maclean had arranged to
buy secondhand plates following their use in art books abroad; these
and various Italian, etc., examples were representative in the main
of a school of art that has faded into oblivion. Occasionally, it is true,
there was a masterpiece, such as *Napoleon, 1814,* by Meisonnier, or
the chubby, naked *Twins* by Canada's Paul Peel, or Alma-Tadema's
idealized documentary, *Antony Meets Cleopatra.* But in the main,
*Art Weekly* leaned heavily on the specific late nineteenth-century type
of picture that can be readily visualized, even now, by such titles
as *Rutting Stag, Village Wedding* and *Gathering Dandelions.*

Each week's issue, as it came from the presses in New York, was
shipped in bulk to a list of contracting newspapers which paid anywhere from six to nine cents per copy, according to the size of their
order. In turn, the dailies sold the supplements to their readers at ten
to fifteen cents per copy, but with the essential "plus" requirement of
a coupon clipped from one of the paper's issues for the current week.
Thus the *Art Weekly* quickly became a potent circulation stimulant.
And if the daily's management so decided, the plain white cover of the

booklet could be used for "house" advertising, with a stamped or printed name of the paper and its slogan: "The *Soperville Sun* . . . shines the year round!"

The largest customer was Toronto's *Mail,* yet within a very short time after the *Art Weekly*'s launching Maclean's bulk buyers in the United States had risen to thirty or forty newspapers, and their individual orders ranged from 500 to 5000 per week. As the break-even point for the whole operation had been carefully estimated at 12,000 copies per week, profits rolled dizzily on and up when that modest figure was left far behind. Another highly gratifying phase of the business—one that may have developed en route, so to speak— emerged with the secondary or rerun use of the material. At the end of each sequence of twenty supplements, all were bound together in sturdy board covers sheathed in a handsome moire finish and bearing the title the *Art Weekly,* in chaste gilt lettering. These volumes sold at $20 apiece and the remarkable fact is that they *sold,* even in the great American depression of the '90s.

The manager and the bookkeeper-secretary he had hired were soon swamped by office work, but an appeal to Miss Forbes in Toronto to come down and organize all details solved that problem effectively. Maclean realized he also needed help in choosing the pictures and presenting them for maximum effect. For this job he selected Ernest Rolph, young architectural graduate from Toronto, later to become a partner in the distinguished firm of Sproatt & Rolph, who were to bestow on their native city some of the handsomest university towers and spires this side of ancient Oxford.

It seldom happens, however, that a promotion scheme lasts forever. After a year or so the *Art Weekly*'s business began to fall off. Some of the smaller participating newspapers were slow in settling their bills; several lawsuits had to be initiated, to the detriment of the net profit situation. At the same time competitors with brand-new promotional plans were making their aggressive rounds. So, shortly before the end of 1894, the Dyas-Douglas-Maclean partners decided to wind up the enterprise. Maclean closed the New York headquarters, yet with a triumphant final project. All supplements and bound volumes on hand were sold to his good friend of early *Grocer* days, J. E. Ganong, New Brunswick's "Surprise Soap man," who could always use an art premium in his business with Canadian housewives and their carefully saved bundles of soap wrappers.

The New York venture had been a profitable experience in many

ways. In addition to his salary, Maclean received a share of the
$500 or $600 extra profit that rolled in every week during the peak
period. Such dividends may have added up to some $3000 or $4000,
even more, in his bank account, yet one would be foolhardy to try to
arrive at exact figures from Maclean's bookkeeping, even after Miss
Forbes' careful efforts. All through life he had a casual attitude toward
ledgers and balances, etc. In his early days he tended to put his
personal income along with payments from advertisers and subscribers
in a single account—or pocket; what more natural than to write a
cheque or draw out as needed, whether to pay a printing bill or buy a
new shirt? Thus, after studying all the bits and pieces of records from
the New York project, the only report that can be safely proffered is
that they neither confirm nor deny the statement which the Colonel so
often made to many of his friends: that the basis of his fortune was
laid during the publishing of *Art Weekly*.

Greater by far than the monetary success, however, were the inevitable widenings of his horizons and the acquiring of important new
friends. In New York he lived handsomely—in contrast to his boardinghouse life in Toronto. He joined the Sphinx Club, a favorite
rendezvous for publishers and advertising men. There he met William
Randolph Hearst, his junior by a few months but (with the help of a
rich father's backing) now the successful owner and remodeler of
the San Francisco *Examiner,* and soon to produce a New York paper,
the *Morning Journal,* which at the unheard-of "give away" price of one
cent per copy would rock all newspaperdom.

Sometime during Maclean's visits to the Sphinx he had his first
handshake with another innovator, the man who had already thrown
the sedate nineteenth-century magazine world into a state of alarm:
Frank A. Munsey, owner and inspirer of *Munsey's Magazine,* a monthly
publication, fat with good fiction and lively features, and selling to
a huge public at just a dime a copy. That brief encounter of the
pink-cheeked young man from Canada and the rather dour, long-
faced forty-year-old was surely supercharged with Fate at her most
unpredictable. From the first casual meeting would develop a lifelong
friendship, one which was to survive even the crisis of rivalry for a
woman they both loved, one which never faltered even through their
later years of arguments concerning basic publishing ethics. Munsey,
a poor backwoods boy equipped with only elementary schooling,
was to become a restless, brilliant impresario of publishing, the
man who in the early 1900s reshaped the New York newspaper

structure by ceaseless acquisitions, mergers, and, when he deemed it necessary, hatchetings. A clear-eyed view backward from today's vantage-point would seem to indicate merely that he was born a half-century too soon.

Another new and close friend, emerging from Maclean's New York interlude, was S. S. McClure, founder in 1893 of the highly successful *McClure's Magazine,* a neck-and-neck competitor with *Munsey's,* and thus eventually forced to meet the latter's dime price rate. But *McClure's* outshone the other in literary quality, presenting first-run material by the great names of the day, such as Arthur Conan Doyle, H. Rider Haggard, Rudyard Kipling, James M. Barrie, even dispatching Mark Twain to Europe for a series of pieces, and Robert Louis Stevenson on a special voyage of discovery to his beloved South Seas. Perhaps S. S. McClure is remembered best for his introduction of the *exposé* type of article, as early demonstrated by his favorite contributor, Ida M. Tarbell, in her series on the rise and history of the Standard Oil Company. Some critics denounced McClure as a muckraker, and indeed he was an all-out fearless campaigner when he felt the subject justified the means, yet at the same time his magazine bristled with lively, informative, man-to-man discussions such as how to steer the new horseless carriage, and a brilliant explanatory piece on the principles of Signor Marconi's amazing new wireless telegraphy.

*McClure's* began to backslide after the turn of the century, when publisher Sam became involved in a sequence of grandiose expansions. The magazine and his long-established newspaper syndicate were to be just segments within a completely reorganized complex, which would publish textbooks, promote a McClure insurance company, a McClure savings bank, and eventually finance housing projects and social services. Before any of these plans could materialize, his buoyant Irish good health began to weaken and he turned over the magazine to a son-in-law. Later there was a succession of owners, none of whom could cope with the constantly multiplying intricacies of periodical publishing. In the year 1921 John Bayne Maclean was offered *McClure's Magazine* for $150,000. It was still substantial as to circulation, selling 350,000 copies per month, but its advertising revenue had fallen to a mere $25,000 per year. The Colonel, while strongly tempted, was wise enough to decline. The next year, his old friend Sam, returned to his namesake publication as editor, and the Colonel sent him a note of congratulations. The doughty Irishman cheerfully replied, "I imagine that with the May number, the magazine will satisfy the older readers." But most of them had probably passed on—and that was to be the fate of famous *McClure's* too, in the year 1924.

During Maclean's absence in New York, brother Hugh had faithfully tended shop at Toronto headquarters, at the same time keeping a watchful eye on Jack's activities. As a printer he could not approve the quality of reproduction in the early issues of the *Art Weekly* . . . "you are always one for trying to get your engravings and printing from the cheapest firms and now that I'm not around to check, the poor results certainly show up," wrote Hugh with family-style candor. Eventually Hugh found a printer in Buffalo who could upgrade the presswork at a reasonable figure; thereafter *Art Weekly*'s quality improved.

Both men, even in those years of scurry and worry, were inveterate letter writers, and Hugh's reports often carried bad news as well as good advice. On December 19, 1893, he wound up a doleful recital of events with the stark statement, "We have never been so short of cash for nearly two years as we are now. We have not a cent to meet wages on Saturday." Nevertheless he did meet them; indeed the little company was earning a modest profit. Hugh managed to reorganize production of the trade papers on a more efficient basis and he had some success in speeding up collection of advertising accounts. It was probably natural that he should resent Jack's absence —a reaction underlined by the complaints of "hard work back home here."

Now, nearing the end of 1894, Hugh looked forward to his brother's return and the resumption of the old arrangement of specific responsibilities assigned to each. Everything would be normal once again —with a proper division of routine.

But from the moment of the reunion it was obvious that Maclean had a quite different plan. He announced his decision to move his personal headquarters to Montreal, continuing as president of course, with offices in the St. James Street branch of the company. The decision was a shock to Hugh who was disposed to argue about it. But John found a neat way to avoid his brother's strictures. On the pretext that advertising business from Britain had shown a lively upswing, Hugh C. was persuaded to pack a bag and visit the Old Country on an intensive selling campaign. Success attended him—even to the point of expediting the sale of the plates that had been used in

the New York production of the art volumes. This little sideline
netted $1500, of which Hugh was allowed to keep one-third.

Next was the appointment of an editorial manager to work with
Hugh—and very quickly W. L. Edmonds, a black-bearded, nimble-
minded five-footer of versatile talents joined the group at Front Street,
where he would remain for many years. Sometime during those hectic
months Maclean made a trip to the Maritime Provinces, attending a
meeting of their joint Board of Trade, calling on advertisers and no
doubt dropping in on friend Ganong, perhaps even concluding the
deal concerning the leftover bound volumes of *Art Weekly*.

It was on this tour that his eyes were opened on the matter of
aggressiveness among the average Maritime merchants. He called on
one of his *Hardware* subscribers, noting a window full of scythes,
plus a single copy of the New Testament priced at ten cents. Maclean
was a little surprised at this departure from the rules of good window-
dressing but decided not to mention it. Instead he asked, "Well, how's
trade?"

The retailer said: "Not very good, what with competition and all
that." Then, he added "Why, know what that damned so-and-so down
the street is doing? He's offering the New Testament at seven cents!"

On his return to Toronto, Maclean put everything in readiness for
his move to Montreal as soon as Hugh got back from England.

Why did Maclean remove himself so summarily to the eastern
metropolis when he was so badly needed right in Toronto? He had no
capacity with the French language. His little office in Montreal handled
business efficiently; there was no need for the top executive to take
over; indeed, the announcement of his impending arrival must have
caused consternation among the staff. All his relatives and most of his
old friends were in Ontario. Why go to Montreal?

The New York interval had been partly responsible, of course.
There he had glimpsed a new and exciting world of big business and
the powerful figures who controlled it, of friendships just waiting
to be made, it seemed, and a downtown world of club life and palatial
hotels. In New York he had lived expensively and enjoyed it. The
prospect of returning to the familiar routine in Toronto had little appeal. Why not try Montreal, Canada's biggest city and financial
center, with its cosmopolitan blend of two cultures, its port that attracted world traffic? Besides—and this was the clinching argument—

by establishing himself in the eastern metropolis he might find opportunities for quicker advancement in the militia.

The situation with the Grenadiers had changed during his period
abroad. A new colonel had been given command, various other officers
automatically advanced in rank, and, necessarily, the man on extended leave in New York ignored. Another five years might pass before promotion for a mere captain was possible.

The move east would keep him within commuting distance for the
Grenadiers' important occasions in Toronto; meantime he could study
the local militia scene and hope to arrange a transfer to one of
Montreal's excellent units that promised faster rewards. Maclean's
urge to wear a lieutenant colonel's "crown-and-pip" on his shoulders
had, in short, reached a feverish intensity.

(Today, it is difficult for the average citizen to appreciate the glamour
that attached to the militia in the 1890s. Ambitious young men were
attracted to it then as today they might take up sport car racing, or
work toward the presidency of the local "Jaycees," or the chairmanship
of an important civic charity campaign. An officer who served his
regiment faithfully, year in, year out, had a known value in his community. As for the "other ranks," the men who were happy to wear the
issue uniforms and keep boots and buttons polished, the militia offered opportunities for personal friendships as well as group activities,
a highly respected masculine atmosphere, and the chance—in peacetime—to learn the art of soldiering for the better defense of their country. Here, for all ranks, was public service at its finest, totally voluntary,
entirely without monetary remuneration; indeed, the only possible reward consisted in moving forward to new responsibilities, as when
corporal became sergeant or the company captain won his "majority.")

So the scene for Maclean changed. He moved into an exclusive
boardinghouse at the top of Beaver Hall Hill, organized an office to
his taste at the St. James Street business headquarters, and devoted
most of his spare time to initiating or expanding friendships among
Montreal's leading regimental groups. Naturally, having got the habit
of success, he was confident his plan would work, given a little time.
It did too, but that story can wait its telling while we look into the
development of a rather unusual publishing project in which he suddenly found himself. He bought for a song, the *Canadian Military
Gazette*.

That paper had begun under the name of the *Illustrated War News*, which was a modest little sheet issued in Toronto during 1885, when Canadian militiamen from the east were stalking Riel and his rebels in the final phase of the Northwest Rebellion. With its eyewitness accounts of skirmishes and battles, plus full-page drawings of action on the treeless plain, the paper had an astounding success though an abruptly short life, for with the third issue and its report of the troops' victory at Batoche the publication ceased. A little later one of the Northwest veterans, returned to Ottawa, decided to reinstate it as a journal under the new name, the *Canadian Militia Gazette*. After several years of struggle he sold it in 1893 to two keen young regimental officers in Montreal: E. J. Chambers, a major in the 6th Fusiliers, former correspondent at Batoche, and now a member of the *Star*'s editorial staff; Edward Desbarats, lieutenant in the 3rd Victoria Rifles, in civilian life the very capable advertising manager of Maclean's Montreal office (and, eventually, founder of one of the earliest and most highly respected advertising agencies in Canada).

For two years they had done a steady, constructive job with the little magazine, now slightly retitled as the *Canadian Military Gazette,* and occasionally they had discussed its policies with Maclean. It wasn't always easy to give force to the decisions arrived at, for Chambers' full-time association with the *Star* could be a hampering factor. But by 1895 the owner and many others realized that the militia situation in Canada had reached a point where a strong, uninhibited voice was urgently needed. Ottawa's political leaders showed little sympathy with the volunteer part-time Army; headquarters staff, under control of imported Imperial officers, viewed the militiamen as amateurs and "mere Colonials"; and, as Maclean wrote later, "the climax came when the Government canceled all rural corps training and cut off four days, i.e., one-third, of the annual pay to all city regiments." An alarming state of affairs, for everyone knew that virtually all militia units channeled the full pay allotment from Ottawa into regimental funds to meet maintenance and training expenses; in many cases the dwindling cash on hand had to be eked out with private contributions from such officers as could afford them.

A delegation of commanding officers hastened to Ottawa and pleaded with Sir George Foster, Minister of Finance, to replace the four days' pay deduction. When the answer was a chilly "No," they went into hurried conference and agreed that (a) a real fight must be made and (b) John Bayne Maclean plus the *Canadian Military Gazette* would be the ideal team to handle it. Honorable J. M. Gibson, a minister in Ontario's Liberal Government and Colonel of the 13th Hamilton Regiment, with Colonel George Taylor Denison, identified for a lifetime with the Governor-General's Bodyguard, Toronto, and Major Labelle of Montreal's 65th Regiment, "all intimate friends of mine," wrote Maclean years after, "finally talked me into buying and carrying on the *Gazette,* which I did in late 1895. Chambers continued as editor, but with no public responsibility for the paper's aggressive, perhaps offensive, but always fair, constructive policies. I had to assume that as well as the political and social punishments that followed." Desbarats carried on as business manger.

Thus John Bayne Maclean found himself in the front line of the kind of battle that excited him, vigorously fighting for causes which he knew were right, and using a type of weapon he understood—the printed word. By early 1896 the magazine, a semi-monthly appearing on the 1st and 15th, had improved its paper quality, general makeup and typography. It had started a barrage of exposé editorials concerning the deplorably slack conditions which had been allowed to develop at Royal Military College, Kingston, under Commandant General D. R. Cameron, who happened to be the brother-in-law of the Prime Minister of that year, Sir Charles Tupper. Thus goaded, the government appointed a high-ranking commission to investigate; the resulting report proved the allegations correct; the House of Commons went into a righteous uproar; the *Gazette* received commendation for service rendered the country; the Commandant resigned, and eventually Maclean's beloved R.M.C. returned to its precisely disciplined life.

By 1897 there was another famous victory, brought about by the tactical skill, operational courage and tireless editorial campaiging of the *Gazette*'s publisher. Shortly after Dr. Frederick Borden had been installed as Minister of Militia in the new Laurier government, he traveled to Montreal to discuss the militia pay situation with the man who was quite obviously Canada's best informed expert on the matter. Maclean had the satisfaction of seeing the follow-up of their private chat in the newspapers a week or so later, when the Minister's announcement of a retreat by the government was made to a hushed Parliament. That night probably every regimental mess across Canada celebrated both Borden and the *Canadian Military Gazette* with a special round of toasts.

The *Gazette* never hesitated to do battle, even when there was no hope of winning. Several of its 1897 issues had sharp criticism of the arrangements for the Canadian contingent to be sent overseas to Queen

Victoria's Jubilee celebrations; just two hundred, all ranks—"from this great country, a parsimonious showing!"—and, as they would be chosen from many different militia units, the result would be a "crazy quilt" appearance of clashing uniforms, line by line. In the June 16 issue, a disheartened *Gazette* correspondent describes the chaos at Quebec's Citadel where the chosen few were sent to form up the contingent, have final outfitting and drill before sailing; his last sentence is in itself a neat summation . . . "The boots issued appear to be all one size."

Authentic bylines were scarce in the *Gazette*. To be sure, the straightforward, informative type of article, perhaps concerning the coming importance of the bicycle in military operations, would carry the writer's name, complete with rank and decorations. But revelations, scandals and challenges appeared anonymously, most frequently as editorials which sometimes occupied more than three of the opening pages. No one had any doubts as to their authorship, even if the publication's masthead omitted any reference to Maclean or his publishing company. The *Gazette*'s business location also had its certain air of mystery, with no street address but merely a post office box number in Montreal. There was never any listing of editorial staff— perhaps just as well, considering that after Chambers' departure there were occasional gaps in news coverage which could only be filled by conscripting the local *Dry Goods Review* correspondent to run around to the various barracks or parade occasions with notebook in hand.

Anyway, it was Maclean himself who stood ready to bear the full brunt of outside reaction, as in the year 1899, when the *Gazette* became the country's first publication to announce that Canada would be sending a militia force to fight the rebellious Boers in South Africa. On this occasion, Major F. S. Dixon, then the nominal editor, had written the unsigned piece, but Maclean had not only inspired it but supplied the factual details which were climaxed by the statement that all such volunteers would be absorbed into British units under Imperial officers. Immediately controversy swept across the nation like a summer hurricane. The French Canadian press spoke out fiercely against any participation in South Africa's troubles. At the same time Toronto's Empire-minded population and papers were loudly vocal for going to the assistance of the British on the grounds that Canada's own safety was involved. Yet everywhere the suggestion that Canadian troops would serve under non-Canadian officers met with indignant protest.

The little *Gazette* had started something which even the Prime Minister could not ignore. Sir Wilfrid Laurier summoned the press for a special interview. He denied that Canada had offered a contingent. He defined the constitutional law, which, he said, allowed Canadian troops to be sent anywhere for their country's defense; but when there was no menace, as in the present situation concerning South Africa, they could not be so used, unless Parliament passed on it and voted moneys. And he wished to declare, unequivocally, that the statement in the *Canadian Military Gazette* was "pure invention."

The Prime Minister was wrong. Behind the article had been a series of talks between Maclean and Major General Edward Hutton, Chief of the General Staff at Ottawa, who at that very juncture was promoting, through the Earl of Minto, the Governor-General, the plan for a Canadian contingent, to be officered, of course, from the Imperial Army, of which Hutton was an exceedingly proud member. It is quite unlikely that Maclean agreed to keep the secret, for as an expert interviewer he would realize the possible entanglement of such promises; moreover, he had no doubts as to the responsibilities which must be accepted by the country's highest-ranking military command. And he was perfectly aware that public opinion would reject Hutton's plan for British officering of a Canadian force. Maclean had calculated each of the moves with nice exactitude; he was probably the least surprised member of the whole coast-to-coast community when Ottawa announced approval for the recruitment and dispatch of troops to South Africa, specified that they would be officered by Canadians and would serve alongside other Empire contingents in British brigades.

The South African War gave the *Gazette* a considerable boost in public recognition, which, in turn, led to a remarkably successful, though non-military, career for its editor of that period. When Dixon eventually left for duty on the far continent (one of the total of 7300 Canadians who served there) he was replaced on the *Gazette* by James S. Macdonnell, a staffer with Maclean's trade paper group in the Montreal office. Son of a Toronto preacher, Macdonnell had formerly been a junior master at Upper Canada College; he was still young and well supplied with intelligence and initiative, when Maclean hired him at a starting salary of $5 per week.

Dixon's numerous letters from the front to his former associates captured the interest of everyone, including Macdonnell. They couldn't be published in their original form, or under the by-line of a serving soldier from the battle front, but they just might be salvaged as the basis of a series of "first-person" articles, and signed with a *nom de plume*. So Macdonnell sat himself down and produced a well-written and factual continuing story from the South African theater of war—to make an exciting feature for the *Military Gazette,* but, better still, to have widespread impact through full reprinting in newspapers from coast to coast. John Bayne Maclean was delighted.

Too bad that Macdonnell's next project was hardly in the same category. The young editor happened to meet an Austrian chemist who had produced an emergency ration for use by troops in the field. Samples had been sent to Ottawa and tests were under way among members of the Canadian permanent force stationed at Kingston, Ontario. Eventually the news came through that the ration was unacceptable and would not be adopted. The chemist, embittered and out for revenge, sent Macdonnell information about the inadequacies of food and equipment supplies now being shipped to the Canadians serving in South Africa. The young editor, never one to delay, wrote a damning article. As soon as the news reached Maclean, he ordered the piece withdrawn from the issue, but he was too late; the *Gazette* was already off the press and in the mails. The result was a political scandal that shook the House of Commons and the country. F. B. Monk rose up from his place in the Conservative Opposition front bench and preferred formal charges against Militia Minister Borden.

For days the matter was hotly debated, and the *Gazette*'s article constantly quoted, sometimes with respect and confidence, just as often in terms of ridicule and denunciation. Again, the well-known safety device of a Royal Commission was resorted to, but when in due course its findings were presented there were still unreconciled party differences. The majority (Liberal) report exonerated the Minister. The minority (Conservative) statement held to the stern charge of gross inefficiency against him and his Department. The episode was to form a main point of attack on the Laurier administration in the general election of 1900, yet without noticeable effect, for the government was swept back into power, and Nova Scotia's Frederick Borden would continue to be the Liberals' Minister of Militia and Defense until 1911 and would receive a knighthood. Perhaps more incredible, though, is the fact that the friendship between him and Maclean was to stand firm through all the Ottawa muckraking; indeed, they were to have closer contact in the years ahead, through shared interests in the St. John's Ambulance Brigade.

Did a private man-to-man explanation of the whole case take place between Maclean and Borden? It's a possibility. Yet in an issue of the *Gazette* some months after the original explosion, the "publisher" printed a special statement that was notable for lack of any retraction. By that time Macdonnell had resigned, and the rumors asserted he had been fired. So it was now Maclean's opportunity to state the facts, boldly yet calmly. In a few sentences he declared he had neither repudiated nor apologized for the article, nor had he found its facts without foundation; the gentleman who wrote it, now no longer with the *Gazette,* had not been dismissed but had resigned of his own volition.

Years later Macdonnell cheerfully recalled the whole event in his autobiography. He had left the *Military Gazette,* he said, simply because R. S. White, publisher of the big, bustling daily, the Montreal *Gazette,* liked the article so much he offered the author a job as a reporter. Macdonnell in double-quick time became one of the city's most popular journalists, but his local career was cut short by a threat of lung trouble. He moved to the warmth and sunshine of California, where he worked first as a farm laborer, next as a bank messenger at $40 a month, and ultimately, in the popular Horatio Alger tradition of the period, became president of the First Trust and Savings Bank of Pasadena, and, as a happy sideline, the acknowledged leader of a growing Canadian colony roundabout.

John Bayne Maclean occasionally included the *Canadian Military Gazette* on mastheads and letterheads of his other publications. On other occasions, he ignored it. *Gazette* revenues seldom exceeded a few thousand dollars a year—hardly enough to pay for printing, paper, mailing. Advertising ran the gamut from Johnston's Fluid Beef "for strength" to band instruments and secondhand uniforms. A column of classified ads, open to readers at very low cost, covered an interesting variety of subjects, from a Crimean veteran's collection of medals and saber to "Automobile, brand new, must be sold; $450," and then to a Major L. B. J.'s announcement of "Cow for sale, 2 weeks in milk, good producer, 31 Garden Ave. (Parkdale), Toronto."

In 1900 the owner decided to broaden the appeal of his publication by expanding the title to *Canadian Military Gazette and Gentleman's Magazine,* and opening several pages to general topics such as "Masculine Modes" with a report on men's fashions in London, occasionally a theater review feature, and often a column dealing with the new books. A photograph of Ella Wheeler Wilcox, the homebody versifier, adjacent to a chat about her new volume, even today has total shock value as one turns from lists of winners in the annual rifle competition; what the members of a Sergeants' Mess had to say about it must be firmly left to the imagination.

In 1906, Maclean, deeply involved in other matters, sold the *Gazette* to a group headed by his good friend, Lieutenant Colonel Andrew T. Thompson, M.P., formerly of Cayuga, Ontario, but recently moved to Ottawa as member of the law firm of Thompson, Coté, Burgess & Code. Little cash changed hands in the transaction for the seller was quite willing to accept shares and a directorship; anyway, there would be some regular revenue to his company through the continued production and mailing of the magazine from the Front Street plant in Toronto.

His pride and interest in the *Gazette* never faltered. Maclean's filing cabinets at this moment have bulging folders of letters, reports, memoranda concerning the publication which he had made uniquely his own over a decade, and which remained a favorite offspring when farther afield in the world. In 1914, he thanked Thompson and his group for the check for $120, a 4 percent dividend on his thirty shares. In 1946, well into his eighties, he readily agreed to the suggestion of the *Gazette*'s then owner, Major R. B. Farrell, Ottawa, to prepare a series of articles detailing the paper's early days and fighting moments.

The *Canadian Military Gazette* has now passed into history. If ever a publication deserved a medal for courage on the journalistic battle-line, this was it.

# CHAPTER VII

# OFFICER COMMANDING

"Time spent in reconnaissance
is seldom wasted."
*Old army maxim*

WITH EYES WIDE open and ears alert, Maclean carefully reconnoitered Montreal from the special standpoint of his own future, and he rejoiced in what he saw and heard. The local militia was devoted and lively, eager to accept a trained officer of the same mind. So he was pleased, if not greatly surprised, when within a few months after his arrival he was invited to transfer to the 6th Battalion Fusiliers, assuming the rank of major. The uniform was appealing—a smart redcoat, a busby with a crisply upthrust cockade—and parades were a pleasure, especially the occasional battalion turnout for church service.

The tempo of life had quickened on all fronts. There was hardly an evening without an engagement, whether at the St. John's Ambulance meeting or the Red Cross committee or among the Highland social group known as the Clan Maclean Society of America, of which he served as president for one year. New friendships among the Montreal business community, both English and French, were agreeable results of these activities; so, too, the constant extensions of acquaintance through his trade papers' chief advertisers, the larger wholesale grocery, hardware and dry goods firms, many of whose top people also sat on bank and railway boards. He was to become the close friend of a pair of rising executives in the Bank of Montreal: Vincent Meredith and Frederick Williams-Taylor, both of whom would wear a knighthood for many years, the former as bank president, the latter as general manager and later vice-president. Williams-Taylor was a year younger than Maclean, Meredith a dozen years older.

Two successive presidents of the Canadian Pacific Railway were interesting new contacts: Sir William Van Horne, who was to die in

1898 at the age of fifty-five, and that gentleman's efficient protégé and successor, Thomas G. Shaughnessy, then in his mid-forties, soon to receive a knighthood from Edward VII and later to become one of Canada's handful of lords. Both were enthusiastic supporters of St. John's Ambulance; both enjoyed lunching at the exclusive St. James Club, where the young publisher, a new member, was easily persuaded to join their table. Often, of course, he brought in his own party, either there or at the other executive *rendezvous,* the Montreal Club. The well-turned-out bachelor from Toronto was moving up the business and social ladder, steadily but without fanfare, and local observers accorded him their approval. One of the city's leading journalists wrote of him: "As a commercial editor, Mr. Maclean has perhaps no superior in the Canadian press. He knows personally almost every prominent merchant and manufacturer in the Dominion."

From country excursions round about the city would emerge memories to be enjoyed through the next half-century. In 1942 Maclean wrote to Walter C. Wonham, head of an old-established importing firm: "Your father and mother and your whole family were so kind and cordial to me during the years I lived in Montreal. I shall never forget them and the weekends I used to spend at your country house . . . among the splendid French-Canadians and many interesting scenes and monuments of Canada's earliest days." That was in the Richelieu River valley, and one of the long-remembered "scenes" was the Chambly home of the famous singer, Madame Albani, born Marie Louise Lajeunesse in 1847, destined to become a favorite performer before the crowned heads in Europe: Queen Victoria, the Czar of Russia and the German Emperor.

And there was so much more that Maclean wanted to recall for Wonham . . . "how your younger brother and sister made me come out there and nursed me when I cracked a rib when my horse had a nasty fall one morning, cub-hunting." He had appreciated their kindness then, "but now, looking back, I appreciate it still more." The box of fine cigars, presented to him each Christmas by the Wonham firm, became the pivotal point of another cherished reminiscence. "I was not a smoker but I kept this box in the lower drawer of my desk in the Board of Trade Building." Dr. William Henry Drummond occasionally dropped by for a chat, to discuss the Irish terriers which they had enjoyed raising and showing in partnership, or, again, to go over the doctor's new *habitant* poems. (In those days Drummond insisted it was just "scribbling"; he could become extremely annoyed when friends referred to his hobby as "poetry.") Anyway, Maclean recalls, "He got in the habit of writing these verses and bringing them to read to me. I was always delighted to give him a cigar which he smoked as we chatted. It became a habit with him"—to the extent that the visitor soon bypassed the amenities and simply opened the drawer and helped himself.

One March day Drummond burst in early, very angry and clutching another manuscript sheet on which the ink was barely dry. It seems the newspapers had carried a dispatch from a town in England where all citizens were loudly condemning (for reasons not apparent today) the "effrontery" of an Irish regiment which had paraded through their streets on the 17th of the month with shamrocks stuck in every rifle. Drummond had sat himself down at his desk and, as befitted a native of County Leitrim, had immediately gone to work "on the English." When Maclean finished reading the verses, he said, "Bill, let me have this to publish in my *Military Gazette*." Instantly the expression on the face opposite changed from rage to alarm. "Oh, no, Jack, you mustn't do that. It would hurt the feelings of the English."

Both men were ardent anglers, members of the St. Maurice Fishing Club, and when the pair returned from a triumphant day on the river the larger group gathered round the clubhouse fireplace could sometimes persuade Drummond to recite "The Wreck of the Julie Plante" or one of his other popular pieces. Indeed there was always an eager waiting audience, whether close at hand or across the length and breadth of America, for Drummond's rhymes in the Anglicized patois of the French-Canadian. If they have not survived as Canadian classics, it is probably because later generations have construed his dialect form as ridiculing or somehow demeaning. Yet Drummond loved his fellow *Québecois,* and no doubt their early delighted, non-critical acceptance of his published stories in verse was a spur to the steady output in the decade before his death in 1907, at the age of fifty-three.

As contacts and interests increased, so did Maclean's reputation as a campaigner, mostly through his journals, occasionally outside. Sometimes, of course, his efforts ended in failure—as when he tried to persuade Sir Mackenzie Bowell, Prime Minister of Canada from December 1894 to April 1896, to reopen negotiations with Newfoundland for joining the Dominion. He came into the picture this way: Sir William Whiteway, Newfoundland's long-time Premier, and the man responsible for spanning the island with a railway, had come to Ottawa in 1895 to seek Bowell's support for a series of discussions concerning union. The Island government had been in a poverty-stricken condition for many years, and appeals to its sovereign authority, the British cabinet in London, met with only partial relief, grudgingly given. Most Canadians, especially public leaders, knew the situation and were concerned. Yet Bowell (a type who reserved his strength for the whim of the moment) curtly dismissed the visitor and his project, refusing even to submit the suggestions to cabinet.

Disappointed and frustrated, Whiteway was brought by a mutual friend—an advertiser in *Canadian Grocer*—to see Maclean in Montreal. If Canada would assume Newfoundland's debt of some $750,000, the Premier declared, the Island colony would readily agree to joining Canada. Maclean was impressed. Here was a deal of the greatest importance for the long future. Bowell, thought Maclean, could not have understood the significance of his decision; after all, he was a busy man with many problems, but as a former editor and still publisher-owner of the Belleville, Ontario, *Intelligencer,* as well as a long-service militiaman, surely he could be persuaded to give some consideration to rounding out a nation.

So Maclean hurried to Ottawa and pleaded the case with the Prime Minister. The effort was totally wasted. Maclean never forgave Bowell and never forgot. When Newfoundland finally joined Canada as the tenth province in 1949, John Bayne Maclean was probably the only man alive who could explain exactly how and why it had *not* happened a half-century before.

The year 1895 was memorable as well for another project that did not come off, but in this case it was Maclean who made the decision. Montreal's Charles R. Hosmer, a man of wealth (Ogilvie Flour, British Columbia Zinc and Lead, the Mackay Cable-Telegraph chain) sought out Maclean and broke the news that the *Gazette,* the city's highly respected daily, was for sale. He knew he could buy it for half-a-million, and this he wanted to do—if Maclean would move in and run the paper.

A compliment indeed to the thirty-three-year-old from Toronto— but he declined with thanks. The reasons were not far to seek: his trade papers had expanded satisfactorily in size and influence, and he was now about to try his hand at a gossipy-chatter weekly to serve the local area. Under the name, the *Metropolitan,* with subtitle *Montreal Life,* the little magazine was to continue for several years during the late '90s, reporting the doings of visitors, travelers, theatres, concert halls, club groups, and the like, and attracting enough advertising to break even, most of the time, from such a miscellany of sources as the Carpet Beating Co., the Academy of Music, the Raleigh Hotel in Washington, D.C., and Henry Birks & Son. When the paper finally gave up the ghost, sometime in 1900, probably the owner heaved a sigh of relief, for the magazine had never warranted the effort, and Maclean himself was hardly the type to be confined, mentally or physically, to a single locality. By that time he was a well-traveled man, one with influential friendships in high places, one whose long-term convictions and aspirations had been released, as from an open floodgate, after several months' sojourn in England in 1897.

That was the year of the old Queen's Diamond Jubilee, and, just as significantly, the period of the final, dazzling fortissimo of Imperial glory. Maclean, bitterly disappointed that he was not included in Canada's official military contingent, determined to make the trip on his own, and to that end drew up a careful program. He attended as a journalist the Colonial Conference at which the new, all-important Canadian proposal for Empire tariff preferences (Laurier's pet scheme that was to cut the ground from under the Canadian Tories) was presented by Minister of Finance Fielding.

Years later Maclean recalled the mixed reaction that followed. Laurier, immediately on arrival in England for the Jubilee events, had been subjected to special pressure, to the point where "he unfortunately publicly announced that Canada expected no favors in return" for the concessions he was offering. Again, the plan "raised a vicious storm in Germany and they at once struck back. But most amazing was the opposition that came from British interests. Mr. Fielding and I traveled about England, gossiping with business leaders. It was surprising what narrow, selfish views prevailed in many sections." However, the attitude was not general, as he and Fielding discovered when they attended the annual dinner of the ancient Society of Master Cutlers in Sheffield, where the Minister's speech outlining the mutual advantages of tariff preferences received "tremendous applause."

Nevertheless British opposition from other quarters continued, and in fact the Colonel was moved to add a rider to his brief memorandum: "British big business has, through the years, treated Canada unfairly and often brutally. I have had many a fight with these interests. But the Mother Country primarily and the Dominions and Colonies have been by far the best buyers of our surplus products, raw and manufactured. For that reason I have always stood strongly for preferential trade." And, as an afterthought farther down in his memorandum of recollection: "In 1925, in an interesting chat with President Coolidge, I happened to remark that for some years I had held the view that Canada should gradually reduce duties, leading eventually to complete free trade within the Empire . . . at the same time gradually developing similar relations with the United States; that finally between the British Commonwealth of Nations and the United States there should be complete free trade. Mr. Coolidge instantly remarked, 'I believe strongly in such a policy.' His comment was passed to Mr. Hoover, then Secretary of Commerce, and that evening the latter cordially expressed his agreement." Whether or not Coolidge, Hoover or Maclean himself really believed in this dream depends upon the interpretation of the word "finally."

In spite of the first resistance and criticisms, an Empire preferential tariff system was to become an accomplished fact before too many years had passed. Maclean took special satisfaction in having been in at the birth. And—who knows—he may even have had some modest influence on final British business opinion in its favor, for he spent many days that summer calling on important advertisers in his trade journals.

Several weeks of his 1897 visit were apportioned to a special military course at Aldershot, and here he was to meet a number of Britain's future field marshals and generals, notably John French and Ian Hamilton, the latter to become a lifelong friend. There were glittering occasions aplenty to which Maclean, as a military man and a staunch Imperialist, was invited: Royal jubilee reviews of the Army and the fleet, banquets and meetings, two of which brought him into the orbit of his old friend from Toronto, Colonel George Taylor Denison, who as president of the British Empire League in Canada headed a special delegation to the London festivities.

It was a summer to remember. He could hardly wait to get back to see Professor Goldwin Smith and inform him he was wrong: Canada's future did *not* lie in close economic association with the United States, as Smith insisted, but rather as a sturdy partner in an expanding British Empire, joined together not only by elements of sentimental attachment and a common link to the Crown but by a system of virtual free trade.

British hospitality had been frequent and lavish—to the point where his suspicions were aroused. Over the weeks of constant invitations and a crowded schedule of receptions and dinner parties, a certain

Rev. John Bayne, D.D., of Galt, Ontario, who brought the young Reverend Andrew to Canada and inspired the naming of his son

Reverend Andrew Maclean, pioneer minister at Crieff, Ont., father of John Bayne Maclean

The family group in 1873: Mrs. Andrew Maclean, recently widowed, with her two sons, eleven-year-old John Bayne and seven-year-old Hugh Cameron Maclean

Toronto in the 1880s as young John Bayne Maclean beheld it. Above: Looking west on King Street, the view dominated by the tower of the *Mail* building where he worked as a reporter. Below: The city's distant skyline across the bay from Hanlan's Point, favorite spot with him and others for a Saturday afternoon's boating

# THE CANADIAN GROCER
## & GENERAL STOREKEEPER

PUBLISHED WEEKLY • $2.00 PER YEAR

Vol. III.        TORONTO, JANUARY 4, 1889.        No. 1.

## The Canadian Grocer.

PUBLISHED IN THE INTERESTS OF GROCERS,
CANNERS, PRODUCE AND PROVISION
DEALERS, AND GENERAL
MERCHANTS.

PUBLISHED BY

**THE GROCER PUBLISHING COMPANY, LIMITED**

H. C. McLEAN,                    J. B. McLEAN,
*Assistant Manager*                *Sec.-Treas.*

Subscription    .    .    $2.00 per year.
*Invariably in Advance.*

MONEY may be sent by Postal Money Order,
Accepted Cheque, Bank Draft, or Express Co. All
Drafts and Money Orders should be made payable to
the order of THE GROCER PUBLISHING CO., Toronto.
COMMUNICATIONS upon all subjects of interest to
the trade are solicited. THE CANADIAN GROCER is
entirely independent, and will state facts and express
opinions regarding topics of importance to the trade
in a fearless and independent manner. Any information our readers may wish to obtain shall be
cheerfully given, and prompt replies will be made to
all inquiries addressed to us on any subject of interest to the trade.
ADVERTISING RATES made known upon application. It is the aim of the publishers that none but
reputable firms be represented in our advertising
columns; our subscribers will confer a favour by
notifying us if they find them otherwise.

ADDRESS ALL COMMUNICATIONS TO
THE CANADIAN GROCER,
No. 5 Jordan Street, Toronto.
**Telephone 630.**

## Official Directory
### — OF —
## TRADE ASSOCIATIONS

### WHOLESALE GROCERS' GUILD.
*President:*                        *Secretary:*
WILLIAM INCE.                EDGAR A. WILLS.

### TORONTO RETAIL GROCERS' ASSOCIATION.
*President:*                    *Vice-President:*
J. BERWICK.                    ROBERT BARRON.
*Secretary:*                        *Treasurer:*
J. F. THACKERAY.            A. K. WILLIAMSON.
*Inner Guard:*
FRANK JOHNSTON.
*Executive Committee:*
D. W. CLARK.                    WM. CALHOUN.
R. MILLS.                        F. S. ROBERTS.

### CANADIAN
## PICKLERS AND PRESERVERS' ASSOCIATION.
*President:*                    *Vice-President:*
C. RICHARDSON,            WM. MARSHALL,
Toronto.                        Hamilton.
*Secretary-Treasurer:*
F. JAMES GIBSON, Toronto.

### CANADIAN PACKERS' ASSOCIATION.
*President:*                    *Vice-President:*
A. E. CARPENTER,            S. FENTON, Jun.,
Hamilton.                    St. Catharines.
*Secretary-Treasurer:*
J. B. McLEAN, Toronto.

### CANADIAN CONFECTIONERS' ASSOCIATION.
*President*                        *Secretary:*
A. W. PORTE, London.    G. W. COTTEREL, London.

### SPECIAL TO OUR READERS.

**As the design of THE CANADIAN GROCER is
to benefit mutually all interested in the business,
we would request all parties ordering goods or
making purchases of any description from houses
advertising with us to mention in their letter that
such advertisement was noticed in THE CANADIAN
GROCER.**

### OUR THIRD VOLUME.

With the present issue THE CANADIAN
GROCER AND GENERAL STOREKEEPER enters
upon its third volume. Its progress during the past year has been marvellous.
Over two thousand new names have been
added to the list of subscribers in the past
eight months. The paper is now to be
found in the hands of the leading merchants all over Canada. It is satisfactory
to know that both subscribers and advertisers are more than pleased with it.
During the present year we will endeav-
our to make it still more valuable to both.
A new dress of type has been ordered, and
with it the general appearance of the paper
will be materially improved.

### THE BUSINESS SITUATION.

Business in Canada during the year just
closed has been quite satisfactory, both as
regards volume and net profits. At the
same time it has been a very trying year.
There have been numerous failures ; large
quantities of bankrupt stocks have been
thrown on the market and profits have
been hard to get. The honourable merchants have had a hard struggle to keep
their business on a paying basis. The
large advance in the prices of wheat and
barley in the early autumn revived trade
very considerably and, for a time, quite an
active business was done. The farmers,
however, were not content with the high
prices, but, as usual, wanted more. These
most of them did not get, and there is
now every probability that values will not
again, this season, touch the high point
reached in the early part. Latterly business has been quiet, but as soon as snow
falls and deliveries of grain again com-
mence, a more active trade is looked for.
This will be warmly welcomed, especially
by the country trade, who have still a larger
quantity of staples on hand than usual at
this season. There are numerous complaints on the scarcity of money. The
only excuse given is, that farmers not having sold their grain cannot meet their
obligations.

### CANNED GOODS PACKERS.

Mr. W. Boulter, of Picton, has received
a letter from Mr. Wm. Ballinger, President
of the Western Packers Association, inviting him and through him the other Canadian packers and manufacturers of packers
machinery to attend the meeting of the
Western Packers' Association, to be held in
Chicago, Feb. 13. It is likely that a
number of Canadian packers and manufacturers will attend the meeting. Arrangements have been made with Messrs. Norton
Bros. of Chicago to provide a building with
ample space for the exhibition of all kinds
of machinery used or intended to be used
in canning factories.

### TO BE WOUND UP.

The Rising Sun Canning Co., of Hamilton, as stated last week, is to be wound
up. This course was rather unexpected
by many of those interested. They thought
there would be no difficulty in effecting a
compromise. Among the shareholders are
a number of market gardeners, several of
whom are said to have invested their entire savings in the now insolvent corporation. It is whispered that a competing
firm which suffered a good deal from the
reckless way in which the Rising Sun
people had cut prices, induced one of the
principal creditors not to agree to a compromise of any kind.

### COMMERCIAL TRAVELLERS.

WESTERN ONTARIO TRAVELLERS.

The Western Ontario Commercial Travellers' Association is in a flourishing condition. President Samuel Munroe, in his

The *Canadian Grocer,* first-born of the Maclean line of publications,
appeared in September 1887. Its newsy, no-nonsense style of cover
continued for a number of years, as shown on the January 4, 1889, issue

By the 1890s the company was growing and could afford a few fancy touches—such as this seal on its cheque forms. "We never sleep" is the motto line under the owl

John Bayne Maclean's rough draft of letter accepting the post of Commercial Editor of the *Empire,* the new Toronto daily organized for all-out support of Sir John A. Macdonald and the Conservatives. The Maclean handwriting stayed much the same throughout his lifetime

# The Canadian Grocer

### PUBLISHED WEEKLY

## IN THE INTERESTS OF THE GROCERY, PRODUCE, PROVISION, LIQUOR AND CONFECTIONERY TRADES.

J. B. McLEAN, General Manager.

5 Jordan Street
Toronto, 14th Nov 1887

Mr O.D Creighton M.P.P.
Toronto

Dear Sir

I beg to state that I have much pleasure in accepting the situation of Commercial Editor of the new Conservative organ at the salary of $1200 per annum provided that I am permitted to retain my connection with The Canadian Grocer as its editor

The Maclean company's second publication, introduced in 1889, clearly described its field with a cover design that ran unchanged for five years. The name was later expanded to *Hardware and Metal*

In a quarter-century of devoted service to the Canadian militia, John Bayne Maclean wore a variety of uniforms. Here, in his early twenties, he is lieutenant in the 10th Royal Grenadiers, a Toronto regiment

For special Scottish occasions such as a gathering of the Clan Maclean Association, he had ready the full Highland regalia—not, it's true, identifiably military but nonetheless warlike with sword and pistols

By 1898 a great dream was realized, and Maclean (seated, second from left) achieved commanding officer status. Here, with other "pillboxed" officers of the Duke of York's Royal Canadian Hussars, Montreal, he attends a field-training exercise

The Colonel, resplendent in full-dress uniform of the Duke of York's Hussars. From white-cockaded fur busby to the spurred boots, the complete outfit, as supplied by the best London makers, cost $1500

By the early 1890s the Maclean company had expanded sufficiently to install its own mechanical department. This is a view of the first mailing room at the Front Street East headquarters

Below: The first pressroom, installed in the basement at 10 Front Street East. Here, *Canadian Grocer* and *Hardware* rolled off regularly week by week; there was a little commercial printing as well

conviction had taken root: the English were very, very clever people, and one of their highly developed skills consisted in knowing how to take advantage of the "colonial" from overseas while entertaining him handsomely.

Perhaps so, but a few of them also had a quick appreciation of brains and experience, for during that visit he was offered several tempting posts as publisher of newspapers or magazines. One of the invitations came from Lord Northcliffe, another concluded a pleasant luncheon with Sir Arthur Pearson, and a third, from the *Morning Post*'s owner, Lord Glenesk, stressed the exciting future that awaited just such a candidate for the top appointment. But Maclean remained aloof from these overtures. Once having gone into trade paper publishing he seemed to lose all interest in daily newspapers, and he would not leave Canada for he was convinced the opportunities at home were greater than anywhere else. Life there could be full to overflowing with variety and achievement. And always the great spaces beckoned.

Maclean's militia career—eventually to cover a quarter of a century from the moment of signing-on in Owen Sound during high school days—was now about to quicken in pace, expand in responsibilities, and challenge his capacity not only to adapt with new groups but to pay his way. During the year 1898 (long before the khaki era) he would be required to turn out in three different regimental uniforms and badges. His name would appear six times in Militia General Orders issued from Ottawa, and each of those terse announcements had to do with either a promotion or the correct preparation for same. He loved every minute of his militia duty—and understandably, for here was compensation for his failure to realize a young boy's dreams of serving as an Imperial officer on one of Her Majesty's distant frontiers.

He was a good soldier, one who drew respect from all ranks, including the decision-makers at headquarters. In March 1898 he earned his certificate for equitation—the art of military horsemanship—which at that period was required of every infantry officer of senior rank. Just two weeks later Major J. B. Maclean was promoted to Lieutenant Colonel of the 6th Battalion, Fusiliers. Within the next month that unit would amalgamate with the 1st Prince of Wales Regiment, also of Montreal. As a result of the merger, officers were now in oversupply—and so Militia General Order 57 states that Maclean will serve as a major in the P. of W. at mid-June. Within another fortnight he figures in the official lists again as having completed a special course from a Royal School of Military Instruction—and perhaps this had a bearing on his rising reputation for careful training procedures. He was intensely proud of his riflemen, and of the fact that in a few months five from his P. of W. Company were selected to join Canada's Bisley team of twenty crack shots who would compete in England for Empire honors.

At that point any other man might have been content to subside into his regimental niche for the rest of his active days—but not Maclean. With his love of horses, his passion for uniforms and his continuing desire for social recognition, there was an obvious, ultimate experience still awaiting: the cavalry. Sometime during the summer of 1898 he went to England, ostensibly on trade paper business, but perhaps even more eagerly to join a special course with the Hussars Cavalry Brigade at Aldershot, under Sir John French (later to command the BEF in Flanders). Here, again, there were stimulating new contacts, such as Robert Baden-Powell, recently returned from service in Matabeleland (but still with ten years to go before founding his Boy Scout movement). Maclean never forgot one piece of advice which Baden-Powell proffered. "Always be firm but always be fair. With a smile and a stick you can get anywhere in the world." B-P went on to emphasize his point by mentioning the motto of a certain community of African natives: "Softly, softly, catchee monkey" and the vital word, as Colonel Maclean told the story many times in later years, was "softly."

In November 1898, Militia General Orders contained two significant paragraphs: the first stating that Major (Brevet Lieutenant Colonel) J. B. Maclean is transferred to the unattached list; then, immediately below, the announcement that the same officer is to be Major, Commanding the Duke of York's Royal Canadian Hussars (Montreal), as of the first of the month.

This was a small but proud unit, tracing its history back to the "troubles" of 1812–15 when the Royal Montreal Cavalry had been hastily organized to resist a possible American invasion, later undergoing various affiliations, notably with the British 13th Hussars who, after the Crimean War and their participation in the charge of the Light Brigade at Balaclava, had been posted to Canada. Now, the year 1898 would witness a glorious rebirth. Victoria's grandson, the Duke of York (eventually King George V), had been graciously pleased to approve the renaming in June, and to permit use of his personal insignia for finishing touches on the officers' newly designed uniforms.

These had been ordered as soon as Maclean took over—or, to put it with stark accuracy, as soon as he raised a loan of $6000 for the purpose from his friend, Vincent Meredith of the Bank of Montreal. With that sum the squadron's eight officers could be outfitted in a few weeks, but it is quite probable the compassionate O.C. arranged for repayment of the individual share to be spread over twelve months if necessary. In the 1890s a cavalry major "earned" $3.90 per day for about a dozen days' intensive training (as at summer camp) but the grand total of $46.80 for his year's activities was promptly and without exception, signed over to his unit's funds for general upkeep, horse rentals where required, and prizes for special training contests between the sixty-nine "other ranks" that composed the squadron body. The volunteer cavalry was, in short, a costly business for each officer.

But from Maclean's point of view, it was worth every cent of the investment. As the officer in command of the Duke of York's Hussars, an upright, handsome figure on a gleaming black charger out front, he had at last realized his dreams. Now, instead of the modest green uniform of the rifleman or the redundant scarlet of the fusilier, he turned out in almost armorial splendor on each parade occasion. His black jacket had six rows of heavy gold cord ending in large looping frogs across the front—a device adopted far back in time as a protection from the slashing cuts of an enemy's sword. The sleeves were emblazoned with a series of Austrian knots, having the appearance of curvaceous feather shapes; centering these was the treasured emblem carrying the Duke of York's insignia, which consisted of the white rose of York surmounted by a royal coronet, all displayed on a golden maple leaf and carrying the unit's initials, "D.Y.R.C.H." Officers of field rank, such as the O.C., were equipped (perhaps "encumbered" is the word) with a sabretache, which from Napoleonic days or even earlier served as a sort of elegant brief case for field maps and orders. This, along with the sword, hung from the gold-embroidered sash. Headgear was a fur busby with high-rise white feather cockade clamped at the center by a gold band. Nevertheless the topper had its practical value for heavy leather lining made it in effect a crash helmet; the wearer had a sporting chance of surviving a direct slash on the cranium. Black leather boots to the knee were decorated with gold swirls around the top. (The only feature missing—familiar today to all lovers of *The Merry Widow* or *The Chocolate Soldier*— was the "pelisse," the fur-trimmed top jacket, always suspended

jauntily from the left shoulder, and merely awaiting a light rain shower
to prove its serviceability.)

Given a sunshiny day, what a sight they were—Montreal's Duke of
York's Hussars in close formation, decorously prancing down the
slope of Côte des Neiges, each trooper with one hand on the reins,
the other holding a long lance topped with a fluttering pennant, and
every helmet a-glitter! Two regimental marches were exclusively theirs
in the city's military district: "St. Patrick's Day" and "Men of
Harlech" and the lilt of the former or the solid chords of the latter
inevitably drew crowds from the side streets. The elaborate *guidon,*
embroidered with the regimental motto, *Non Nobis sed Patriae* ("Not
self but country") excited the admiration of the ordinary folk lining
the curb. No wonder the face of that mustachioed, fine figure on the
polished horse leading the procession wore an expression of fulfillment. He was O.C. of Montreal's finest regiment, and, although the
single-squadron size of the unit would normally justify only a major in
command, his qualifying as lieutenant colonel the year before had
been recognized by Headquarters and his appointment confirmed in
that rank. Thus shortly after his thirty-sixth birthday emerged the
"Colonel," as he would be known, often affectionately, to several
generations of employees, publishers, politicians, royalties and their
deputies, and international figures in a dozen gathering-grounds the
world over.

During Maclean's term of command, the Duke of York's Hussars
were given just one serious assignment. On October 22, 1900, a strike
developed at the Montreal Cotton Mills' plant in Valleyfield, Quebec,
where men engaged on hurried construction work before the winter
freeze-up voiced strong objection to "standing belt-deep" in water and
receiving wages of just $1 per day. When the company suddenly an-
nounced dismissal of the crew and discontinuance of the project until
the next spring, there was still louder reaction. Hastily a group of
citizens headed by the mayor requested military protection for both
plant and community. Four days later selected details from one artillery
and three infantry regiments, plus a goodly muster from the Hussars,
appeared on the scene: 400 in all, including a multiplicity of officers.
Now the strike went into its second phase, with all 3000 employees
of the mills joining the construction gang in protest against the military
turnout. Soldiers were stoned and otherwise ill-treated; after-dark
scuffles broke out between strikers and the patrolling guard.

The situation had approached the ugly stage when a certain twenty-
six-year-old by the name of W. L. Mackenzie King, just recently made

Deputy Minister of Labor in Ottawa, decided to go to Valleyfield on his own and make an effort for peace. His plan worked. After a day and a half of talks with the bosses and the workers, both separately and together, the strike was settled. By October 29 most of the troops were leaving, although the Hussars had to mark time, waiting for box-cars to ship their horses back to Montreal.

The officer commanding, however, had not been present, for that happened to be the week when he had a most urgent prior engagement in the city of Boston, Massachusetts—of which more, much more, later.

But there is little doubt that Maclean gave a great deal of study to all angles of the Valleyfield incident. He had admiration for the young Mr. Mackenzie King, and expressed indignation on his behalf when five months later the Conservative opposition in Parliament criticized the whole affair, militia and all, and declared the mediator from the Department of Labor had turned up for the purpose of stimulating support for the Liberal candidate in the forthcoming election, rather than for settlement of the strike. After King had prepared a sworn statement, to be read in the House, refuting all such charges about "political activities" during his brief visit to Valleyfield, Parliament grudgingly dropped that angle, only to switch to hours of debate as to who would pay the $5000 earned by the troops, especially "all those high-ranking officers at their high rates of pay." Finally, a shared arrangement, as between town, mill and Department of Militia, was worked out.

The Colonel's greatest moment with the squadron came in 1901, when its colonel-in-chief, H.R.H. The Duke of York, accompanied by his Duchess, visited Canada. In September a vast military review, involving some 5000 troops, awaited his pleasure on the Plains of Abraham at Quebec City. True, the rain poured down relentlessly, and the second half of the program had to be canceled; nevertheless the Duke made a keen, careful inspection of "his" cavalry, later congratulating the Colonel for the splendid turnout and military bearing of all ranks, including the mounts. Within a few days the Royal guests were in Montreal, and there the honor of furnishing escorts in full regalia for every suitable occasion on the program was conferred on the Duke of York's Hussars.

Maclean remained in command of his cavalry for five years. For his military services he received two decorations: one, the Colonial and Auxiliary Forces Long Service Medal, inaugurated by King Edward; the other, George V's Silver Jubilee Medal of 1935, which was probably awarded as much in recognition of Maclean's Red Cross and publishing work as for military activities.

Colonel Maclean was convinced that the militia was one of Canada's great establishments, a force for stability in national life, a proven influence for good among the country's young men. During 1931 he spoke out twice on the subject. In a letter to the editor of a country weekly and published therein, he suggested that "if one looked into the faces of the men who are continually running past signals and breaking other motor laws, one would find few, if any, of the type who belonged to the militia." The same idea underwent careful expansion when he addressed a military group in Toronto: "The militia is the greatest single factor in the maintenance and development of national unity and loyalty in Canada and the Empire. It is the best training school, and perhaps the only training school, in which young men are taught discipline, and through their military discipline are inspired to discipline themselves in their private lives and to discipline themselves to the obedience of law and respect for order."

The same positive pronouncements were no doubt ready on his lips in June 1947 when, as guest of honor at the first of the Hussars' post-war annual dinners in Montreal, he rose in his place and waited, patiently, happily, for the cheers to subside. Of course, times had changed rather drastically in the half-century since his final parade in the gold-embroidered uniform. At the opening of World War II the regiment took its place in history as the last of Canada's militia cavalry to dismount; within months the Hussars were deep in intensive training as a reconnaissance regiment of the Canadian Armored Corps; on the fateful "D-Day" of June 6, 1944, they went ashore in Normandy with the 3rd Canadian Infantry Division and played their part in the push across France and Belgium. Was there ever a nostalgic moment for remembering the old horse stalls and saddle racks which had been piled away neatly, perhaps even hopefully, under lock and key in the barrack storerooms in Montreal? It could be—for not until 1951 did the Hussars bring themselves to dispose of all such paraphernalia from the past, thus making way for the complex equipment of an armored regiment in the peacetime militia. If John Bayne Maclean could have dropped by of an evening, after that change-over, and watched those neatly uniformed groups busy at their technical studies, blackboard mathematics and weapon demonstrations, he would certainly have discovered pointed new significance in the old motto, still proudly in use: "Not self but country."

## CHAPTER VIII

# DEAR HUGH, DEAR J.B.

"We were brothers . . . (and) brothers closely allied in business almost invariably disagree and separate."
*J.B.M.*

JOHN BAYNE MACLEAN had entered his eighties when he drafted the three-page letter containing the comment quoted above and sent it along to "Dear Hugh." By that time their partnership belonged to the far past, indeed to the previous century, and those mellowing years of the 1940s could have been filled with happy exchanges between the brothers who, each in his separate way, had built up one of Canada's two leading houses for periodical publishing. But that was not to be. The reminiscences that drove them into a frequent interchange of long typewritten scripts or scribbled notes of afterthoughts harked back almost invariably to their business break-up in 1899. Both men were fully aware that the decision at the time had been mutually acceptable, yet neither would agree with the other's explanation of why the split had come about.

It probably never was necessary and, over the years, each of them must have recognized that fact.

Throughout the correspondence each brother stayed in character. Hugh's message to "Dear J.B." (the invariable salutation) was often an accusatory tirade as blunt and direct as the man himself. J.B.'s letters bore the mark of their author: calm, unhurried, reasonable in tone even while rejecting Hugh's charges, and leaving the over-all impression that the writer is saddened by the willful and stubborn behavior of a younger brother. Such an attitude was bound—perhaps even calculated—to raise the blood pressure of the junior partner who knew that he had carried the heavy burden of administration during the other's Montreal experience; no wonder a heated rejoinder would be in the mail within twenty-four hours.

Yet to interpret these arguments and recriminations as an all-out feud would be a mistake. Jack and Hugh never forgot they were brothers, descendants of proud clans; true to the rugged Scottish tradition, they accepted their right and desire to stand staunchly together as a family pair before the world, even while privily brandishing their claymores at each other. Occasionally they joined forces during important gatherings of publishers or other related business groups— although casual twosome lunches or downtown calls were never indulged in, regardless of the fact that their offices were less than a mile apart.

Most important of all, however, were the social occasions at each other's family headquarters, when guests around the dinner table could not help but remark the affection and loyalty existing between the two brothers, "even though they're competitors in business, my dear!" At one point well along in the twentieth century, the Colonel tried to bolster his "competition" by giving $50,000 out of his private purse to help Hugh in a final attempt to preserve the *Canadian Magazine*. And in his last will and testament John Bayne Maclean made a generous bequest to his brother's son, the only surviving third-generation member of the Reverend Andrew's line.

Of course the quarreling had started many years before the period of "the letters." One of Hugh's favorite recollections from childhood days sheds some light on the conflict of characters. During their time with Uncle James Cameron in Chatsworth, an aunt with a pronounced limp made occasional visitations to the parsonage. The boys were highly diverted: here, they were sure, was an actual person with a wooden leg! But they'd have to prove it . . . "so," suggested Jack, "after supper, when they change the white cloth to the plush one with the long fringe, you hide under the table and jab this hatpin into her ankle. You're the small one—they won't see you." The leg turned out to be flesh and blood, and Hugh was sent to bed howling, after a thorough Victorian spanking. A half-century later he laughed when he told the story, but he never forgot to point its moral. "It was Jack who always got us into trouble," he said, "but I was the one who took the punishment."

The incident was a forecast of the later business relationship. It was Jack who initiated the various publishing projects between 1887 and 1899 and his brother who often supplied the muscle and perseverance for their successful execution and, as a result, sometimes suffered, in term of hard work and a sense of injustice. But never in silence—

as proved by Hugh's contributions to the several pounds of correspondence and memos exchanged by the pair over some sixty years (and still in existence in the Colonel's "Family Files").

Jack's obvious appetite for the simultaneous handling of several jobs, whether with or without increment, was a continuing source of irritation to Hugh. In 1890, just after the latter had organized the first branch office in Montreal, he was stunned to receive a note from his brother requesting immediate inquiries about an interesting opening on Montreal's *Herald*—for a general manager, it seemed, and who could fill the bill better than John Bayne Maclean, equipped with both newspaper and publishing experience? By return mail Hugh replied in characteristic staccato style: "Whatever is the matter with you? How do you think our papers would get on without you? The idea of wanting to leave Toronto to come to this damned place. You must be crazy . . ." For other reasons as well, Jack dropped the idea.

Hugh had never approved the *Art Weekly* enterprise in New York; in fact, some of his letters in after-years suggest that, from an over-all point of view, this venture had actually lost money. Then, when the two brothers switched geographical locations, and Jack began his meteoric rise in Montreal's military circles, there were periodic growls from Head Office: "You should be paying more attention to your business and less to your supply of horses." But this did not indicate a disinterest in soldierly activities, for Hugh was a militiaman himself, having been commissioned first in the Prince of Wales Regiment, and, after his return to Toronto, becoming an officer in the newly formed 48th Highlanders. Eventually he acquired the title of "Major," which would remain an inseparable part of his name for the rest of his life.

There were very real differences of temperament between the brothers. Jack was a man of considerable vision, industrious enough —as he demonstrated during his start-up days in publishing—but alway bored by administrative details and office routine. Hugh was a more practical person. Jack presented the outward appearance of calm and unemotional detachment. Hugh was earthy, irascible, gruff, with a square, hard-jawed face to match the manner. He was direct in speech and action. If he wanted to fire an employee he did it himself and explained the reasons for his decision; Jack's method was to assign the task to someone else, at the same time suggesting a polite, face-saving excuse. It was more than once left for Hugh to patch up his brother's occasional mistakes.

One example had to do with Uncle John Cameron, a non-reverend in that large family. Sometime in the early '90s this gentleman was brought into the business by the founder and listed on the masthead of each publication: "John Cameron, General Subscription Agent." The brothers liked him and stood by, ready to help with the mysterious details of mailings, records, change-of-address, etc., but they soon realized the appointment had been unfortunate, not because of the man but because of his voluble womenfolk, specifically his wife and sisters.

On October 7, 1895—when Maclean was snugly settled in Montreal and just about to take over the *Military Gazette*—Hugh sat himself down to write his uncle the letter that would either (a) end it all or (b) necessitate a fresh beginning. He stated that this notification of dismissal was directly attributable to the constant complaints from the aunts that "we have been treating you unfairly . . . We have stood this talk now about three years, lately it has been getting worse and now it is unbearable, and rather than stand it any longer JB and myself feel that we would rather break the pleasant business connections we've had with you for some time." In an undated note to Montreal, Hugh reports his action and goes on: "When Uncle John gets my letter there will be a great row in the camp. I'm afraid it will strike Mother harder than anyone else. She cannot look at the matter in any other way than that we are expected to support the whole Cameron family. She will now feel that we have disgraced her and ourselves. I'm also afraid that Uncle John will be too proud to ask to come back; well, if he doesn't make Aunt Jane come to me and apologize he will have to stay away. I feel rather sorry for Aunt Jane as she has been exceedingly kind to both of us but I must admit that I never knew a more grasping woman."

Apparently Aunt Jane had no apology to offer, for Uncle John Cameron stayed away. More surprising, however, was the fact that Maclean expressed strong disapproval of Hugh's "high-handed" move, especially the wording of his letter which "would only stir up family strife." Yet there exists to this day J.B.'s signed note, dated October 5, 1895—two days before Hugh opened the *cause célèbre*—instructing his brother to "fire" Uncle. "If you could keep him suspended for a month," the note goes on, "it would probably teach the other relatives a lesson, if we can force them to come down to ask that he be reinstated."

No wonder Hugh gave vent to a long, cranky letter on October 30.

"I'm now getting too old to allow this constant nagging which I stood for a lifetime," he writes to J.B. "When I have time to reflect on the past I cannot help thinking that if I'd been encouraged instead of being told that I was of no use, I should be now far above my present standing . . . I say again that I don't propose to allow you to browbeat me any longer. At present your head is a little too big and you forget that other people have rights that must be respected."

A contretemps of that kind can happen in the best-regulated families, especially if there is a business involvement. But "the real differences" between the brothers, as the Colonel was to point out to Hugh in a 1937 letter (which, like Tennyson's brook, goes on forever) had to do with "your use of Company money in mining speculation, and using our name in flotations, particularly in association with certain promoters whom I knew to be absolutely dishonest from every angle."

One of the get-rich-quick projects to capture Hugh's interest and cash was the Hawk Bay Company, of which the promoters, quickly sensing his excitement plus his dependability, had made him "Honorary Secretary-Treasurer." J.B., still in Montreal, suffered total shock at the news. He immediately wrote to Toronto: "Who ever heard of an honorary secretary-treasurer of a business corporation? You have more work to do than you can possibly overtake in the Maclean Publishing Company and here you go in with this gang of fakers and, worse than that, you allow our name to be blazoned forth in a flaming advertisement. On no account allow their advertisements to appear in any of our papers; otherwise I shall insert an article which will not be at all complimentary to you."

In 1899 the quarrel came to a head. On February 17 of that year J.B. wrote to Hugh: "It looks like a period of very great prosperity. I'm getting on in life"—he was thirty-six—"and must make my money. We cannot, however, continue as we have been going on. Our best year was in 1895, before your foolishness (I ought to use a stronger word) brought on family troubles." Was the reference to Uncle John Cameron or to Hawk Bay? One can't be sure. Anyway, to continue with the letter: "I have made several attempts to bring about a better state of affairs but receive no encouragement, only the reverse. In the last three years, neither of us has given the business fair attention and it has gone down." He said he had endured more mental suffering than in "the whole of my previous life put together. My health is now broken down and I must take a rest.

"First, however, I must settle our business relations. Only my love for my mother has prevented me doing so before. I hope the change can be satisfactorily explained to her, so that she will have nothing to worry her.

"I will sell you my two-thirds or buy your one-third. Let me know by return mail what you will buy or sell at. When this is satisfactorily arranged, we can toss up a penny as to which shall remain. The other shall agree not to embark in any competing trade journal." It seemed a fair enough offer.

Hugh made a counterproposal: he would (a) step out and let the Colonel run the business for five years or (b) the Colonel could take a five-year rest while he, Hugh, kept the Company going. The profits would be divided every quarter. Then, at the end of the five years, the business would be carefully evaluated and disposed of as per the Colonel's wishes.

The Colonel requested an opinion on the plan from Toronto's top legal light of the period: Zebulon A. Lash, Q.C. The lawyer pointed out that the business was run as a partnership which could be dissolved at any time by either partner. The two Macleans had been operating as if they were an incorporated company; nevertheless what they had was simply a private partnership. No steps had been taken under the charter for the organization of a company, the issue of shares therein, or the transfer of the business to a company. With Lash's help, the partners came to an agreement: J.B. bought Hugh's interest for $50,000, at the same time canceling the latter's $23,000 debt to the Company for stock market activities.

The arrangement sounds simple, direct, easy to grasp. Yet for the rest of their lives, these two brothers, who actually liked and respected each other, would argue back and forth in endless letters about that "deal," and its fairness or otherwise. Hugh would insist that "up until 1898 I believed I held a half interest in the business . . . You claimed a two-third interest, and on this ground final settlement was made." Then J.B., calmly and at considerable length, would point out by return mail that he had paid his brother what he'd asked, "i.e. $50,000, and canceled your debt of $23,000, making $73,000 in all; that is, you put in $1000 and six or seven years later withdrew $73,000 which was really very much more than the business was intrinsically worth . . . I certainly did not want you to retire. I was quite happy in Montreal, far happier than I would be in Toronto, and with its people." Nevertheless, he could say, looking back on it from this point in time —1937—"I think the separation was a very wise move."

Was it "a very wise move"? Did the qualities of each brother not complement the other's weaknesses?

If Jack had not gone to New York, if the two brothers had continued to work side by side in the same office, they would inevitably have accommodated themselves as they did in the early days of *Canadian Grocer* and *Hardware & Metal*. But if Jack had not gone to New York and if there had been no Montreal period, what would have happened to his future? Instead of emerging as a mover and shaker, an originator and a fighter, he might have settled for the dull, safe routine of the Front Street office for the rest of his days.

The agreement of dissolution and sale was dated March 7, 1899, and although both men must have been exhausted from the strain, it appears that each had his immediate plans well laid. Within just a day or so the Colonel was on his way to England. That trip was to have its unforeseen delay and anxious moments, for the ship he had boarded in Portland, Maine, the Allan Line's new *Castilian,* struck a submerged rock ledge off Nova Scotia on the first night out, March 11. Fortunately no lives were lost and by the next evening all passengers, including Maclean, had been transferred to rescue vessels and landed at Yarmouth. The following day he took the train to Halifax and made the crossing on the S.S. *Vancouver*—and an unpremeditated treasure of his luggage was the March 13 issue of the Yarmouth *Daily News,* to which he had been a contributor. The five-column story of the disaster featured "A Passenger's Statement," and, although no name was mentioned in print, the Colonel's unmistakable handwriting added the initials "J.B.M." under the heading of the carefully saved clipping. The style, too, confirms the authorship. "I was asleep when the steamer struck," the account begins, "and the shock awakened me, but I merely thought a heavy wave had struck us, and then the gentleman in the next cabin knocked on the door and announced, 'We are on a rock,' and shortly after appeared the steward, who quietly suggested, 'You had better get up, sir, and pack your clothes, in case there should be any necessity of leaving the ship.' All people, whether passengers or crew, showed fine composure, although there was some anxiety when the deck in the dining saloon and music room was thrown up. This was supposed to have been caused by the swelling of the grain in the forward hold." And admittedly, "it was a sad sight to see the dead sheep being thrown overboard" after they had drowned in their smashed pens.

The long statement, which ends with a grateful tribute to the courage and calm efficiency of the captain and his crew, was obviously written out by the anonymous "passenger." The teasing question that springs to mind now is: when and how did he manage it? By burning the midnight oil in the Yarmouth hotel, either downstairs in the parlor, or upstairs among the suitcases in that low-ceilinged bedroom? And what was the *Daily News'* closing time for "rush copy"? If the paper circulated in the morning, an outside contribution would have to be in the editor's hands well before midnight; a little more latitude—say to 6 A.M.—might be allowed for an afternoon edition. But the veteran of a thousand deadlines had met still another one. Certainly he had delivered his article, and on time, and then, with the little eight-page paper under his arm, went happily forward on his interrupted journey.

Brother Hugh's 1899 plan also called for a trip overseas. For several months he traveled about Britain and on the Continent, calling on business friends, sightseeing and having a rest. In addition to the recent office turmoils, Hugh had suffered tragedy in his personal life. His wife, Bessie, daughter of Maclean's early associate, T. W. Dyas, had been buried a couple of years earlier; one of their children had died too. Now his family consisted of just one son, Andrew, born in 1896. Eventually the two would be closely associated in the Hugh C. MacLean Publishing Company, with headquarters in Toronto. Before that was to happen, Hugh MacLean would inaugurate the business in Winnipeg, where, in 1903, he purchased the Mortimer group of western trade papers, and established his own name in this field. The two brothers tried not to compete directly with each other but over the next fifty years it was inevitable that minor encroachments should happen and the "non-compete" rule gradually disappeared, to the accompaniment of many letters of protest.

The name itself was to remain defiantly, perversely different. In fact, both brothers had gone through years of individual troubles with the spelling of their surname—all in the best Highland tradition.

The Gaelic spelling is Macgilliane. Over the entrance to Duart Castle, ancient stronghold of the clan's chief, the name is carved out as "Mac-Lean," but the family within sign their names "Maclean." The father of John and Hugh was recorded as "Maclean" during his student days in Edinburgh, but when he joined the ministry he adopted the form then approved in church circles, using "M'Lean," and later adopting the other abbreviation, "McLean." It was under this confusion of spelling that he migrated to Canada. When his sons were born at

Crieff he wrote each name in a beautiful copper-plate hand, and in full: "Maclean." Then, perhaps just to ensure continuing confusion, he signed his own name at the bottom of the page, "Andrew M'Lean."

So it arose that Jack, at the time of forming his business, confronted complete freedom of choice. What influenced his early decision for the "J. B. McLean Company" was the need to avoid identification in the public mind with another publisher, the famous "Billy" Maclean, owner of the newspaper, Toronto *World,* and for whom he had worked as a reporter far back.

With incorporation of the Company in the early '90s, J.B. decided to change the name style to "MacLean," (note the capital "L") which had been used, perhaps unwittingly, on his military orders and records. Thus by 1895 all his publications proclaimed "The MacLean Publishing Company Limited" on their mastheads. Now, he and his brother and their business were obviously one family with the same name. There was to be another change, well along in time—in fact, between the two Great Wars—when, after a visit to Scotland and Castle Duart, the Colonel decided to follow the correct clan tradition and decapitalize the "L." But only for private use, as by that time the MacLean Publishing Company was a long-familiar term, and the final synchronization had to wait for a special corporate development in the 1930s. Thus, for years John Bayne Maclean was president of the MacLean Publishing Company Limited, which published *Maclean's Magazine.*

But Hugh C. MacLean was never to change his style, in either character or name. Until his company was finally bought out by Southam's, it was known as Hugh C. MacLean Publications and, in an interim period, Southam-MacLean.

CHAPTER IX

# THE GIRL HE STOLE FROM MUNSEY

"That weary, gray wolf."
*Elinor Glyn, describing Frank A. Munsey*

IF JOHN BAYNE MACLEAN had not been equipped with a special talent for forming, sustaining and deepening friendships . . . if Henry M. Flagler had failed in his monumental plan to make Florida the winter playground for the rich . . . and if a certain eminent Boston family had elected to stay put among the snows and mists of Chestnut Hill in the early months of the year 1900—then certainly this record of a man's life would have been vastly different. The career itself would have lost in brilliance and sweep, and any attempt to analyze the total picture would have resulted in just another story of business success. That the John Bayne Maclean saga has its provocative differences, its procession of colorful characters, is attributable to the man's personality and his unquenchable zest for new places and experiences and the close, abiding associations which inevitably followed, chiefly through his nurturing.

Consider the Maclean friendship with Frank A. Munsey. Their casual acquaintance in New York during the *Art Weekly* period had flourished vigorously, chiefly through the flow of letters from Canada, plus occasional visits, and now both men had arrived at a point of complete mutual respect and confidence. Their backgrounds were not dissimilar. Munsey, born on a struggling Maine farm, had left school at sixteen, "picked up" the technique of telegraphy, moved to the state capital, Augusta, where he became a key man, literally, between the legislators and their contacts near or far, and, of more importance, between the news of the outside world and the local publishing industry, which included a group of cheap magazines as well as newspapers. "I lost no chance to make the acquaintance of men prominent in business and in public affairs, through whom I sought the opportunity to throw my life and energy into the work that they had in hand," he recalled many years later. But as there were no takers, he set forth to carve out a career on his own—which he did by moving to New York in the early 1880s, equipped with a satchel containing $40 in cash and a clutch of manuscripts bought with the remainder of his savings, something under $500. From that unlikely beginning and an office just large enough for one table and two chairs, he launched himself as sole owner, publisher, editor and frequent contributor for his new publication, *Argosy*.

The Munsey success story would make a book—and two separate attempts at that project were undertaken after his death by former employees but neither of these volumes discovered the real man-behind-the-empire. His early years of playing off one creditor against another ("I bought paper on time. I bought everything I could get on time. The very audacity of it all gave me credit, and more and more credit all the while."), of storming ahead with such unheard-of and costly experiments as advertising and free sample copies, and eventual price reduction to make it "the first 10-cent magazine!" (which, because of the reduced profit per copy, started an immediate war with the distributing agency and promptly inspired the publisher to organize his own handling service) have some of the thrills, chills and exciting crescendo effects of the Alger serial which *Argosy* so proudly presented: *Do and Dare, or a Brave Boy's Fight for Fortune.*

By 1900 Munsey was forty-six and had become the greatest money-maker in a magazine world that included such formidable competitors as Cyrus H. K. Curtis and S. S. McClure. His net earnings, chiefly from *Munsey's Magazine* and *Argosy,* but nicely rounded out with returns from such incidentals as a hotel, a refrigerating plant, an umbrella factory and the first of his Mohican chain of groceries (soon to number seventy-five, scattered through half-a-dozen eastern states) were close to a million dollars a year. His peak was still to be reached, after entrance into the newspaper field.

The reason for the Maclean-Munsey friendship, which was to stay solid "with hoops of steel" on both sides for a quarter-century more eludes complete definition. They had shared the same experience of venturing into the complex field of publishing, backed with little or no capital, and had reached a point where the rewards of hard work could be enjoyed. They saw eye to eye in the matter of good writing, believing it to be the basic requisite for any successful publication. Both

were proud of their achievements in journalism, especially after having
had to learn by the lonely, grueling method of doing, discarding and
doing over again. (Munsey's self-tuition had been the more remarkable: within a few months of "deciding" to be a publisher, he was
studying words, dictionaries, setting assignments for himself each
evening; in his first four years of struggle with *Argosy* he wrote two
long fiction serials, the second of which, *Afloat in a Great City,* occupied him in midnight toil, as he later reminisced, over an entire
winter. He "put into it elements of dramatic interest that would get a
grip on the reader. I wrote and rewrote the first chapters many times."
Far from receiving any remuneraion for his effort, Munsey borrowed
$10,000 to advertise the spring-summer issues presenting *Afloat.* From
that point forward *Argosy* started to bring in "a clean hundred dollars
a week.")

But aside from certain parallels in their early business careers,
Maclean and Munsey had little in common as to personal interests or
character. No one ever heard the Colonel raise his voice except for
military commands; Munsey enjoyed thundering at his employees, and
indeed seldom missed a chance to underline the low estate of the Help
as contrasted with the Boss. Even by the year 1907 when he owned
two newspapers and half-a-dozen magazines, he could write the story
of his success for one of friend Maclean's publications and never at
any point in the course of 10,000 words refer to an editor or assistant
or valuable department within the Munsey organization. The Colonel's
special introduction under the heading, "America's Greatest Magazine
Publisher," came close to the stark truth, though certainly without
malice aforethought, when it wound up a sincerely complimentary
sketch with the comment, "His staff never know what to expect from
him. All his great moves have struck them like a thunderbolt." Quite
so, for Munsey was one of the original and one of the last Loners.
That tall, awkward, shaggy-armed figure with stony, unsmiling eyes,
deep-sunken cheeks and thick out-curving mustache had no need for
confidantes or advisers or pleasant exchange of opinions. He was a law
unto himself, and that law permitted no wasting of time on the amenities.

The Colonel, on the other hand, valued all the opportunities for a
well-rounded life, each day, every day. He had a delight in the airs
and graces of the drawing room, the gay badinage of sophisticated
people. He could, and often did, criticize or reprimand any employee
for less than the expected perfection on the job, but there was never

any abating of agreeable manners. His militia experience had instilled in him respect for all levels of activity, especially "other ranks."

Was it the attraction of differences that held the Munsey-Maclean association together? Aside from opposite character traits, there were several other factors worth noting: the spread in ages, which may have encouraged a Big Brotherly feeling in Munsey; the well-separated non-competitive areas of business operation, i.e. the U.S.A. versus Canada; and the simple yet overwhelming circumstance of their respective monetary power. Munsey was well on the way to his final fortune of $40,000,000; Maclean, head of a modestly prospering publishing house with five trade papers and the *Military Gazette,* offered no serious financial rivalry. In fact, Munsey was glad to pass on stock market tips received from such wizards as Judge Elbert H. Gary and Charles M. Schwab; acting on these, as well as certain whispered confidences from Montreal's wealthy "fur traders," Maclean had been able to accumulate a nest-egg competence quite outside the returns from his publishing business.

Thus he was ready to respond enthusiastically when Munsey suggested a holiday in Florida.

On the 20th of February, 1900, Munsey from New York and Maclean from Montreal signed in at the Royal Poinciana Hotel in Palm Beach. For both it was a first experience in the fabulous new winter resort, and for both this visit, which lasted until late March, would establish a habit almost as unvarying as each new year's calendar.

Florida had everything that the Munsey-Maclean pair, so totally committed to big dreams of a glittering future, could ask for. Moreover, its very existence as the playground of the rich was proof of the power of one man's dream, plus his skill in making it come true.

Henry Morrison Flagler, long-time Rockefeller partner and president of the Seaboard Railway, had spent over $35,000,000 to extend the line south along the east coast of Florida; then, out of a separate $20,000,000 reserve that happened to be handy, he had launched forth on hotel-community development, notably on the virtually uninhabited strip of land separating the length of Lake Worth from the Atlantic surf. By that time the thousands of coconuts washed ashore from a cargo ship years before had made themselves vigorously, happily at home, and here now was a forest of majestic tall trunks, umbrella-topped with fronded green. Palm Beach, in short—the perfect setting for the most "ultra" of Flagler's resorts!

The world of wealth, celebrity and fashion showed unanimous agreement with him as soon as his Royal Poinciana—largest wooden building in the world, with thirteen miles of corridors and carefully appointed rooms for nearly 2000 guests—opened its doors, which not too surprisingly faced the flower-banked train stop a few yards distant. Down from the private cars and Pullman parlors stepped the diamond-studded names. The merchant prince, John Wanamaker, put in regular appearance; so, too, the Thaws of Pittsburgh—that is, before there was a murder in the family. Charles Dana Gibson, America's most popular artist, brought his wife, the original "Gibson Girl," whose sister would eventually become famous as England's Lady (Nancy) Astor, M.P. Occasionally, if his concert schedule permitted, Paderewski would arrive for a week or so of sunshine and rest. The actor, Joseph Jefferson, familiar to millions as the stage's Rip Van Winkle, enjoyed the deep-sea fishing by day and was happy to give readings for charity by night. Cyrus H. K. Curtis, Philadelphia's magazine magnate, and Lewis Nixon, recently elected head of New York's Tammany, formed a holiday twosome. The Vanderbilts were Florida devotees, sometimes arriving in single units, occasionally in complete boardroom quorum. A couple of British duchesses sunned themselves languidly on the terrace; Mark Twain, tossing his white plume, was the animated center of a group of strollers; Admiral George Dewey, hero of Manila Bay just two years back, seemed always to have his little audience too.

Maclean and Munsey met them all, and for the younger man especially, the one who had a longer way to go in order to reach the top, it was a memorable experience. Here were the people who caused things to happen: men of power and decision, famous public figures, and women who led the world in beauty and fashion. Quickly he learned their habits and followed suit. Night after night Colonel Edward R. Bradley's newly established gambling club attracted an exclusive clientele; now Maclean from Canada stepped up to the tables and took his chances at the roulette wheel—not because he liked to bet but because this was the way to mix with the people who did. He attended the Palm Beach ball on Washington's Birthday —an occasion which the local society editor, frank and fearless in her conviction, described as "the swellest social event in the whole world." Several times the Colonel invited a few of his new friends to join him for afternoon tea or a round of pre-prandial refreshment, and before he left for home there was a certain handsome young woman starring importantly among those present.

Maclean had been introduced to Miss Anna Denison Slade of Boston by Munsey, who had met her a year or two earlier when he was making frequent visits to that city to study the possibilities of establishing his publishing headquarters there. That Munsey was attracted to her is clear; that he was too busy to think of proposing marriage is equally obvious. Now, here against the exotic backdrop of sea, sand, and sunshine and moonlit nights, two men were in love with her, two devoted friends competing for her interest and approval. John Bayne Maclean won out. Munsey lost and remained a bachelor for life—his frequent explanation in later years conveyed in the statement that when he was young he hadn't had time to marry, and when he reached wealth and middle age women wanted him only for his money.

For Anna, however, there was never any doubt in her mind as to the eventual decision. From the moment of their meeting she had been interested in the Colonel from Canada, so well-groomed, neat and trim of figure, calm and smiling; it was an agreeable experience to talk with a man who was incapable of gushing or resorting to the empty endearments of "Darling" or "Little girl," who at no time modified or downgraded his conversation to the supposed female level.

Far on in life she liked to reminisce about the month of March 1900. Jack was a very warm, human person, "and handsome too," she would say. "Mr. Munsey was a cold, strange man whom I never understood. They both wanted to marry me. Mr. Munsey used to send me an orchid every day. But Jack arranged with the florist and with my maid to have a tiny bouquet of violets on my breakfast tray every morning." Jack, in short, had time to fall in love and obey the instinctive impulses that led straight to a woman's heart. Munsey, it seems, could only stand by and watch, mystified. In this contest for a wife, the arid gaps in his personality showed plainly, and he was already on the way to becoming "that weary, gray wolf," as Elinor Glyn, expert observer of menfolk, would later describe him.

For John Bayne Maclean the months following were to move with happy acceleration. There were trips to Boston to meet the numerous Slades and their friends. In early summer he welcomed Anna to Toronto for a short visit, and saw to it that the *Mail & Empire* had the facts correct for the June 7 social column: "The engagement is announced of Colonel J. B. MacLean, of Montreal, and Miss Slade, daughter of Mrs. Denison Slade, of Boston. Miss Slade is in town, the guest of Mrs. MacLean in St. George Street"—the Colonel's mother of course, and at that time living in one of the city's quietly exclusive *pensions.* Anna and Jack agreed that Toronto would be their place of residence, and for him this meant frequent trips to and from Montreal, settling both personal and business matters there and taking thought for the morrow in his old stamping ground of the Queen City.

By early July the morning social column (as confused as the Colonel himself about the spelling of the name) reported "Colonel McLean has taken up his quarters at the Hunt Club, for the season." But apparently during those crowded weeks he managed a little change of air in Bar Harbor, the fashionable resort of New Englanders—for on September 11 the *Mail & Empire*'s social editor published this paragraph: "Colonel McLean is in town again after the summer vacation and is staying at the Toronto Hunt Club. Colonel McLean's marriage with Miss Slade is to take place in Boston in October."

And it did—in the Unitarian Church on Walnut Street, Boston, at twelve noon, Wednesday, October 31, 1900. (In Valleyfield, Quebec, the strike at the cotton mills had subsided, but Maclean's Hussars still awaited the railway boxcars for shipment of their horses back to Montreal.)

According to the wedding report in the Boston *Sunday Globe* a few days later, "the chancel was filled with towering tropical plants, all in green, and at each alternate pew was a huge bunch of yellow chrysanthemums, tied with yellow satin ribbon." There were appropriate selections by the church organist during the seating of the guests; then in due course the procession appeared, with first the ushers, viz., Conrad Slade, Frederic R. Tudor, Jr., Lieutenant R. B. Van Horne of the Duke of York's Hussars, M. G. Haughton, Jr., Arthur W. Wheelright and Elisha Flagg II. (Nowhere in the report is there any mention of Hugh. Was he there?) The bride was escorted by her brother, Denison Slade. She had no attendants. The groom had for his best man a cousin, Lieutenant C. W. Weldon Maclean of the Royal Horse Artillery, "just home from service in South Africa." The Slade residence was the setting for the wedding breakfast, where the guests (including the defeated Munsey) passed down the receiving line composed of the newlyweds and the bride's mother. Her gown of black velvet and old pointe lace, etc., her matching toque, and certain other ladies' ensembles were carefully described in the report, yet there is not one word about what the bride wore!

That she was beautiful in a distinguished, regal way can, however, be taken as fact, and quite aside from the details of costume. Her golden hair gleamed in a smooth pompadour above a high forehead, large blue eyes, straight patrician nose, and a delicately fair complexion. She moved unhurriedly, and perhaps it was the combination of the poise of her carriage, the unvarying habit of "chin up," plus the height of her coiffure that made her appear taller than her husband. All her life she showed an inborn sense of style, especially as it applied to her own wardrobe or environment—hence, the wedding dress, whether traditional white or otherwise, would have been carefully selected to enhance the total picture.

She was now thirty-three years of age, four years younger than her husband; a woman in the full bloom of maturity, and one of those rare persons of either sex who qualify for the term Individual. Her influence on the Colonel's life, which up to this point had lacked any close feminine alliance, was to be profound; suddenly there were windows opened on a larger world than any he had previously experienced. And the basic, inescapable factor in this development deserves to be clearly recognized for what it was: in short, not merely the impact of a woman's character, important though that would be through a long life together, but the full force of her remarkable family history.

The Slades went back in an undisputed straight line to the original colony in New England—and, as their claim to that distinction was supported by the careful researches of one of Harvard's leading professorial investigators, none other than Anna's scholarly father, it is hardly likely that twentieth-century skepticism can flaw the statement. Two of the ancestors were among the *Mayflower*'s passengers: Mary Chilton, alleged to be the first woman to step ashore, and Edward Winslow, still remembered as a leading official and sometime Governor of the little Plymouth settlement. Within another few years the Denison name, carefully preserved by the later generations of Slades, entered the picture by way of Major General Daniel Denison, who emigrated with his father to America. One of his descendants, Richard Clarke, won a permanent place in history texts as the merchant who waited months for that famous consignment of 342 boxes of tea, worth $18,000, which, on December 16, 1773, was to be dumped into Boston Harbor in the first overt act of the American Revolution. And, finally, a Clarke daughter became the mother of Professor Daniel Denison Slade, identified throughout his life with Harvard University, a man whose various degrees and pursuits ranged from medicine (he witnessed the first capital operation with ether) to osteology, applied zoology, horticulture and, in his spare time, astronomy. His lectures were consistently popular, having, as a learned colleague expressed it, "the power of stimulating original observation on the part of his students." Slade produced several books and countless treatises, and the subjects were as catholic as his interests—all the way from syphilis, presented in a thick volume of translation from the original French, to Massachusetts' wild turkeys (a charming piece for general reading) and, in the year before his death, "Abnormal Attachment of the Atlas to the Base of the Skull," which appeared in a leading medical journal.

He was a completely happy, gregarious type. On his fiftieth birthday he jotted in his diary: "I am in health, and in the enjoyment of all needful blessings—*riches,* in the form of a fond wife, and darling children, a well as riches which the world calls wealth . . . My dear home, my darlings within it . . ."

The home was a Chestnut Hill house, set in a pleasant garden, and sufficiently ample to accommodate any social influx, which often included Francis Parkman, Oliver Wendell Holmes, and others of the nineteenth-century Boston intelligentsia. The place had been designed of necessity for a large family, and from it would go forth, in their separate ways, ten adult sons and daughters, including Anna, who occupied a middle position in the range of ages. At the time of her wedding, Professor Slade had been in his grave for four years, but over the next half-century members of his coterie and their descendants would become valued friends of the son-in-law he never knew.

Yet this was only part of the story of John Bayne Maclean's highly valued acquisitions through marriage. By the simple act of falling in love with a daughter of Mrs. Slade, he became the nephew-in-law of a King's widow, still very much alive as a gay hostess in a fanciful chalet on a mountain slope in Portugal. Some day soon he would meet her, and another inviting avenue to a cosmopolitan future would open up . . .

He would take Munsey along, too, for their friendship had suffered no setback from the romantic rivalry. The Macleans and the New Yorker were to form up as a happy threesome on travels over many years. Frank could, and did, remain fond of Anna but with no thought of jealousy toward Jack. As for Anna, the situation was saved by her wit and good sense; she was confident her choice had been right, and every day the attentions of an affectionate, considerate husband underlined her convictions. As a happy wife, she saw no possible objection to the continuing friendship of the two men—and thus did Maclean's favorite companion stay for the rest of his days as the essential third party of the group.

# CHAPTER X

# LIFE BEGINS AT FORTY

"The house shows the owner."
*George Herbert*

THE MACLEANS' first Toronto residence was impressive from all points of view. It was located on the east side of Queen's Park Crescent. The circular roadway that coiled around the pleasant green open space dominated by the massive new Parliament Buildings (opened three years before) represented the ultimate in social environment. Just to the north of the Colonel lived B. B. Osler, Q.C., a leading criminal lawyer. After his death a year or so later, the house was occupied by Herbert C. Cox, heir apparent to a father's insurance empire. Farther along stood the family headquarters of dry goods wholesaler W. R. Brock, and then the huge, *porte-cochèred* domain of the "biscuit people," the Christies. Queen's Park was admittedly a showplace, the heart of Ontario and its government, and the property owners lived up to their responsibilities as evidenced by the spanking upkeep of gravel drives and lawns and the geometrically precise flower beds.

No. 13, the Macleans', spread over an ample corner lot at the junction of Grosvenor Street and the Crescent. Set well back behind the low fence of black iron spikes, topped every so often with gilded balls, the imposing, three-story buff brick house showed itself a hearty Victorian modernist. There were window groups of varying sizes and fanciful paning, a central doorway rising up to form a square entrance tower fringed with iron railing. Along the south side, a deep semi-circular bay could only mean a cushion-padded cozy corner as an interesting interruption in the length of the drawing room. At the back of the property stood the sizable stables, with second-story accommodation for the groom and ample space below for at least one riding horse as well as the carriage-and-pair which Anna loved to drive.

In short, the establishment had something of the expansive character of a country manor, even though situated in the center of town. The fact that John Bayne Maclean could make this type of transition after his bachelor years in rented rooms, hotels or clubs led Toronto's teatime gossips to the inevitable conclusion that *"She* is the wealthy one, my dear; she comes of a well-to-do Boston family." True up to a point, yet the late Harvard professor's realizable assets, aside from the house which remained the Slades' headquarters for years, had had to be divided between eleven immediate heirs. Even the most brilliantly successful academician, especially in the '90s, could hardly have amassed sufficient fortune to make any of them "wealthy." Anna's share was probably a matter of twenty or thirty thousand dollars— which would still be intact a half-century later.

John Bayne Maclean himself provided this elegant new household. The careful investments, entered into on the advice of his friends, had been bringing in excellent returns during the past few years; indeed, it was from his private account that he had been able to make the single, total cash settlement with his brother in 1899.

The Company, too, was prospering and its five trade papers expanding in size, subject coverage and advertising revenue. Gone the first timid days of 30-page issues! In the year 1900 *Dry Goods Review's* twelve numbers contained a total of 1312 pages, of which no fewer than 825½ were filled with advertising. Its big Spring Trade issue, presented for January, was a triumph not only in size—190 pages —but in that new magazine development called "color," featuring a cover painting of a brown-eyed Miss in the latest fashion of pink, puff-sleeved blouse, nicely displayed against a pale green background criscrossed with pink apple-blossom sprays. In the same year *Bookseller & Stationer* jogged along profitably, though not so spectacularly with 151¾ pages of advertising out of an over-all of 320. But *Canadian Grocer,* cherished first-born of the group, remained the unrivaled leader, presenting its 52 weekly issues in a total of 2528 pages, of which well over half were revenue-producers. A special Export number, published in midsummer, had accounted for 108 pages —and also, according to editorial announcement later on, for a virtual sell-out of the issue to eager enquirers in the United States, Britain and far corners of the world.

The profits were gratifying (and necessary too considering the new scale of living) but to Maclean, the born campaigner, the fact that he owned these important pulpits or platforms from which he could preach the gospel of better business represented the ultimate in personal satisfaction.

When *Canadian Grocer* was in its earliest tentative stages he had found himself in an argument, in print, with the Wholesale Grocers' Guild which he accused of operating a price-fixing ring, to the disadvantage of the retail merchant and the public. That campaign, diligently pursued, led first to examinations by the Dominion government, then to the eventual launching of a series of official interventions in such rings or "trusts," and years later culminating in the Combines Investigation Act.

In 1900 there was seldom an issue of *Grocer* without its arousing piece on the scandalous situation among certain British Columbia salmon canners, who were packing putrid or otherwise undesirable fish and labelling it to sell at first-grade prices. It was up to the government "to lay a heavy hand on this evil." Eventually the Department of Inland Revenue began an investigation, and from that point, step by step in official slow-motion action, grading standards were not merely set up but enforced through constant government testing routines.

In the early '90s, Maclean had opened fire on the Ontario Department of Education through his *Bookseller.* He had discovered a situation of favoritism, whereby a certain few publishers were automatically given all contracts to produce textbooks for the schools of the province. Not only the system but the quality of the products incurred his wrath, so in a straightforward editorial he demanded open tendering for all standard works and greater opportunity for every legitimate publisher to submit new manuscripts for special subjects.

Thus it was up to the Deputy Minister of Education to act, and he did, first by drafting a highly commendatory statement concerning Ontario textbooks, and then asking Maclean, as publisher of the leading book trade paper, to sign it for public release! Of course the suggestion was met with a firm refusal. Nevertheless, the official had a second plan ready: he would use the statement in the platform speech he had been invited to make next week, and he would—and did— manage to leave the impression that the words were Maclean's. The young publisher, righteously angry, revealed the entire plot in the next issue of *Bookseller,* much to the embarrassment of the government.

By 1900 he was taking a strong stand against that new menace called "trading stamps." In *Grocer* he pointed out that only a few stores, chiefly those of doubtful standards of service, had fallen victim to the smooth talk of the distributors of these "costly, wasteful extras" (the word "gimmick" had not been invented); in *Hardware & Metal* he warned the men of the hammers and nails to stay carefully away from the fallacy of trading stamps, no matter what a few other retailers were doing.

And in *H & M,* December 1900, there was an extended, calmly reasoned message for Toronto readers—one that, while losing pertinence with age, has undoubtedly gained in charm. It seems that certain Toronto municipal representatives were seeking to establish a city-owned telephone service, requiring just $675,000 initially, but well worth the effort, they believed, in order to halt Bell's monopoly. Under the heading, "Two Telephone Systems from a Business Standpoint," the article explores all the angles, pointing out that because of the nature of the service a single system must be considered essential—otherwise, a divided public could not communicate with each other—and also that a municipally operated rival for Bell would inevitably add to the tax burden. But the crux of the argument seems to be as follows: "Many ratepayers who do not use telephones are opposed to the idea," and, when all is said and done, "In a city like Toronto there is a limit to the number of persons who are or would be telephone users."

The trade papers' campaigning features were not all written by the Colonel. By the early 1900s he had a keen, hard-working though small group of editors at the Front Street headquarters, ready to translate his approval of good business methods or his objection to questionable practices into clear, forceful writing, always directed in a straight line to a special segment of the community. All such blasts appeared in print without bylines; hence, if and when there were repercussions from outside, it was the Colonel who took full responsibility. His crusading spirit had attracted attention from areas remote from his actual influence—and this was the reason that on an evening toward the end of May 1902 a certain young man in quest of a job set out eagerly for No. 13 Queen's Park Crescent to which he had been summoned. The experience proved so unusual, that he was inspired to set the details down on paper . . .

His name was William Arnot Craick, and for this important first encounter with the publisher he had worn his best suit; blue serge and carefully pressed. His black boots shone, his hard collar was sparkling white, and a straw boater sat on his head, jauntily but not too jauntily. As he hurried up the Crescent, carriages passed him, liveried coachmen at the reins, wheels and hoofs scrunching the gravel. An automobile rattled by—enough of a novelty that he paused briefly to watch it.

His thoughts were on the future. At the University of Toronto, where his senior year had just finished, he had majored in mathematics. Now his urge, a powerful one, was toward journalism. And although many of his classmates were departing for the glittering opportunities in the United States, Craick wanted to work in Canada, which seemed to him to be on the verge of an era that would overflow with adventure, excitement and achievement. Admittedly, the population on this side of the border was still only five and a half million —less than one-fifteenth of the eighty million in the U.S. But the wave of immigration from Europe gathered strength every year, washing across the incomparable wheat lands of the West, and inevitably expanding the growth and opportunities of city life as well. Toronto was getting close to a head count of three hundred thousand.

The place was on the march: more factories, able to produce everything from windmills to egg-beaters, from locomotives to canoes for Yukon's gold prospectors, from shovels to spoons, from pianos to whistles, from ermine capes to overalls. Toronto's products were exported in increasing quantity (the windmills, for instance, had a waiting market in Argentina and China). The city was a prime merchandising center. The biggest store, Eaton's, stood ready to dress the whole family, furnish the whole house, equip the whole farm—and shoppers could make their decisions in person at the counter, or sitting, catalogue in hand, in their rocking-chairs a thousand miles away. (That mail order business, incidentally, was not to be overlooked by Maclean's trade publications; several outspoken articles were later to suggest that Eaton merchandise was not always as represented in the annual catalogue and to offer practical advice to local merchants across the country on how to combat mail order competition. As a result, the Eatons, highly prizing their honor and reputation, were to threaten to sue Maclean and in the meantime ban his periodicals from their store newsstands.)

Maclean's editorial fearlessness was one of the main reasons young Craick hoped for a job on his staff. And now, thumping the bronze knocker on the door of No. 13, he swallowed hard, realizing that the big moment of a face-to-face meeting was just a moment away.

The Colonel's batman admitted the visitor and ushered him to an upstairs sitting room. Maclean rose to greet him and introduce him to Mrs. Maclean. She was handsomely gowned, and her sleek pompadour and aristocratic air of self-assurance seemed exactly right for a dignified hostess.

She glanced up from the embroidery in her lap to murmur a polite welcome, then lowered her eyes again over the needle. She stayed through Craick's entire interview with the Colonel, but she didn't say another word. Maclean, by contrast, talked freely about politics, economics, western crops, northern minerals, the Army, Palm Beach and those old friends, Munsey, McClure, *et al.*

Craick studied Maclean intently. The Colonel was of medium height, five feet nine or thereabouts, but his erect military bearing created the illusion that he was taller. His hair, brown but sprinkled with gray, was receding from the dome; nevertheless he looked fit and youthful. His Scottish parentage was discernible in the round cheekbones, ruddy complexion, astute blue eyes, bushy brows and bristling moustache.

He moved, Craick noticed, with the grace of a swordsman. His voice was soft and clear and he gestured with well-shaped hands to emphasize what he was saying. His stiff shirt gleamed, his black tie was precisely in place, his dinner jacket showed perfect tailoring. (Throughout his married life Maclean, like the legendary Englishman on safari, dressed for dinner almost every night, guests or no guests.)

Craick suddenly realized that he himself was being carefully watched and evaluated. Abruptly, the Colonel's easy flow of general conversation stopped, to be followed by a bombardment of sharp, penetrating questions. He concluded it, finally, by asking Craick why he did not intend to pursue the career in mathematics for which he had been educated. Because, said Craick, he had discovered that he preferred journalism. But had he not paid the university to teach him mathematics? Of course. Then should he not be willing to pay to be taught journalism? Craick searched the Colonel's face for a smile that wasn't there—and realized that not once through all their light chatter, had his host smiled.

Craick was understandably confused, and he was uncomfortable in this baroque sitting room with the elegant Colonel and his lady, who, at her embroidery, listened with a trace of amusement. But he managed to say he *had* been a reporter. Where? The Port Hope *Times*.

When? In summer vacations. Was that all? No, said Craick; besides that
he had written a book. What kind of a book? A history of Port Hope—
and it had been published, too. Well, then, said the Colonel, Craick
*did* have a little experience, but not much. Would seven dollars a week
be satisfactory as a salary? Yes, said Craick, he guessed it would do
for a start. But he was uncertain in his mind whether to be elated or
depressed. Toronto's factory hands were averaging ten dollars for a
week of fifty-four hours. Craick, with his university degree, would toil
longer for less.

The Colonel accompanied him downstairs. "Craick," he confided
as he opened the front door, "you will be interested to know that Mrs.
Maclean is related to the King of Portugal." He did not elaborate.
Craick was puzzled as he thanked his host and bade him goodnight.
One thing he was sure of: his new employer was no ordinary man.

Those frequent and sudden references to "the King of Portugal"
were to mystify many Maclean editors and others over the years.
History books offered little help, for the simple reason that one of the
principals in the great morganatic romance was still very much alive.
Now the story can be told, and it goes like this:

Anna Slade's mother had been born Mina Louise Hensler, in
Neuchatel, Switzerland, although her ancestry was probably Austrian.
Sometime during the 1840s the Hensler family emigrated to the United
States, taking up residence in Springfield, Massachusetts, where her
father opened a small tailoring business.

Both Mina and her sister Elise loved to sing, and in their teens
they not only joined the North Church choir but were regularly
sent for lessons with the best local teacher, Signor Guidi. So impressed
was he with Elise's talent that when he moved to Boston he persuaded
the Henslers to come along too, for the further training of her voice,
which he recognized as of platform quality. So, in the old port city
Mina known as "the pretty sister," met her Harvard professor husband,
while Elise concentrated on her voice, at the same time engaging in
a course of interpretive dancing.

Within a few years the name of Elise Hensler, member of the
Boston Opera Company, was drawing eager crowds in most of the
larger centers of the United States; inevitably her success led to bookings for a European concert tour. Thus it came about, sometime in
the 1860s, that she sang in Lisbon, capital of Portugal. Ferdinand II
was in the audience and was captivated by what he saw and heard.

He was now in his middle age, having been born in 1816, the eldest son of the Duke of Saxe-Coburg-Gotha, thus a blood-relation of both Queen Victoria and her husband in England, and indeed during his British cousin's younger days one of her favorite partners for the waltz and gallop. In 1836 he had married Maria II of Portugal, receiving the title of King Consort, and after her death he ruled as Regent until his two sons were of an age to succeed, the first having died young.

From various contemporary accounts it seems Ferdinand was endowed with a pleasant personality and had a fine appreciation of music. The fact that he was respected as well as popular, and even beyond Portugal's borders, is demonstrated in his having twice been offered a foreign crown, first by Greece and some years later by Spain. But by that time he had married the singer from America, who had been granted the title of Countess Elise d'Edla of Saxe-Coburg-Gotha; even so, he quite understood that a non-Royal wife would be unacceptable to the Spaniards. Some historians go so far as to say that, as a result of his refusal, plus the Western European intrigues and turmoils that followed the presentation of any other royal candidate's name, there was immediate gearing-up for the Franco-Prussian War in the 1870s. Out of that chaos and its causes emerged Edla's place in one historian's footnotes, as "the woman who changed the map of Europe." More important to us is the fact that her relationship to Anna led Maclean to give Europe high priority on his annual calendar of travel and news-gathering.

Ferdinand and his wife enjoyed their life together—much of it spent fifteen hundred feet above the plain of the River Tagus, in the Castel da Pena which clings to the top of a pinnacle at Sintra. The palace still stands and has never lost its power to amaze or amuse visitors. The architecture is a wild blend of Gothic, Moorish, French Rennaissance, fake Manueline; the clash of materials and colors and menacing statues, not to mention cannon, suddenly encountered as one emerges from the road that winds up through thick gardens, has a frightening impact on the unprepared eye. But by the time the visitor strolls about inside, that first shock has subsided and one becomes the normal sightseer, able to study, for instance, the room fitted out entirely with porcelain furniture, or to set up the camera for a shot of the life-size Turkish figures which hold up ornate candelabra in the yellow banquet-hall. And from the fancy battlements the view, when the clouds part and let the eye absorb the miles of landscape far below, is almost bound to clinch the final impression that here, indeed, was the ideal royal setting for "living happily ever after."

By the time of the Colonel's marriage, ex-King Ferdinand had, of course, left one heaven for the other; his death took place in 1885. But Anna remembered him, having made at least one trip to Portugal during her girlhood. Now, to her delight, she was joined in her admiration for the late Ferdinand and her devotion to his widow by the Colonel, to whom Portugal was as yet an unknown country. Eventually Aunt Elise would become his close friend and confidante, as well as a thoughtful hostess on his frequent trips abroad. One of his visits with her resulted in his appointment as Honorary Vice-Consul for Portugal in Toronto—a post which carried with it a sort of semi-diplomatic visa, enough to speed him through European customs formalities for many years to come. He never attempted to undertake the routine work of a consul, but left such details plus any fees involved, to his secretary. The social obligations were another matter, however; these he shouldered willingly, and his services eventually won a special tribute from the government of Portugal in the form of honorary membership in a military order.

Thus, for a full half-century of his life, John Bayne Maclean was to find a constantly stimulating interest in a far-off country, its people, its long-gone royal line, and especially in Sintra's fascinating lady, the Countess Edla.

CHAPTER XI

# COLLECTOR OF PEOPLE

"An unselfish listener? Cherish him
as a good friend."
*Beverley Baxter*

JOHN BAYNE MACLEAN could never have been a happy hermit. People
were as essential to his daily well-being as food and air. Indeed, on
looking back over his life and into the bulging (if disorderly) files of
records he left, one comes to the conclusion that he was a collector of
friends, in much the same way as other eager hobbyists pursue early
maps, English pewter or first editions of Lewis Carroll. With him,
however, it was an unconscious urge, the active expression of an
inner need to meet, learn, discover, communicate, and then, finally, to
remember.

He was constantly at the ready for any new encounter, and any
person could walk into his office without an appointment and be
entirely welcome. If a stranger were to stop him on the street and start
a conversation about the slackness of municipal paving, within minutes
the Colonel would soon know all about the person's ancestral background and present circumstances.

If he met an unfamiliar employee in the corridor he would startle
the newcomer by a searching enquiry. It might go like this:

"Your name is Anna Koo? You must be related to Dr. Wellington
Koo. Your people come from Shanghai, don't they? Did you visit him
when he was minister to Washington? I used to meet him every
summer in Paris. Do your family see him now? Please tell him I was
asking after him."

And a puzzled little third-generation Canadian typist with almond
eyes would make her excuses and her escape.

Almost as inevitably he would take a liking to anyone who made
a point of talking with him or listening to him. In fact, he tended to be

suspicious of people who seemed to avoid these little confrontations. Some of his editors remember how his long-harbored distrust of certain leading businessmen, who, he was sure, had intentionally slighted him, would vanish forever once the person involved would pause for a handshake and a greeting, "How are you, Colonel? I enjoyed your articles from Europe."

John Bayne Maclean's "people collection" operated along catholic lines, in that all kinds were included, even those he strongly disapproved of. One such was Winston Leonard Spencer Churchill who at the age of twenty-six made his first visit to Canada. Even then his name had acquired an aura, not particularly by reason of his Marlborough ancestry, but rather because he had proved himself a young man who could make things happen. He possessed extraordinary bravery, which was not entirely the product of his desire for recognition, even notoriety. Just recently he had been elected Tory M.P. for Oldham and was wont to forecast that he would one day be Prime Minister. A few months prior, when serving as war correspondent in the South African campaign, he had been the hero of an exciting escape from the hands of the Boers, into whose hands he had no right to fall in any event. His new book. *From London to Ladysmith via Pretoria,* detailed that experience in lively fashion, and, as *Bookseller & Stationer*'s review in the August 1900 issue declared, "made its way at once to the hearts of readers by reason of the vigor and vividness of the narrative."

Churchill had earned good money as a war correspondent *cum* fighting man in Egypt and South Africa; then, to pay off debts and accumulate cash to promote his high political ambitions, he decided on a lecture tour in Britain (very profitable) and later in the United States (profitable, but less so). When he expanded the program to include several Canadian cities his American agent, Major S. B. Pond, engaged the Colonel's old reporter colleague, Stewart Houston of Toronto, now manager of Massey Music Hall, to arrange the Toronto and Montreal meetings. Houston, remembering that Maclean was a Hussar officer in Montreal, knew he could count on his friend to promote the lecture visit of another now world-famous Hussar. The Colonel gladly went to work on the press, the business brass and the public.

Small wonder, then, that a group of reporters surrounded Churchill when he stepped from the Boston train in Windsor Station, Montreal, on December 23, 1900, or that his opening remark—"a fervent ejaculation," as one of them described it—was immediately jotted down in notebooks. "Thank God, we are once more on British soil!" he said. He answered many questions and within an hour he boarded the train for Ottawa, to spend Christmas with the Governor-General, Lord Minto. The fact that the young visitor's current romantic interest, Pamela Plowder (who was ultimately to marry someone else) was also a guest may have speeded his departure for Government House.

The lengthy, glowing newspaper reports of the interview excited many of Montreal's distinguished citizens who had been badgered by Maclean to attend the lecture on December 26. So, the forthcoming appearance promised to be an important event.

With characteristic zeal and careful detailing, Maclean had organized a brilliant setting for the lecture, with appropriate social events before and after. Colonel E. A. Whitehead, leading militiaman and successful insurance executive, would be host at a special luncheon in the St. James's Club. Senator (later Sir) George Drummond agreed to move the vote of thanks after the evening lecture and also to use his influence in ensuring a distinguished platform group of high court judges, business leaders, top military men and others. His Worship the Mayor accepted the duty of chairman. And after the speeches, this hand-picked roster of Montreal's best would move to the Mount Royal Club, where millionaire banker Edward S. Clouston had offered to entertain at supper.

The preliminaries were impressive. The actual occasion in Windsor Hall and its sequel added up to unfortunate disillusionment for many, including John Bayne Maclean. For Churchill was in his most exuberantly arrogant mood.

Even the newspaper reports did not attempt to conceal the unfavorable reaction. The 1200-odd in the audience "were disappointed if they attended anticipating any new light on the all-absorbing subject" of the South African War, for virtually no information not already in their possession was imparted. Nonetheless, it was conceded that "Lord Randolph's son has a very taking way with him," through his witty asides and running comment—especially when he branded as false those rumors about the imprisoned Britishers (himself included) calling out "incivilities" toward the ladies of Pretoria. The fact was that the street running by the prison seemed to hold peculiar attractions for the local womenfolk, but he wanted to assure his audience, in the same breath, that the ordinary Dutch "vrau" was hardly one to arouse susceptibility.

The newspapers described the "backing" of a large group of influential citizens on the platform as a courteous gesture, yet hardly necessary as "he is a young gentleman quite able to play a lone hand."

At several points in the speech he introduced lantern slides of photographs showing "your gallant Canadians" on the march across the veldt or hoisting the Union Jack over a hard-won objective. When a member of the audience, Dr. Francis J. Shepherd, McGill's Professor of Anatomy, rose to ask why all the Colonial troops pictured seemed to be Canadian, the lecturer was ready with a breezy comeback: "Oh, those troops will all be Australian when I get to Australia."

The flamboyance remained undiminished at the supper party, where the guest of honor was inspired, after suitable refreshment, to proffer a few off-the-record remarks, including a repetition of his frank prophecy that he would one day head the British government.

"A very bumptious and conceited young man," was Dr. Shepherd's summing-up. And the Colonel, who had attended all the occasions that day, could but agree. He apologized to his wealthy business friends for having imposed Churchill on them. He had found the visitor "shamefully disgusting and offensive to all."

It was a first impression that would become a fixed conviction over many long years. Even when, sometime later, he made a special, cherished place in his "collection" for General Sir Ian Hamilton, twenty-one years Churchill's senior but one of the politician's closest friends and admirers, Maclean steadfastly refused to modify his judgment, despite numerous persuasive letters from Hamilton. More than two decades were to pass before there was any relaxing of his private opinion—and the conversion would be in large measure due to Mrs. Churchill whom he met at a special occasion on the Riviera in the mid-1920s and found totally charming. Obviously there must be *some* worthy qualities in the man this lovely being had deigned to marry, and by the time the statesman and the publisher were to have their first private meeting Mrs. Churchill had, through her own personality and quite unconsciously, removed most of the Colonel's prejudices.

Maclean had a special way with women. Unlike most Victorian males, he indulged in no unctuous flattery, no special conversational gambit reserved "for the ladies." He treated them exactly as he treated men—in other words as equals—and this may have been the secret of his success. He assumed that a woman read the newpapers and kept herself otherwise informed, and that her interests in politics, industry, etc., were no different from a man's. Possibly, from time to time he might run into an unreconstructed nineteenth-century deb or dowager who would be bored by his lively dissertation on, say, freight rates; even so, that sort of reaction was not entirely unknown among Maclean's male friends as well. In the main, however, women interpreted his attitude as a compliment; here was a business leader who obviously considered them as mentally capable as the menfolk.

His instinct proved to be right at many points in his life, but never more brilliantly than in the case of E. Cora Hind, one of Canada's most respected journalists of all time. Ontario-born Cora had moved to Winnipeg in 1882—to become the country's first public stenographer and typist west of the Great Lakes. Her services were frequently engaged by agricultural organizations in conventions assembled, and, as a logical outcome, she was sometimes asked to prepare condensed reports of the doings for Winnipeg's *Free Press*.

In 1897, when she was thirty-six years old, a vital new phase in her career began when she opened a telegram from the Colonel in Toronto, requesting her free-lance services as a prairie market and general news correspondent for his trade papers. It would be necessary for her to travel through the major crop-bearing areas during the growing season, talk to the producers, and then draft careful estimates of the forthcoming harvest in size, quality, etc. Such news would be eagerly studied by manufacturers, wholesalers and merchants in all such lines as groceries, hardware and dry goods, books, for a bumper wheat crop "out west" always meant good business for suppliers in the east.

Miss Hind gladly accepted the offer, which would supplement her regular earnings by a hefty $10 per week during the spring, summer, fall. Right from the outset she was a success. Her "Manitoba Markets" column in *Canadian Grocer* was studied with great eagerness, not just by readers but by the Maclean editors; one week after her published report on the season's disastrously reduced feed-corn crop, the publication's staff came up with a major editorial feature showing how that situation would inevitably raise the price of live hogs, all pork meats, plus lard and, by the cost-push process, all baked goods—and the condition would continue throughout Canada during the next ten or twelve months.

Or again, when "the rains came mainly on the plains" at a crucial moment in early October 1901, Cora Hind brought everyone to the alert with her comment: "There is no disguising the fact that the long and heavy rains have seriously injured all of the grain that was in stook, and in many instances where stooks were not well built, it is little better." Thus the expected bonanza crop had suddenly shrunk to merely average size.

Grain market operators, businessmen and bankers found her summaries, statistics and predictions invaluable. By 1904 they had so impressed John W. Dafoe, editor of the *Free Press,* that he offered her a full-time job as his agricultural writer and crop forecaster for the Winnipeg paper, but with the courteous stipulation that, as Maclean had made possible her first big chance, she should continue to free-lance for the Colonel's papers. Over the next quarter-century Cora Hind, the plain, pleasant, common-sense spinster, was to become famous in Chicago, Toronto, Montreal and even around the world.

Colonel Maclean's likes and dislikes were seldom mild. If he liked someone, he could and did ignore any weakness, even when exhibited in flagrant social or public indiscretions. If he disliked someone, he tended to harbor deep suspicions of everything that person said or did.

He distrusted intellectuals (particularly Rhodes scholars, although he admitted he had found them generally of "high character"), university professors, British politicians, Baptists, heavy drinkers, teetotallers, international bankers, paper manufacturers and Winston Churchill. He held to the conviction that most missionaries were sent abroad to spread subversive ideas. (A note in his files reads "Often the heathen led really better and happier lives before missionaries arrived"); the single exemption from this charge would be Scots, especially if they were Presbyterians. He admitted the value of missionary schools and hospitals but maintained that the export of religious dogma to the far places of the world constituted a menace because it led to unrest, and unrest always led to Socialist thinking. Although he was wary of most politicians, those who served on municipal councils or school boards were, in general, "sound." He had great respect for civil servants, always excepting the types with whom his business must have dealings, such as tariff and postal officials.

If anyone in the special groupings of trusted people made a mistake, the Colonel would set out on a hunt for the evil influence behind the scenes. When Ian Mackenzie emerged from British Columbia and into the House of Commons, all the while proclaiming his Scottish background in fiery Gaelic, he immediately had the ardent support of Maclean. Then, as soon as the newcomer proved a monumental failure as Minister of National Defense, the Colonel quickly concluded that the fault must lie with Mackenzie's Deputy. But that theory proved untenable with the discovery that a *Québecois* now held the post—and all French-Canadians had for years occupied a proud position on the Colonel's list of "likes." So, the whole sad mess of Canada's military situation must, therefore, be attributed to unidentified, evil operators working under cover in Ottawa—probably as a conspiracy of Communist-inspired Rhodes scholars and a sprinkling of university professors.

Indeed, when a good man went wrong, "they" (a generalized term which the Colonel skillfully avoided defining) were responsible. "They" were the grafters and intriguers who, out of their nefarious experience in international rings, knew exactly how to pull strings and cause trusting leaders, including honest Scots, to join, quite unknowingly, in costly outlays, heavy taxation, bad government and even world revolution!

The Colonel's steady favorites among the human race were Mrs. Winston Churchill, French-Canadians and Scots as indicated, plus Jews, Roman Catholics, Presbyterians, United Empire Loyalists, most of European royalty, almost all the people of the U.S.A., and a sizable group of their leading captains of industry in particular. This still left a large area in which to be distrustful.

No American on the list, not even Munsey, could compete for place with Charles M. Schwab, the magnate who revolutionized and revitalized—more than once—the American steel industry. Here was a man John Bayne Maclean could thoroughly understand and appreciate: a man of the same age, one who after minimum schooling—considerably less than the Colonel's—had made his own way up. From the first humble job as stake driver in the Andrew Carnegie steel works, Schwab had risen rapidly to chief engineer, then continued his ascent to the presidency of the company in 1897. That was merely the beginning, for by 1901 he had become the first president of the huge U. S. Steel Corporation merger, and after a few years moved on to form and master-mind his own company, Bethlehem Steel, which quickly became the largest independent producer in the field.

The Schwab-Maclean friendship, begun in a casual encounter at Palm Beach, was to flourish for the rest of their lives. Schwab steered the Colonel toward several highly profitable investments on the American stock market. At one point, in 1904, there was a place on the International Nickel Company directorate made ready for Maclean, and Schwab was disappointed when he received a note of refusal with the explanation: "I prefer being a power behind the throne, keeping in the background rather than exposing myself to public view where jealousy or rivalry might defeat or make more difficult the accomplishment of any of my plans."

None of Maclean's employees could escape the influence of Charlie Schwab or his theories and methods. The Colonel loved to recount how his friend, after selling out Bethlehem to a group who proceeded to wreck it, returned to take over and, as a first move, immediately selected a completely new executive corps "from out of the plant." One of the fifteen thus promoted had been a $75-a-month mill hand; he rose eventually to the presidency and an annual income of $1,368,-000.

Perhaps the Colonel, operating on a more modest scale, put a little too much emphasis on his American friend's fame and fortune. To Schwab, however, millions were the plain stuff of everyday life. He had earned $1,000,000 per year during his top post with Andrew Carnegie's steel empire back at the beginning of the century. Seven nice round figures in a straight line were easy to deal with. At a World's Congress of Salesmanship in 1917 he was to declare in a careful speech: "I have had some experience as a salesman and I have found that it is a great deal easier to sell a big thing than to sell a little thing. It was easier to sell the Carnegie Steel Corporation to Mr. Morgan for $500,000,000 than it would be to sell a $100 piano to a farmer who has no interest in music."

Schwab loved his old boss, Carnegie, and, 'way back in 1905, both these men of money were to be gratefully in debt to the Colonel. The project had its initiation when Schwab wrote a private note to Maclean, conveying his concern and mystification about the "apparent unpopularity" of Mr. Carnegie with Canadians. Could "dear J.B." explain, or, better still, make any suggestions?

Promptly the Colonel took off for a conference with the two in New York. He proposed that Mr. Carnegie—now seventy, retired, and spending most of each year in his native Scotland—agree to appear publicly in Toronto, make a speech, and let people meet him at first-hand. The plan was accepted, and within a day or so of Maclean's return a cordial invitation from the Canadian Club was on its way across the border. In due course, the great Carnegie addressed what was described as "undoubtedly the largest audience ever assembled by that organization." The impression left with his listeners was obviously favorable, and Mr. Carnegie returned to New York a happy man, warmly appreciative of Maclean's service.

Schwab, too, was delighted, and for many years thereafter, he made a special point of welcoming the Colonel as a distinguished head-table guest at two of New York's big occasions: the annual dinners of the American Iron & Steel Association and of the Pennsylvania Association, of which Schwab was president over a long period. At one of these festive gatherings, a-glitter with a thousand guests in full evening dress, the Chairman had ready a little anecdote when he introduced the Canadian publisher to the audience. "A few hours ago I read over my remarks for tonight to the Colonel," he said. "I wanted his reaction. Well, he just looked at me. Not one word of praise. All he had to say was, 'Charlie, you'd better stick to steel-making. You are hopeless as a writer.'"

After the First World War, Maclean suggested that the Pennsylvania Association have a Canadian speaker for the banquet. Schwab agreed —"and so now it's up to you to suggest one." Maclean took it from there, and for the next few years he struggled manfully either to persuade Charlie to accept those who were willing to appear, or to get co-operation from the "famous" Canadians Charlie wanted. The Honorable Ernest C. Drury, then Premier of Ontario's Farmer government, and Bishop Fallon of London, Ontario, could have been available, but Schwab turned down each suggestion (Americans had never heard of either). Next the Duke of Devonshire, Governor-General, was mentioned; Schwab agreed enthusiastically, but the Duke did not, even though Prime Minister Arthur Meighen was induced by the Colonel to add a little special pressure. "Why not do it yourself?" Maclean asked Meighen. But the Tory leader felt that the time was unpropitious for Canada's government head to make even a simple, non-political speech south of the border.

In 1922 Schwab revived the scheme with a request to the Colonel to line up Stephen Leacock, certainly a famous Canadian, and one well known to millions of U.S. readers, including President Warren G. Harding, who was to be an honored guest at the forthcoming dinner. The Colonel promptly got busy and invited Leacock to make the trip down from his "Mariposa" country retreat near Orillia and discuss the plan over a quiet dinner at the Maclean residence. Leacock was in his usual jovial mood; the Colonel saw nothing but success ahead—until his guest launched forth with a counterproposal. The Pennsylvania Association, he remarked, had heard many great after-dinner speakers; it was obvious that the members had set themselves very careful goals over the years, and thus they had earned the right to be critical. They would expect Stephen Leacock to be entertaining, even mirth-provoking. But, he pointed out, this was exactly what he could not be in any post-prandial delivery at a dinner where the only cold drink consisted of ginger ale. He had always refused to speak at "dry" dinners in Canada, and how could he possibly lower his standards for an audience in the U.S.? However, reviewing the whole situation and wishing to please Colonel Maclean, he would like to propose that the Pennsylvanians change the location of their affair to Montreal where the members would be *his,* Leacock's, guests, free to select from a civilized, complete, non-Prohibition menu. With these slight amendments he would deliver a speech guaranteed to raise the rafters.

Poor Maclean, poor Schwab! They rallied from the Leacock blow sufficiently to make one more effort for a speaker from Canada: this time, the Governor-General, Viscount Byng of Vimy. The Colonel did his valiant best, as from one humble soldier to a great Army commander, but His Excellency declined, with thanks.

By such extra-curricular activities, Maclean's circle of acquaintance continued to expand. The two decades flanking the turn of the century were to represent possibly the most productive period of his life, both as to friendships established and, as their logical outcome, certain highly gratifying advances in his private financial status. Nowadays, quarterly earnings reports, the more generous sharing of "inside" information with investors at large, plus stricter controls on director trading have lessened the cash value of close acquaintanceship with company board members. In the 1890s, men in controlling situations felt freer to buy and sell, and to advise their friends to do the same. During the years in Montreal he had acted promptly on the advice of two new friends, Lord Shaughnessy, CPR's president, and C. R. Hosmer, both of whom urged purchase of Canadian Pacific stock during a market depression. With the next boom period Maclean sold to brilliant advantage.

Schwab, as mentioned, was constantly interested in J.B.'s financial welfare. Just as helpful, too, were three other American friends, all vastly wealthy. Bernard M. Baruch, eight years junior to Maclean, yet a self-made millionaire before the age of thirty, stood ready with advice for the enquiring Canadian, even as in later years for the U.S. government which constantly sought him out. Jules Bache, banker and art collector, and James Speyer, New York representative of his family's century-old financial house, steered the Colonel to various profitable operations with American stocks.

In the case of Speyer there was to be an interesting sequel when he sought Maclean's influence with new underwritings in Canada. Thus in 1921 the Toronto publisher suggested to both the Ottawa Minister of Finance and CPR president Edward W. Beatty that Speyer have a chance to bid on Canadian issues. Later, however, Maclean was to advise Speyer against certain other ventures north of the border. It seems that Robert J. Magor, president of National Steel Car, had asked Speyer to finance a merger of his company with Canadian Locomotive Company, Hamilton Bridge and Dominion Foundries & Steel. Although rating Mr. Magor highly, the Colonel recommended against the proposal on the ground that bridge and railway car plants in Canada were already "overbuilt." Speyer acted accordingly—yet eventually, National Steel Car would be one of the great production arsenals for shells in World War II, still later its freight cars were in demand around the world, and inevitably the company was merged with Dominion Foundries & Steel. By 1926 Speyer had another notion: take over the British Empire Steel Corporation (one of the stages in the development of Dominion Steel and Coal Corporation). But, again, the Colonel hastened to keep his friend from any entanglement of that kind "unless you can get Judge Elbert H. Gary, president of U. S. Steel, to join you. This Canadian corporation has no talented executives, no one who actually knows steel." Today, in the light of the checkered history of Dosco, Maclean's judgment seems to have been rather shrewd; yet who can say what the company's record might have been, under Speyer, *et al?*

The Colonel's advice may not always have been infallible, but he certainly believed he was right. So far as financial deals were concerned he took a ramrod-straight stand, worthy of a son from a nineteenth-century manse. Over the years he enjoyed telling a story which came from old Lord Strathcona, head of the Hudson's Bay Company, and which, for Maclean, underlined for all time the fact that big business could and must be conducted on an honorable level. It went like this: "I happened to be in London (England) and saw Lord Strathcona at the time Harriman—I think it was—started to work hard to oust the J. J. Hill interests in the old St. Paul, Minneapolis & Manitoba (railway) line. I had heard his agents had offered Strathcona $1000 a share for shares he had originally bought for 25 cents, and asked him why he did not sell, as that price would have been a great fortune in itself. The old man said he was offered more than that, but all the money in the world would not induce him to desert his old friend, James Hill."

It would be a mistake to carry away the impression that John Bayne Maclean of the 1900s moved entirely in a rarefied atmosphere of millionaires. They just happened to be the later accrual (and an exceedingly profitable one) to his long list of friendships reaching far back. The newspaper cronies of former days never lost their interest for him. In one of his typical, handwritten, rambling reminiscences—undated, though definitely of the early years of this century—he extols Harry J. P. Good, just resigned from the editorship of the *Sunday World* to become press agent for the Canadian National Exhibition. "Mr. Good is, after W. F. MacLean (the *World's* owner) undoubtedly the best all-round newspaper man in Canada," and lists the sound reasons, such as Good's capacity as a sports editor, "when he knew every harness horse on the track." Maclean recalls with relish a certain night of crisis on the old Toronto *Mail,* when Bunting, the managing editor and also a Member of Parliament, bade the staff goodbye as he left to catch the Ottawa train for the session, and made it plain that everyone must stay constantly on the job during his absence. But he missed the train, and on returning to the office found not a soul in sight except an exploding, cursing city editor. After an hour's search up and down adjacent streets Bunting found his staff, including the Good boy, in McGinn's saloon. (Was Maclean of the party too?)

But reminiscences, once begun, tend to go on, and they usually did in the Colonel's case, whether in conversation, letters or memos. So . . . "On another occasion Mr. Good was seriously ill, so ill that the doctors held out little hope." Half-a-dozen associates gathered at the bedside for a last farewell, and specifically to ask if they could help in any way. Mr. Good suggested a Bible reading—any passage at all. After some scurrying, a Bible was found and one member of the group who had formerly taken oratory lessons was appointed reader. He opened the book at random and started with the first chapter of Matthew, that famous "begat" column: "And Jesse begat David the King; and David the King begat Solomon of her that had been the wife of Urias," etc., etc. Within the space of another half-dozen lines (the Colonel would recall), "Harry began to revive. He always was an authority on stock pedigrees."

There, indeed, is the noiseless chuckle of John Bayne Maclean, connoisseur of people.

# CHAPTER XII

## *NEW FACES*

"Keep thy shop and thy shop will keep thee."
*Sir William Temple*

LIFE AT NO. 13 Queen's Park Crescent ticked off at decorous pace during the first year or so of the Macleans' tenure, and this was precisely as the Colonel and his wife wished it. Both were staunch traditionalists, and in their daily schedule violent innovation was decidedly unwelcome. For even a small dinner party formal invitations must be mailed at least two weeks in advance, to permit of the "R.S.V.P." acknowledgment, also by mail. It was to be many years before Anna Slade Maclean caught up with the new craze known as "telephone occasions," involving, as reported, in the social columns, a gathering "to which the guests were bidden by telephone that very morning." Mr. Bell's invention, recently installed in the Macleans' main hall, a long awkward wall-box with the essential crank for ringing "Central," had practical uses, especially in emergencies, but it was slow to supplant Society's approved routines.

The gracious Anna adhered strictly to local protocol. She and the other hostesses on the east side of Queen's Park kept Tuesday as their at-home day. Thus the ladies from the west side, who received on Thurday, and the north-of-the-Park group, whose day was Friday, could complete all calling duties in the eastern sector between three and six o'clock, knocking on each door in turn, having ready a sheaf of cards to drop into the inevitable silver tray on the hall table, and pausing for a pleasant word, perhaps a cup of tea, with each hostess. All present, the visited as well as the visitors, wore hats.

Quite often an at-home day would have to be canceled because of family matters or absence from town, but, given enough forewarning, the lady involved could resort to an announcement in the daily press notifying her friends that she would not be receiving that week or, in certain cases, "until further notice."

The latter phrase had ominous overtones when it appeared in connection with Mrs. J. B. Maclean of Queen's Park in the late autumn of 1901. Her husband was seriously ill with one of the scourges of the period: typhoid fever, which, according to census figures, would kill off some 2000 persons in Canada that year. The doctor's assessment of the case indicated that the disease had been contracted a few weeks earlier when the Colonel was in Quebec for the ceremonies of welcome to the Duke and Duchess of York. For a proud officer like the Colonel, there was no question that the occasion had been worth the resulting miseries and slow convalescence; in fact, the struggle against *salmonella typhosa,* the fever caused by contaminated food and water, seldom merited attention in his later reminiscences.

Nevertheless, one aftermath was to linger for decades: his concern about diet. The rules were subject to constant change, according to the latest fad of, say, "all protein at one meal per day," or depending on his own whim, as when he announced that melons were "dangerous," or during the bran boom of the 1920s made it a rule to have a bowl of the dry flakes on the table at every mealtime. Never one to keep valuable discoveries secret, the Colonel became a zealous spreader of dietary gospel among his friends; indeed his convictions re bran were to be shared with all employees patronizing the Company cafeteria, where he would appear from time to time, pausing at each table to win converts to the flaky brown stuff which, by his order, had recently joined the center cluster of sugar, pepper and salt.

A month or so in Florida would certainly benefit a man still exhausted from the long fight with typhoid, and so, early in 1902, the Macleans took off for Palm Beach. As they stepped from the train, Frank Munsey came forward to meet them, and the loyal trio was again complete, just as on that auspicious occasion two years before.

On this trip their headquarters was Flagler's new hotel, the Breakers, flanked by gardens and soaring palms, facing the sand, the surf and the Atlantic horizon. With six hundred other guests the threesome sat down to seven- or-eight-course evening meals in the dining room, where the well-advertised "580 incandescent lights" picked up the constantly shifting gleam of jewels, satins, (and the gold dental crowns now the vogue among wide-smiling ladies of fashion). Huge audiences

## Do you know **Why?**

If you are an advertiser you know that some newspapers bring you better results than others : : : :

Here are three of the many reasons that might be given why

# The Globe
#### Toronto

gives you better results than any other paper in the Dominion : : : : : :

**1st**—It has 25 per cent. greater circulation than any other morning paper in Canada.

**2nd**—It has 33⅓ per cent. greater circulation than any English evening paper in Canada.

**3rd**—And most important, 98 per cent. of its whole circulation goes directly into the **homes** of the best families of Canada.

### THE GLOBE

Phone Main 5400                    Toronto, Canada

# Business
## The Business Man's Magazine.

"There are occasions and causes why and wherefore in all things."—Shakespeare.

## THE REASON WHY

# The Toronto Daily Star

Carries more General Advertising than any other Toronto Daily is

## "It Brings Results that Make a Profit"

### CIRCULATION 39,000

Forerunner of *Maclean's Magazine:* a 16-page publication aimed at a readership of Canada's business men. The Colonel acquired it, along with the modest subscription list, in 1905

*Busy Man's Magazine* became the second phase in the development of *Maclean's*. This lively promotion piece, circa 1906, was printed in maroon. The Colonel probably wrote the "copy"

# THE BUSY MAN'S MAGAZINE

## CONTENTS FOR NOVEMBER, 1905

V.  **The Rothschilds of France.** By VANCE THOMPSON - - - **35**
Something about the French branch of the family, whose
fabulous wealth is a household word.

VII.  **The Richest Woman in America.** NEW YORK TIMES - - - **44**
Something about Hetty Green, of New York, who is known
as the Rockefeller of her sex.

XVIII.  **From Station Master to Prime Minister.** - - - - **92**
Follows the career of Serge Witte, the Russian diplomatist
and statesman, from his humble origin upward.

XIX.  **Perils in Retiring from Business.** - - - - - - **95**
Views the question of retirement in a new and interesting
light.

XXI.  **The First Steps of Famous Business Men.** - - - - **102**
Tells how succesful business men from Andrew Carnegie
down made their start in life.

## CONTENTS FOR DECEMBER, 1905

I.  **D. D. Mann, Railroad Builder.** By AUGUSTUS BRIDLE - - **7**
A capital sketch of a Canadian self-made man, who has had a
remarkable career.

III.  **Madame Tussaud's Exhibition.** - - - - - - - **20**
Descriptive of the wonderful wax-work establishment, which
is one of the sights of London.

IV.  **Originality, the Secret of Success.** By SIR WILLIAM VAN HORNE **25**
Freedom from the trammels of rules and traditions is Sir
William's code of success.

VII.  **Beveridge, a Study of the Self-Made Man.** By G. H. LORIMER - **38**
Some account of the career of Senator Beveridge, with
remarks on the phenomenon of the self-made man.

VIII.  **How Burbank Produces New Plants.** By GARRETT P. SERVISS - **47**
Showing how Luther Burbank performs feats in the world
of nature that are almost miraculous.

X.  **The Story of the Franklin Syndicate.** By ARTHUR TRAIN - **57**
A graphic story of one of the greatest swindles of modern
times.

XII.  **The Automobile's Service to France.** By FRANK A. MUNSEY - **73**
An estimate of what the automobile has done in the way of
increasing tourist traffic.

XIII.  **The Making of the Modern Newspaper.** By SIR A. HARMSWORTH **79**
Pointing out the superiority of the newspaper of to-day over
that of yesterday.

XXIII.  **Railroad Rebates.** By RAY STANNARD BAKER - - - **119**
A definition of the rebate, showing how it is paid and its
general effect on industry.

*Busy Man's* offered a wide variety of subjects and authors. November
1905 issue had 27 articles in over 140 pages. Many features were reprints from other magazines, but gradually Maclean developed his own
writers and established a policy of "all original" material on the main
pages. Above are shown a few examples only

Fifteen Cents

# MACLEANS

## August

Is Permanent Peace
Possible?
By STEPHEN LEACOCK

A New War Poem
By ROBERT W. SERVICE

Business---*and*
The Fatal Spiral
By AGNES C. LAUT

*and*

ARTHUR STRINGER
ARTHUR E. McFARLANE
L. M. MONTGOMERY
H. F. GADSBY

An All-Star Canadian List of Contributors

THE MACLEAN PUBLISHING COMPANY LIMITED TORONTO CANADA

The August 1916 cover of *Maclean's* offered an impressive group of
contributors—proof that the publisher was well on the way toward his
goal of "Canada's national magazine"

# MACLEAN'S

### ▓▓ ▓▓▓▓ ▓▓ MAGAZINE ▓▓ ▓▓▓▓ ▓▓

| Volume XXXI | FEBRUARY, 1918 | Number 4 |
|---|---|---|

# Why We Are Losing the War

## By John Bayne Maclean

FAILURES and disappointments have been our experience during the past twelve months. War conditions are growing steadily worse. The general outlook to-day is just about as black as it can be. The greatest shock to our pride seems to be developing—a setback to the insane strategy forced upon our military by interfering politicians. The first sign of our partial defeat is the shading down of our war aims. The Asquith-Churchill-Grey-Balfour family laid down very definite objects which we proposed to attain — which could easily have been attained but for the damnable incompetence and the refusal of these men to listen to the naval and military heads and the other great executives of the nation. Now we are told by Lloyd George, Henderson and others that it was never intended to humiliate the Germans by war or to exterminate them in a business way after. I pointed out at the time that the Paris Economic Conference was a joke—made up as it was of unpractical men, like our own Sir George Foster, while Asquith refused to allow Premier Hughes to attend. Later Mr. Asquith made a statement in the House of Commons concerning it, which Mr. Hughes described as a deliberate falsehood. It looks as though we were now being prepared for a compromise peace with Germany. Any peace but the complete defeat of Germany means a German victory. Germany could give up and indemnify Belgium and France; give up Alsace-Lorraine and all her colonies; and still win the war. More important to Germany are Austria-Hungary, the Balkans and Turkey. They will become part of a German Empire. They, and perhaps Sweden, will be absorbed as Prussia took in the states now forming the German Empire.

There are some rays of hope. It is not yet too late to help Russia back on our side, and there are signs that the influence of the family compact, that has so woefully misdirected our Imperial affairs, is weakening.

*Sir Charles Macara, Bart., who says if Asquith and Grey had acted on expert advice the war would have been over in 1914.*

We can't win Russia back with prayers and statesmanship, but we can with cash and saloon politics. I am not belittling prayer. I have had to say more prayers than most men. But there are times when they do not seem in place—as the late Bishop Strachan told his clergy, "What's the use of praying for rain when there's not a cloud in the sky?" To bring Russia back we need entirely new methods, and we can't have new methods until we get new men. As Frank Munsey, the publisher-financier, once said: "You can't get out of a man what God Almighty did not put into him. You can't fit the job to the man, you must fit the man to the job." The success of British recruiting in Boston and its failure in New York is an example of what I mean. Colonel Guthrie, a New Brunswick lawyer, a member of the Legislature and a clever local politician, whose regiment was practically wiped out in France, went to Boston to recruit men for a new battalion. He was told he could not expect much success as the British had already worked the city, but perhaps they might be interested in a Canadian regiment. In Boston they had a strong Irish Home Rule anti-British mayor, a powerful man with the masses. Guthrie's first move was to call on him, figuratively slap him on the back, tell his story and ask his help. That was an approach no human man could resent. The Mayor dropped everything to help. He soon had all the "boys" and the press in Boston working. When the Mayor and the Colonel had their last drink in a saloon in the Irish ward at the end of the first day's recruiting they were calling each other by their pet names. No outsider ever got such a cordial reception. He needed about 500 men to complete, but in a few days he had over 2,000 and had to stop.

His success reached the ears of the British authorities in New York. They sent an urgent call for his assistance; but they would have none of his methods. Instead, the procedure had to be dignified. A public meeting was held, opened with prayer and conducted in the usual orthodox style. The clergy and other distinguished citizens were on the platform. Fashionable society was in the audience. But eligible recruits were not. Colonel Guthrie was entertained. He was popular in exclusive society circles, but possible recruits saw him only when he marched through the streets with his pipers. At the end of a week only fifty-seven recruits had come in. It was not the fault of the men of the British Mission, who are splendid

John Bayne Maclean's article that rocked the country and resulted in a summons to Ottawa. When editor Costain mentioned he had contributed only the heading, "Why, that's the worst part of it!" shouted the censor. Undeterred, Maclean continued his criticisms

1904, and the Maclean Company's first banquet—with the President-host in evening clothes at centre, Miss Forbes in dark dress immediately in front. There is a noticeable absence of gaiety, and understandably, as this was not merely the wind-up of a full day of staff conferences; it happened also to be New Year's Eve, and a Saturday too!

View of the corner of University Avenue and Dundas Street at the time John Bayne Maclean purchased the property, a full city block

The old cottage that originally stood on the site of the company's administration-editorial building

For many years this building fronting on University Avenue served as the executive and editorial headquarters of the Maclean Publishing Company. The mechanical plant adjoined at the rear. The building was razed in 1956

The Colonel's office at University Avenue headquarters was impressively "period," yet the Tudor paneling (brought from a Devonshire manor) did a functional service in supplying secret file drawers along the wall at left

gathered for such special events as the annual "cakewalk" for the Negro staff, or the Parlormaids' concert where enthusiastic millionaire claques awaited the appearance of certain favorites.

Maclean and Munsey were always present, obeying their inflexible rule, "When visiting Florida, do as the other visitors do." Perhaps they joined the Shakespeare Club, the first cultural effort at Palm Beach; the high society patrons, rather than the high-minded purpose, would have been their motivation. By day there were strolls along the beach, with frequent pauses to chat with rich men's wives, all of whom came equipped with brilliant parasols to keep complexions from burning or (much worse) tanning. For everybody it was always a lark to board Flagler's mule-car which ran back and forth between the Breakers and the Poinciana—especially as each passenger had to pay five cents for the service, and people accustomed to writing a $2000 cheque for their family's weekly hotel bill never seemed to have a nickel handy. A whole afternoon's laughs up and down the sands resulted from one such embarrassment for Munsey.

In the relaxed atmosphere, friendships were waiting to be made, and the Colonel seized every opportunity that was presented. This was his reason for going to Florida, whether in 1902 or over the many years to come: not to holiday or improve his health but "to meet and talk with the people who made the news." For him Palm Beach had an essential second title, "the winter news capital of the world," which was brought forward conspicuously in every article, letter, confidential memorandum he would write from or about the place. In short, he held to the belief that he went to Florida to work. His success at the self-assigned job must therefore be measured by the number of "news sources" added to his list.

The two Woolworths of the "five-and-ten" chain—even in 1902 it consisted of several hundred stores—were among the early encounters, along with various other figures already mentioned. One of the impressive additions to the Maclean roster was the E. T. Stotesbury group from Philadelphia, where the husband, as head of the J. P. Morgan interests in that city, had by middle age accumulated a nest egg of some $70,000,000. But the Stotesburys were not merely rich, they were "fun," contributing endlessly to the gaiety of the Palm Beach scene. Mrs. "Stote" was to become one of the Colonel's closest friends, and he and his wife were to enjoy many visits, year after year, to El Mirasol, the Stotesburys' huge, rambling house (designed by Addison Mizner, architect-impresario of the neo-Spanish cult), set in a 25-acre estate which included a private zoo of tropical birds, monkeys, etc.

Both host and hostess Stotesbury were Characters in the grand manner. The Colonel often related how "Stote" would insist that he, too, was an Army man, having served as a drummer boy in the Civil War, "but," added the Colonel, safely back in Toronto, "I rather doubted that claim, as he could have been hardly more than ten years old when the war ended." Anyway, El Mirasol's master had his own way of substantiating the story, for sometimes, at the proper climactic point during a soirée, he would call for his drums, and proceed to beat out the stirring rhythms of "Marching through Georgia" for a little spontaneous singing.

Mrs. Stotesbury's children and their diversified careers, especially in wedded life, were a constant source of interest to the Colonel. Before becoming Mrs. Stotesbury she had been married to a Cromwell. A daughter, Louise Cromwell, made a quick shift from a first husband to marry a military man who, as commander in the Philippines, was definitely on the way up: Brigadier General Douglas MacArthur. That alliance lasted for almost seven years, or until the Broadway star, Lionel Atwill, came on stage. All three of Mrs. Stotesbury's sons-in-law were known to and liked by the Colonel.

James H. R. Cromwell, Mrs. Stote's son by her first marriage, was to be given a special opportunity to study Canada, when President Franklin D. Roosevelt appointed him U. S. Minister in Ottawa. An amateur economist, Jimmy was not taken too seriously by the professionals. His wife, tobacco heiress Doris Duke, constant headliner in the tabloids, appeared in Ottawa for a month or two of skiing in the Gatineau or Laurentian hills and then took off for gayer spots. The Colonel asked one or two senior Maclean Publishing executives to help the young man get established in Ottawa, but this turned out to be a bad deal for the new Minister. At the suggestion of one of the Colonel's editors, the Canadian Club invited him to be a luncheon speaker; Jimmy accepted with alacrity, and delivered an address which, because of its embarrassing implications for FDR and current policies, resulted in early recall to Washington. Cromwell argued for less neutrality and a more positive anti-Nazi stand by the American people; Roosevelt was not yet ready to abandon neutrality. A trumped-up reason for the vacating of his post was hurriedly invented.

By April 25, 1902, Toronto's *Mail & Empire* could report in the social column: "Lieut.-Col. and Mrs. J. B. Maclean have returned from their southern trip." That may have been the year they initiated the practice of pausing for a week or so at White Sulphur Springs, in West Virginia, on the way north; over the long future the Colonel was to insist on a break in the return journey, believing that the change from Florida warmth to Canadian chill might be too abrupt.

Occasionally there would be a stopover in New York, and this inevitably meant the old Waldorf-Astoria on Fifth Avenue at 34th Street, his favorite Manhattan caravanserai. Here, too, he could count on renewing acquaintances with important news-makers, most of whom he had met through Munsey; Henry Clay Frick, Judge Gary, J. P. Morgan, John W. ("Bet-a-Million") Gates, *et al.* Through careful observation he had learned from them the basic rules of hotel life: "Always tip generously" . . . "Always know the *maître d'hotel,* the head waiter and the doorman by name" . . . "Always engage a suite." In later years these directives would be stressed *ad nauseam* in conversations with Maclean Publishing's promising young men, about to voyage forth on Company business. By that time the Colonel had forgotten the stern disciplines concerning expense accounts; what concerned him was simply the sharing of his own hard-won education in cosmopolitan ways. On a certain occasion during the depression of the '30s, he ran into one of his editors in the new Waldorf-Astoria on Park Avenue. "Come," said the Colonel, "I want you to meet the General Manager and, of course, Oscar." So immediately there were introductions all round, and the hotelman and his famous *maître d'* solemnly accepted the Colonel's charge to them "to look after this young man," whose smile never wavered, even though he knew he was limited to $10 per day expenses.

Maclean used his favorite hotels as exclusive clubs. The old Waldorf-Astoria appealed to him for its unassailable ancestry—the first section built by William Waldorf and opened in 1893, the second brought into being alongside four years later by John Jacob Astor IV, and then the two piles linked by the elegant architectural "hyphen." Not to have experienced that famous gathering-point for New York's Four Hundred, would have been tantamount, from the Colonel's standpoint, to admitting one had never heard of the world. Of course ladies were not expected to be familiar with the Gilded Bar or the Men's Café, for these remained for many years exclusively male territory—the ideal atmosphere for a big steel merger that would shake the continent

tomorrow, or, as highly probable in the spring of 1902, a friendly
Maclean discourse concerning the upcoming coronation on June 26.
What an occasion that would be! The first British coronation in sixty-
four years, the first crowning of a king in more than seventy!

To the Colonel, it was clearly evident that a coronation stimulated
business—even in Canada and even in the Maclean trade papers.
*Dry Goods Review*'s spring issues for 1902 bulked large with reports
and special advertisements announcing "Union Jack table centers with
red silk frills" . . . "Coronation bibs for Coronation babies" . . . "King
Edward tartan"—a hot introduction for men's neckwear . . . "Coronation velvets" and the totally uninhibited new color, "Coronation red,"
which *DGR*'s London correspondent mentions as a trend in dress
bow ties but hastens to express doubts that any wearer would be
"admitted to the opera in one." Sometimes an advertiser got carried
away with all the excitement, as when an old-established English
firm, inviting Canadian buyers to drop in during their coronation
visit, stated unequivocally, "We are a Fancy House and our aim is
always to have ready the latest novelty." Again, there may have
been a few raised eyebrows among *DGR* readers when they opened
the 220-page issue of late June and came upon the full page of
heavy red paper, featuring portraits of the two leading figures of
the coronation, and the message in bold type: **"If King Edward and
Queen Alexandra were living in Canada they would not hesitate to
recommend your buying Oil Cloths made by The Dominion Oil Cloth
Co., Limited."**

It is quite likely the Colonel might have queried such copy if he
had seen the early press forms, as was his custom then, but by
mid-June he and Mrs. Maclean had sailed for England to attend
the ceremonies in Westminster Abbey. The Colonel had been offered,
by friend Borden, Minister of Militia and Defense, the command of
one of the squadrons in the Canadian Coronation Contingent but,
as his strength was still below par for the exhausting demands of
military ceremonial, he had to decline the honor.

For the Macleans and thousands of others there would be shock
and disappointment when two days before the great event the new
King was laid low with a serious illness necessitating surgery. All the
royal pageantry had to be postponed (until August, as it turned out);
the street decorations became dull and streaked with weeks of wet
weather, and the Colonel had no occasion to unpack his full-dress
Hussars uniform.

Nevertheless he was to remember that London visit for certain unanticipated opportunities to meet both old and new friends. He attended the dinner given by Lord Strathcona, Canadian High Commissioner, and sought out the special guests, the Earl of Minto, Governor-General, and Sir Wilfrid Laurier, Prime Minister, for a chat afterward. Colonel George Taylor Denison, doughty companion and campaigner, was in London, not just for coronation doings but to discuss with key government men his carefully drawn-up plan for free trade within the Empire. Kitchener, hero of the Nile and South African campaigns, returned to a cheering London on a midsummer day. The great Bisley shoot took place as scheduled. And at one of these occasions John Bayne Maclean was pleased to be "presented" to the new Prince of Wales, better known as the Duke of York, whom he had saluted at the Plains of Abraham review the year before.

In July the Macleans sailed for home, and happily, for now a different, special, private excitement confronted them. A baby was coming.

All previous plans were now completely revised in order to prepare for the great event. Florida, of course, was dropped from the winter program; so, too, the weekly receiving-day routine at 13 Queen's Park Crescent. Mrs. Maclean would live the secluded life that was then considered the only correct procedure for an expectant mother. On sunny afternoons there would be a pleasant drive in the carriage behind the coachman; the rest of the time would be given over to fine sewing for the layette.

If she felt in the mood for a good book, there was always the Colonel's special shelf of recent titles. Only a few months previous he had been dismayed to discover that *Bookseller & Stationer*'s young editor, after finishing his pages of reviews of the new volumes sent in, was actually taking the books home. "I am the owner of this trade journal," he told young Arnot Craick, "and therefore all such book-review copies must be considered my property." Henceforth, the hardworking *B & S* man, although still firmly of the traditional opinion that "To the reviewer belongs the book," made a practice of dividing the spoils, i.e., retaining those volumes he wished to keep, and sending along the remainder to his employer. If the latter noticed any short-changing, he was sufficiently discreet not to mention it.

As a matter of fact, the Colonel could never have been called a bookworm at any point in his life. Much more to his taste were the newsy summaries of the literary business as presented in *Bookseller*. Its 1902–3 issues were packed with such: Ralph Connor's *Glengarry School Days* had been "far and away the best-selling book in Canada," but close behind came (Sir) James M. Barrie's new one, *Little White Bird*, and of course Marie Corelli's novels continued in lively demand. Old friend Andrew Carnegie had underwritten fine new public libraries in Winnipeg, Galt, Goderich and Collingwood; there were more to come. A vigorous editorial in early 1903 demanded "a push" in souvenir post cards: "Canadians as yet have not come to appreciate such cards, and sales are consequently small . . . but there are great possibilities in the business," as shown by the recent post card boom in England and on the Continent. Another lively paragraph forewarned specialty stores of "a big croquet summer ahead."

For proof of publishing success, none of the Maclean journals of the period could compete with *Dry Goods Review* in actual weight of argument. Even the solidly established first of the line, *Canadian Grocer*, stayed fairly consistently to 48 or 52 pages per issue; and thus for the month of December 1902 its four weeks' numbers totalled 204 pages inside the covers. But the January 1903 issue of *DGR* sprang forth with 266 pages! More than half that total consisted of advertising, all revenue-producing with the possible exception of the New York Skirt Company's sales message, which, unfortunately, was printed upside down.

In a magazine of that bulk the editorial content could, and did, range over the whole wide field of fashion: men's and women's wearables, all the way from woolen underwear, corsets, woven bustles and hip pads, to new coat and cape styles in furs from the Peace River and Athabaska country, plus forecasts of spring millinery; then on to style as applied to home interiors—featuring the last word in Cozy Corner treatments, especially with the draped or "tented" top, followed by an informative assessment of the recent Art Nouveau Exhibition in Paris and its eventual influence on room decoration, and winding up with an interesting article concerning "flats" in Canada's larger cities. "The apartment house has come to stay," the anonymous writer declared, and, even though something should be done to discourage a "tall, six-story factory-like building" from being built in fine residential areas, he maintained that thoughtful Canadians should be ready to accept this new trend in simplified living for the small family. "The heating is done from the basement by the janitor, and for a small sum he will do all the housecleaning."

That *DGR* issue was able to expand to six pages its regular department headed, "Good advertising—for wide-awake retailers," wherein various types of presentations from daily papers, catalogues, etc., were reproduced and analyzed. Window dressing, too, had become an important subject, month by month, and one of the features at this period discussed and illustrated the best displays of umbrellas for the early spring trade.

The year 1903 would be a highly significant landmark in the forward-march of John Bayne Maclean. In February there was the birth of the son he had longed for and, indeed, named well in advance: Hector Andrew Fitzroy—the first and last inspired by their ancient usage in Clan Maclean, the middle name commemorating the long-dead Presbyterian minister of Crieff. Frank Munsey became the child's godfather.

This great moment for a husband and wife approaching middle age—the Colonel now in his forty-first year, Anna in her mid-thirties—also brought with it certain anxieties which would never be entirely eradicated. The infant was undersized and had obvious digestive difficulties. Eventually the cause of that condition would be medically established as "an abnormally small passage from stomach to lower organs": meantime the little occupant of the new nursery was to become the constant concern of nursemaid and household staff, as well as parents. For months and years ahead the Colonel and his wife, setting forth on a special engagement, were to leave not only careful instructions but full details as to where they must be notified in case Hector was taken ill. "There go the Macleans—they've been called home again," got to be a fairly frequent comment among their friends at dinner parties or concerts.

Down at 10 Front Street East, the Colonel's company headquarters, there was expansion too. With the larger issues of the Maclean-owned trade papers, extra editorial staff must be hired—to join Mr. Edmonds, and his two or three co-workers in the rickety little offices on the second floor. Few of the writers were exclusively committed to just one publication; most of them could switch readily from a *Hardware and Metal* feature concerning lamp chimneys, which were advancing in price, "due to the scarcity of soft coal . . . plus higher workmen's wages," to a careful analysis of the recent year's honey crop for *Grocer*'s pages or a thoroughgoing report concerning engraving methods for *Printer and Publisher*. When news from far corners of Canada was required on any public issue or local business transactions, the staff had merely to walk two or three paces to the recently organized Canadian Press Clipping Service, occupying a cluttered desk in the middle of the floor. In summer, 1902, a young university graduate, W. H. F. Addison, took charge of that department; a few months later he left to enter a medical course, from which point he would rise, step by step, to a distinguished career as Professor of Anatomy, Graduate School of Medicine, University of Pennsylvania.

On the third floor of the Front Street building, the Colonel's office had a certain lonely splendor, from the simple fact that the rest of the space was unused. Even the busy composing room, with its typesetting machines and make-up stands, did not occupy more than half the area available on the fourth or top floor. From here a primitive hoist carried the forms down to the three presses in the basement; on completion of the press run, the printed sheets were gathered and fixed between their covers in the bindery, and then sent to the mailing room which occupied the rear area of the main floor. To the front here was the all-important business office, with its imposing broad window and arched glass door directly adjacent to the street pavement. Friends passing by could nod their "Good Mornings" to Miss Forbes, seated at her bookkeeper's high desk, or to the Business Manager, Captain Burns, old friend of the Colonel and complete ex-Army type, or to one J. Meredith McKim, a young man of distinguished appearance, who was in charge of advertising for all trade papers. Within a few years McKim would move to London, England, to represent the Maclean business there.

All told, there were some thirty or forty employees from top to bottom at 10 Front Street East, and a dozen more in offices in Montreal, Vancouver, New York and Winnipeg. A few of those originals at the turn of the century were to remain for many years, and one of them, H. Victor Tyrrell, was to emerge eventually as Vice-President and General Manager. In 1947 the Colonel, reminiscing about the old days, said: "Often at night I would go back to work and find a light burning in the composing room. There would be a young figure, working long after hours. I would ask him what he was doing and why didn't he go home. He would reply, 'I'm learning something.'" True enough, for Tyrrell was a man stubbornly, totally determined to achieve, and by 1903–4 he had already proved it.

For some time the Colonel had been concerned about the constant delay in delivery of advertising plates or copy, with resulting dislocation in press and mailing dates. What was needed was an expediter thoroughly familiar with the publishing routine, and one who could have straight man-talk contact with all the outside miscellany of manufacturers, advertisers, and those few new groupings called "agencies." Tyrrell, the young, long-eared compositor who enjoyed learning, was the choice. From that point forward his hands would be immaculate, free of the inevitable black grease of typesetting machines; within a matter of months he had smoothed away virtually all the problems of advertising deliveries and lateness of press schedules. His future was inevitable.

In October 1903 an event destined to leave its mark on the Colonel's publishing enterprise for the next fifty years, took place with the hiring of twenty-two-year-old Horace Talmadge Hunter. Perhaps the Colonel at that first interview had one of those mysterious flashes of intuition; indeed he often arrived at swift decisions which, in later years, made him appear to be a man of great wisdom and foresight. Undoubtedly he was impressed with young Hunter's poise and with the details of his "previous experience." It was clear this fledgling already knew the discipline of concentration toward a definite goal. He had put himself through the University of Toronto by selling advertising for *The Presbyterian*—a weekly review published locally; his original part-time arrangement there had developed so satisfactorily that he had been promoted to advertising manager, which of course necessitated careful budgeting of spare hours outside of classes and study periods. Yes, he had found the work fascinating; he was now convinced advertising could play a great role in the growth of Canada. After graduation a few months ago he had accepted an offer to join the Halifax *Chronicle,* but Nova Scotia seemed just too far away from his favorite headquarters, Toronto—which had the advantage of being close to Markham, where a certain charming fellow graduate, Miss Christine Fleming, lived.

Hunter was promptly engaged as advertising salesman on *Hardware & Metal,* and almost as promptly the Colonel knew the decision had been overwhelmingly right. On the young man's first official swing through Ontario, he succeeded in selling, among other business, a contract for fifty-two full pages—one page per week for the entire year —to a Hamilton wholesaler, whose former use of the publication had been only sporadic. No one at the Front Street office was surprised when, some ten months later, the Colonel announced the appointment

of Hunter as *H & M*'s manager. By the time he had reached his
thirtieth birthday, Hunter had been given almost complete control of
the Colonel's operations, making those day-to-day administrative decisions which J.B.M. found irksome.

Hunter was to become the ideal partner for the Colonel. The first
few years after the break with brother Hugh had been difficult ones,
and the weakening effect of the typhoid illness had further served to
stress the need for finding a joint administrator. Now, month by month,
these worries smoothed out, faded into the past as merely transitional adjustments. Hunter, a young man of careful judgment, incapable of anything less than absolute integrity in any plan or action,
gifted to the point of brilliance in matters of analysis and policy-
mapping, was on the job, the Colonel's right-hand man. His name
was ultimately to be joined with Maclean's in the company name.

Thus the year 1903 held several milestones for Maclean: the birth
of a son and heir, the discovery of the right partner for his business
future, and retirement from active militia life. Undoubtedly this last
was a relief in some ways, with no more commuting to Montreal for
regular parades or special regimental occasions; certainly it was time
to relinquish command and transfer to the Reserve of Officers. But
the break must have caused inevitable pangs as well—and one proof
still exists in the typewritten copy of a round-robin notice on Maclean
Company letterhead offering his uniforms for sale. The date is May 22,
1908, some five years later, and probably the final decision to part
with the equipment lay in the fact that the Quebec Tercentenary celebrations would be an important royal occasion for the militia that
summer. Let's listen to his description of the merchandise, with its
revealing facts concerning size (no lumberjack need apply), quality
(absolutely superior) and offering price (a bargain).

I will sell a complete Hussar outfit, made by Hamburger,
Rogers & Co., Tyzack and others, very best makers in London,
everything of the finest quality, at a great bargain.

Size: Chest 38 in., Height 5 ft. 8 in., Boots 7½ to 7¾, but
can be stretched.

The Tunics are for Lt. Colonel, but lace can be removed to
make them suitable for any rank.

The attached is copy of photo of this particular uniform levee
dress, which will be found necessary for officers who desire to

be presented to the Prince of Wales at Quebec, or for use on other important occasions; also list and memo of original cost of each article.

The greater part is as good as new, and it cost about $1,500, without duty. I will sell the whole (excepting Sabretache, Macintosh and Chest of Drawers) for $400.

The Tunics, Busby and Shoulder-belts are alone worth that. I will not sell any part, but in case of officers wanting only part, they can no doubt distribute the remainder among others in their own corps.

May be seen in Toronto.

Yours truly,

So, all that spanking smartness of the former O.C., Duke of York's Hussars, was sold, and probably distributed piece by piece among Montreal's rising young lieutenants. All, that is, except the military chest of drawers which made an excellent filing cabinet for home use, the Sabretache to be cherished as a unique reminder of his cavalry career, and the Macintosh, which in the eyes of any frugal man, could deliver several more years of service.

CHAPTER XIII

# A MAGAZINE IS BORN

"Some enterprise that hath a stomach in it."
*Shakespeare*

---

THE PERIOD of 1904–5 found John Bayne Maclean thoroughly immersed in his publishing business—and quite understandably. Extended family travel was set aside during the baby's first year or so; constant interruptions from militia responsibilities had ceased, and there were no substitute hobbies sufficiently interesting to claim his time. Church life had dropped almost entirely from the curriculum, unless he had to turn out for a wedding or a funeral.

What he lived for now, in his early forties, was the continued growth of his business, both as to profits and influence—and the former would not only guarantee the latter but justify further additions to his list of publications. Such expansion was bound to come; he had only to look around him in the Front Street offices to gauge the progress already made. There had been staff additions in all departments, and Miss Forbes was no longer the sole female employee.

It was necessary, of course, to train the newcomers in the proper Maclean tradition. Old-time Scottish thrift showed itself in various rules. TURN OUT THE LIGHTS WHEN NOT IN USE warned the printed signs throughout the building; just the same, he still made an inspection round each evening after quitting-time to ensure the completeness of the blackout. Another stern directive, DON'T WASTE PAPER, may have been attributable to the fact that paper represented the costliest item of supply in his publishing business. He did not, however, insist that the staff emulate his own triumphs of salvage, such as slitting used envelopes to arrive at good clean reverse sides for memorandum purposes, or keeping last year's (or last century's) desk calendar because of its many valuable blank spaces, fore and aft.

Among the employees, especially the editorial group, he was known as a perpetual fault-finder, never completely satisfied with this report, that heading, those editorials ("They should have been *stronger*"). He drilled his writers with prodding and criticism reminiscent of a tough sergeant major on the parade ground—but with this conspicuous difference: the Colonel never shouted. His voice stayed in the same median key and his words were delivered at the same calm pace whether he was indulging in social pleasantry with a friend or delivering a quite devastating criticism to a harassed employee.

Such constant striving for perfection was perhaps only to be expected, for he had experienced, and managed to survive, various threats to success. There had been, for example, the horrible night of April 19, 1904, which witnessed Toronto's great waterfront fire. From its starting point in a neckwear factory on Wellington Street, around 8 P.M., the blaze had been fanned by the westerly wind into a spreading holocaust, leaping east across Bay Street, south to the Esplanade, and devouring all the close-set rows of buildings within an area of fourteen acres. Maclean executives and office staff had rushed back to help with the removal of all portable files and equipment, realizing that 10 Front Street East, just across the Yonge Street intersection, would obviously be the next victim. But mercifully, by 4:30 A.M., the situation was under control and the fire stopped west of Yonge Street. There would be no serious shut-down or costly aftermath for the Maclean publishing business. The only loss suffered was a batch of thick folders containing much of the Colonel's early correspondence; carefully taken from the building for safety's sake, they were to disappear as completely as if totally consumed.

Some two hundred firms, many of them wholesalers in hardware, dry goods, books and paper—and thus regular advertisers in the trade journals—were burned out, completely or in part. The Colonel and his editorial group set to at once to give complete coverage to the disaster from the specialized interest of each publication's field, at the same time welcoming emergency advertising concerning temporary quarters, incoming stocks, etc. *Bookseller* brought out a special issue before the first of May; *Dry Goods Review*'s forthcoming number even had some mischievous announcements of "Red Hot" values from belt and neckwear manufacturers. And all the Maclean journals presented strong editorials, in the familiar vigorous style of the Colonel himself, denouncing the action of Canadian and British fire insurance companies which had promptly increased their premium rates by 25 to 100 percent following the disaster. True, that group of institutions had paid out nearly $11,000,000 of the total estimated loss of $13,000,000; yet the Colonel insisted that this proper fulfillment of their contracts could not justify the sudden "intransigent move," made without discussion among other responsible bodies such as the Canadian Manufacturers' Association.

For years to come old-timers on the Colonel's staff would talk of the two memorable events of 1904: "The Fire" and "The Banquet." Each was exciting in its own way, the second having the advantage of being an exclusive company affair, without precedent, and carefully organized and looked forward to for weeks. Only John Bayne Maclean could have selected the date, which was December 31 and a Saturday as well. New Year's Eve *could* be a sober occasion of review and resolutions!

Some sixty people were present: a complete turnout from all departments at Toronto headquarters, plus company representatives from New York, Montreal and Winnipeg offices. The morning was given over to a general meeting; the afternoon program allowed for study of each publication in turn. Then the staffers hurried home to change into their finest as befitted the next item on the agenda: a ten-course dinner in the luxurious Queen's Hotel. Some came in white tie, some in dinner jackets; some in their Sunday best. Everyone was invited, from general manager, Edmonds, to the younger apprentice printers. After the several desserts (plum pudding followed by cheese, ice cream and great platters of fruit) the host rose and thanked his guests for contributing to this truly "historic day" for the Company; there were solemn toasts to the New Year; a boy's choir sang several carols and, as the next *Monthly Bulletin* to Macleanites described it, "The approach of the hour of midnight, when the Sabbath day would be ushered in, brought to a conclusion a profitable conference and a delightful evening." A flashlight photograph of the event is still extant and, as this is written, two survivors of the party are alive.

The *Bulletin*'s full coverage of the gathering featured certain interesting angles on the state of the business. Each day of the year the company's presses spewed forth an average of 45 pages of print in the "most complete" publishing plant in the Dominion. "Omitting reports of murders, suicides and other crimes, scandals, local happenings and similar occurrences, the Maclean papers contained more original and exclusive news than any daily in Canada." And that the total product represented responsible journalism at its best was emphasized by the

Colonel when he informed the audience: "The Maclean newspapers have never published a line of paid reading matter in their editorial columns. Many advertisers and some trade associations have attempted to dictate the editorial policy but none have tried it a second time."

January 1905, saw a sixth trade journal added to the Colonel's family of publications. *Canadian Machinery and Manufacturing News,* an outgrowth of a special department in *Hardware and Metal's* regular pages, would now come forth proudly month by month with its own name and format, presenting all the news concerning machinery, engines, turbines, pulleys, and other equipment for Canada's booming heavy industry.

Right from the start it was a vigorous offspring, dedicated to the masthead motto, "Forward Is the Word." The second (February) issue's editorial headed "A Universal Unit of Measurement" urged that the metric system be adopted as the international standard of weight and measurement, the benefits of which would justify the inevitable initial cost in millions of dollars and enormous labor, plus the "entire revolution in the design of machinery and machine tools." The editor admitted that "the bitterness of the opposition to be overruled before such can be accomplished has already been shown"; nevertheless, after marshaling all current thoughts on the subject, he closed on a hopeful note, declaring "Throughout the manufacturing and commercial world a feeling favorable to the metric system has been growing stronger and stronger, so that there is every evidence of its universal adoption within a few years." He was a little out in his timing but not in his logic.

*Canadian Machinery's* early editorials had a robust, red-blooded quality which automatically selected the readership aimed at: chiefly owner-manufacturers and mill superintendents, but also foremen, machinists, even the young hands on their way up among the grease, steam and noise. Here was a Maclean paper removed from the concerns of wholesaling, retailing, window-dressing and over-the-counter transactions; a paper industrially oriented. It proclaimed boldly, "We are not on the eve of a great industrial revolution in Canada; we are in the very midst of it, and that without anticipation on the part of some, and, with the many no realization of the fact whatever." Some of the country's cabinet ministers obviously belonged in the latter group; they still insisted that Canada's one destiny lay in agriculture, that here would continue to be "the granary of the Empire," and to that end all other interests must be subservient.

The Colonel could not agree. January 1906 issue listed the impressive reports concerning the country's mineral prospects from coast to coast—among them "the world's richest veins of asbestos" . . . "the recent startling finds of silver in the Cobalt district" . . . "Sudbury's nickel." Now the need was for a rapid building-up of refining plants, so that the full value of these national, natural assets could be realized by and within Canada.

That last reference may have had a launching-pad in the Colonel's conversations and correspondence the year before. Friend Schwab was one of the New York financial interests behind the Sudbury nickel group that was rather significantly involved in the U.S. refining plants to which the Canadian unrefined nickel "matte" was regularly shipped. Maclean had courageously brought up the possibility of completing the refining process in Canada "and," as he reminded Charlie later, "you looked on it most favorably." Then, one evening in December 1905, Honorable Alexander Grant MacKay, Ontario's new Minister of Crown Lands, was the Colonel's guest for dinner and a chat, the outcome of which was a long letter to Schwab, reporting that this member of the government had welcomed the idea too.

In the final paragraph comes what amounts to a direct challenge, however amicably expressed: "If you could kindly tell me why the nickel industry cannot transfer its refinery to this country now, and the bonus you would want to enable you to do so and for what term of years it would be necessary to continue the bonus or bounty; also if there was any additional assistance you would require," that would be most helpful, etc., etc., but "please do not mention my name as I occupy a peculiar position and my motives might be misjudged."

Within a couple of days Schwab wrote to acknowledge "your very interesting letter" and promised "my careful consideration . . ."

Of course the project took time; it was years before International Nickel's great refining plant was opened at Port Colborne, Ontario, with the Colonel's business papers unceasingly reminding the company of the need. But by the time the refinery was built, the publisher stood totally free from any possible charges of "motives," he having sold all his Canadian stocks by that time.

Indeed 1905 was to be a very special red-letter year. The Colonel produced his first magazine—one that was to become a national institution.

The conditions were encouraging. The six trade papers continued to realize a clear profit, however modest, after all expenses. The editorial staff had demonstrated ample capacity for hard work and diversification; one more publication would not be too upsetting. Anyway, the Colonel seldom worried about gaps or replacements in the ranks; as fast as men left him for better-paying jobs there were always young university graduates eager for a chance to learn the mysterious art of writing and editing. The training was stiff, and they were apt to find themselves with simultaneous story assignments ranging from the upcoming trend toward electric refrigeration (*Machinery*) to a survey of all Canadian-made writing papers (*Bookseller and Stationer*) and an analysis in depth of the failure of Ontario's tomato crop (*Grocer*). When a novice showed he could stand up to such indoctrination there might be a raise in title, though not always in salary; the Colonel saw no objection whatever in appointing a twenty-three-year-old to managing editor, especially if the title helped the young man stay put.

Two or three key executives, notably Hunter, held the enterprise together during the Colonel's frequent absences. Whether these trips were of a routine nature—a few days in New York—or a more extended trip, his companion, of course, was Frank Munsey, and just as inevitably much of their conversation turned to publishing, and especially the kind in which the Munsey millions had been made: general magazines.

Was this the next logical step for the Maclean establishment? The longer the Colonel pondered the question, the more definite was the answer: Yes! Canada had few magazines of national circulation. In the English language, only three made any effort to serve a coast-to-coast readership. One was the monthly *Canadian Magazine,* national and informed in its point of view, outstanding in the caliber of writers and material, but never prosperous. *Canadian Home Journal,* started in 1904, was still in an uncertain early period of experimentation, not yet sure whether its mission was to women or to both sexes, or whether the fiction presented should be all-out literary or back-porch romantic. *Saturday Night,* the weekly, had built up a devoted following over almost twenty years, but its specialties of political comment, high society reporting and extended reviews of current drama and literature ruled out any likely development of "mass appeal."

The Colonel's first idea was to create a magazine for women. His initial move was a private conference with Arthur T. Vance, the brilliant editor of *Women's Home Companion,* at that point the sensational success of the American publishing field. By the time the New

York interview took place a specific proposition was ready to be presented: Would Vance come to Canada to found a similar publication for the women of that country? Vance countered with a scheme of his own. He announced he could buy for half a million dollars 70 percent of the shares of the Crowell Publishing Company which then owned the *Companion* with its 500,000 monthly circulation, as well as *Farm and Fireside,* distributing 350,000 copies twice a month. In fact, the company was making between $130,000–$150,000 clear profit per year, and capable of much more. Would Maclean join him in buying out Mr. Crowell?

Shaken as he no doubt was, the Colonel explained that this was hardly what he had in mind. Vance, in turn, declined the invitation to come to Canada.

Now, it seemed, the decks were cleared for a project quite different —one that appeared more practical for a publisher of the Colonel's experience. The comfortable state of his trade papers proved the existence of a sizable, interested male audience, coast-to-coast. Why not introduce a general magazine packed with lively, leisure-time reading for the same group?

No sooner said than begun—not entirely out of thin air either, but, more craftily, by the purchase of a small house organ owned by a Toronto advertising agency. In this way Maclean immediately acquired a nucleus of subscribers, about 5000 in all, some of them paying, others on the free list. For five years the little journal with the cumbersome and slightly repetitive name, *Business: The Business Man's Magazine* had been issued regularly. Now, reasoned the new owner, this might represent the first move toward a better-balanced general magazine.

From that cautious, inconspicuous beginning would grow the most famous of all Canadian magazines, *Maclean's.*

In October 1905 the Colonel's first issue appeared under the shortened name of the *Business Magazine.* The hefty thickness—144 pages plus covers—justified the price of 20 cents per copy ($2.00 per year); at the same time the page size of $5\frac{1}{2}'' \times 8\frac{1}{4}''$ depth gave it attractively compact book proportions. That first issue contained no original material but the range of features and sources was impressive, even at this distance of sixty-odd years. Here was, in short, the first digest magazine, deliberately designed to help businessmen by mining the world's periodicals for them, and then selecting, reprinting in full or condensing as necessary, to make a balanced collation of news and thoughts on many subjects.

There was fun—with "Pigs Is Pigs," by Ellis Parker Butler, as recently debuted in *American Illustrated;* there was a stimulating group of career features, as in "George Washington, Genius," and "A Canadian-named Automobile," the latter (from the Toronto *Sunday World*) dealing with the amazing new Russell car and its gifted inventor, T. A. Russell, Ontario-born, graduate of the University of Toronto, and at that date General Manager of the Canada Cycle & Motor Company. (Oshawa's famous McLaughlin automobile would not see the light of day for two years.) Other articles ranged from a study of "Christie's," London's great auction headquarters, to an exposé of the "Wiles and Ways of the Counterfeiter." Indeed, reading enjoyment to suit every mood seemed to be guaranteed by the variety of sources, which included *London Magazine, Cosmopolitan, Cassel's, Success, Pall Mall, American Illustrated, Grand, Pearson's, Arena, Leisure, National Geographic.*

For all this wealth of content the Colonel paid nothing. His arrangement with the other publications was simple and explicit: if they gave him permission to reprint, he would credit the piece to its original vehicle, and also publicize their regular issues by listing major article titles as featured therein. To publishers at home or abroad, this seemed a fair offer, although in one or two cases they added the proviso that no more than 50 percent of the original wordage should be reproduced.

Most of the material was selected by the Colonel himself, but young Arnot Craick stood by to help, if his already overburdened timetable permitted. As all editors know, "the first is the worst," and no wonder the launching of the periodical that would one day be the familiar *Maclean's* had its troubles, as indicated by the following "Note" over the October listing of contents: "Owing to the confusion consequent upon the publication of this first number of the *Business Magazine* under new management, a few mistakes have been made. In some copies the folios will be found to be a little out from page 72 onward. Readers will kindly overlook this small error."

They did. Subscriptions poured in and there was a brisk demand for individual copies at the newsdealers' counters. A bigger, better audience awaited the November issue with its first original article: the success story of patent-medicine-man Senator George Fulford of Brockville, Ontario, and his "Pink Pills for Pale People." The Toronto author, Augustus Bridle, witty, urbane, gifted with a rich vocabulary, equal to any analysis of human personality, would continue for many years as a leading contributor; eventually, in 1916, an excellent selection of his biographies written for *Maclean's* and its predecessor would come forth in a popular book, *Sons of Canada.*

The Colonel's third issue, December 1905, proved to any doubters still around that this was a magazine capable of swift improvement and expansion. The title was now simplified to the *Busy Man's Magazine,* by which it would be known for almost another six years. The subhead underneath described the publication's contents and purpose: "The Cream of the World's Magazines Reproduced for Busy People." Three of the covers and ten consecutive full pages at the back of the 160-page book carried advertising for insurance, typewriters, long-distance telephone service, filing systems, beer, and, rather surprisingly, table syrup for the discriminating hostess. In all, there were twenty-six feature articles. One was another Bridle profile, this time presenting "D. D. Mann, Railroad Builder," the young friend who had stood out long ago against the Reverend Andrew Maclean's advice. A few weeks previous Mann had driven the last spike on Canadian Northern's main line into Edmonton—a memorable event for all Canada, as the story indicated, yet, "He said the least of any of the orators. He was cheered the loudest."

The Colonel liked that; in fact, there were certain high points in *Busy Man's* No. 3 issue which he would enjoy discussing in detail ten or more years hence. Among these present in its pages had been his chums; Schwab and Munsey, and each in his best form with something pungent to say. From the New York *World* came the interview with Bethlehem Steel's president (he had left Carnegie and now headed his own company) following his return from Germany. In the great steel plants there, he declared, quality had undisputed top place, whereas in the United States, quantity, cheapness and speed were sought first, with quality trailing. He warned that "a titanic struggle" between those two points of view, "the American love of brute bulk" versus the German pride of scientific perfection, would be inevitable, unless U.S. manufacturers saw the danger and changed their philosophy and practices. At the Bethlehem works, he had immediately altered and expanded certain procedures on his return from abroad. Result: the improved product had already brought in orders for the next twelve months, necessitating quadrupling of services.

Munsey's piece, written in his own vigorous style for the magazine bearing his own name, was, oddly enough, along comparative lines, too, this time with America losing out to France in the matter of motoring facilities. True, Napoleon's fine roads had been there for a century awaiting the automobile age; but the speed with which that country had set about modernizing the routes, establishing car maintenance depots even in the remotest spots, refurbishing old inns and building new accommodation had now placed France well in the lead of any nation so far as motoring pleasure was concerned. And the Americans going there in increasing numbers discovered that just *one* license number and *one* set of highway rules would see them through their happy holiday—so different from the situation at home, where if a man were to drive through the whole United States "he would have to plaster every available inch of space on his car with numbers, and would have to equip himself in the outset with licenses from all those States and Territories, and familiarize himself with the different laws therein." No wonder France was experiencing a great, profitable tourist boom, as Munsey summed it up. No wonder, either, that the friend who had sat beside him on the trip and shared, perhaps inspired those observations, had adjudged the article worthy of reprinting.

For even in those groping, early days of *Busy Man's,* the Colonel was moving inevitably toward the policy that would establish Canada's national magazine. Here was, in the first place, a publication entirely and uninhibitedly of the twentieth century, one with its windows open to the whole wide world of experiences and ideas and history-in-the-making. And, accepting that basis as an already accomplished fact, here *could* be the medium of essential information for Canadians concerning all the great movements, at home and afar, which would affect their lives. Such a magazine, honestly conceived, scrupulously edited in lively fashion, attractively produced, could be a national force. It would not merely inform Canada but also express it! The argument that no publisher had yet succeeded in such an achievement only showed, according to the Colonel's reasoning, that none had really tried.

The challenge was there, clear, unmistakable; for a man of Maclean's character, there was no choice but to take it up. Issue by issue, over the next half-dozen years, the groundwork would be well and truly laid: by an editor-in-chief who happened to be the owner and whose pioneering would earn the respect of a long line of brilliant successors; a Canadian whose name continues to be worn proudly by the national institution he founded—*Maclean's Magazine.*

# CHAPTER XIV

# ENTER, THE FINANCIAL POST

"I don't want economic essays; I want the news,
told in simple words."
*J.B.M.*

---

"IT IS AMAZING the amount of work one can do under pressure.
This does not mean pressure of a boss or slave-driver, but one's
own personal pressures. Under such pressure one can do as much in
a day as in a week under ordinary routine."

So reads an undated scrap of note, penciled in the Colonel's hand,
and filed (with dozens of folders on subjects as diverse as soil
drifting and Empire relations) in a bulky package labeled "Pressure"
and in the correct slot marked "P." As a journalist Maclean placed
high value on that sort of four-drawer cabinet of ideas and observations, ready to be brought forward for study and expansion at the
psychological moment. More notes went in than could ever be used.
Some are obvious platitudes, others have the dust of the nineteenth
century on them, like heaped discards in an attic, but a few supply
interesting confirmation of the Maclean character and habits.

He was well qualified to comment on the achievements possible
under "one's own personal pressures," for certainly the Maclean inner
drive never relaxed. He was a man incapable of idleness. He could
and frequently did put in the same nine or ten daytime working
hours at his printers. An evening at home often meant concentration
over a special editorial for one or all of the trade papers. Or if
Anna's engagement book necessitated attendance at a social function
as it frequently did—well, no one knew better than John Bayne Maclean how the nod of greeting across a drawing room could lead to
an informative conversation, and often a happy relationship that would
survive over the years.

From his point of view, friendships, whether in the bud or fully flowered, merited support and sympathetic help throughout all their phases. Thus it followed that any day's agenda at home or abroad might include hours of correspondence, interviews, investigation and thought—all on behalf of another man's pet project. Such activity was taken on enthusiastically, voluntarily, and never once, with any idea of "commission" or profit. For him, it was reward enough that the plan promised good things for someone he valued as a friend. Of course, when the latter happened to be an important international figure, the Colonel's enjoyment of the role of expediter or intermediary heightened noticeably.

One interesting venture of the kind had its start at a Carlsbad spa in the early summer of 1906. The Marquis of Doria, well known in Florentine society, happened to be taking the cure at the same time as the Colonel; they enjoyed each other's company, and within a few days were deep in serious discussion of the Italian's cherished dream, i.e. to move thousands of his fellow countrymen from their overcrowded, poverty-stricken rural communities to the wide-open land spaces of Canada. The Marquis had little money of his own, but surely there must be a way, and what would the Colonel recommend? The answer: a steamship line, to be named the Italian-Canadian, and, as to the necessary capital, the Colonel felt confident the initial amount could be raised.

As soon as the Carlsbad farewells were said, Maclean pursued the plan entirely on his own. Stopping in London, he had a first discussion with his publisher-capitalist friend, Sir Hugh Gilzean-Read; then the two met with Sir Christopher Furness, head of the Furness, Withy's salt-water empire. It was decided that two ships, each capable of carrying 1500 immigrants, would be required, and at a total outlay of £225,000. Furness, Withy and Gilzean-Read quickly signed up subscriptions amounting to £165,000—an excellent beginning, and the Colonel was sure he could find the balance in Canada. So, back at the Front Street office, he wrote to several of his friends with money to invest but all were wary.

Another source still remained: the Dominion Government. Maclean went to Ottawa and laid his plan before Sir Richard Cartwright, Minister of Trade and Commerce, requesting an outright subsidy of £50,000, plus a subsidy per head for all immigrants delivered to Canada. Cartwright, liking the general idea but balking at the cost, stated he would participate with a subsidy of $50,000 (dollars not pounds) provided the Italian government would also contribute. Letters and diplomatic contacts now followed, yet without avail; Italy refused to join in, and the scheme collapsed. At no point in the lengthy correspondence (which, to this day, makes a thick bulge in the Maclean files) did the Colonel raise the question of what he might get out of the deal.

That same year, 1906, saw another free-will offering of effort and interest, plus hospitality. This time the enterprise was to be crowned with success, and for the rest of his life the Colonel would enjoy recalling his part in the introduction of the Rolls-Royce motorcar to North America.

Friendship and the strong linkage of the Clan Maclean formed the springboard. During a trip abroad shortly after the turn of the century the Colonel had met the Honorable Charles S. Rolls, son of Lord and Lady Llangattock, and on his mother's side the nephew of the current (26th) Chief of the Maclean Clan, cherished friend of the Toronto publisher. Rolls had impressed the Colonel. Here was a young man of unassailable background including Eton, an outstanding racing cyclist during his Cambridge years, a daring "balloonatic," and already a veteran prize-winner of virtually all the sensational automobile events in Britain and on the Continent. He moved with the speed of light from one achievement to another. By 1902, he had established a garage business in London where cars were stored, repaired and available on rental, special bodies built, chauffeurs trained. He acquired the United Kingdom rights to sell the Panhard, a French automobile; within hardly more than a year of that arrangement he had a hundred new cars on order from across the Channel.

Small wonder the Colonel had marked him down as a man with a future. And why shouldn't that future feature overseas expansion? This was the question implicit in Maclean's letter of 1902, suggesting that Rolls make a visit to the United States and Canada and bring a car with him. Motoring was beginning to catch on in America, and certain wealthy friends on both sides of the border could be considered excellent prospects.

Then, a little later, the Colonel wrote to tell his young friend that Schwab was holidaying abroad. "If you hear of him, I wish you would introduce yourself to him, mentioning my name, and see if you can be of any service to him." But that wasn't all. "It is possible Mr. John W. Gates may be with him. He was a traveling salesman a few years ago, but he has made money and he, more

than any other man, manipulates stocks on this side. Just before he
sailed he cornered the market and is said to have made on that one
deal alone fully one million pounds. I like him very much because
of his ability, but I see he has been criticized a little in the English
papers because of his personal manners. Personally I have never
seen anything in him to find fault with, but in case you meet him I
want you to know this is in confidence, and so that you will not
mind if his manners are not always those one is accustomed to in
average Society."

(It is doubtful that the famous stock speculator's lack of polish
bothered Rolls who, according to the times he lived in, was already
*déclassé* by reason of having entered "trade." His own manners, too,
fell somewhat short of perfection; certain contemporaries found him
mean and discourteous, and one biographer was to sum up the Rolls
character as "unloveable.")

The Colonel's repeated invitations to come to America had to wait
for fulfillment until 1906, by which time Rolls, the passionate addict
of mobile power, the well-to-do businessman with impressive connections, had joined forces with Henry Royce, Manchester's brilliant
designer and engineering genius. The Rolls-Royce automobile, soon to
be world famous, had been born, and—as indicated on the letterhead
in the Colonel's files—its exclusive symbol was already established,
its head office functioning on Conduit Street, with repair shops at
Fulham and factory at Manchester.

Rolls and two companions arrived in New York in November,
with the Colonel on hand to welcome them and to ensure comfortable
arrangements at his favorite hotel. Although Rolls's objective was
specifically to display his new 30 h.p. car at the automobile show
there early in December, he allowed himself and party plenty of time
both before and after the event—enough, indeed, for two separate
visits to the Toronto Macleans, the first in November, the second
over the Christmas period. During the show week, of course, the
Colonel was standing by in New York, ready to bring forward his
well-to-do acquaintances, each in turn, to examine the quite amazing
British creation. And, in spite of the fact that newspapers and automotive journals completely ignored the Rolls-Royce exhibit, orders for
three cars were received by mid-January—all from the Colonel's
list of prospects.

But before that happened the first Rolls-Royce in America was to
leave its tire marks on the snowy streets of Toronto. The planning was

rather involved, especially for Maclean, to whom Rolls, still in New York, gladly left all the problems, contenting himself with a daily note or telegram bristling with question marks. COULD YOU KINDLY LET ME KNOW WHETHER YOU CAN, AS SUGGESTED, ARRANGE FOR MY MOTOR TO BE IMPORTED INTO CANADA, TEMPORARILY, FREE OF CHARGE? After a batch of explanatory letters to the Customs Department in Ottawa, the Colonel was able to answer in the affirmative: the car would be allowed in duty-free, for a period of one month and for exhibition purposes only.

Next question: What did "My dear Maclean" anticipate as to weather conditions? "If the streets are impassable for motorists owing to the snow being soft and deep," Rolls wrote, "then it would not be much good my coming." (And those were the days when a liberal snow-covering was welcomed by Torontonians; indeed it was essential for the regular type of winter transportation, viz. sleighs, which served all needs, whether for family use, delivery services, funeral cortèges, or whatever.) The Colonel replied with a quick succession of weather reports in mid-December. "Cold but little snow," and he could promise the visitors some delightful ice-boating on the Bay. The next note was slightly discouraging . . . "nothing but sleighs now." A week later conditions had improved, with "quite a number of motorcars getting about. The streets in the city are hard. Several of the cars have chains on their hind wheels. I think you will have no trouble in moving your motor about the principal roads."

Rolls decided to take the risk, ship the car north and make himself comfortable for the holiday season at the Queen's Park residence. It was a wise decision, for, through the Colonel's good offices and careful selection of guests for luncheons and a reception, a fourth automobile order would be firmed up within a matter of days. The handsome young John Craig Eaton, successor to his father's mercantile realm, was to become Canada's first Rolls-Royce owner.

In spite of the rather happenstance program, those two or three months of the Britisher's visit would lay the foundations for his car's great North American market. Surprisingly enough, the man who urged the effort in the first place, and then set to in workmanlike fashion to prove it both feasible and profitable, was still a horse-and-carriage owner. The temptation to take the plunge into the twentieth century and buy "an auto" was strong, especially in the early weeks of 1907. Rolls had opened the subject in the course of his dutiful thank-yous before departing (and after his host had tracked down and recommended a competent Canadian agent for the car), but the Colonel remained non-committal, perhaps a little worn after all the excitement, though happy to be of service.

Then, late in February arrived the letter that necessitated a decision. Rolls, back at London headquarters, stated that, while all the 30 h.p.'s had been sold, the 40/50 h.p. "Silver Ghost," fresh from Royce's design lab, offered various improvements, such as "paraffin lamps, electric light to interior, electric telegraph for communicating with the driver and full equipment of spares and tools"; also, the detachable brougham top allowed conversion from a completely closed carriage for winter to an open touring car for summer. "The price . . . would be £1,200 retail or £1,057.10.0 to you," representing 15 percent off the chassis value. Rolls urged action, as "What I am afraid of is that the present negotiations for the Toronto agency will be completed before receiving your order and then it will be quite impossible for me to give you any discount . . ."

But the Colonel had to decline. He was short of cash, having recently invested $15,000 in presses required for an important new publication. A Rolls-Royce must be deferred—until 1909, as it turned out, when he bought (at full market value) the same model which would in later years be the desert companion of Lawrence of Arabia and the favorite vehicle of Lenin in Moscow.

The career of the Honorable Charles S. Rolls was to end tragically before his thirty-fourth birthday. By that time his interest in motorcars had been superseded by total absorption in "heavier-than-air" flying. He had sought out the Wright Brothers during their experiments in France, bought one of their machines and within a few weeks mastered it to the point where he could, and did, chalk up the first return flight ever to be made across the English Channel. Some months later, in July 1910, he was killed in a crash during an emergency landing manoeuvre at a flying meet in Bournemouth.

Those new presses in the basement at 10 Front Street were amply to justify their right of priority over any such frivolous venture as an automobile. From them would issue a completely new and different type of publication, *The Financial Post,* soon to be one of the most powerful of the Maclean media, and eventually to outrank all the others in profitable operation.

For several years the Colonel had been mulling over the fact that the average Canadian retail merchant, wholesaler or manufacturer had no publication specifically designed to help him with investments. The trade papers showed the reader how to make money, yes, but for a businessman's logical next step, the conserving of profits and their deployment for further earnings, he was left to stumble on alone. The financial papers of the day offered little assistance; their columns were filled with learned economic treatises by stuffy academic types. What they were talking about was beyond the comprehension of the Colonel; so how, he reasoned, could a small-town bank manager or pickle manufacturer make sense of it?

A weekly publication that would sort out, analyze, interpret in direct, understandable language all the news that had a bearing on a businessman's prosperity or daily decisions involving money could render an important service.

Such were the Colonel's preliminary thoughts, long-cherished but carefully disciplined to await the discovery of the right man to implement them.

As luck would have it, that man was to come forward sometime in 1906—of his own volition, and eager to explore various ideas for new publications with that admitted expert, his old friend Maclean.

From the Colonel's point of view, Stewart Houston's history and demonstrated versatility made him a highly desirable candidate. He was the son of an Anglican clergyman in Waterdown, not many miles from Crieff; back in the '70s the two pastors had struck up a pleasant acquaintance on their occasional encounters along country roads. After graduating from Trinity University, Houston had moved on to a law course, at the same time taking a job as reporter and sports writer on the *Empire,* where Maclean was functioning as commercial editor.

A firm friendship developed, and through the next few years the older man watched with interest as Houston successfully tackled new projects. He was chief founder, as well as manager, of the Toronto Spring Horse Show and Military Tournament, manager also of the Hunt Club's fall race meet. Finding the legal sphere slow and uncongenial, he decided to step forth as a full-time impresario—first in the capacity of Massey Music Hall's manager, and then quickly broadening his booking services to other major Canadian centers where audiences were ready to pay good prices for the world's best in music and lectures. He had married a well-known Toronto singer who belonged to one of the province's top families, the John Beverley Robinsons, former occupants of Government House. The Houstons moved in the upper circles of society, and everyone admired the handsome male member of the pair, that tall, fair young man with the distinguished manner.

Now, as Houston explained to the Colonel, the tour management business had lost its earlier excitement; so much traveling kept him away from home; he was ready for a change and seriously considering a return to journalism. He could buy out that waning periodical, *Canadian Sportsman,* and breathe some life into it. What would Maclean advise?

The answer was prompt. Certainly, journalism and publishing represented an ideal field, but make the vehicle a financial newspaper!

Houston got busy immediately. He analyzed the three existing publications—the *Monetary Times, General Commerce* and *Financial Chronicle*—and quickly discovered that, while advertising volume was constant, impressive and thus profitable, the editorial content had to be rated even below an adequate minimum in scope, service or interest. He undertook interviews with various leaders in the downtown community, and wound up with a series of calls on all the general managers of Canada's chartered banks. This last group proved unanimous in the opinion that the country's businessmen, and particularly the branch bank managers (numbering over 1400 at the time) stood in real need of a paper designed to serve the financial field, one which would present all pertinent Canadian news, including complete stock market coverage, and one which would be, above every other consideration, readable.

Young Houston had found the challenge he had been seeking, and the Colonel now saw his own secret hopes and gropings translated into a complete plan of campaign. Gladly he contributed the full amount of capital required; just as readily he entered into a special partnership with Houston to allow the latter a one-third interest in the new paper.

Its name was chosen by Maclean as a tribute to his friend, Lord Glenesk, publisher of the *Morning Post* of London, England. In a characteristic if unnecessary gesture, the Colonel wrote overseas, explaining his reasons and awaiting approval; Glenesk replied with gracious blessings and best wishes for Canada's forthcoming *Financial Post.*

The first issue appeared January 12, 1907—some 25,000 copies rolling off the recently installed newspaper presses. By the time all mailings were completed, the paid subscriptions were pouring in from points up, down and across the country. Bond and stock firms wrote or wired for full information as to advertising rates, deadlines, etc. Here, at last, was the publication they had been waiting for, one which had for its avowed purpose, according to the standing subhead under the front page's logo: "A weekly newspaper aiming to present, in a popular manner, accurate information relating to the financial interests and legitimate investments of Canada."

It was virtually a one-man operation at the start. Houston, the editor, also served as the complete editorial staff. The trade papers' correspondents scattered throughout the Dominion had been enlisted to file special stories for the *Post,* but Houston, a perfectionist like the Colonel, did his own careful, lively rewrites before passing the material to the typesetters. A normal issue could take as much as 12,000 words, but one of the first *Post* "specials," for which the lone editor was wholly responsible, contained over 25,000 words of copy. The Colonel was impressed—to the point where he memoed all company editors and managers, declaring that, after hearing so many complaints about overwork, it was fitting that he should put before them Mr. Houston's achievements for the issue of January 23, 1909. The message ended with the stern challenge: "Let the quantity, but particularly the quality, be a record for the editorial staff to work to. Let them paste this on their mirror at home." Yet within the next five minutes he was writing in rather different vein to Houston: "I suppose I ought to congratulate you on the tremendous amount of work you did last week, but instead I feel like severely reprimanding you for doing it. You cannot stand it and you must not attempt it. At the same time, after having said the disagreeable things, I want to congratulate you."

With Stewart Houston at the helm, the *Post* stayed on a straightforward course throughout that important early period. He wrote fearlessly; his ethical standards were of the highest. A *Post* review of a certain bank's annual report inspired that organization's president to send the editor a cheque for $5000. Houston returned it.

Problems of a much graver kind were to confront him by the end of the first year. The paper had been introduced during a time of abounding prosperity throughout the country, thanks to continuous immigration, railway construction and ample capital inflow from abroad. But in December 1907 panic hit Wall Street, and the listed stocks in Toronto and Montreal dropped by a third of their market value in a matter of days. Some financial houses and auxiliary services collapsed, others teetered—with the result that advertising revenue suffered, and many of the 1908 *Post* issues were perforce kept at the thrifty eight-page size, or just two newspaper sheets, folded.

Yet Houston was never to relax his rule of honesty in editorial service; *all* the news relevant to the readers' concerns must be given impartially. Sometimes he had encouraging developments to report, as in the July 4th issue: "Curiously the coal companies in Canada have not been affected by the commercial depression and have increased their output," whereas in the United States a very marked curtailment had been noted. Or again: "No less than eleven mines (in the silver area of Cobalt) shipped out ore last week—a total of 820,270 lbs." A certain amount of building was still going on in Toronto; the *Post*'s listing of permits included one at $20,000, for five pairs of semi-detached two-story brick dwellings. Indeed, the lead-in paragraph pointed out that contractors were getting better value for wages paid than in previous good times, and "a building can be done in Toronto for from 12½ to 15 percent less than a year ago."

By 1909 the stock market had recovered its poise, prices were rising under brisk buying, and *The Financial Post* came forth as a sixteen-page paper, week after week. In the June 12th issue a boxed announcement on the editorial page proclaimed that in one recent month new subscriptions had been received from seven provinces and such foreign countries as France, Newfoundland, Bermuda, Holland, the Fiji Islands and Brazil.

Houston had done a job, but it was soon to end—with shock and sorrow to the Colonel and countless others. On February 7, 1910, in his forty-third year, the editor-manager died at his Rosedale residence after two weeks' illness from typhoid fever. That scourge had been rife in Toronto for months; almost every hospital had been forced to set up a typhoid section; eventually the municipal authorities were shamed into action with their oft-postponed water filtration plant and improved handling of the city's sewage effluent.

The *Mail and Empire*'s long obituary included an unexpected and touching bit of news. Mark Hambourg, the Russian-born pianist, just arrived in town for a Massey Hall appearance two nights later, announced that he would rearrange his program to include Chopin's B Flat Minor Sonata with its *Marche Funèbre,* as a tribute of respect to his friend, Stewart Houston, who had introduced him to Canadian audiences eight or nine years earlier.

Inevitably the Colonel was faced with various problems and anxieties following the death of his able confrère. Indeed, at one point early on, when still suffering from the personal loss, he almost sold the *Post*. George M. Morang, the book publisher, had popped up with an offer to buy. What would the price be? After due consideration, the Colonel suggested $100,000, for which figure he would give his personal guarantee that the paper's earnings, when audited, would prove to be not less than $10,000 per year. Morang came back with an offer of $75,000, which was refused. Once this little intrusion had been dealt with, the Colonel could concentrate on careful reorganization of Maclean Publishing Company stock, so that he could turn over to Mrs. Stewart Houston preferred stock shares in Maclean Publishing Company equivalent in value to her husband's one-third *Post* interest plus earnings to date.

During the next dozen years or so, the editor's name, face and capacity for the *Post* job would change several times. John Appleton, a financial writer from Winnipeg, was an early one in the line-up. For a later period R. G. Dingman, under the title of managing editor, had top command. Next came J. W. Tyson, hailing from Guelph, Ontario, who proved a hard-working editor-in-chief. The Colonel liked Tyson because he didn't argue; if the president wanted a specific campaign carried on, this editor would set to immediately, gathering masses of data and preparing endlessly repetitive articles to promulgate his employer's theories. Tyson was a nervous, somewhat cynical bachelor, a non-smoker who suppressed his regular workaday tensions by chewing small wads of copy paper picked up, absent-mindedly, from anybody's desk. Sometimes a minor crisis could result—as when he helped himself to a sheet covered with carefully worked-out percentages, essential to a certain young reporter's article for which the printers were waiting.

In 1925 a different name and face took over the editorship—a new man twenty-seven years old. "Far too young," said the Colonel, and not without reason. Yet, as it happened, it was Maclean himself who had made the appointment.

# CHAPTER XV

# NO SAUSAGE FACTORY

"Never spend your money before you have it."
*Thomas Jefferson*

---

THE ENTERPRISE founded by John Bayne Maclean is today a highly
diversified operation, ranging from magazines, business papers, industrial and trade shows, press clipping service, design services, radio
and television, plus a large commercial printing plant. Activities have
spread to five countries beyond Canada. Such broadening of scope
and services has been recognized as sound practice by most of the successful publishing house, notably Time Inc., McCall Corporation and
McGraw-Hill in the United States, Southam's in Canada, and the
Thomson and similar empires in Britain. Indeed, the company which
once held the world's top position in magazine production, the Curtis
Publishing Company of Philadelphia, came to disaster by failing to vary
and widen its interests.

Diversification of a kind was by no means unknown to the Colonel—
although he would probably be staggered if he could know how his
organization has branched out today. In a little pamphlet brought out
at the end of 1908, chiefly for the reprinting of his speech in Chicago
before the Federation of Trade Press Associations, he devoted the
back page to certain current statistics concerning his company. There
were now ten "chief" papers (the latest being *Power House,* a monthly
"devoted to the Generation, Transmission and Application of Steam,
Gas, Electric, Air and Water Power"), but, counting annuals or
other specials spawned by that group, the company "owns or controls twenty-seven publications." This expanding operation was
served by "a larger number of editors and special writers than any
two dailies or other publishing concern in Canada." Company offices
with salaried editorial, advertising and business staffs were functioning
in Montreal, Toronto, Winnipeg, New York, Chicago and London,

England—the last-mentioned three, significantly, "manned by Canadians who had made good here before being sent abroad."

From such facts and figures it was obvious that a lot had happened since the founding of *Canadian Grocer* some twenty years earlier, yet the Colonel implies that much, much more must be achieved. Many newspaper friends visiting the Maclean offices and plant, he declares, "invariably express amazement at the magnitude" of the business, and "this is a condition we ourselves have not perhaps realized, because I feel we are still in our infancy and have accomplished so little of what is yet to be done."

More, better and bigger periodicals were what he had in mind; that was his understanding of diversification. True, a small volume of outside printing had been developed, for the purpose of occupying the presses during their lulls between issues, but from the Maclean point of view this was merely a sideline. When radio became the new sensation during the 1920s, he ignored it completely; by the time television appeared he had, of course, withdrawn from active participation in company decisions.

He was, in short, a "print" man—and the teasing mystery here is: Why did he never re-enter the field of his first experience, indeed first love, by publishing a daily newspaper? The great names in that area of operation were constantly in his mind or on his lips, whether the occasion was a staff conference or an elegant private luncheon; anyone knowing Maclean inevitably knew something of the latest hard-hitting campaigns of Munsey or Hearst or McCormick in the States, or the history of Northcliffe in Britain. The Colonel admired them all for their vigor and fearlessness. Thus it might have been expected that he too—always priding himself on being "a good reporter"—would have plunged, at some point, into the maelstrom of daily journalism.

Opportunities were not lacking. There had been Hosmer's flattering overture re the acquisition of the Montreal *Gazette* back in 1902; four years later Maclean found himself picked to take over another newspaper, this time in Toronto. The plan was not without its attractive angles.

No doubt a little weary after the first few issues of *Busy Man's,* the Colonel had gone to Florida on schedule, with wife and son, to meet the springtime—and Munsey, Schwab, *et al.* Within a space of hours after his return he found himself caught up in a high-level Tory scheme to buy out the *Mail and Empire* for the purpose of redesigning and revitalizing that once-powerful organ, now in something of a slump.

The plan had the blessing of Robert L. Borden, M.P., leader of the Conservative opposition in the House of Commons, and Ontario's recently installed Premier James Pliny Whitney; the prime movers included well-heeled, resourceful Toronto types such as Albert Edward Kemp, M.P., and Edmund Osler, M.P., head of an influential stock brokerage house (all four were later to add "Sir" to their names). The group agreed that Maclean would be the ideal key man throughout the negotiations and after: a sound, vigorous, Empire-minded Tory like themselves, yes, but with all the specialized knowledge of publishing to boot, and, as a distinct plus, the friendship and confidence of the newspaper's chief owners and executives, the Riordon brothers and W. J. Douglas.

The Colonel entered in with a right good will. By the end of May his file folder marked *"Mail and Empire"* was growing bulky with statistics concerning not only that paper but its local competitors; he had amassed complete records of number of employees, their specific jobs and weekly wages in all departments, from circulation to stereotyping; coal, light and power costs and the like were not overlooked, although of course most of the hand-written memos back and forth to the *Mail* had to do with the vital matter of net profits.

Many of the Colonel's queries were based on the practical advice of Munsey, following the former's urgent appeal for help; but the more "Dear Frank" heard of the antiquated condition of the plant and pondered certain gaps in the paper's financial statements, the less he approved of "Dear Jack's" sudden entanglement. The final paragraph in Munsey's last letter states that he is enclosing all the material sent to him for study, hopes his suggestions may be of use, and goes on: "You know, old fellow, that I am always ready to serve you and delighted to serve you. I hope very much that your good Scotch sense will come to your aid and keep you out of this miserable daily-paper proposition. Do you imagine I fancy for a minute that if it were a sausage factory that offered no way of certainty, and no better prospects of financial reward than this paper does, that you would give the purchase of it an instant's serious consideration? I think you will follow my reasoning. With love to Anna and yourself . . ."

The negotiations eventually did stop—not because of Munsey, but because the *Mail's* owners, in a logical reaction to the zealous pursuit by Maclean and his group, raised their price. The first offer of $300,000 cash was turned down; the new figure would be half-a-million; but when the Colonel, recovering from the shock, added the proviso that this would be agreeable only on a pay-later arrangement, plus five years free of rental in the newspaper's premises, the conversations petered out.

Not so the over-all plan, however. Instead of resuscitating a weak Conservative voice, the Osler-Kemp-Maclean committee, spurred on by Borden and others, decided to create a totally new organ, and for that purpose announced the incorporation of a $500,000 firm to be known as the Toronto Daily Standard Publishing Company. The earlier zest and confidence returned—but for a short time only. No money was forthcoming to put the plan into operation, and certain Toronto observers, such as the *Star,* implied that the acquisition of a charter was merely a final, desperate attempt to force the *Mail's* owners to sell.

The Colonel retired quickly, and in disgust, from the local cabal. Nevertheless his file folder on the matter would remain open for a considerable period. In March 1908 he wrote to the group's lawyers, asking for a rendering of their account and mentioning that he, Kemp and Osler had long before agreed to split the charges. Nothing much happened over the next few years; the legal firm misplaced the letter during removal from one building to another, or the K.C. in charge of the case, another Osler, was on holiday abroad, or the Colonel himself was out of reach.

Eventually, the full account of $501.52 was in his hands. Now he would put in a couple of hours' work dictating two long explanatory letters, detailing the history of the project, recalling the original agreement to share any preliminary costs, and requesting a one-third settlement, viz., $167.18, from each of his fellow committeemen, Osler in Toronto, and Kemp, by that time occupying an important post with the Borden government in Ottawa.

To Kemp the Colonel indicated that "really the Conservative party should bear the total cost," especially as it was well known that the present party funds were ample. The reply was quick and crotchety: Kemp did not remember any "sharing" arrangement in that long-past enterprise; however, the amount was "trifling," and so he enclosed his check; but regarding Conservative party funds, he had "no knowledge, whatever, of any such funds. I remain, etc." Anyway, at last, the Colonel was able to forward to the lawyers the three checks, his own and the two others—and apparently nobody involved, not even the suspicious Mr. Kemp, discovered that the legal bill was being overpaid by two cents.

Now the Colonel could close the file for good. The carbon copy of his short letter accompanying the enclosures still shows the date clearly: "17th January, 1916"—or ten years after it all began.

The prospect of acquiring a newspaper specifically for the Maclean line, and quite outside of political party sponsoring, did not wholly subside. In the early 1920s the Colonel had several discussions with the Riordon and Douglas families who were still eagerly looking for a buyer, especially as the new going rate for the *Mail* had risen to two million. This time he was saved by the solid advice of his banker friend, Sir Herbert S. Holt, Montreal, who emphatically warned that the newspaper's profit position did not justify the price.

After that Maclean lost all interest in daily newspaper publishing. During the depression of the '30s there were many Ontario dailies waiting to be picked up at reasonable figures; two attractive possibilities involved a mere $100,000 in one case, slightly more in the other. Maclean and his vice-president turned down both opportunities, believing they had enough problems in nursing their existing publications through the bad times. Within a few years, Roy H. Thomson— to become Lord Thomson of Fleet, and head of a prosperous chain —bought the two dailies; at this writing each would fetch considerably more than a million dollars.

Why was John Bayne Maclean so bold about magazines and business papers and so hesitant about the daily field? The answer probably lies in his Scottish background and upbringing. To buy a newspaper property involved heavy initial borrowing and he was appalled at the thought of going into debt beyond an amount which could foreseeably be paid off within a year or two. His careful practice was to make a profit, invest it temporarily in good securities and then, cash in hand, launch forth on a new project. By his policy of not paying dividends to himself, he found that substantial sums of money could accumulate with reasonable speed.

In short, he followed a safe, foolproof course, in the sober tradition of nineteenth-century business success. He never realized that this attitude had become old-fashioned. A swift look round could have identified for him many companies which had reached size and influence through anticipating their earnings and going into debt, as needed, for expansion. Investment houses had multiplied and stood ready to do their jobs, i.e. sell bonds and debentures to provide new capital immediately, eliminating long waiting periods while a company's treasury amassed enough cash for a cautious start. Even the banks were ready and willing to advance money for sound business development. Nowadays renting money from a bank is routine. To the Colonel it would have meant simply more debt, with all its anxieties. And because he was a stubborn hold-out against modern financing, his enterprise grew more slowly than it needed. As a result he never built up the chain of daily newspapers that his experience fitted him to establish.

If John Bayne Maclean had entered the daily paper field and at a suitable juncture, it is quite possible that some of his "fights"—as he called them—with certain newspaper publishers would have been avoided. Consider the case of the Canadian Press Association as it affected the Colonel.

Back in 1888 when there were only three struggling journals in the Maclean line, he had joined the Canadian Press Association which brought together owners and senior executives of dailies, weeklies and "class and trade" publications. The organization had been going for almost twenty years, and had functioned harmoniously to solve problems common to the full membership, even though, between meetings, the individuals were often in direct competition with each other. Maclean entered into the activities zestfully, with the result that he was immediately elected to the small executive committee, and in 1891 took over as secretary-treasurer. His chief jobs were to organize the two major annual events: (1) the summer outing for members and wives, generously underwritten by the railways and lake steamship lines with passes, and by the hotels with token rates; and (2) the midwinter workshop session, devoted to discussion of printing costs and technique, the new age of photographic reproduction, and the ugly matter of libel.

That last subject was inevitably assigned to John King, Q.C. (father of a future Prime Minister, W. L. Mackenzie King), who, as a result of always standing ready with free legal advice to the Association, had built up a respectable following, plus a sizable private clientele, among the membership. A banquet in the grand manner wound up the winter conclave; the lengthy toast list called forth replies from such head table guests as government dignitaries and/or the indispensable Professer Goldwin Smith. Occasionally CPA members themselves contributed to the banquet program, as when Joseph E. Atkinson, soon to be the power-house of Toronto's *Star,* sang a patriotic song, "Fair Canada," and was roundly cheered.

The Association had one of the busiest periods in its nineteenth-century history during 1897–98, and no doubt in large measure due to that year's president, John Bayne Maclean. He had just returned from his memorable months in Britain during the Queen's Jubilee festivities; in a spirit of rededication to sovereign and Empire, he decided to take up the challenge of a certain problem which had confronted CPA members for a long time but which had never been fully aired.

In those days the news from Britain reached Canadian newspapers via an American agency, the Associated Press. Although the AP headquarters in London did a thorough, workmanlike job in assembling and filing their cabled news, something happened at the New York receiving end, when the brief messages underwent the necessary padding-out and editing. In short, the reports took on a slant that was obviously American, and not infrequently anti-British—yet these represented the only material available for wire service to Canadian dailies.

Maclean, with the hearty approval of CPA executive and members, went to Ottawa to see Minister of Finance, Fielding, who, as a former newspaperman, was well aware of the situation. The result: a promise of government subsidy if Canadian papers would establish their own direct cable service for news from the United Kingdom. This proved to be a significant early step in a series of moves that would ultimately lead to the formation of Canada's national news-gathering organization, the Canadian Press.

The CPA's president that year proposed certain other innovations as well. He believed it was in the best interests of all members to appoint a full-time Association manager and secretary—but this matter was to stand in abeyance for a few years. Next: Why, he demanded, did English-speaking publishers meet as the CPA while the French-speaking group stayed within the separate Quebec Press Association? "The people of Ontario cannot too soon form a better acquaintance with the people of Quebec," he declared at the 1897 dinner. Within days he proffered an official invitation to the QPA to join the CPA, and from this amalgamation emerged the first completely representative, national group of publishers and editors. To celebrate the occasion he organized a CPA meeting in Ottawa, with the Governor-General as the honored chief speaker and—who else!—Frank Munsey as the lively shot-in-the-arm for those hard-working publishers. After reminiscing pleasantly concerning his own *Munsey's Magazine* and others, he advised his listeners to brace themselves for the merger or disappearance of many newspapers, especially those which spurned business-like methods. At the same time, he deprecated the tendency "to bow down to that little tin god, the advertiser." He said, "The true journalist knows . . . only the reader and the reader's interests."

Undoubtedly John Bayne Maclean enjoyed his CPA presidential year. He approved of such trade or professional associations where members could share the technical knowledge gained in experience, where personal friendships and mutual respect developed, and where, if necessary, the whole body could act as one, either to oppose legislation or taxation inimical to the group or individual members, or to promote the value of the end product and services in the eyes of the public, as in the case of the CPA or, at other points, the advertisers. He drew the line at certain activities, notably price-fixing or lessening of legitimate competition. Cartels and price rings were vigorously opposed in the editorial columns of his business papers, and he stayed consistently with that policy in any trade association he joined.

When the CPA began its slow disintegration as an all-inclusive publishing group, it wasn't cartels, etc., which were to blame, but, instead, a growing sense of competition between the different types of publications. Toronto's leading newspapermen, such as the *Star*'s Atkinson, the *Telegram*'s owner-founder, John Ross Robertson, and its pugnacious editor, "Blackjack" Robinson, didn't hesitate to bring the conflict into the open, whether through certain denigrating references to the trade-paper field in their own columns, or in peremptory terms at CPA meetings. There was, indeed, some basis for their concern, for by 1912 the "trade and class" publications contributed about one-fifth of the CPA membership. Under the pressure—and after Robertson's warning that the dailies could soon be swamped and outvoted by the others—that year's business meeting decided to break CPA into three separate sections: the dailies, the weeklies and farm papers, the magazines and trade press.

But the rearrangement had no time to prove itself, for a year later the whole matter flared into sharp controversy following presentation of a report prepared by a Montreal member, concerning the vital subject of postal rates. He made full use of the opportunity to blast all periodicals. He defined trade papers as "class publications published to exploit various business interests and (they) consist for the most part of advertising." He did not hesitate to add his personal comment: "I do not believe that these publications serve any public interest which warrants their participation in a privilege designed to facilitate the dissemination of news and the diffusion of useful knowledge." Thus, his final proposal was that the basic rate of one-quarter of a cent per pound for second class mail be continued, but that the rate be increased to one cent per pound for trade papers and then gradually increased until it reached four cents per pound.

The Colonel, righteously indignant, took up the challenge and fought back in association meetings. The dailies, he argued, were not really afraid of the trade papers but of the power of the hundreds of small merchants throughout Canada who were served by these publications. Such retailers were struggling to survive and to hold their community markets. The trade papers were teaching them modern methods of merchandising and showing them how to advertise effectively in their local weeklies. The dailies, on the other hand, were interested in building up the big metropolitan department stores and their mail order business.

His arguments, naturally, appealed to the publishers of the country weeklies, and from those vigorous early battles by Maclean at CPA meetings would grow a warm affection and mutual esteem between himself and all the weeklies across Canada. (Later they were to make him an honorary life member of their own organization which year by year received him as a special guest at its sessions.

The arguments within the CPA picked up force and speed; at both 1916 and 1917 meetings resolutions to eject the trade papers were introduced, but the final decision was put off until the next convention. When that took place another violent quarrel erupted—this time because the Colonel had recently presented in his *Printer & Publisher* a summary of the last debate, naming names and quoting from their speeches. Now the immediate concern of the dailies was to condemn him, once and for all, for publishing a "confidential report of a secret meeting." The turbulent tides washed back and forth between the two sections: the dailies on one side, the trade periodicals plus the weekly publishers ranged in defense formation opposite.

The final answer was the obvious one, initially proposed seven years before: partition. In 1919 the CPA split into three associations, viz., dailies, weeklies, periodicals, each of which continues to flourish today. Perhaps as a gesture toward the happier past, it was decided to continue the CPA as a sort of parent body, composed of ten directors from each association, under an elected president and a secretary-treasurer. But the CPA was never to meet again, although some of the separate organizations solemnly continued to elect their zombie directors each year. In 1941 the representatives from the dailies passed a resolution to wind up the CPA, and prevailed on the secretary-treasurer, at that time a trade press publisher, to turn over the cash in the bank, $152.93, to the Red Cross. No member in any of the three groups objected to the latter decision, although the magazines, by then well established as the Periodical Press Association, did not formally recognize the CPA "liquidation" for another twenty years. Indeed, CPA's last charter of incorporation, Chapter 135, 4–5 George V, stands unrepealed on the statute books of Canada.

The bitterness between the two major warring factions continued almost as long as the participants themselves, although in the Colonel's case he could and did relent in certain directions. John Ross Robertson's benefactions to Toronto, especially in the matter of preserving the city's early history, were hailed enthusiastically by Maclean; eventually both gentlemen agreed to forget their CPA tussles and enjoy each other's company.

But the Colonel could never forgive the Montreal member for the postage report and its disparaging comments concerning trade papers. In fact, the Colonel found his own time and place for retaliation. In 1919, when the offender was director-general of National Information at Ottawa, the Colonel contributed a signed editorial to *The Financial Post* in which he firmly stated: "The fact that [the member] has made a gigantic failure of his two big newspaper ventures should be sufficient to condemn him as a man whose opinion on publishing or news is of little value."

The member issued a notice of libel—which merely spurred the Colonel to write a second editorial, duly published. By careful statistics he showed that the member's former employees at his Daily Mail Publishing Company in Montreal received only 35 percent of the wages owing to them when the company went broke; ordinary claimants got nothing. No more was heard of the libel suit.

If, as suggested earlier, the Colonel had been a newspaper proprietor as well as a periodical publisher, the history of the old CPA might have been different; at any rate, there would have been less acrimonious debate written into its minutes. Today's diversification policies in the publishing field are accepted as sound business practice. A large organization such as Southam's can and does maintain active memberships in both the Canadian Daily Newspaper Association and the Periodical Press Association, and nobody cries havoc. John Bayne Maclean might have had the same experience, if he had aggressively sought a chance in the daily field.

# CHAPTER XVI

## THE COLONEL BUILDS

"When we mean to build
We first survey the plot . . ."
*Shakespeare*

---

ONE OF THE Colonel's favorite mottoes was "The reward of work well done is more work." Behind the high, balding dome and the steady blue eyes, he kept the maxim at the ready for any suitable occasion: a staff conference, the hiring of new help, sometimes the parting wish of an old hand who had proved just too persistent about a more tangible reward. Work was the chief end of man, one good job accomplished merely led to more of the same; only by that process could solid success be achieved. This was the gospel as delivered to Presbyterian Scots, and, in his own way, according to his own lights, Maclean accepted it without question as a motivating principle.

Certainly, by the time the first decade of the twentieth century came to a close, he found himself involved in more work, and of the kind directly attributable to the "rewards" of earlier activities. At no point in the entire landscape of the Colonel's life would there be a period so crowded with important decisions affecting the long future.

For some time it had been obvious that the old Front Street building could no longer serve the expanding needs of the business, especially in the matter of new color presses and other mechanical equipment. Thus in 1909 the Colonel bought the present head office site at 481 University Avenue (originally No. 143, until a southern extension of the street necessitated renumbering). After the deal went through he discovered, to his dismay, that building restrictions prohibited any kind of manufacturing within 90 feet of the Avenue's grassy boulevards. Mercifully, there was a solution, in the fact that, as his purchase covered an entire city block, he could locate the structure on the back of the area and escape the ban.

On Monday, May 23, 1910, Maclean Publishing swung wide its doors in the brand-new four-story headquarters that would become the nucleus for future developments. Although lawns, shrubs and iron fencing (even a bowling green for a few years) eventually would add agreeable touches to the University Avenue front, the building had a sturdy no-nonsense appearance. The interior presented vast sweeps of open space uninterrupted by partitions. Advantageous as this was for the mechanical departments, it promptly drew muttered complaints from editorial, advertising and office staffs who could never escape each other's eyes or noise. That condition would be corrected three years later when the Colonel proceeded with Building No. 2: a six-story structure projecting to the Avenue's street line. Here all executive, editorial and business staffs would be housed, separated from the plant, and guaranteed some privacy by inner enclosures, whole or part.

By 1919, a third building rose, on the back of the block to permit expanded facilities; within another nine years the cluster had its most important expansion with the construction of a nine-story building at the Centre-Dundas corner—the first of the units to be carefully planned in modern architectural terms for attractive office accommodation, and for efficient flow within the mechanical departments on three lower floors. This building, remodeled, still stands—now incorporated within the solid block of the $6,000,000 office headquarters opened in 1958.

Whether the Colonel, far back in the early 1900s, anticipated this whole program seems rather unlikely. Yet his shrewdness in acquiring a complete block of land, facing the city's widest, handsomest boulevard, cannot be denied. With each new project he would ask his staff for ideas. "I would like the managers of departments particularly, and members of the staff generally," he wrote before the second addition, "to send me any suggestions for the layout of such a building [previously described as to functions], and for special features that will promote the economy and efficiency of the business. Members of the staff who visit other offices occasionally see features that could be very profitably introduced. Do not hesitate to send even the most trifling suggestions."

Undoubtedly there was a lively response, especially concerning partitioned offices. But somehow no one mentioned a regular supply of hot water for the washroom taps (was the editor of *Plumber and Steamfitter* on vacation?) and, as for an elevator, that was obviously one of the "trifling suggestions." Anyway, it was installed, equipped with a manual wheel and an operator on a stool beside it. For the rest of his business life, the Colonel was to become inured to the necessity of dispatching his secretary to rescue visiting VIP's from the cage that so often stuck between floors. As for the staff people, the elevator and its whims took on the status of a unifying experience, an enemy common to all, without respect of person or position. For well over forty years the ups and downs of the elevator were to be rated among the delightful diversions of every working day. To some of the staff the elevator's existence was an inspiration to daily exercise; as they preferred to run up two or three flights rather than risk temporary imprisonment. Others, after the Dundas Street building opened, gladly walked around the block to the new entrance and its modern elevators, and didn't mind the long doubling-back process through the mechanical department to their offices on the University Avenue side.

As soon as the company's move uptown was completed, the Colonel felt free to turn to his second building project for the year 1910: a fine family mansion. This, too, had become rather an urgent matter, for his Queen's Park residence had been taken over by the Academy of Medicine some months earlier, necessitating transfer of all furnishings to storage and removal of the Macleans themselves to a suite in the King Edward Hotel.

But the Colonel was not unprepared for this important new enterprise. In 1906 he had acquired several acres of picturesque, thickly treed property on the crest of Wells Hill, one of the highest points in the escarpment running for miles east to west between the Don and Humber Rivers and overlooking the constantly expanding city. He had bought direct from a member of the Wells family after which the area was named: Nina (Wells) de Pencier, wife of a clergyman who would later become a popular bishop in British Columbia. The initial purchase price was $20,500, three-quarters of which took the form of a mortgage to vendor. By 1909, after nearby street lines had been laid out, the Colonel added several lots adjoining his first segment and gave his hand to two more mortgages.

Thus he became the owner of some ten acres on the edge and down the slope of Toronto's "hill"—and at a point suddenly, excitingly, in the local news because of the recent start on Casa Loma, Sir Henry Pellatt's fabulous castle, which was a couple of hundred yards to the east. Before the Colonel got going on his own scheme, he had the satisfaction of seeing the castle's towered stables, behind their great iron gates and the all-encompassing wall of red brick and stone piers, brought to a state of handsome completion. Naturally, the castle itself, containing some fifty rooms under its crown of turrets, and eventually costing $2,000,000, took a little longer—four years more, in fact.

Other holdings in the district assured any newcomer of distinguished neighbors and well-tended estates in the English manner, notably those of E. J. Lennox, Casa Loma's architect, who would build his own triple-sized, spreading bungalow on the hilltop lot between Pellatt and Maclean, and, east of the castle, the Nordheimer family, piano manufacturers, whose house and gardens would soon carry an assessment of a quarter-of-a-million, and John Craig Eaton's recent acquisition where Ardwold would eventually rise to command sweeping vistas over terraces, lawns and across the full depth of the city to the far horizon line of lake and sky.

In planning his new home the Colonel did not abandon his native caution. Just the gatehouse, or The Lodge, as he called it, close to the Austin Terrace roadway, would be completed immediately, thus allowing the architect, John M. Lyle, ample time to develop plans for the great house, which would occupy a dramatic site on the hill's crest. By the end of the 1910 summer, while the Macleans were on vacation in Muskoka, the gatehouse was finished, drawings were probably under way for the next phase, and, depending on the weather, it might even be possible to start the major project before freeze-up.

So simple, so direct and practical! Yet "the next phase," as orginally conceived, would never see the light of day; instead, a grave family problem now suddenly claimed the Colonel's full attention, and in finding the solution he quickly scrapped his original building campaign.

At some point during the hot, steamy weather that settled over the Muskoka lakes Anna Maclean contracted the dread disease of polio- myelitis, better known then under its other name, "infantile paralysis." Even after her careful removal to Toronto and the continuous at- tentions of nurses and medical experts, nothing could be done to prevent the onset of the frightening aftermath, muscular atrophy—in her case centered in the lower limbs and feet. For the rest of her life this handsome woman, once so active and graceful, an admired figure on Toronto's avenues as she turned out each morning to ride or drive the fine horses she loved, would be unable to stand or walk without artificial support. Heavy leg-irons and built-up orthopedic boots of thick leather to lace tightly around the ankles, plus a pair of sturdy canes, would be essential equipment through the many years ahead, until she finally accepted the alternative of a wheelchair.

The drastic first stage of the illness dragged on for many months. Even in June 1912, the Colonel was writing to a friend: "I am sorry to say my wife has been seriously ill with infantile paralysis for nearly two years but is steadily recovering." By that time the three Macleans, three servants and a nurse occupied the lodge, which had been carefully extended at either end to become a sizable two-story mansion. In style it was simplified Provincial French—and several of the Colonel's neighbors, such as Lady Eaton, congratulated him on his "miniature château" which in its smooth stucco finish, painted pale gray, and the contrast of light turquoise for the lower shutters and other woodwork, made a sprightly contribution to their hilltop community.

The first plan for a "great house" was completely abandoned. Over the years the expanded lodge would grow, even as the University Avenue headquarters. Extra service quarters would be added, and an elevator for Mrs. Maclean. The most impressive expansion by far was to take place in the early 1930s, under architects Mathers & Haldenby, when a new wing took shape at the southeast corner. A complete master suite, incorporating sitting room as well as dressing room, etc., utilized the second-story space, but the real reason for the addition was to be found in the Louis Quinze drawing room downstairs. Here, in a 25-foot-square space meticulously planned for the purpose, was installed the carved rosewood paneling done in France, circa 1755, and later moved to Carlton House, London, where the Colonel had made the find sometime during the 1920s. Now the panels had come forth from their storage and wrappings; one by one, in careful sequence, so that the airy ribands, the graceful flowers and scrolls, the clusters of little birds, etc., could match up precisely with the intended neighbors, the rosewood strips were set in place from baseboard to ceiling. Everything fitted precisely, even at the tricky points where the original eighteenth century room's three antique mirrors were to be inset—a wide one over the fireplace, two tall, narrow types in the other walls.

By the time an over-all bleaching had brought the wood to its original light nut-brown tone, the Colonel was in his element. All furnishings, he determined, would live up to the magnificent background. An eighteenth-century Aubusson carpet came from the Wildenstein Galleries in

New York. Several antique Louis XV open armchairs and a brave velvet sofa worthy of Madame de Pompadour's salon were arranged in careful groups. The draperies were of French hand-woven silk, cherry red splashed with cream flowers; they were topped with matching valances finished with red tassel fringe.

Various experts, including one from Paris and another from London, were consulted by the Colonel during this careful decorating project. One of the best, as he was glad to admit, was the Sidney White firm in Toronto, which erected and finished the paneling. The famous Elsie de Wolfe made a trip from New York to advise, but it must be recorded that the pair of chairs she supplied looked out of character in the Louis Quinze setting and eventually moved to the Colonel's downtown office.

The Colonel himself had a keen eye for line, color and harmony; his nature was such that he could never accept second-rate compromises. A professor of art who, as a young man, frequently visited the Wells Hill establishment, knew the French room and the Colonel's library next to it, declared recently: "He was a man of excellent taste in clothes and furniture. He could have decorated his house and office better than any of the expensive decorators he hired."

Maclean's publishing commitments had continued to grow both immediately before and after the great hegira from Front Street to University Avenue. These new papers represented in their own way "the reward for work well done," as in one or two cases they were logical outgrowths of successful departments within the established publications. From *Dry Goods,* for instance, emerged *Men's Wear Review,* brimming in size and vigor from the outset. Its No. 2 issue, dated May 1, 1911, splashed the news of motor coats; indeed, "style in outing garments has been affected to a great extent by automobiles." The popularity of the latter would make caps a big seller in the forthcoming season; another fashion influence, of course, was the city man's sudden interest in golf. At the same time, retailers were forewarned to lay in a full stock of straw hat sizes, especially in the important new types featuring "wide brims and pencil curl."

That year, too, the Colonel was carefully watching his new project for the agricultural community. *Farmer's Magazine* came forth first in October 1910 with an issue nicely expressive of Thanksgiving and the fat of the land: 144 pages inside a costly four-color cover depicting a hearty chap in overalls, pursuing a red-necked turkey, and equipped with a platter in one hand and an axe in the other—the latter concealed behind his back. For the next eleven years no effort, no experiment was spared to make the publication interesting and informative for the farmer and his family: crops, methods, equipment in detail . . . all political developments affecting agriculture (frequently discussed in a signed editorial by the Colonel himself) . . . illustrated fiction . . . a well-planned section for women ("Tasty Lunches for Rural Scholars"—an inevitable subject even in 1912) . . . and a lively correspondence department where readers were often invited to send in their answers to supplement the editor's (as in the case of the original poser submitted by a farmer's wife: "Where should the hired man wash his feet?"—which brought an avalanche of suggestions for the next several issues).

Yet by the end of 1921 the Colonel was ready to admit total defeat. The paper had been losing money steadily for many months. The reason? "Because," as he would patiently explain to all and sundry for the rest of his life, "farmers just will not support their own magazine. They are suspicious of advertising in general, and even more so of the normal businesslike messages addressed directly to them by the agricultural suppliers." It was an easy explanation, perhaps too easy. At any rate, *Farmer's* was summarily dropped from the Maclean Publishing group.

Looking back from this far-along distance in time, it is clear that 1911 was to be one of the Colonel's most important periods of decision. That was the year Horace T. Hunter, after demonstrating his capacities in the development of several of the "split-off" publications, was obviously ready for a major executive post—and the Colonel lost no time arranging his promotion to general manager. Edmonds was eased out, not without some bitterness on the receiving end, but Maclean, while regretting the necessity for the action, insisted there was no other way. The Colonel regarded him as an obstacle to progress but probably he shifted Edmonds out because he felt he had found a better man. The late general manager had received a modest salary of $3000 a year. Hunter took over at $5000, with promised annual increases of $1000 over the next five years.

In announcing the promotion the Colonel stated in his message to the staff: "That Mr. Hunter earned and is eminently fitted for the new position I am sure everyone who knows him will agree, and all will join in congratulating him on his appointment. There are many reasons why it is gratifying to me personally. For nearly nine years, in spite of many temptations from outside and much hard, discouraging, irritating work inside, he has never faltered in his loyalty to and belief in the future of the institution."

It would be some time before Hunter achieved shareholding status in the company, even though the Colonel had discussed the subject some years earlier. He wanted to bring a few of his senior men into partnership as shareholders and, characteristically, had sought the advice of J. P. Morgan's partner, George W. Perkins, as well as Schwab and others. By 1907 he thought of selling Hunter and Tyrrell company bonds, accompanied with generous bonuses of common stock; in a note to Hunter he declared "your investment of $10,000 today can be worth at least $100,000 to you within ten or fifteen years." No deal went through, however. In 1911, the Colonel reopened the subject, this time drafting a prospectus, having it printed, and then circulating it among a dozen of his associates. A few were suspicious; Hunter and Tyrrell were prepared to buy, but again nothing happened. It was not until the company was reincorporated in 1919 that Maclean made arrangements to share ownership with his two chief executives and pave the way for later extension of the plan to others in the firm.

The story of the relations of Maclean and Hunter, whose names were ultimately joined in the corporate name of the company, is one of intense loyalty and devotion of two men.

Very quickly after Horace Talmadge Hunter entered the establishment as an advertising salesman in 1903, the Colonel had recognized the young man's capacities and sound judgment. Here were qualities and talents which he may have instinctively felt to be missing in his own makeup; an understanding of corporate processes and an analytical, objective approach to every problem or project. And Hunter was a man of breeding and courtesy, a good companion at all times; he and his wife would bring distinction to any of the occasions associated with senior executive responsibility.

The extent of the founder's regard was to be put to the test early in the new general manager's career. In 1913, when Hunter was still in his early thirties—proud father of two sons at the toddling stage— he developed tuberculosis. A three months' rest in Barbados, underwritten by the Colonel, failed to check the condition. Hunter returned to Toronto, wrote out a letter of resignation, and then, on discovering that his regular salary had continued to be deposited in the bank, he enclosed a check for the full amount.

The Colonel refused both resignation and refund. His note to Hunter urged him to take all the time necessary to regain his health: "The fact is that the foundations have been solidly laid for a great business, and I want you to share in its future prosperity. I will make temporary arrangements, and I want you to remain away until you are quite strong again. I do not believe you ought to do any work for at least a year, and if you will be still better by remaining away two years, by all means take them. My intention is to hold your place here and have you rejoin us under your old or a better arrangement, in more pleasant surroundings and with less onerous work."

Hunter entered a private sanitarium in Muskoka where he was to remain for over two years. During that period—admittedly a difficult one, with its gathering European crisis, sudden outbreak of war, and countless emergencies confronting the Canadian economy—Tyrrell ran the company and did a notable job, while visibly aging in the process. As the third man in the recently rearranged executive line, Herbert Victor Tyrrell was a rock of dependability, knowledgeable in all matters relating to printing and other mechanical processes, single-minded in his service to the Maclean business. The Colonel had accurately sized him up as the logical complement of Hunter—the one given to complete immersion in practical details of publishing, the other as general manager, assuming the responsibilities for over-all policy and administrative matters.

Through an extensive correspondence that never faltered on either side, the Colonel and Hunter were to deepen their friendship during the latter's illness. To "My dear Horace" or just as often to "Dear H.," the Colonel wrote volubly on many subjects—at one point offering a careful recipe for healthful Bulgarian milk, as served in Carlsbad, but it would be necessary to take full precautions "against Muskoka flies and other insects"; again, detailing the recently discovered graft by certain contractors who had been engaged on the new Maclean building fronting University Avenue. Occasionally he would report temporary appointments for the handling of segments of Hunter's duties. Invariably the reply from the sick-bed stated that such stop-gap arrangements were hardly fair to the others, who could not be expected to give their best when the line of promotion was blocked. Several times Hunter asked that his resignation be accepted; always the Colonel refused.

In November 1915 the office welcomed Horace T. Hunter back to his desk. It was obvious to all that not only had his health been restored but his knowledge, mental alertness and judgment had undergone remarkable development. Small wonder—for this young man's natural aptitude for study and critical reading had taken him through what amounted to a post-graduate course in history, biography, travel and economics during the sanitarium period. He had also spent time and thought in arriving at a philosophy of life which would be revealed in an immaculately ordered mind, undeviating respect for fundamental disciplines, pursuit of any worthy goal by full effort, and, always, in a gentleness of manner and voice.

Within a few weeks of his return Hunter was named vice-president of the company and Tyrrell moved up to general manager. In 1933 Hunter succeeded Maclean as president and seventeen years later it would be his turn to become chairman of the board.

To many of his employees Horace T. Hunter appeared hard and rigid. To the few who worked with him closely and knew him well— including the author of this book—he was not hard, but firm. He established high standards of personal conduct and corporate philosophy and expected others to recognize and share them. He demanded systematic organization, both by a man of his work and by the company of its business. He handed over authority to his junior executives, conceiving his own job to be the drafting of basic policies and the larger plans; other men, supervised yet never interfered with, would carry them out. The senior executive, he believed, should avoid retaining too much responsibility because "the other man will hold you partly to blame if there should be any failure. A man working under an overzealous supervisor is relieved of all responsibility."

This was Hunter's own dictum, carefully arrived at, and not just an echo from the Maclean catechism. During the Colonel's active days scores of good men came into the company and left—many to establish successful firms, to become company presidents and the like; sometimes they resigned because of the Colonel's low salary scale, but also, and perhaps just as significantly, because of the constant, disheartening and often picayune criticism to which they were subjected. The Colonel was as cautious with praise as with money. One result of his attitude was that, while the good men left for more promising fields, the second-raters stayed on, too timid to venture forth. His staff became a mixed bag of brilliant young college men with constantly changing names and faces, and a steady dead-weight of defeated older types.

With the rise of Horace T. Hunter to a place of authority, the situation as to the staff improved rapidly. He raised the standards of hiring, selected the men he regarded as important for the company's future, and paid them salaries that kept them happily, productively on the job.

Did the Colonel know what was happening? Of course; yet no word of question or disagreement can be found among the thousands upon thousands of his business memoranda to Hunter. The confidence of the older man in the younger was total. With good reason too, for together—Maclean with his drive, his Highland flair for derring-do, and Hunter with his mastery of organization and a calm and often impersonal approach to all problems—they made a strong team.

# CHAPTER XVII

# *A BRILLIANT NEW EDITOR*

"In our periodical press we have our closest
approximation to a national literature."
*The Massey Report*

In MARCH 1911, an important landmark in publishing was set firmly
in place when the first issue of *Maclean's Magazine* made its appearance under that title. Such rechristening of *Busy Man's*—as explained in a full-page announcement—would remove any lingering
impression that this was solely a "businessman's" journal, and at the
same time it would better identify the more general nature of the
publication and its breadth of coverage. No further reasons were
offered, and indeed the public needed none during that ebullient
heyday of publishers' namesakes on the newsstands. Now, alongside
the piles of *McClure's, Munsey's, Collier's Weekly* and *Scribner's*
literary monthly, the good solid name of Canada's *Maclean's* would
have its appointed place. The Colonel must have been pleased, even
though there was little time to savor the situation. For at this point
the owner-publisher found himself deeply involved in the day-to-day
problems of the magazine; in short, he was acting as editor.

Nobody could say he came to the job without experience. For almost
six years he had constantly inspired, prodded and harassed the writers
and staff to produce the type of publication he dreamed of. Personality
sketches were of leading importance, and especially when they dealt
with Canadians destined to play a significant role in Canada's future.
As early as April 1908, there appeared a round dozen of such, featuring
among others, Robert W. Service, poet of the Yukon; Adam Beck,
founder of Ontario's hydroelectric power system; W. L. Mackenzie
King, Deputy Minister of Labor in Ottawa, and Dr. A. S. Vogt, conductor of the Mendelssohn Choir. Later issues presented lively profiles

of CPR's Shaughnessy; William Macdonald, the eccentric tobacco king and philanthropist; Lomer Gouin, Premier of Quebec.

Entertainment had always been an important part of the monthly fare; now the Colonel demanded that there be some special Canadian creations on the menu. So the first home-grown fiction came forth in 1908—a gay piece about doings in the Rock Bottom Insurance Company, by Archie P. McKishnie, who would be a popular contributor over many years. Bylines from Canadian experts on various subjects began to appear, notably that of Professor James Mavor, University of Toronto, and an acknowledged authority on everything Russian, including Tolstoy.

Such venturings, of course, cost money. By 1909 the Colonel agreed to allow young Craick, then his chief editorial assistant on the magazine, $75 per month to pay for assigned articles from outside; that meant a good writer could collect as much as $10 for a full-length contribution. But it also meant that the bulk of the Canadian features continued to be written in the office by two or three hard-pressed staff men, the best producer being George Van Blaricom, using several *noms de plume* as well as his own name.

The Colonel spawned the ideas and in quantity, but he was seldom satisfied with the results in print. After each issue appeared he called a conference and gave forth with opinions; this was invariably followed up with a flood of memos reiterating his complaints, sometimes amplifying them, and ending with a warning against all such practices in future, especially in the handling of those excellent new subjects he had just suggested. Small wonder that the men invented their own grim little joke. "We're certainly going to enjoy our vacation, as soon as the Colonel leaves for Palm Beach," they would say.

Maclean himself seemed totally unaware of their reaction. It never occurred to him that some people reacted unhappily to blunt criticism; that perhaps there was a more tactful way of achieving improvement. There were several on his staff who could not understand how, within an hour of deflating every ego present, he could revert smoothly to the urbane gentleman-about-town and invite the group to lunch with him at the St. Charles or McConkey's Restaurant, both of which were considerably beyond a regular staffer's budget.

Craick, a quiet, dispassionate person, not easily ruffled, suffered keenly under the Colonel's nagging. He worked off his silent anger by nighttime entries in his diary. "A *Busy Man's* conference . . . more exasperating than usual." "Severe criticism from the Colonel which he said he hoped I would consider not serious, merely friendly." And then: "I drink to the day when I can shake the dust of his establishment off my feet."

It was the Colonel who picked the day. Just after the October 1910 issue had been distributed, he appeared beside the young man's desk and, pointing to a spread in the open book, announced in clear, measured tones: "Craick, this is damnable." The resignation took place then and there. Yet, curiously enough, Craick continued to write for various Maclean publications, chiefly the *Financial Post,* until he accepted a full-time position in 1919 as editor of the Canadian Manufacturers Association's *Industrial Canada.*

By the time the new name, *Maclean's Magazine,* blazoned forth, the Colonel had virtually taken over the editorship. Van Blaricom was no longer around, having left the company shortly before Craick; and now the only experienced man from the original group was the Colonel himself.

It was he who commissioned the articles—and tried hard, sometimes quite successfully, to meet his own standards. Canadian features in an early 1911 issue ranged over such subjects as political campaign funds, contemporary architecture, foreign spies, expanding industries; there were also several profiles of newly knighted Canadians and five pieces by local poets. Robert W. Service's *The Trail of '98* was being serialized. From an unidentified source an O. Henry story was picked up. As usual, about one-third of the issue consisted of a review-of-reviews section, with selected, condensed material reprinted from various publications near or far.

And it was the Colonel who also took on the hard, grinding job of editing the material for the printers, deciding on length, necessary rewriting, etc. At one point this caused a small crisis with Sir William Van Horne, the railroad builder. During a pleasant chat in Montreal Van Horne had told Maclean an anecdote concerning Charles Tupper, one of the Fathers of Confederation and still alive. Here was real Canadiana, just the stuff for the magazine! Maclean asked Van Horne to write the story—and within a week or two the following single-paragraphed article arrived at the Toronto office:

About 20 years ago when Sir Charles Tupper was High Commissioner for Canada in London, and when Canadian cattle were yet freely admitted to Great Britain, a consignment of Canadian cattle was condemned at Liverpool on the ground that some of the animals were affected with pleuro-pneumonia and the owner appealed to the High Commissioner by wire. Sir Charles immediately started out and procured at the public libraries and elsewhere the best and latest works on pleuro-pneumonia—a dozen or more of them—and drove quickly to Euston Station to catch the first train for Liverpool. In the cab and on the train he studied his case furiously. His long experience as a physician enabled him to master it in the few hours available and by the time he reached Liverpool he had perhaps a more sharply defined and more up-to-date knowledge of pleuro-pneumonia than any living man, for knowledge acquired with an immediate object in view and with intense interest is far more vivid and definite than that acquired in the usual way. At Liverpool he drove immediately to the cattle yards, asked to be shown the condemned cattle, demanded the attendance of the several inspectors who had condemned them and put these inspectors through a sharp examination on the reasons for their action, requiring them to point out the particular animals affected and to state what would be found, on dissection, to be the condition of the heart, the lungs and other organs, if the case were really pleuro-pneumonia. He pinned each inspector down to the most exact particulars, ordered the animal which was indicated as having the most pronounced symptoms to be slaughtered, called for surgical instruments, took off his coat, rolled up his sleeves and proceeded to open up the carcass. Removing sections of the lungs he presented these bloody fragments under the noses of the half dozen inspectors in succession, demanding to know if they saw in them the conditions they had described. Then he proceeded in like manner with the heart, the kidneys and the other organs until the inspectors were obliged to admit that they had made a mistake. Then he made them indicate another animal, and yet another, with like results, and in less than an hour the condemnation was raised and Sir Charles left the cattle yards in triumph, covered with blood and glory; and after that, there were no more condemnations of Canadian cattle lest 'that old Devil from London' should come down again.

It was a little too terse for Maclean's taste, and any magazine reader will appreciate that the great Van Horne hardly rated as a writer. The Colonel turned the manuscript over to a staff man for rewrite. A few imaginative touches and added bits of conversation helped to make it more palatable.

Van Horne bridled when he saw the finished piece in print and under his byline. Immediately he wrote to the Colonel, objecting to the "extension of my remarks," and saying, "It may be, and no doubt is, a great deal better from a literary point of view than what I wrote, but it isn't mine."

The Colonel replied in soothing vein, stating that while condensation was an established policy in all his trade, technical, financial and similar papers "in the case of the magazines, which are read at leisure, we have found from long experience that the average reader likes the small talk, and it was with small talk your article was padded."

By this time Van Horne's temper had subsided and he was able to write back with a twinkle in his eye: "I am not a little amused at the idea that a magazine article must be padded out to certain proportions. I know that this is the prevailing idea with magazines, but isn't that the reason why they are nearly all so dishwatery?"

No answer to that has come forth from the Colonel's files. Perhaps by then he was wholly absorbed in scouring the market for new fiction, for this, too, had become one of his responsibilities for *Maclean's*. When suitable reprint stories were unavailable, it was necessary to buy first rights material. Here his native talent for haggling could have significant results, as in the deal with a certain Englishwoman, a popular writer of the day, who, after stressing that her fixed price stood at £3 to £4 per thousand words, graciously accepted his final bid of £2. Result: a 3500-work piece of enthralling romance for just £7 outlay!

In spite of these occasional triumphs, the magazine was in a period of drift. True, the Colonel had efficient help standing by; his stable of staff writers on the trade papers and *The Financial Post* had grown along with the publications; from those groups he could summon first-class reporters for a *Maclean's* assignment or a "desk man" to handle layout and copy processing. And there was no immediate worry about the business health of the magazine. The May 1913 number, for instance, had a total circulation of over 25,000 and contained within its covers 272 pages, of which 150 were solid with advertising.

But something was missing: a great editor.

As it happened, the man who would eventually earn that title beyond all chance of contradiction, was already an employee of the Maclean Publishing Company. His name: Thomas Bertram Costain.

He had been born in Brantford, Ontario, on May 8, 1885, and from the time he could read a line of printed words he had devoured books of history and biography. Great deeds of the past inspired him to try his own hand at creating heroes and heroines; before his seventeenth birthday he had written four novels, sent them off to publishers and promptly received them back. Nonetheless he did manage to get into print locally when the Brantford *Expositor* presented a mystery story written in a few hours stolen from his high school homework. He received no pay for it but his initiative got him a job as reporter on the paper at $5 a week. In his early twenties he had moved to the Guelph *Mercury* where he became editor at a salary of $28. In 1912 he happened on an advertisement concerning an opening on a Toronto business paper; his letter to the box number resulted in an interview with John Bayne Maclean. They liked each other: the middle-aged publisher ready with a docket of shrewd questions, the strikingly handsome young newspaperman just as eager and forthright with his answers. "You will be hearing from us," the Colonel said.

Within a few weeks Horace Hunter brought him to Toronto to become assistant editor of the hardware paper and the plumbing journal. This was merely the successful first step, for, almost before he had mastered the building's geography, he found himself promoted to editor. Before another year had passed, he was given the same post on the dry goods and men's wear papers and provided with an assistant for each.

He had little time for writing. The work of supervising four papers was heavy, especially in view of the constant staff changes. Yet Costain enjoyed the expanding responsibilities, and, to the delight of the observers in the "front office," it was obvious that he possessed organizing capacity and a gift for training young recruits. Inevitably his duties broadened to make him, in effect, the general managing editor of the entire trade paper group.

Somewhere along the line of this steady forward march, Costain was asked to lend a hand with *Maclean's,* and somehow, in spite of existing commitments, he contrived a place in his schedule for the Colonel's nearest and dearest. But soon it became apparent that an occasional morning or weekend was quite inadequate for full study of the problems and opportunities involved in a national magazine; even the most brilliant and all-encompassing policy would be valueless without firm, enlightened application day by day. Costain's early moves had demonstrated how new shape and substance could be achieved; he must be allowed to continue. Thus it came to pass that over the next year or so the business papers received less of his time, and *Maclean's* claimed more. By October 1914, when the line "T. B. Costain, Editor" first appeared on the magazine's masthead, this young man, not quite thirty, was already a veteran of countless decisions, plans and accomplishments on behalf of *Maclean's*.

(The lag in the actual appointment revealed another of the Colonel's quirks. Job titles meant little, even concerning himself. Over the years he had several times changed his own designation on new batches of Company letterhead: sometimes he was described as "publisher," again "general manager," once or twice "managing editor." Around 1912, it seems, he finally made up his mind that he would stay with the title of "president.")

Now, with the announced authority of "editor," Thomas B. Costain could and did move rapidly ahead, causing things to happen far and near. A recent extension of *Maclean's* page size had permitted important improvements in general makeup; large illustrations and special heading effects added eye-appeal to the main features; advertising was released from its former bunching together at the back and brought out into the open among the columns of editorial turnover. Thus a reader was encouraged to continue his perusal right through to the back cover—and that meant better impact for the advertisements.

The Colonel was pleased. He felt he had been wise to disregard the advice of friend Munsey. Several times the calculating, dollar-conscious Frank had warned against continuing *Maclean's*. "Drop it," he'd say. "You're never going to get anywhere with that sort of publication."

But the Colonel remained confident. Canada, he believed, needed a magazine that would be thoroughly Canadian. He expressed his philosophy in a memo to Costain: "The two features that should distinguish *Maclean's* from others is the Canadianism of the original matter and the educational and informing character of the review section. Nearly all letters received from readers show the Canadianism of *Maclean's Magazine* appeals to them. This is the strongest feature in the magazine. Make it the guiding principle of your work. Keep it before you every minute, when you are reading or editing copy, when you are writing index headings or putting captions under pictures."

And, on that final point, he had a specific criticism concerning the recent issue: "Mary Pickford is a Canadian, born a few doors from

our office. Yet you make no reference to this under her picture."
The rebuke was not forgotten, for, in December 1917, a full page of
movie stills of "the best-known Canadian" proudly stressed the fact
that she had been "born on University Ave., Toronto, just a few blocks
above the home of *Maclean's Magazine.*"

Canadianism had Costain's enthusiastic approval too. It was a theme
to be pursued in a variety of ways: subjects, ideas, exposés when
necessary—and, always, the top Canadian talent to discuss or illustrate them. *Maclean's* art roster was to become a goal for a rising new
generation of painters and sketchers. C. W. Jefferys and several of the
original members of Canada's "Group of Seven" contributed regularly.
J. W. Bengough's cartoons added their inimitable comment to political
pages. The editor wondered why Arthur Heming's paintings and
stories of Canada's northland were published in *Harper's* and *Century*
but never in a Canadian magazine. A visit to the artist disclosed the
happy fact that he was only waiting for an invitation; so, in the
April 1916 issue his dramatic feature on whaling off the British
Columbia coast inaugurated what was to be a long association with
*Maclean's,* involving covers and various self-illustrated article series—
the latter eventually to be published in book form.

Well-plotted fiction with believable characters was dear to Costain's
heart (he somehow found time to contribute several short stories of his
own in 1913–14), and he took special pride in presenting such upcoming authors as Arthur Stringer and Alan Sullivan, perhaps forgotten today but writers of mark in their time. One of the leading
novelists of the period, Canada's Sir Gilbert Parker, then living in
England, appeared frequently. Arthur Beverley Baxter, later to be a
*Maclean's* fixture with his reports from the British capital, had the
thrill of first seeing himself in print, at the age of twenty-three, with
some amusing short stories.

It is known that Baxter's future boss, Lord Beaverbrook, made
the grade with several contributions in his plain Max Aitken days.
The story goes thus: at Toronto's Arts & Letters Club the editor
ran into Max, who just happened to have a manuscript in his pocket.
"Look at this, Tom," he said. "Would you like to publish it?" The
answer next day was in the affirmative, and so began another lively
editor-writer relationship. A close search through the bound files of
*Maclean's Magazine* for that period reveals no Max Aitken byline;
however, it could be that certain outspoken current-events dissertations,

presented anonymously with an introductory note assuring readers of the brilliance and reliability of the writer, were his handiwork.

Costain's zealous pursuit of Canadianism did not mean that he was limited to the home-grown product. He kept in touch with international sources for the best in English-language fiction, comment and unusual personal experiences—with important results under names as famous as H. G. Wells and Jack London. Yet one of *Maclean's* greatest successes watched avidly by editors abroad, was to blossom forth on native soil.

It happened that in 1915 the editor dropped a note to Stephen Leacock, professor of economics at McGill University, suggesting possible contributions. A few weeks later that shaggy-haired, smiling gentleman called at the office and asked for Costain. It was lunch time and the editor was out. On his return he found a rumpled sheaf of papers scattered over his desk. The handwriting could hardly be deciphered, but manfully he struggled with it to the last page, and realized (in his own words later) that here in his hand he held an "elegant piece of Leacock."

So, in the September 1915 *Maclean's,* three full pages were devoted to the professor's chosen theme, "The Lot of the Schoolmaster" as currently existing in Canada's secondary schools. A serious subject, yes, but with the unique Leacockian wit—and the cartoons this had inspired—brought to a state of full, foaming sparkle for even the most apathetic reader. At one point he started a paragraph thus: "Now in my opinion (which is a very valuable one, so valuable that I am being well paid by this magazine merely to state it)"—a matter of satisfaction to the editor, who had just persuaded the Colonel to permit an increase in *Maclean's* rates. Writers of established caliber should get $100 per article, Costain insisted, and after considerable reluctance the Colonel consented.

Leacock was worth any investment. Following that début he would become a fixed habit with *Maclean's* and its readers for the rest of his life. Generally the subjects were of his own choosing, as when he came forth now and then with a freshly contrived incident from the old sunshine days in "Mariposa," actually Orillia, Ontario, the town which he had known as a boy and to which he returned in later years as a summer resident. Many of the magazine pieces were to be preserved in his numerous collections brought out in book form over the years.

Costain was the complete antithesis of the general concept of writer-editor. He stayed unruffled through any crisis; never tore his hair (which was thick and beautiful, whether in the golden-brown stage or its snow-white climax); never shouted; was more of a listener than a talker. For virtually all his life he had just one favorite beverage: tea. He had been a lacrosse fan in youth; later, when he took up bridge, cribbage and chess he got maximum enjoyment only when the stakes were stiff.

He budgeted his time as carefully as his editorial expenses. He calmly accepted, and promptly answered, the Colonel's endless flow of memos. At least one such gave a special glow to his smooth pink cheeks—following publication of a poem in a decorative layout. The Colonel congratulated him; those verses, unlike others in the past, "were understandable, so human." Costain took the news home to the author, who happened to be the wife he adored, and who had signed her maiden name, Ida Spragge, to the simple little stanzas extolling mother love.

The editor's demonstrated capacity for systematizing operations could be useful with the trade and technical group, the Colonel thought. Cheerfully Costain set to work, studying each phase of every paper's activity, and finally coming forward with a plan for complete reorganization involving merging of staffs and "cross-pollination" of writing, with resultant salary savings and higher efficiency. The confidential report ran to more than 8000 words—proof, even then, that he could pour forth uninhibitedly. Some of his suggestions were acted upon, although the all-out consolidation was deemed hardly feasible for publications which might occasionally have quite opposing points of view on trade or public matters.

Indeed, Costain's agile mind, careful judgment and capacity to deliver were kept continuously employed. During the 1914–18 war they were to be recognized by the Colonel as among the most valuable assets the Maclean Publishing Company possessed. Together the president and his editor would undergo severe testing times, suspected, berated, officially reprimanded; yet the loyalty of each man to the other, and their joint acceptance of total wartime reponsibility to the people of Canada through the medium of a national magazine stayed absolutely firm.

And that is a story in itself . . .

CHAPTER XVIII

# THE WAR THAT JUMPED THE GUN

"In the jungle book of our aristocracy
Sam Hughes should have been Lord Valcartier."
*"The Masques of Ottawa"* by *"Domino"*

---

"SO HE'S OFF on another jaunt," said the stenographer to the messenger boy when they met on the elevator. "See—it says here: 'Colonel Maclean left on Thursday for a short trip abroad' " and she held up her new copy of *Maclean's Weekly,* the pocket-sized house organ distributed every Saturday morning to company employees. "Some people have all the luck!"

That opinion would undergo drastic change very shortly, for the date was July 18, 1914, less than three weeks before Europe would be in the turmoil of a total war.

The Colonel, like many other observers of the international stage where the German Kaiser strutted in the role of braggart villain, had for some time believed that war was inevitable; however, his visit to the Continent the year previous had strengthened the conviction that peace would continue at least until 1915, even 1916. To be sure, certain friends back home, Colonel George Taylor Denison among them, had recently urged him to forego the Carlsbad "cure" this year; but their concern, though kindly meant, was not justified according to his own inside sources of information, which included "a distinguished French financier and public man," whom he frequently quoted but never named. Neither the Parisian, nor Maclean, nor millions of others could foresee the inexorable march of events following the assassination of Archduke Ferdinand, heir to the Austrian throne, in the town of Sarajevo across the Serbian border at the end of June.

The Colonel with his wife and Hector, now eleven, duly arrived in Berlin on July 26, just three days after Austria had sent its belligerent ultimatum to Serbia. The streets were jammed with people—unusual for a Sunday morning—and on the Unter den Linden there was constant movement back and forth in front of the various newspaper offices and the displays of late bulletins. Eventually the cab got the trio through to their hotel, the Adlon of course, Berlin's best, situated at the corner of the Linden and the Pariser Platz, virtually within shouting distance of the British, French and Russian embassies, and thus the favorite gathering-place of the international community. Undoubtedly the Macleans relaxed and made themselves comfortable in one of the spacious suites with window balconies, although the view of the swarming throngs on the pavement below and the sound of cheering and frequent bursts of "Deutschland Uber Alles" may have caused the Colonel some uneasiness.

Nevertheless when he called at the British embassy next morning to report his group's arrival (Canada's own foreign services of the kind were still years away), any little fears were dispersed; indeed, the diplomats were glad to remind their annual visitor from Toronto that the Kaiser himself was still on a yachting vacation off the Norwegian coast. "The present situation will be settled in Vienna," they declared. "It is merely an incident." A second call, this time on his friend, the managing director of the Hamburg-American steamship line, produced the same sort of reassurance. Those huge headlines proclaiming Austria's rejection of Serbia's reply were, it seemed obvious, just another case of sensational journalism. The alarming behavior of prices on the Berlin bourse the previous Saturday could be put down to merely superficial reaction.

So the Colonel determined to proceed with his plans. The family's trunks were promptly checked through to Carlsbad. After a couple of days' rest at the Adlon the party would follow—to that favorite holiday spot situated some two hundred miles to the south, in old Franz Josef's Austro-Hungarian empire. Munsey was already there, waiting to greet them; perhaps Jimmy Speyer, the other regular, had arrived by now.

True enough: Speyer had reached Carlsbad but stayed hardly long enough to taste the waters. Over the weekend he had hurried to Berlin to consult with German financial authorities concerning the monetary situation; on Monday afternoon—just where or how is not clear—he and the Colonel met by chance, and Jimmy, the astute New Yorker and expert assessor of futures, had nothing but somber advice for his friend. "You must take your family away at once," he said. "Leave the continent. Things are bad."

But how bad? The Colonel probably wrestled with that question for the next few hours, after Speyer had said his hurried goodbye before catching a train for Frankfurt to meet his wife. Certainly the sudden return of the Kaiser boded no good; the newspapers announced he would spend the evening "in conference" at his palace in Potsdam. The stock exchange had just closed in a state of near-collapse, and one trader's suicide was reported. (Others would follow in the next twenty-four hours.) Yet as the Colonel walked back to the hotel through the side streets, he found the atmosphere normal, even pleasant: the sun shining, the shops open and doing business, and occasionally from a bar's doorway he could hear a three-piece band giving forth with the American ragtime sensation which Berliners loved: "He had to get under . . . get out and get under . . . to fix his auto-mo-bile!"

The telephone was ringing when the Colonel rejoined wife and son in the suite, and its message, Speyer-inspired, banished all ifs and buts effectively. The caller, head of the Deutsche Bank, exhorted "Herr Colonel" to leave the country and return home: in the interests of the family, the grave voice went on, it would be wise to take action without delay.

The luggage, of course, was beyond recall, already heading south; anyway, the important project was to conduct his little group to safety. England would be the immediate destination—and on Tuesday, July 28, the day Austria declared war on Serbia, the Colonel addressed himself to the business of obtaining transportation to a Channel port. Just how, or through whose good offices, this matter was arranged cannot be established now; perhaps the Adlon services or the Hamburg steamship executive came into the act. Or it is entirely possible that the Colonel's tickets and reservations were promptly supplied in the regular way, for, as all later histories of the period show, the German metropolis continued with daily business, there was no panic in the pre-war week and the Kaiser had still not spoken. Britishers on European holiday were inclined to dismiss the crisis as just another Balkan wrangle. In that interpretation they were joined by many others at home, including certain members of the Cabinet, but always excepting the First Lord of the Admiralty, Winston Churchill. At the moment Maclean made his decision to change course, the man who had been a source of irritation on that occasion in Montreal fourteen years earlier was proving a staunch bulwark. He had suddenly ordered the British fleet, just finished with a special manoeuvres program and Royal review, to stay at the ready. The seas around Britain would be safe.

On Wednesday, July 29, Frank Munsey was heard from—and the

Colonel, always the journalist, was apparently glad to share his news with one of the foreign correspondents on the local scene. Toronto's *Globe* next morning featured an anonymous cabled dispatch from Berlin under the heading, "The Last Message from Carlsbad," which opened this way: "Americans who are marooned at Carlsbad, which is now cut off from the rest of Europe, both by telegraph, telephone and railway, are warning friends and relatives . . . not to come under any circumstances. One of the last wires to get through from the famous Bohemian spa was early this morning by Frank A. Munsey of New York to a brother publisher, Lieut.-Col. J. B. McLean (sic) of Toronto, who is at the Adlon. Mr. Munsey said: 'Leaving here next week. Don't come. Weather bad. Only few people are left.'" Between those close friends there would be complete understanding about the "weather."

On Thursday, July 30, the headlines announced that both Austria and Russia had ordered general mobilization—and the three Macleans were speeding by express to Ostend, the Belgian resort facing the North Sea. It was the last train on the line to adhere to regular schedule; within another day or so passengers lucky enough to reach the Belgian frontier were compelled to dismount and walk—in some cases as much as twenty-five miles—in order to continue the journey away from war.

By Friday, July 31, even the optimists had lost hope. German troops were massing near the Belgian border; Berlin sent an ultimatum to Russia to demobilize within the next twelve hours; at 6 P.M. the Kaiser, in his favorite uniform and spiked helmet, greeted the citizens of the capital from the Royal Castle balcony and, as soon as the cheers subsided, made his first statement to the nation he had relentlessly disciplined for this moment. "A fateful hour has fallen upon Germany," he began . . . "The sword has been forced into our hand . . ."

On Saturday, his commander-in-chief, General Helmuth von Moltke, ordered general mobilization—and Maclean, after waiting overnight in Ostend, hoping for the arrival of the trunks in answer to his urgent telegram, decided against further delay and shepherded his lame wife and little boy onto the sea-ferry leaving for Dover. The crossing was uneventful, except for the comforting presence nearby of several British destroyers.

By Sunday, August 2, German troops occupied Luxembourg, ensuring handy access to France and Belgium—and the Macleans were in London. It was just a week since they had arrived in Berlin, and,

although August 3 was England's popular Bank Holiday, everybody
had stayed in town and the crowds around Whitehall, in front of the
bulletin boards along Fleet Street, or listening to curbside orators here
and there, were depressingly reminiscent of that first view of Unter
den Linden. Nothing, it seemed, could hold back the tide now.

And on Tuesday, August 4, when the Kaiser and his special circle
of *Generalstab* supermen disdained to reply to the British ultimatum
to withdraw their troops from Belgium and respect that nation's
sovereign rights and long-standing neutrality, Britain and Germany
were at war.

Although the Colonel stayed calm through those weeks, the atmosphere at University Avenue headquarters several thousands of
miles away was anything but tranquil. Horace Hunter had been im-
mobilized for months in a Muskoka sanitarium. Victor Tyrrell was in
sole charge, doggedly determined to carry on for the company and the
Colonel. To the latter in Berlin he had cabled reassuringly: STRICT
RETRENCHMENT ORDERS. REDUCING STAFF. EXCHANGES TORONTO-
MONTREAL CLOSED. HAS STEADYING INFLUENCE. COMPLETE YOUR
HOLIDAY.

The message never reached the Colonel. But in London there were
other bulletins awaiting him from Tyrrell, who had suggestions for
wartime economies, plus requests for rulings on certain projects,
especially concerning the new administration-editorial building. At least
one of the Colonel's cabled replies may have puzzled the censors. It
read: STAIN GROUND FLOOR, ECONOMIZE EVERYWHERE. That the instructions were accepted *in toto* is obvious from an announcement,
signed by Tyrrell, in the *Weekly* later that summer, warning the staff
that furniture in the main office must never be shoved across the
floor but moved only by lifting, as "a great deal of money was spent
in laying an attractive floor and in finishing same."

The Macleans turned down one or two ship bookings, preferring to
wait for the *Olympic,* due to sail August 28. Suddenly the liner was
commandeered, and as a result their return to Canada was delayed
until mid-September. In the meantime the Colonel and his wife made
the rounds of London's smartest shops for new wardrobes to replace
the clothes in the missing baggage; as currency was scarce and the
exchange rate was $6.00 Canadian, for each pound note, all pur-
chases, as well as the hotel bills, were charged, with payment to be
made from Toronto later, at a more favorable rate.

As a change from London, he decided to move the family to Harrogate, where they spent three weeks. "I am drinking the waters and taking the baths," he wrote to Tyrrell. "I have never tasted viler stuff than these sulphur waters; I have to take four big glasses a day." The place itself couldn't compare with Carlsbad "where, for 600 years, the world's leaders have been taking their bodies in for annual overhauling." Obviously, the Colonel was in a state of depression. He had no patience with the optimistic opinions of certain voluble public men concerning "a short war" and its assured outcome. "I would not be surprised to see the war last five or six years," he wrote. "There are still some who think it will be over in three months. I do not think we can expect a final settlement for years. Then we may have to fight Russia."

And it may have been at this point in his melancholy musings that John Bayne Maclean experienced one of his great flashes of inspiration. Canada should get into production of war equipment and shells—*immediately*. He sat down and carefully drafted two cables. The message addressed to Tyrrell directed that *Canadian Machinery* arrange at once for a continuous series of technical step-by-step articles on shell manufacture. No sooner ordered than started, and with such important results that *Machinery* quickly became the "how-to" guide for Canada's vigorous new munitions industry. One of the April 1915 issues devoted 45 of its 190 pages to "Shells, Shells, then more Shells" (the quote from Sir John French, Commander-in-Chief of the British Expeditionary Forces in France), and in a series of infinitesimally detailed and fully illustrated articles showed how existing plants, such as locomotive engineering or machine tool shops, could be efficiently switched to shell manufacture.

For the next two or three years, *Canadian Machinery*'s series would be in demand in all the Allied countries—full translations being made, for example, to circulate to heavy industry in Russia and Japan. When Australia, about to start on shell production, was suddenly confronted with a paucity of basic technical material, an urgent request to *Machinery* resulted in distribution of the articles in booklet form by that government; later, when Australia undertook to supervise shell production in India, the same Canadian step-by-step "recipes" were circulated to the wartime plants there. And still tucked away in the Colonel's files today is a note of thanks from the Australian government, stating that the information contained in *Machinery*'s articles had saved months of precious time in the process of tooling up for war.

The Colonel's second cable from England on that 1914 summer day of decision went to his old friend, Honorable Sam Hughes, dynamic Minister of Militia in the Conservative government headed by Sir Robert Borden, (cousin of Frederick B., the Liberal). A long war was certain, the sender declared, and Canada should immediately take up the production of shells, guns, uniforms and other vital equipment.

Hughes probably did not need such prodding, but he appreciated the message and its obvious support of what he was trying to accomplish in his Department. Canada's first contingent had been mobilized and almost 30,000 men were assembling under canvas on the Valcartier Plain, near Quebec. Not everyone approved: the troops complained of inadequate sanitation and the generals grumbled that discipline and training were bound to suffer during such a high-speed program. So far as armament production was concerned, the iron and steel industry, after agreeing to accept orders from a swiftly organized shell committee, showed a tendency to criticize the latter for delays and incompetence.

Mistakes a-plenty were made, yet by October, Canada's first contingent was overseas and Hughes had been promoted to major general— a preliminary to his elevation to knighthood the following year when he received the first KCB since the 1867 award to the one and only John A. Macdonald.

Such honors had the full, delighted approval of the Colonel, for never at any moment of Sam Hughes' colorful, controversial career was their lifelong mutual esteem allowed to falter. The two understood each other perfectly; indeed they had much in common, although Sam was the senior by nine years. Both had attended Toronto Normal School, had taught for a time, and enjoyed their long militia service. Both believed wholeheartedly in the destiny of the British Empire, each in his own way anticipating and working for an ever closer union of the Motherland and the "colonies," regardless of the fact that the latter had for decades been emerging into parliamentary independence. And both were steeped in the publishing-editing tradition, Hughes having supplied the thundering voice of the weekly *Warder* in Lindsay, Ontario. As members and officers of the Canadian Press Association, the two had met in the early '90s; from that point forward, and especially after their shared experiences during the Queen's Jubilee celebration in England, they kept in constant touch.

Hughes entered Parliament in 1892, a Conservative stalwart, and yet as a total individualist ready to do battle within the Tory ranks whenever necessary. Recalling his early years in the House, he once wrote to Maclean: "The party, as you know, had been on the downgrade, was torn by factions and imbecility. We had autocrats and tyrants on the one hand trampling on constitutional methods, and would-be autocrats and tyrants on the other. The public weal and the Tory party seemed to be cast into the background." As a result, he decided "to navigate the troubled waters and not become allied with the wreckage of the contending fleets of Toryism."

He was a man insatiable for action. When the South African War broke out, he applied for an active commission in the Canadian expeditionary group but was turned down. This didn't trouble him too much, for, with the permission of the Prime Minister, Sir Wilfrid Laurier, he boarded the troop ship as a civilian; on arrival in Africa, he presented himself to a British General and got immediate posting as a Transport Officer; later, he moved up to Intelligence, and finally took over command of a mounted brigade that spread havoc among the enemy and at one point rounded up 300 Boer prisoners, plus an immense stock of animals and equipment.

At the end of a year or so, he returned to a tumultuous welcome in Lindsay, where thousands from the countryside roundabout cheered their very own hero, now a Colonel, gallant, daring, and "thrice mentioned in dispatches." Neither for him nor for the populace did it matter that several Canadian newspapers had spoken out ironically, even maliciously, about some of his published letters that showed bumptious criticism of senior officers at the front and at the same time stressed his own superior tactical skills. His frequent reference to his batman as "my man, Turpin," was also a rather jarring note for super-democratic Canadians, even those in the Lindsay area. No one, however, was mean enough to seek corroboration of the whispered rumor that the British Command had *asked* him to go home.

From Maclean's point of view, the newspapers were free to express themselves pro or con—indeed, he scrupulously saved all the clippings about Hughes, whether of praise or ridicule; yellow with age, they were still among the Colonel's papers a half-century later—but he was never to deviate from his total confidence in Sam Hughes. When the Liberal Prime Minister made his famous statement about the crusading

Orangeman and needling political opponent, "He [Hughes] has done more in his day and generation for the upbuilding of the militia in Canada and the Empire, than any other man," Maclean was in full agreement. And when, in 1911, following the defeat of Laurier's Liberals, Borden announced that Hughes would be Minister of Militia and Defense in the new Conservative cabinet, Maclean saw a matchless opportunity to help from the sidelines.

Immediately he began to feed ideas to Ottawa. The officers of the permanent Army (i.e., the full-time or "professional" soldiers, as distinct from the local militia units) should be given accelerated staff training in all branches of operation, preparing them for brigade and divisional commands in the event of war. They should also be urged to co-operate more closely and enthusiastically with the militia. In that way, Canada could create for itself a disciplined force capable of efficient mobilization in an emergency.

Hughes valued the suggestions and lost no time in putting them into effect, along with his own abundant ideas. He built drill halls, always known as "armouries," in scores of communities. He initiated summer camps where high school cadets could receive concentrated military instruction. More controversially (and probably without Maclean's prompting), he decided that messes would be better off without strong drink; so the officers lost their liquor privileges and the sergeants their traditional beer. Yet all the while a new, cohesive military organization was forming up, thanks to the speed of the man in Ottawa abetted by the flood of ideas from the man in Toronto.

Both, in their separate ways, were to enjoy the reward of their collaboration when Canada's first contingent was swiftly mobilized in 1914 and sent overseas. Hughes, in his freehand style, wanted to express his thanks in a positive way. "If you see any place where your services could be utilized, bring the same to my attention," he told the Colonel. But Maclean, unlike numerous "friends" on the Minister's list of suppliers, contractors and go-between opportunists, had no interest in sinecures or recompense, public or private.

It wasn't the first time that Hughes had offered a reward to the Colonel for his friendship and advice. Shortly after taking office, the Minister had asked if there was anything Maclean wanted. "Nothing for me personally," was the answer, but he did have a request. Could a Fenian Raid Medal be awarded to Sir Charles Fitzroy Maclean, Bart., KCB, chief of the clan? As a young soldier, he had come to Canada with his regiment, the 13th Hussars, to fight the Fenians, although, admittedly, the Britishers were a little late as the raiders had been turned back at the U.S. border four months earlier. Hughes could not comply; experts in his Department had refused similar requests in previous years. The Colonel was never to give up, however; he continued to press Ottawa for recognition of the 13th Hussars, and at last, in 1933, his campaign ended happily when medals were issued to Sir Charles, then ninety-nine years of age, and a few others slightly junior.

Hughes' achievements in office were prodigious, but so, unfortunately, were some of his blunders and blatant acts of favoritism. Almost simultaneously with his feat of Valcartier and the first contingent came shocked outcries from the press and public; the scandals in the Militia Department must be stopped! Characteristically, Hughes spoke out brusquely about "the fools who didn't know there was a war on"; just as characteristically, his friend in Toronto decided to come to the Minister's defense, using the printed word as the weapon. *Maclean's Magazine* for January 1915 presented a major feature, "General-The-Honourable-Sam," a profile by Robson Black. The intention was to put the man's life and work in full and thus impressive perspective, yet a careful reading of the article today suggests that the author wrote with tongue in cheek, as when he mentioned Hughes' recent conversation with Kitchener at the War Office, followed by a direct quote from London newspapers, "Kitchener and I were in perfect agreement." Thus the next paragraph by Black: "Do you wonder, now, that Kitchener makes so few mistakes?" Nevertheless, both the Colonel and Hughes were pleased with the piece, and the Minister wrote his friend a long, meandering letter of thanks. "Today," he said, after harking back to his past activities, "the public are beginning to realize that there was method in my madness." He misjudged the public, for the great majority of Canadians had finally concluded there was too much madness in his method.

Oddly enough, in that same January 1915 issue of *Maclean's,* the editor presented—no doubt with the Colonel's approval—a lively spy fiction feature in which the detective masterminds were none other than Prime Minister Sir Robert Borden, under his own name, and his brave, clever "Minister of Militia," otherwise unidentified. No reader in the briefest glance at the page could miss the real-life angle of the story, as both these characters were drawn with photographic accuracy in the illustration. The unsolved mystery is how the Colonel escaped a libel writ, for the nasty, highly ingenious spy of the plot turned out to be none other than the military secretary to the Minister of Militia!

But a bigger and better thriller awaited readers of the next issue, which devoted its three opening pages to the special feature, "How the Canada Armada was Saved." This time, Sam Hughes, the Minister, was right there in name and illustration, occupying the leading male role, ready to be accosted in the Château Frontenac restaurant by "a fascinating woman," a study in grace, with a face of striking pallor, topped by heavy coils of black hair. She introduced herself as "Madame de Tourneauville," and over the candlelit table (the illustration depicted the scene with almost photographic realism), she reveals to him the German plan, by which a Zeppelin concealed in the forest wilds of northern Quebec will within hours sail forth to bomb the ships carrying the first contingent overseas. But never fear: Hughes took immediate action, planes were dispatched to the lonely site, the Zeppelin was blown up, and the Canadian soldiers saved. Next day, the story related, Hughes determinedly went on a search for his beautiful informant, finally found her and announced that he intended to follow the transports to England and personally tell Lord Kitchener "what we, and the Empire, have to thank you for." The tale concludes with the starkly simple statement: "And he did."

Canada's daily press pounced on the feature—understandably, as, although it was indexed in the magazine's "fiction" grouping, its front position and general appearance over the pages left the impression of a real-life episode. Several newspapers summarized the piece as if it were an actual inside story out of Militia and Defense headquarters in Ottawa. Immediately, other sections of the press demanded that, in the interests of the public, the Minister reveal whether the *Maclean's* feature was indeed fact or fiction. Within hours, Hughes received a batch of interviewers and faced up to them manfully. Asked if all events described had actually occurred, he replied in resolute tones: "Yes! Every word was true except for one minor error. There wasn't one woman; there were three!"

It was ironic and perhaps a little sad that the year following his elevation to knighthood would witness his removal from the Cabinet. Reluctantly, the Prime Minister had concluded there was no alternative but to ask for his colleague's resignation; the public outcry against Sir Sam Hughes' "scandals" had been too continuous. Viewed from a half-century later, these seem rather minor, especially for a department engaged in building up a vast war machine in a matter of months. For example:

The issue boots, excellent for wear in the Canadian bush, were unable to take the mud of England and France. This led to a catchy new nickname for the Minister, "Sir Sham Shoes."

There was a problem with horses—and a great to-do resulted after the discovery that a small percentage of spavined jades had been included among the thousands of remounts purchased during the first Valcartier weeks. Hughes' close personal friend, J. Wesley Allison, was glad to help out with the assigning of shell contracts; unfortunately, he pocketed a sizable cut now and then on the orders. Eventually, a Royal Commission put Hughes in the clear but condemned both Allison and the system.

And then there was the famous case of the Ross rifle, which had been found unsuitable immediately the Canadian troops went into action in France. It heated up too quickly, the bolt jammed, and the weapon showed *prima donna* behavior with other than Canadian ammunition, which was not always available in quantity. Hughes continued to defend the Ross, "the best rifle in the world," long after public concern had risen to panic level.

The Colonel, too, had considerable respect for the Ross; in fact, he had played a modest role in its selection, a decade earlier, as the official rifle for the Canadian Army. The story goes as follows:

For years, the Northwest Mounted Police and most of the permanent forces stationed in Canada had been equipped with military rifles, such as the English Lee-Enfield and one or two others. The equipment behaved admirably in mild weather, but winter use brought problems. Indeed, in 1900, Colonel Maclean had sent two of the non-com's of his Hussars regiment on a firing-test expedition in the Gaspé Peninsula; they found that the bolt of the famous Lee-Enfield would not operate properly in below-zero temperatures. So it was that Sir Charles Ross, Scottish baronet, inventor, landowner, gunsmith and a wealthy man with mining interests in Canada, was asked to develop a rifle to stand up to all weathers in the Dominion. He kept in constant touch with Maclean, informing him of experiments. As soon as the NWMP had made their tests with the new Ross and reported complete efficiency at between minus 16 and minus 47 degrees, the Colonel lost not a moment to open a campaign in his *Military Gazette* for the

rifle's adoption. That decision was finally made by Sir Frederick
Borden, Laurier's Minister of Militia.

An interesting footnote to history is the fact that in the early 1900s,
Canadians had no thought of possible battle engagement in Europe;
military equipment was designed or selected primarily for the defense
of Canada, and particularly for service in the rugged lands of the far
northwest. Hence the Ross rifle, produced in a Quebec factory quickly
erected and brought into operation in 1914, and turned out in huge
quantities, along with its special ammunition; hence, too, just as
inevitably, the total jettisoning of the weapon, along with its ardent
advocate, Sir Sam, at the midstream point of World War I.

But nothing happening to the dynamic, stubborn Sam, nothing that
he caused to happen, was ever allowed to diminish the Colonel's
affection for him. Maclean stood ready to defend the summarily
retired Minister of Militia when he seemed to have not a friend left.
Small wonder that one of Sam's letters to University Avenue, Toronto,
wound up with the line: "I have always regarded you as a trump."

By 1916, the Colonel felt the urge to take up his pen again. For one
thing, he had some of that valuable commodity, time. Responsibilities
at the office had been effectively lightened the year previous with the
return of Horace Hunter in excellent health and spirit. Now installed
in the newly created post of vice-president of the company, "HTH"
could relieve the Colonel of dozens of decisions. Travel abroad was
cut off by the same war that had sent the Macleans fleeing from
Berlin. Just recently he had been reminded of that strange interlude by
the arrival of the family's lost luggage. It had been delivered intact
in Toronto, in two lots at well-spaced dates, and just how the
shipments were organized remained a mystery—beyond the known
fact that the Hamburg-America line agent brought the collection from
Carlsbad to a Belgian border station, where on August 2, 1914, German soldiers took charge. Obviously, a good friend could still be
helpful even from within an enemy country in wartime.

Both at home and at downtown headquarters, the Colonel's daily
life now resumed a normal pace. He remembered the memo he had
sent to Costain months before, indicating that, while it was the editor's
responsibility to provide "gripping articles strongly human rather than
abstract . . . as near sensationalism as possible but of course absolutely
accurate," he, Maclean, would contribute the "controversy and opinion

pieces." Now, with the war gaining momentum and with his own mouthpiece ready to hand, he must speak out.

The byline of John Bayne Maclean appeared over outbursts against the generals and the politicians; in the latter grouping Winston Churchill and Lloyd George got the roughest going-over. The Colonel's statements concerning the Dominion's conscription crisis added up to a vigorous defense of the French Canadians against the charge that they were not doing their share. A reprint of the article was widely distributed to cabinet ministers, M.P.'s, editors, and business leaders; in fact, a quarter-of-a-century later the Colonel ordered the piece dug out from the files and reproduced in facsimile for similar distribution during World War II. His memory was a long one—not merely for a proud appearance in print, but capable of stretching back to the '90s and his happy days among Montreal's French population.

Admittedly those World War I articles made difficult reading. Sometimes Costain was impelled to insert a special introductory note, striving hard to sum up the points the reader would find. Yet even for a skilled editor this was an almost hopeless task. The Colonel's wandering style could lead him from long-ago militia recollections to the present food shortage, on to a blast at undercover manipulators in Ottawa and forebodings about the future war debt, plus the disgraceful waste of money on extension of streetcar service in Toronto. His inability to hold to a selected theme, with clear premise, reasoned arguments and proper conclusion, had once inspired his banking friend, Sir Frederick Williams-Taylor, to remark, "If the Colonel ever built a railroad it would be all branch lines."

Nevertheless certain newspaper editors and M.P.s did manage to read enough of his printed polemics to get mad. Editorials here and there came close to calling him a traitor; roundabout the House of Commons the mere mention of his name could cause thunder in the air.

Strangely enough, his first encounter with wartime censorship arose from articles he had contributed to *The Financial Post,* rather than *Maclean's,* and, just as oddly, involved a private campaign he had voluntarily launched on behalf of a U.S. publisher. William Randolph Hearst's newspapers were violently anti-British; indeed the Hearst name was anathema in Canada. He and the Colonel met frequently in New York; now at this critical juncture Maclean believed it was imperative that every effort be made to keep Hearst, the powerful shaper of American opinion, on reasonably friendly terms with Canada.

It wouldn't be easy, as Maclean realized; Hearst was a Jekyll-and-Hyde character, one to be watched rather than trusted. "His ideals and policies wouldn't last in our organization ten minutes," Maclean wrote to a staff editor . . . "All the same, I like him and particularly I like his wife, a model mother."

Soon after New Year's, 1917, an order-in-council was passed at Ottawa forbidding entry of any Hearst newspaper into Canada "for the duration." Maclean was shocked; this precipitous action would confound and destroy his current missionary enterprise. In the *Post* he vigorously denounced the move, quite disregarding the fact that most of Canada's dailies had welcomed it. He went to Ottawa and saw members of the Cabinet, including the Prime Minister. To find out just how far the order applied, he wrote to the chief censor, none other than Colonel Ernest Chambers, old comrade from the Montreal period. The question presented was simple: "Would it be legal for me to reproduce any article from a Hearst newspaper?"

"No," replied Chambers, quoting the Justice Department and War Measures Act, "and consequently I am unable to sanction the republication in Canada of matter which has appeared in Hearst publications." Indeed, it was an offense to have clippings from one of the prohibited Hearst newspapers in one's possession. (All bureaucrats are subject to silly intervals in wartime.)

Meanwhile a long letter arrived from Hearst, thanking the Colonel for his stand in the *Post,* praising him for remaining "calm and just in the midst of the excitement and violent prejudice and high antagonism of war times." Hearst insisted he was not antagonistic to Canada; he was fond of Canadians, knew the country well, had traveled its rivers and lakes, camped in its Rockies, and seen more of Canada than most Canadians. "I do not object to being hanged in effigy any more than I object to having the Hearst papers excluded from Canada. One of these performances is about as harmless and aimless as the other." He was reminded of the story concerning the young fop who called on his sweetheart and found her engaged to his rival. Fop, on departing, discovered his rival's umbrella in the hall, picked it up, broke it in two and said, "Now I hope it rains." Probably Canada's officialdom wished the same sort of fate for Hearst publications, "but it hasn't rained yet"; indeed they would "continue to advocate cloudless skies and friendly sunshine in all matters affecting the common interests of the United States and Canada."

Thus, in spite of Ottawa's ban, it looked as if the Colonel's private patriotic scheme had worked in some degree. Within three months the United States entered the war, and the Hearst skies immediately cleared on both sides of the international border.

Early in 1918 John Bayne Maclean and his top editor found themselves in a serious crisis with the chief censor. The Colonel had written an article criticizing the conduct of the war and, in particular, lambasting British politicians for interference with the generals. History has not proved him wrong, but during that crucial period it was hardly the "popular" thing for publications to present discussions likely to arouse distrust or disaffection. The piece had been prepared for *Maclean's Magazine,* and after Costain's careful reading the Colonel asked: "What heading shall we use?" In ten seconds flat, Costain came up with the answer: "Why We Are Losing the War."

Such an article, especially under such a heading, was bound to produce a sensation even beyond the Colonel's wildest dreams. When the February issue appeared, with the feature title boldly displayed on the cover, the country rocked. Some people burned or tore up the magazine publicly; perhaps others found themselves agreeing with the author after following his *exposé* to the end; but no adult Canadian could ignore it.

Anyway, Colonel Chambers did not. He wrote: "Certain features of this article are calculated to have an injurious and harmful effect. The title of the article expressly and distinctly states that we are losing the war, consequently expressing the hopelessness of further effort to resist the pretensions and aims of the enemy . . . it is almost certain to be republished in Germany and Austria for the encouragement of the populations of the enemy countries."

The Colonel was summoned to Ottawa. He sent Costain instead. Before leaving, the editor was warned by the Colonel: "Don't let them push you around. Stand up to them." Yet the chief censor was inclined to treat Costain gently and to sympathize with him for having John Bayne Maclean for a boss. The atmosphere changed abruptly when Costain casually remarked that the heading had been his only contribution. "That's the worst feature of it!" shouted Chambers. The meeting ended with the editor's agreement (1) to submit any further articles of the kind to the censor's office for advance clearance, and (2) to persuade the Colonel not to circulate reprints already processed from the February pages.

For Costain and Maclean the crisis was over—yet there would soon be another result from their daring collaboration. A sudden govern-

ment order-in-council came forth; after numerous "whereas's" it for-
bade the press "to print, publish, or publicly express any adverse or
unfavorable statement, report or opinion concerning the action of Canada, the United Kingdom of Great Britain and Ireland or any Allied
Nation in prosecuting the war."

*Maclean's Magazine* presented its best controversialist just once
more during 1918. The Colonel's manuscript was, as promised, submitted to the censor. The article, which was chiefly a reply to the
author's critics, came back badly mauled. The censor had gone beyond
his appointed role; he edited the article as a slot man might hatchet
a junior reporter's copy. One passage, totally removed, had read:
"How weak and helpless our management in Russia was will be understood when we consider the fact that two strangers—walking delegates—could come from abroad and in a few days take the situation
completely out of our hands as did Trotsky and Lenin. They took
control of 200,000,000 people. Think of it. It is one of the most
amazing things in history."

In another section the Colonel had expressed admiration for the
generals, those now in high command, whom he had met during his
cavalry training at Aldershot. They would show their splendid capacity, he said, "if given the support and opportunity our damnable
politicians refuse them." The censor struck out "damnable." On moral
grounds, perhaps?

The great Costain period on *Maclean's* was drawing to a close;
soon he would find himself ensconced in a senior editorial chair in
New York—and well on the way to fulfilling a certain prophecy
of the Colonel's.

Sometime during the war Costain had been on a business trip to
New York where he happened to run into John Bayne Maclean.
"I'm going to dinner at Munsey's place," the latter said. "He has
wanted to meet you, so you must come along too." At last the young
editor would meet the man whose publishing philosophy was delivered,
in warmed-over servings, at every major conference on University
Avenue. The Munsey apartment was impressive, furnished in the taste
of a Spanish grandee. Over the dinner table the trio discussed—what
else?—magazines. Very soon it was obvious to Costain, as he later
reported, that his host knew very little about the editing end of the
business, yet the Colonel sat there, "accepting every remark of Munsey's as if it were spoken by a sacred oracle." Finally the visitors said
goodnight, and when the door of the vast suite closed behind them

Maclean said, "Some day, Costain, you will live in an apartment like that."

It was just one of the Colonel's little pleasantries, half encouragement, half jest, but eventually Costain did have his own beautiful apartment in New York. It differed from Munsey's in being furnished in excellent taste. Costain's Toronto salary never exceeded $100 per week, plus a bonus on the rate of *Maclean's* subscription renewals. In 1919 the Colonel sold him five shares of company stock, later raising it to ten shares. There were no strings attached, but when Costain left Maclean Publishing in 1920 he sold the shares to H. Victor Tyrrell. That extra $1000 would come in handy during this major move to the United States.

Costain had accepted the invitation of George Horace Lorimer, editor of *The Saturday Evening Post,* who immediately appointed him senior associate editor at more than double his Toronto salary.

A day or so after announcing his departure, Costain had a chat with Lord Beaverbrook, then on a visit to Toronto. "The Beaver" was concerned about the decision; wasn't it a mistake to give up a really senior job such as the editing of *Maclean's?*

"Well," said Costain, "I have a wife and two daughters, and my first obligation is to them."

"But if you must leave Toronto to make more money, why don't you come to England?" Beaverbrook demanded.

"Because there are no good magazines in England," Costain replied. "And other than yourself, who in England ever heard of me?"

# CHAPTER XIX

# TRAGEDY IN THE FAMILY

"Sorrow concealed, like an oven stopp'd
Does burn the heart to cinders . . ."
*Shakespeare*

DURING THE WAR, life at 7 Austin Terrace had gone on with little change in the decorous pace approved by both the Colonel and his wife. All thoughts of overseas travel must wait until the guns were silenced and, although there were trips here and there in Canada and the United States, the Macleans spent longer intervals at home between 1914 and 1919 than at any other period of their active years. They were seldom alone, for the constant wartime visitations of the Colonel's military, political and business friends almost inevitably resulted in extra place-settings at the dinner table and, just as naturally, in the special pleasure of host and hostess, both of whom loved company.

Hector, the only son, now in his teens, automatically became one of the party, chiefly as a listener. He had always been a quiet, rather lonely child, undersized for his age and with a permanently pale complexion. Relatives and close friends whispered that he was "delicate," but would undoubtedly "grow out of it." Retinues of medical experts, however, had agreed that only surgery could correct the congenital fault in his digestive system. But the parents could not bring themselves to consent, and perhaps this resistance to professional advice merely increased their solicitousness and slowed the boy's development. He evinced little interest in sports, either as participant or observer; he seldom asserted himself.

Yet on one point he did manage to take a stand—and against that formidable expert, his father. Hector enjoyed his chums at Upper Canada College; often he would persuade one or other to come home with him for dinner. The minute Father arrived, and almost before he could be told, "This is Tom Smith," there would be the standard question, "Who are his parents?" Hector seldom knew, didn't care, and was glad to explain with considerable firmness later, "I'm not interested in who his people are. I just like Tom!" This was a normal child's healthy reaction to the dull business of family trees, but in Hector's case it was probably intensified by special experiences. During the annual travels abroad, he would frequently be left to his own devices—and what more natural than making good friends among the junior bellhops at Carlsbad or having a lively round of chess with the son of the steward at the castle while the grownups were deep in conversation and champagne?

During the time when the Macleans lived at the King Edward Hotel, awaiting completion of the house on Wells Hill, Hector had the whole of downtown Toronto as his playground and he frequently showed up at his father's office, where he was always welcomed. In summer, he wore a smart "sailor suit," the approved garb for boys of his age, and sharply reminiscent of the male chorus in *H.M.S. Pinafore.*

By his fifteenth year, there was excitement of a different kind. Each Saturday morning, the Colonel took him to University Avenue headquarters, turned him loose in the composing room, and there, teamed up with his new pal, Ralph, the caretaker's boy, he would explore some of the mysteries of setting type by hand. With a canvas apron protecting his suit jacket and "knickers," he quickly learned the case and began to know exactly what happened to the neat, handwritten "copy" he prepared each month for the Upper Canada school newspaper, of which he had recently become a regular editor. Now, with this extra experience, along with his good grades, he might be able to plan a career in journalism. Would Father allow that?

Already the Colonel had discouraged the idea of a military career— possibly because of the boy's constitutional handicap. International banking seemed an ideal choice, and (as one of the Colonel's letters to Hector explains) especially if taken up "in conjunction with the study of law, the latter being a splendid mental training . . . Banking is the greatest business; it gives you the broadest outlook and the best training without, at the same time, tying you down to a desk in later life." But he did not mean association with a Canadian chartered bank where a young man could be a "mere cog"; rather, "a banking business of your own, or a partnership in a big private financial firm. That would probably mean settling in New York or London, if you want to be in the biggest things in the world."

If Hector elected for journalism, however, his father promised to work with him. A college course to include that subject would be essential (this from a writer-publisher who had learned only by doing), but it must be understood that while "you may desire to come into this business, and I would like to see you do so . . . you will have to fight your own way and not be the sole proprietor as I am today. You will be one of a number; a unit in an institution. My aim is—and I have arranged for this—to make the successful men and women in the organization part owners. Think it over, whether the big but less strenuous career as a banker or the more interesting and sensational life of a journalist-publisher is preferable."

In 1919, when he was sixteen years old Hector had two opportunities to meet most of the "units" in the organization. He accompanied his father to the first formal evening dance held by members of the staff— an occasion that celebrated the return of peace, plus various staff men just back from military service—and then, in June, attended the first mammoth picnic given by the Colonel for all employees and their families. At both events, the lad showed "keen enjoyment," according to reports in the *Weekly,* and years later many Maclean men and women were to recall the happy impression he left with them.

They were never to see him again. Soon after the picnic, he was off with several of his Upper Canada friends for an exhilarating summer at a boys' camp on Lake Timagami in northern Ontario. Everything went merrily until the customary climax of the season's program: a lengthy canoe trip far down the lake, involving *portages,* overnight camping, and rough-and-ready meals prepared over an open fire. It was shortly after one of these that Hector became violently ill. His counsellor commandeered a passing launch and rushed him to the nearest source of medical help, the town of Temiskaming on the east side of the lake of similar name. Two doctors worked over him but nothing availed. Within a few hours, Hector Maclean had died. The date was August 17, 1919.

Next day's Toronto papers carried the dispatch from Temiskaming, attributing the death to "an attack of acute indigestion," and mentioning the fact that the boy's parents received the news by telegraph at St. Andrew's-by-the-Sea, in New Brunswick, where they had been vacationing.

The effects of this family tragedy were to be manifest at various points throughout the remainder of the Colonel's life—indeed, they are still discernible today in the ownership-management of the company he built. But no one, at that moment of shock and sorrow was giving any thought to the eventual or practical results of his bereavement. Messages of sympathy flooded in, and, as was the custom of the period, a procession of callers knocked on the door at 7 Austin Terrace to offer condolences in person. But Anna had collapsed and was under continuous nursing care. Even five months later, when an Ottawa friend asked the Colonel if he would entertain a Japanese dignitary, the reply had to be in the negative, as "we are in mourning; my wife is not able to see anyone"—although he would be glad to welcome the visitor at downtown headquarters.

Through it all the Colonel stayed as firm as a tower. He enjoyed reminiscing about his son, in conversation, letters or even in print. The December 13, 1919, issue of the *Weekly* contained a little vignette, unsigned yet of unmistakable origin, concerning the late Hector A. F. Maclean's favorite motto which hung on his bedroom wall and faced him on rising each morning: "When it is finally settled that the thing is *impossible,* watch some fellow do it." That was the challenging statement which Hector wholeheartedly believed and followed, "particularly in the matter of mechanics. On several occasions where automobile mechanicians (sic) agreed that things were impossible, he showed them how, or did it himself."

At the Christmas-tree party given that year by the Colonel to employees and their families—an event that became an annual company fixture—he took special pleasure in distributing all books belonging to Hector as extra gifts, gaily wrapped and ribboned, to staff members' sons. Even the *raison d'être* of the afternoon, the tree itself, was a link with the past, having come from the Colonel's garden, where Hector had planted it years before. The host, in his speech of welcome, expressed regret that his wife was not well enough to be present, but on her behalf thanked the men and women of his company for the beautiful roses sent to her that morning.

The Colonel's calmness and control after the family tragedy did not mean he could forget. A couple of years later his first full-time secretary, who had left in 1918 at the time of her marriage, called at the office to thank him for the kind note just received, following the death of her child. He ushered her in, made her comfortable in the visitor's chair opposite his own, looked at her steadily for a full minute and then remarked, in quiet level tone: "It's hell, isn't it?"

For Anna Slade Maclean, the death of her son was a traumatic experience which would leave a scar on her personality and habits for the rest of her days. True, she emerged by slow degrees from her year of mourning and resumed her place at her husband's side for all social events and ever more frequent travels. Yet there was always a risk involved. The view of a cemetery, even a mile away, would cause a nervous reaction. In any group where she found herself confronted by gay young people, whether toddlers or in their twenties, she would weep uncontrollably.

For her, the fall-winter season of 1921 must have been a program of misery in full evening dress. That was Toronto's great year for debutantes, the first all-out opportunity since pre-war days for brilliant parties and "presentations." The popular setting was Jenkins' Art Gallery, considered ideal with its great central dance floor surrounded with richly furnished alcoves under a balcony. Protocol stipulated that the first alcove near the entrance be reserved for the receiving line of debutante and her parents, the others occupied by the important dowagers and their husbands, who stood and greeted the pretty girls and escorts after the hosts' welcome.

Almost every week during that glittering season the Macleans were on hand in their section, as close friends of the principals, and the Colonel would blithely go through his routine of "placing" family names and recalling his association with this young lady's uncle or her companion's father. "The whole proceeding from alcove to alcove lasted about an hour before the dancing started," one of the 1921 debs recalled many years later, "and all through that formal handshaking and unimportant chitchat with dozens of people, Mrs. Maclean never stopped weeping. She stood there, supported with a cane in her left hand, wearing a lovely floaty dress of pale chiffon, her jewels flashing, her hair a regal work of art in its casual pompadour style—and the tears streamed down her cheeks. There was no contortion of the face, no sobbing; occasionally, she would even venture a comment or question, socially correct; yet the tears continued to flow and one handkerchief would have to be replaced by another from her bag." The Macleans' good friend, Mrs. Stewart Houston, whose daughter came out that year, sometimes joined their group to give extra support and to help the conversation along. After one particularly harrowing evening, she found herself struggling with the question that had bothered many others: *"Why* does Jack put Anna through this?"

No ready answer was ever forthcoming, beyond the plain fact, known to all their associates, that the Colonel loved to meet people and Mrs. Maclean, despite her sorrow, loved social occasions. At a completely adult affair, such as a Government House reception, or any of her own dinners or teas, she remained the perfectly poised, confident society matron. Only the presence of youth in numbers could shake the façade. But inevitably that meant an ordeal awaiting her at any of the company parties—the Christmas gala with its swarms of tumbling, laughing children; the other all-out family affair of the summer picnic; the annual dance that brought forward the gay young crowd from every section of printing plant and offices. During the dance event, she would occasionally retreat to the powder room to daub at her wet cheeks and repair make-up; sometimes, and certainly at least once, it happened that her neighbor at the mirror, a new staff girl unindoctrinated to the ways of the Colonel's wife, became alarmed and cried out, "Are you not well? Is there anything I can do?" Mrs. Maclean responded with more tears over a little, wry smile, and said, "No, thanks." Then, as if talking to herself, went on, "I'm a fool, just a fool!"

Despite the trials of those special occasions, within her own environment Anna remained an excellent and willing hostess. Sunday afternoon generally found a large group gathered for tea in the drawing room or, in summer, on the porch, with Mrs. Maclean, hatted of course, carrying out her gracious duties at the urn. About once a week, there would be a major dinner party, often involving eight or ten guests; other evenings the number might be reduced to a couple of relatives or old friends. And, frankly, from the standpoint of both the Macleans, it was a dull sort of evening when they dined alone.

Were they bored with each other? This could very well have been true. Or was this insatiable urge for people and conversation and ideas and reports of personal adventures, big or little, merely the obvious concomitant of the pair's lifelong disinterest in books? The facilities and staff at 7 Austin Terrace were constantly kept at peak preparation for entertaining. James Ritchie, the chauffeur who would spend thirty years driving the Colonel's succession of Cadillacs, Rolls-Royces or Chryslers, was ready to fetch guests. Once delivered to the house, they would be met at the door by the butler whose accent might change now and then from Swiss to Polish to English, but whose solicitous concern for the wraps he stowed in the hall closet never varied. Ladies were never invited "to go upstairs"; Mrs. Maclean's

bedroom suite was off-bounds, for even her most intimate acquaintances.

Guided by the butler, the guests reached the drawing-room doorway where the Colonel stood with hand extended. One by one, the
ladies and gentlemen made their way across the room to be greeted
by the hostess, seated in smiling dignity at the end of a French sofa,
her handsome face brought into dramatic cynosure by the flood of
light from a tall lamp nearby. Against the rich mulberry velvet of the
upholstery, the delicate tone and sheer stuff of her evening dress gave
the whole figure a gossamer distinction. "Those beautiful, pale-pale
chiffons or lace gowns were by Worth of Paris, her favorite designer,"
a guest of those days recently recalled. "Yet the impression left on me
and other women in the party was of American smartness, even
'Palm Beach style'—perhaps because at that time most Toronto women
of her age group stayed in dark clothes." For jewelry, she often
favored three strands of pearls—one long, the others much shorter—a
diamond watch on her left arm, at least two magnificent bracelets on
her right, always including a certain pearl and diamond circlet of
baroque design, and for earrings, the quite simple pearl type without
drops.

The dinner ritual never varied. The hostess was the first to leave
the drawing room; thus, her slow progress with the two canes would
not hold up the rest of the procession. By the time the guests entered
the dining room, she was standing at her place at the far end of the
table; when all were ready to be seated, the butler helped his mistress
into her chair. A neatly uniformed maid—two of them for a large
party—now appeared from the kitchen to help with the serving of the
courses under the major-domo's direction.

Mrs. Maclean's infirmity dictated a slight alteration at the end of
the meal, as well as at the beginning. The butler led the female
guests to the drawing room. On his return, he helped the hostess
to her feet, and with canes in hand, she made her way past the
gentlemen standing in their places and, in all likelihood, warned
them not to let her husband detain them too long. Indeed, if the
menfolk lingered more than seven or eight minutes over their coffee
and liqueurs, the butler would be dispatched with a crisp message
from hostess to host.

After-dinner conversation in the drawing room stayed general for
a small group but tended to split into animated twosome debates
when there were numerous guests. The Colonel moved about happily,

switching subjects vis-à-vis each person, according to that individual's known interests or recent enterprises. Anna, too, was always ready with dependable leading questions; installed again in her favorite corner of the sofa, she would invite each of the guests, in turn, to sit down beside her for a chat. And all guests were of equal importance to Mrs. Maclean. The wife of the Washington diplomat, with her gossip from the embassies, was worth listening to; so, too, the new wife of one of the Colonel's junior managers—and she just might have some interested comments, plus congratulations, for Mrs. Maclean's cook.

The atmosphere remained formal; the conversation, safely decorous. Any breach of etiquette was seldom forgotten or forgiven. A certain distinguished Winnipeg lawyer committed the horrible faux-pas of resting his shoe on a Louis XV petitpoint chair during lively argument with the Colonel; that was to be the westerner's last visit. The frankness of modern "woman talk" dismayed Anna. Once, during a quiet chat with the wife of a Maclean company executive, the name of Mrs. So-and-so happened to be mentioned. Mrs. Maclean's guest broke in spontaneously with some interesting news, "Oh, by the way, did you know she is pregnant again?" The stately figure in ivory ninon-and-lace straightened perceptibly and the sculptured pompadour rose by at least an inch as the hostess replied with emphasis that was not intended as playful, "In Boston we never discussed such matters."

# CHAPTER XX

# THE JOYS OF BATTLE

"Sir Adam (Beck) has the kind of egotism that is content with Sir Adam's own good opinion of himself."
*Augustus Bridle in* Sons of Canada

THE 1920s were to mean many things to many people: jazz, an automobile with side curtains, Prohibition and the brisk new business of bootlegging, family evenings around the "console" radio set, stock markets booming and crashing, the eight-hour workday, novels tentatively exploring something called Sex rather than Romance. The tempo was fast, urgent; nobody could escape it.

In Canada, waterfalls were being dammed up for power; the farmers in the West were setting up a pool to market their wheat; bankrupt government railways were being put together in one coast-to-coast national enterprise; tariffs were being cut while the country's natural resources were spawning huge paper mills and new mines.

Certain interesting figures emerged on the political horizon, some ephemeral, others with staying power. Parties were realigned and Prime Minister W. L. Mackenzie King, watching the agrarian unrest in the West produce a new Progressive party, contrived to take it into partnership preparatory to swallowing it up. Across the border such conservative politicians as Harding, Coolidge, Mellon and Hoover rose to power. Individualism flourished, and ruggedly free enterprise was extolled.

For John Bayne Maclean, now in his sixties, it was a time to be on the alert; to crack down both on those who would destroy the "profit system" and on those who would exploit it, such as promoters who presumed too much upon the public's gullibility; to warn equally of Communist "agitators" on university campuses and business profiteers in the market-place. In *Maclean's* and *The Financial Post*, the Colonel carried on campaigns against those who, in his opinion, put their selfish ambitions above the public good, whether in or out of government. Such campaigns were sometimes lively, generally persistent, occasionally boring and always enormously consuming of time and space. He wrote thousands of words a week, all by hand in his neat, minuscule script, and his secretary, Miss Ethel Dove, impersonally copied the sheets and gathered up (for permanent filing) the dozens of scraps of paper on which his preliminary notes had been scribbled at the desk, in the garden, in the bath or in bed. The stream of words the Colonel poured forth during that decade represent his most vigorously productive period as a journalist.

His gadfly tactics were by then well known and frequently irksome, yet his pronouncements had to be watched and read, though not always understood, by those in the seats of the mighty. In 1915 Ottawa had been stirred to wrath by a contribution to *Men's Wear Review* in which the Colonel had exposed conditions under which military clothing was being made. Others, he said, were being given to shady contractors who farmed out much of the work to sweatshops in Toronto and Montreal, and "It is doubtful if the public recognize the menace of sweatshop work in clothing—that is, clothing made up in homes of the very poor: mostly foreigners, crowded together in small rooms. It is in these places where tuberculosis is most prevalent and certain other loathsome and infectious diseases are not uncommon."

Honorable A. E. (later better known as Sir Edward) Kemp, chairman of the recently formed War Purchasing Commission, replied that no such conditions had come to his attention. Who were those sweatshop contractors? In the Colonel's absence from town, Costain answered briefly, suggesting that Kemp do his own research which would show Toronto's clothing district honeycombed with sweatshops. Kemp came back again, demanding names and addresses. So Hugh Eayrs, editor of *Men's Wear* (in after years a leading figure in the book world, as managing director of Macmillan's of Canada), sallied forth, gathered a mass of factual details, prepared and mailed a report that substantiated the Colonel's charges, silenced the Ottawa argument, and improved the handling of contracts for service uniforms.

That sort of stirring-up had its practical value. But occasionally the Colonel could be astonishingly naïve in his preachments, as happened in the climax of a series of articles contributed to the *Post* shortly after he had escaped from Europe in 1914. Disturbed by the apparent complacency of the Canadian people, he stated that the war might last "five, perhaps six years"; in an October 1914 issue he predicted that Canada would eventually have 250,000 men under arms and that the national debt would rise by four or five hundred million dollars. (Though much too timid with both those statistical forecasts, he was right in general.) Now, for such an enormous investment—and altogether aside from the inevitable domestic sorrows brought about by war—surely Canada should "get something in return." So here was his plan, as carefully set forth in the *Post:* Canada should have the right to select 100,000 families a year from the best agricultural population of Germany, over a period of ten or twenty years; those families would be brought to Canada and established, at German expense, on Canadian farms. This would be a great gain for the country, for, as any careful observer would agree, the Germans already settled in Canada were thorough, industrious and "among the best farmers in the land."

The reaction from press and public was violent. The suggestion that the country worth fighting for would eventually have its vacant spaces filled up with vast hordes of the hated Kaiser's people, forcibly removed from their native soil, exported on demand, drew shocked condemnation. At that anxious moment of a war that had barely started, Canadians could hardly be expected to settle for an enemy invasion, however peaceful, as a future "return" on their investment.

The Colonel reached his best campaigning form when he confronted foemen worthy of his steel, flesh-and-blood contemporaries ready to return thrust for thrust. That he realized this is apparent from one of his notations kept for years in this "stray thoughts" file. The handwriting starts off with a quote from Dr. Johnson in Boswell's *Tour of the Hebrides:* "It is advantageous to an author that his work should be attacked as well as praised. Fame is a shuttlecock. If it be struck only at one end of the room, it will soon fall to the ground. To keep it up, it must be struck at both ends." Then the Colonel adds: "Quite unconsciously, has this not been my policy and experience when trying to arouse attention of public to solution of important and serious problems? I have, on a number of occasions, injected in a story, a startling, sensational, but true statement of facts contrary to current belief and understanding. This got the readers fighting over the sensational and, unconsciously, absorbing and understanding the points I wanted to make."

For sensational reading bound to invite attack, nothing quite equaled his all-out effort against the powerful Canadian Manufacturers' Association (CMA). He had quietly studied the group's activities over the years, not only as a journalist but as a publisher-member who served for some time on its Executive Council; and when, shortly after Armistice Day, 1918, he discovered that the same old policies were to be dusted off, brought forward and presented intact as the Association's postwar program he immediately took up battle position.

The Colonel's chief complaints seemed to be that the CMA supported combines, opposed organized labor and virtually ignored the point of view of agriculture. By long dedication to the sole purpose of raising tariffs for their own protection, the manufacturers, he declared, had alienated their best customers, the farmers. What the CMA should do now was to invite rural leaders to "sit down at the same table" and draft a plan mutually acceptable: one that would (a) keep Canada a low-cost country and (b) give adequate protection for *efficient* industries only. But obviously, he went on, a prerequisite to that move was enlightened leadership of the CMA. For far too long, a Toronto clique, "a little group of narrow-minded pinheads," had been in control; in this important new era, the CMA should take a giant step forward by appointing a $50,000-a-year general manager.

Such was the thesis the Colonel would return to, countless times over two or three years, in his bylined articles in the *Post*. Here, indeed, was a "shuttlecock" that could hardly fall to the ground—not in the all-out game Maclean played! Inevitably, to give fresh point to the campaign, he resorted to CMA case histories and loud naming of names—especially those of two Torontonians, S. R. Parsons, president in 1917, and Sam Harris, another potent figure in the CMA. The repercussions were swift and vituperative. At a big meeting of the manufacturers in June 1919, a speech by Harris referred to Maclean as a "yellow cur." Next week's *Post* offered a neat rejoinder: "If Mr. Harris had called me a lap dog, it would have been different. I know something about dogs, particularly about the yellow dog, the name given by the ignorant to the grandest breed of all—the Irish terrier. I have owned and bred a great many of them. You will find my name in the prize list as an exhibitor at shows from New York to San Francisco." Then, "Mr. Harris should apologize to the Irish and the Irish terrier. They have breeding."

The Colonel had the courage of his convictions, too. Several times at the height of his career, he attended CMA meetings and rose in his place to explain his over-all plan, yes, but also to expose to the full membership what he considered the selfish, stubborn shortsightedness of "the Toronto clique," seated in plain view nearby. It seems likely that by such personalizing of his criticisms, he confused his audiences as to the basic points of principle he was trying to establish. Although some members later expressed interest in his campaign, and a few top industrialists wrote letters of encouragement, the majority of Canadian manufacturers were distressed, and scores of them showed their resentment by refusing to advertise in his publications.

But not all officers of the CMA joined in the "hate Maclean" movement. The Colonel's files contain a letter written in 1926 by W. S. Fallis, recently retired president, who, after expressing thanks for the publisher's support, went on to say: "In reviewing the whole work of the Association, it does seem to me that we have in some manner failed to secure a place in the estimation of the Canadian public that would enable us to use our influence for the good of the country at large. We are looked upon as being self-seeking, in the interests of manufacturers only, which is not the case."

Of course, by then, the Colonel's fight with the CMA had passed into history and peace of a kind had been restored. His campaign for a $50,000-a-year manager had failed, but perhaps the recriminations drawn forth from both sides were to have certain salutary effects in the years ahead.

Like any good strategist, the Colonel was perfectly capable of waging war on several fronts at the same time. So it happened that the CMA project had hardly got under way when he found it necessary to open a major campaign against Sir Adam Beck, chairman of the Ontario Hydro-Electric Power Commission.

Beck's postwar dream was to establish—at a cost of $200,000,000 —a system of electrified "radial" railways, linking Toronto with other important centers east and west in Ontario.

The Colonel discussed the plan with friends experienced in the electric railway business in the United States. He discovered that suburban and interurban service of the type was rapidly becoming obsolete; indeed, at that moment in early 1919, many lines had gone bankrupt, and more were to follow.

What was about to emerge there, and what would just as surely be needed here in Canada, was a network of good roads for automotive travel. The motorcar had suddenly become the urgent "next" investment for families, businessmen, *et al;* farmers looked forward to doing their own trucking of cattle and produce to market, once the highways were built.

All these angles were carefully presented by the Colonel via the *Post,* and each article made it abundantly clear that Beck, with his outmoded scheme for a lacy fan of electrified railways, to be financed out of the provincial treasury, deserved nothing but contempt and utter rejection.

Shortly after the Colonel had launched forth in this new engagement, he found himself joined by an important ally, none other than the recently elected Premier of Ontario, Honorable Ernest C. Drury, who happened to be an old friend. The Drury family had been Simcoe County neighbors of the Colonel's maternal Camerons. The Premier's father, Honorable Charles Drury, who in 1889 became the province's first Minister of Agriculture, had won young Maclean's respect, back in the early *Canadian Grocer* days. With interest he had watched Ernest's career, which included graduation from the Ontario Agricultural College, operation of a large modern farm, and occasional contributions to *Maclean's Magazine.* In February 1914, for instance, a Drury article had urged adequate salaries for country schoolmasters—and both the subject and its method of handling had won the Colonel's enthusiastic approval.

When the United Farmers of Ontario swept into power with the election of 1919, they were totally surprised and quite unprepared, having not even settled on a party leader. Filling that gap was the first item on the new government's agenda; after being turned down by several hurriedly suggested choices—including the old Tory, Sir Adam Beck!—the UFO group conscripted Drury. Almost overnight, he faced the task of forming a cabinet from ranks innocent of experience in political life or governmental administration. "A disaster for this province!" said the business-financial community. But the Colonel, always a free-standing individual with his own reasons, thought otherwise. He not only welcomed a government fortunate enough to have Drury at its head, but gladly lent Frank M. Chapman, editor of the company's farm paper, to help select cabinet members and assign departments. *The Financial Post,* in its first report concerning the regime, followed the Colonel's lead—and no one seemed to notice the highly pertinent—unintended—pun in the heading: "Farmers Will Give Ontario Stable Government."

While Maclean stayed on the alert to offer general support through the next few years, his chief effort, pursued without letup, was in battling Beck and uniting with Drury to kill the project of electric radials.

Opposing—and exposing—Ontario's Hydro-Electric czar was hardly a new experience. The Colonel had kept an eye on the former cigar-box manufacturer ever since 1906, when the Hydro-Electric Power Commission, under Beck, then M.P.P. and admittedly an enthusiast for publicly owned power, was established to produce electricity, "wholesale" it to the muncipalities, which in turn retailed it to consumers through municipally conducted utility systems.

Beck was a born politician, crafty in achieving his own ends, either impractical or deceptive in matters of costs and/or results. At a Toronto meeting where he had been holding forth for an hour concerning a certain subsidiary scheme, he was queried as to which of the figures mentioned, $3,000,000 or $5,000,000, was the correct estimate. "Oh, say, five million dollars," he replied. "Anyway, what's the difference?"

In 1917, he had started the Chippawa Falls project at Niagara; this, he announced, could produce 100,000 h.p. at a cost of $10,000,000 or 200,000 h.p. at only the slightly higher investment of $13,000,000. Maclean scoffed at the figures, in his *Post* piece he declared that this undertaking would cost over $80,000,000 and might bankrupt the province. (Actually, the finished job cost $85,000,000 but it delivered over 500,000 horsepower. The capital cost per h.p. worked out to more than three times the $50 per figure which Beck had always quoted in his speeches. However, the province did manage to stay solvent.)

Another feature of the Hydro program drew down the Colonel's invective. Beck was installing 25-cycle power. Maclean pointed out that 60-cycle had become almost universal on the North American continent. Ontario would ultimately have to switch to 60-cycle, so why not do it now, at the outset? (He was, of course, right; after World War II the change-over from 25-cycle power cost the province more than a quarter-billion dollars.)

Beck, who lived on and for adulation, could not endure such criticism and close-questioning. He knew he had the full backing of the *Star, Telegram,* and *Globe* in Toronto, yet it was infuriating to find those Maclean columns reprinted or quoted by various small-town papers—whose editors kept a canny attitude toward any public servant who tossed millions around. He had one last resort he could turn to—

Anna Slade Maclean, the Colonel's wife: handsome and dignified, gallant and uncomplaining in the face of personal tragedy. Anna's remarkable family history, Boston-based, presented her husband with a wealth of social contacts, including European royalty

A pleasant summer afternoon, and the Macleans at home with their two spaniels. Behind: The loggia across the west end of the long, chateau-like mansion at 3 Austin Terrace

No. 13 Queen's Park Crescent, the sprawling Victorian residence where Colonel and Mrs. John Bayne Maclean lived during the first ten years after their marriage. From the entrance front there was an uninterrupted view of the park and the Ontario Parliament Buildings

The main entrance at 3 Austin Terrace, the house the Colonel built, stage by stage, on a picturesque property along the crest of Toronto's "hill." With its modified French-Provincial styling, low roofline, smooth grey stucco finish and light turquoise trim, the structure even as finally expanded maintained an unpretentious charm

Maclean of Toronto, at left, and, at right, Frank Munsey, multimillionaire head of a U.S. publishing empire. The setting is San Sebastian, Bay of Biscay resort; the host, at centre, Alex P. Moore, U.S. Ambassador to Spain, former Pittsburgh newspaper publisher, and one of the husbands of actress Lillian Russell. The date: 1925, a few months before Munsey's death

The Colonel's Carlsbad routine began well before World War I; by 1935, the date of this snapshot, he was the complete habituée, "taking the waters," glass in hand, during the morning stroll, relaxing for an hour each day in a bath of the same hot mineral-spring stuff

April 1916—baseball training season in Florida, with the great Connie Mack of the Philadelphia Athletics pausing for a chat with his Toronto friend. They were almost the same age

A visit to Murray Bay on the St. Lawrence—and the Colonel is greeted by Lady Williams-Taylor, for many years Montreal's leading social figure, and wife of his banker friend

The Company's top triumvirate in the 1930's: Horace T. Hunter, President since 1933; John Bayne Maclean, who had then become chairman of the board; H. Victor Tyrrell, vice-president and general manager. Hunter's span of service dated from 1903, when he graduated from university; Tyrrell's went back even farther—to a humble job in the Colonel's first printing plant

The scene is "El Mirasol," 25-acre estate of E. T. Stotesbury, a J. P. Morgan associate. The Macleans were regulars on the guest list, and each occasion yielded the Colonel—here strolling with another visitor—new data concerning great names, garden design, even the upkeep of a private zoo such as his hosts had installed

# Chatelaine

*The Canadian Woman's Magazine*

APRIL, 1946
TEN CENTS

## The Fashion Story...and its new elegance

The day Mrs. Bayne Maclean received this issue of *Chatelaine* she telephoned her thanks to the editor for "that beautiful hat on the cover," adding "If I were twenty years younger, I'd be ordering it right now." She was then in her seventy-ninth year and frequently did: the association of municipal electric officials, which he himself had organized as an "opinion forming" group. Thus, when the going got tough, Sir Adam would summon the members to Toronto, entertain them lavishly, deliver a one- or two-hour harangue, hammer through a resolution ensuring support of his current plans, and, always, beat his breast concerning the injustices he suffered at the hands of his enemies, especially No. 1 on the list, John Bayne Maclean, who was indubitably the foe of public power development and thus of the people of Ontario.

Beck was a tedious sort of demagogue; given to interminable and repetitious speeches that were duly reported almost verbatim in the columns of the *Telegram* and *Star*. Their fulsome and constant praise of him on the editorial pages might have embarrassed a man less vainglorious, but Beck remained totally committed to his own myth. He was the knight in shining armor, the brave Sir Galahad, fighting the "big interests" of private ownership.

The Colonel was only mildly opposed to public ownership of power, but he had no use whatever for Beck. Having distrusted the methods and extravagances involved in hydro-electric expansion, Maclean could find no merit in the new project for radial railways. Through his columns in the *Post,* and in many letters and private talks, he urged Drury to kill it. The Premier turned the matter over to a Royal Commission for full investigation; when that body's report emphatically advised against the scheme, Sir Adam's postwar dream was abandoned.

For the Colonel the memory of that famous victory never dimmed. In the last dozen years of his life he could have a certain serene satisfaction when he passed, each noon hour on his way to lunch at the Toronto Club, Emmanuel Hahn's super-life-size statue of Beck on lower University Avenue.

# CHAPTER XXI

# BATTLING THE BOLSHEVISTS

> " 'Tis best to weigh
> The enemy more mighty than he seems."
> *Shakespeare*

---

THE COLONEL was fated never to win any of his wars against Bolshevism—but declared over the ensuing years that the real reason for his failure was not the superiority of the enemy but rather the stubborn ineptitude of Canadians in high places.

There were to be two major offensives, several years apart, and both, interestingly enough, launched as the direct result of private information from top-ranking sources in "Intelligence" abroad. For almost a quarter-century—probably ever since he became a friend of Sir Robert Baden-Powell, the Empire's famous Boer War celebrity, later author of the best seller, *My Adventures as a Spy,* and known around the world as founder of the Boy Scouts—Maclean had kept contact with certain members of the British and U. S. Intelligence Services. From time to time, they sent him confidential reports and queries concerning individuals in Canada, sometimes native-born, more often visitors, engaged in mysterious activities; his return comments and summations were often helpful, and as a result several close personal friendships had grown between the Toronto publisher and official investigators in Washington and London.

It was through a memorandum from the American capital that the Colonel first heard of Leon Trotsky, who with Lenin would lead the Bolshevik Revolution in November 1917. The date of the Colonel's advance information is not exactly determinable now, but that he received it before Trotsky was permitted to sail from New York on March 27, 1917 (a fortnight before the U.S. entered the war) is a certainty. By the time the ship had put into harbor at Halifax, N.S., and the Trotsky party taken off at the request of British Secret

Servicemen aboard, Maclean had forwarded copies of the U.S. documents to Ottawa's chief of Intelligence, Major General William G. Gwatkin, and was pressing members of the Cabinet to make the obvious decision of holding Trotsky in detention. It is not clear if Washington had already alerted Ottawa directly, or whether the sole pipeline between the two governments was the Colonel in Toronto. Stranger things have happened, especially in wartime—and a possible inference is that two opposing points of view obtained among the American group. If the seniors vetoed the suggestion for immediate detention, those in favor of such action might well have decided on the unofficial way round, via their dependable friend, Maclean.

He did his best to complete the mission, yet, in spite of "the file" placed in Ottawa's hands, plus other evidence readily available from the New York City Police's crack Bomb Squad which had shadowed the wild man, Canada let Trotsky go—back to the country he had not seen since his escape from Siberia in 1905, and back to make a quick peace with Germany, thus eliminating the Russian front and enabling full enemy concentration against the Western Allies.

The frustration of the Colonel can well be imagined. All through his remaining days he would bring forth this wartime episode as an example of the powerful, unseen influences which could be brought to bear upon gullible officials whom he grouped under the general term, "Ottawa." He would recall how he had "asked Ottawa not to let Trotsky go. My American friends had warned me that he wanted to get back to Russia, link up with other revolutionaries and take Russia out of the war. My friends in New York sent me copies of his speeches to show that he was a subversive character. I sent these, too, to Ottawa. But they would not listen to me."

Actually it appears now—with the help of dispassionate hindsight —that Ottawa was not to blame for either of the vital decisions: (a) the initial detaining or (b) subsequent release of Trotsky.

To be sure, the U.S. and British Intelligence people had put him under close surveillance almost immediately following his arrival in New York from Spain in mid-January 1917. They knew his regular activities: editorial writer for a local Russian language radical sheet and frequent contributor to a German publication of the same slant; a minor office employee in the British War Mission, where his superior was a well-known Canadian executive from the CPR, also an expert in Military Intelligence, Colonel John S. Dennis; evening lecturer to certain small Manhattan gatherings where the wispy-whiskered zealot held forth on the Marxist Utopia which would arise after the world revolution—the essential next move. Plain-clothesmen followed Trotsky on these rounds and had complete information concerning his family life in the dingy three-room flat in the Bronx. The reason for this constant attention had little to do with his anarchistic theories; rather he was suspected of working in the interests of the Germans.

Apparently no specific charge could be laid against him, for when he determined to return to Russia to play a role in the upheaval just beginning (under the Lvov-Kerensky provisional government, which had taken over after the downfall of the Czar), arrangements at the New York end went through without a hitch. The pause at Halifax was routine, as all neutral ships, such as the Norwegian *Kristianafjord* on which he was booked, were required by the British to stop there for examination. The decision to remove Trotsky & Company had been made by the senior Naval Officer, acting on instructions of the British government.

Mrs. Trotsky and her sons spent the next few weeks in a Halifax hotel, living comfortably; "they were never short of money," observers later reported. (Yet the family wage-earner had pulled out of New York in such haste that he was still owed three weeks' salary by the War Mission; months later Colonel Dennis' various letters to him on the matter were finally acknowledged from St. Petersburg with a cryptic reply—"No, keep the money; I'm not interested.")

From the ship, Trotsky and his little group of four neophytes were taken to an internment camp in a converted factory at Amherst, N.S., and there he quickly became conspicuous for his constant harangues concerning the proletarian revolution. He had time, as well, to cable Prime Minister Lloyd George in England, demanding immediate release. Soon that worried head-of-state was being besieged by many such messages; Trotsky sympathizers throughout the world suddenly spoke up, urging that he be allowed to proceed overseas, arguing that his presence in Russia could stabilize the situation and reinvigorate the war effort on the eastern front.

The British government had to come to a decision quickly, and practically with eyes blindfolded. There had been no time to assess the full implications of Kerensky's take-over; he himself had volunteered no information to his "Allies" as to the withdrawal of Russian troops from the combat lines, although the persistent rumor of mass desertions through the utter powerlessness of his pseudo-government would soon be verified. So, when St. Petersburg made its official request to London that Trotsky be released, the British acquiesced. He and his party, eight in all, sailed for Russia after almost a month on Canadian soil.

The Colonel seethed. Regardless of the plain facts apparent at the moment, or of the more carefully reasoned appraisals by historians later, John Bayne Maclean held "Ottawa" solely responsible for the decision. It is interesting, though, to note that he waited until well after the Armistice to declare himself in print. Was he avoiding further clashes with the censor, or did he just wish to spare his old friend, Prime Minister Sir Robert Borden, another ruckus during that critical stage of the war? At any rate, the date was June 1919, when both *Maclean's Magazine* and *The Financial Post* presented his signed article under the heading, "Why Did We Let Trotsky, Bolshevist Leader, Go?"

He opened with the statement that "some Canadian politicians or officials were chiefly responsible for the prolongation of the war, the great loss of life, the wounds and sufferings of the winter of 1917 and the great drives of 1918. While our armies were hanging on in France, they were being betrayed in Ottawa and down in Halifax." In the lengthy dissertation that followed, he ranged far and wide to muster all the points he deemed salient: that Trotsky, originally "Braunstein," was German-born and "a German spy" during his months in New York; that this creature, a boasting braggart on a platform, had "whined and cried in abject terror" when taken ashore at Halifax, and then, "when he found he was not to be shot, his bluff returned"; the British Secret Service, knowing his record, had fought bitterly against his release; moreover, U. S. Intelligence people had been so astounded by the decision that they had dispatched an official to Ottawa to make inquiries at the Secretary of State's Department.

Just there the Colonel's piece abruptly detours to deplore what he considered the general weakness and incompetence at that period in the British Embassy in Washington; it just might have happened, he guardedly implies, that the final maneuvering for Trotsky's release had occurred there. Suddenly the Colonel's next paragraph of just two sentences arrests the eye: "Yet Hon. Mr. Burrell tells Parliament there are no records. Who are they trying to protect or hide?" From that unanswered challenge, the article just as swiftly reverts, in typical Maclean *non-sequitur* style, to further description of Trotsky's habits and methods.

How the Honorable Martin Burrell, then Secretary of State, managed to rate a mention—in fact, the only member of the Ottawa

government to be named—might remain just one more mystery in
this jumbled puzzle were it not for the plain, solid fact that the Colonel
never liked him. On one occasion, he had described Burrell to the
Prime Minister as "a charming but hopelessly impractical Secretary of
State." When the two had first met during a tussle concerning censorship, which came within that Department's purview, the Colonel had
resented Burrell's officiousness, a way of delivering "instructions and
dictations." Perhaps this little temperamental disharmony lay at the
root of the Colonel's conviction, still thriving even twenty years later,
as set forth in a memo from Palm Beach, that "Burrell, along with his
deputy, was all the time working against the detention of Trotsky in
Canada."

Whether the Colonel's interpretations were close to the mark or not,
certainly the Trotsky affair had a permanent, galling effect on the
Canadian who had in this case only tried to serve his country. At
the same time, it spurred him on to still more intensive effort. Under
the title, "Planning Soviet Rule in Canada," his next article in
*Maclean's Magazine* discloses that one Sauteri Nuorteva, alias Nyberg,
a German ex-convict and head of a propaganda bureau in New York,
"has been wielding great power in Ottawa." Through his sinister
activities during the recent Winnipeg strike he had "almost accomplished
part of his scheme," which was to set up "a Soviet government" in the
western city.

The Colonel held firmly to the theory that Canada's recent enemies,
the Germans, were behind the Bolshevist threats. The industrial unrest,
at home and in other Allied countries, would, he predicted, spread
and increase, becoming "a war for trade, for money, and it is the hired
agents in Germany's employ" who were fomenting the trouble. And
suddenly, as usual, the Colonel interrupts his theme with a truly
amazing revelation: "Now it is definitely known that at least one
German accompanied every Corps leaving Canada"; indeed, from
1914–18 there was a well-organized network to which "regimental
spies" reported and from which they took orders.

As to a remedy for the current postwar situation, the Colonel
seemed a little uncertain, although he suggested that the Minister of
Justice in Ottawa detail a capable, trusted agent to investigate "the
real facts," and punish the guilty; at the same time, the government
should start a counterpropaganda campaign against subversive operators from outside. And much, much of the present menace would
have been obviated had Trotsky been kept in detention . . .

Campaign No. 1 against the Bolshevists had been lost but not forgotten. With that bitter experience to sharpen his strategy, he could now, at the opening of the 1920s, drive ahead with Campaign No. 2.

This fresh effort had been inspired by a file of special documents dispatched to him from friends in the British Secret Service. Carefully assembled data showed that several of the new Communist-front organizations in the United States were involved in a plan to win recruits in Canada and to that end were concentrating on two important areas: the labor unions and the universities. After careful study of the reports and a quick glance round locally, the Colonel decided such activities would certainly bear watching and exposing, especially those on the campuses. Possibly he was not unmindful of Hearst's recent public avowal to hunt down all "the Reds" now teaching Young America in the classrooms.

Canada may have needed a little stirring-up, for it was a fact—as amply borne out by the files of Ottawa's official *Labour Gazette* covering those years—that Communism was being not merely debated but preached at meetings organized among college populations. In most cases, the proselytizers were "visitors from abroad," attractive, studious young men, seemingly wholly caught up in the high-minded ideal of production for use, not for profit. From the Colonel's point of view, such theories were not merely impractical, they represented what he called "revolutionary radicalism," designed primarily to weaken Canada and the British Empire, and also to deride and destroy the reputations of sound business leaders. Once or twice the Colonel discovered the *agents provocateurs* in the act of using highly respected names for their own devious purposes, as when one young man, publicized as "Mr. Rothschild of the famous banking family," lectured to a University of Toronto group on the happy prospect of the collapse of private enterprise. The Colonel lost no time exposing the hoax.

But in spite of an occasional minor factual revelation of the kind, Campaign No. 2, carried on for two or three years in both the *Post* and *Maclean's Magazine,* was a dismal failure. The only person to pay it any heed was Sir Arthur Currie, principal of McGill University and former commander of Canada's troops in France. He wanted no Communists on his campus, and from time to time he would write to the Colonel for confidential reports or opinions concerning certain speakers who had offered to address the students. Currie quite arbitrarily kept all suspicious characters off his premises.

Around Toronto's University, however, the Colonel's allegations met with vehement rejection. Of course there were radicals at student meetings, just as there always had been and are today, whenever inquiring young minds join to search out the problems of social organization. But the governors, including Sir Edmund Walker, president of the Canadian Bank of Commerce, saw no threat to the peace and security of the country in such activities, and said so in firmly worded public statements. The man most deeply hurt was Sir Robert Falconer, the university's distinguished president, renowned scholar and theologian; he may have suffered as much from the Colonel's patronizing tone as from the accusations. Under the heading, "Anti-Capitalism Encouraged at University of Toronto," the campaigner wrote that, while Falconer was an intellectual, "a great, good, kindly Nova Scotia Presbyterian of the old type," (he was five years younger than the Colonel), he knew nothing of the intrigue and crookedness of the world; presumably "he has heard of Bolshevism, but doesn't understand it," etc.

The university's staff, the student body and countless local educationalists and well-wishers joined in the Toronto resistance movement to the Colonel's attacks. Letters to newspapers ranged from savage criticism to ridicule. But the matchless *finale* in defense of the university, the retort courteous as well as sharply thrusting, was to await the masterhand of one of the Colonel's fellow journalists, unquestionably none other than Joseph E. Atkinson, owner of the Toronto *Star,* in which the following unsigned editorial appeared on June 22, 1923:

### COLONEL MACLEAN IN HIS HAUNTED WOOD

In the olden days, it was not uncommon for the Crusaders to see the air filled with phantom armies, men on horseback riding down the clouds with swords a-shining.

One is reminded of those strange manifestations when reading in Colonel John B. MacLean's paper, *The Financial Post,* the curious articles in which it is alleged that secret and sinister influences are at work in the University of Toronto.

It is all so deeply and darkly mysterious. Colonel MacLean wants the reader to understand that he could tell you things that would make your flesh creep and then he tries to make your flesh creep without having told you anything.

What he wants you to feel is that there is a secret, insidious conspiracy of Red internationalists going on at midnight in the vaults under the university, that the cleverest spies and plotters in the world are engaged in this malign business, but that, with all their cunning, their doings are known to Colonel John Bayne MacLean and *The Financial Post*. The gage is taken up. The battle is joined. Colonel MacLean leads on. Nobody knows against whom he is contending, nor can anybody ever learn, unless he tells them, how the war is faring. It is a phantom fight in which the Colonel is engaged. He leads a phantom army against a phantom foe, he fires soundless cannon at unseen targets, and all the casualties are shadows. All this seems to be going on in a sort of haunted wood the whereabouts of which nobody but Colonel MacLean knows.

The people who have got into controversy with Colonel Mac-Lean and the *Post* about this matter are substantial enough. President Falconer and Sir Edmund Walker are real persons and they dismiss lightly fanciful imaginings in support of which not a particle of evidence has been produced.

The charge is that sinister work has been going on at the University of Toronto, deeply under cover. When asked to produce a single item of proof, *The Financial Post* flourishes the names of Nicholas Murray Butler, Samuel Gompers and Elihu Root. It can scarcely be suggested that they know what is going on in the vaults of Varsity. If the flourishing of these names does not impress you, the *Post* flourishes other names, that of W. A. Dowler and another name, that of—let us quote so that we may convey the full effect—"a great loyal Canadian like the Roman Catholic Bishop of London, M. Fallon, of whose earnestness there could be no doubt when he said with deep emotion (do not overlook the deep emotion): 'If they would only take foreign influences out of Ireland, the Free State would be the happiest country in the world.' "

If that doesn't convince President Falconer and Sir Edmund Walker that Colonel John B. MacLean knows dark, deep and mysterious things that are going on at Varsity, why, no doubt, *The Financial Post* can publish another article and flourish even greater and more impressive names with similar relish and irrelevance.

Although the campaign against Communists on Campus was his major task, the Colonel managed to keep a wary eye on their penetration in other directions. Thus in 1922, he was quick to pounce when the "Save the Children Fund," organized for famine relief in the Ukraine, opened its cross-Canada appeal. Surely all well-informed persons, he declared, would realize this was actually a machine for raising money for Communist propaganda and merely adopting a humanitarian theme as a mask. Then he popped the inevitable question: What was "Ottawa" doing?

Well, in this case, Ottawa acted. The Colonel's articles disturbed Prime Minister Mackenzie King, especially in view of the government's recent decision to support the fund and delegate a Cabinet Minister to serve as honorary member of the Committee. An investigation was ordered, and the Colonel gladly turned over some of his special information to the Honorable James A. Robb, Minister of Trade and Commerce. Soon an order-in-council went through, safeguarding all contributions, and promising government co-operation only if a suitable voluntary agency, acting for Canada, could be formally established. In the end, the Canadian fund amalgamated for administrative purposes with the British operation, and a highly respected British Quaker accepted the appointment to supervise allocation of all moneys raised.

The Colonel's original suspicions may have been farfetched; nevertheless, he was instrumental in forcing the government's concern and in ensuring that contributions actually went to famine relief.

Through these exciting times of peering and prodding, his range of acquaintance had widened to include certain exotic characters—some of them volunteering enthusiastic support of his program, others having to be ferreted out and exposed as dupes or active workers in the proletarian movement. At one point, the Colonel was in direct touch with the man he believed to be Communist Russia's chief propaganda agent in Canada.

His name was Louis Kon. He had been born in Russia, son of a wealthy factory owner, but, by disdaining the traditional Tolstoyan career of a cavalry officer and preferring the stimulation of "cell" meetings with fellow students, he had come under surveillance and decided to leave the country. In 1907, at the age of twenty-five, he arrived in Winnipeg, took out naturalization papers, and very quickly rose to the post of immigration and colonization chief for the Grand Trunk Pacific in that city. After World War I, he was comfortably ensconced in Montreal as public relations officer for Montreal Light, Heat & Power and its top man, Sir Herbert Holt, long-time president of the Royal Bank, and recognized throughout the land as Canada's No. 1 capitalist. Holt installed him in an office next to his own; there he could be instantly available to plan the necessary new forays in the constant war between private power interests, as in control in Quebec Province, and public ownership as represented by Ontario Hydro and Adam Beck.

It was their separate campaigns against the common enemy of socialized electricity that first brought Maclean and Kon together. Within a very short time, however, the latter's revelations re Beck had become very old-hat indeed compared with the Colonel's quietly accumulating evidence re Kon. The man had managed to keep in touch with friends in Russia: in 1916, he had served as secretary to a Canadian Economic Commission sent to St. Petersburg—and probably there were old chums from student days waiting to greet him; by 1925, when the Soviet government announced a "chief trade commissioner in Canada," Kon got the appointment and said goodbye to Montreal Power and the gospel of private enterprise. His first job was to tour Western Canada to buy horses urgently needed in the U.S.S.R., and soon he was placing sizable orders for binder twine and farm machinery. But he had not forgotten his former "confrère," the magazine publisher. Sometime in 1926, the Colonel received an invitation from Kon to join a few other leading Canadian businessmen in a sponsored visit to the Soviet Union; there they could see for themselves this great market's needs for various types of imported goods. The suggestion met with a polite refusal from University Avenue headquarters.

Then came another Russian overture. Two large packages arrived from the Soviet's trade commissioner; one was addressed to the Colonel and the other to this author, who had recently become editor of *The Financial Post*. Each parcel contained a quart jar of caviar— at that period virtually unprocurable in Canada, an extremely valuable luxury. Over the next week, the Colonel managed to drop in on the *Post* group almost daily. "How are you feeling, Chalmers?" he would ask, and the answer, "Just fine," stayed the same, almost to the point of monotony. Finally, the editor ventured to inquire the reason for this sudden concern, and he was countered with a second question that told all. "But have you been eating the caviar sent by that Bolshevik in Montreal?" Yes, and it was good! That evening, no doubt the Macleans broached their jar of caviar, knowing it was all fish eggs and quite innocent of poison.

Kon would have joined in the laughter, had he known. To most of his acquaintances, he appeared a decent, studious fellow, with nimble wit and a not unattractive personality. Yet his *dossier* would seem to offer some support for the Colonel's suspicions. After Prime Minister King severed relations with Russia, the trade commission closed down, but by 1930 Kon had a "front" job again, as secretary of the Friends of the Soviet Union. Under the regime of Quebec's Premier Duplessis and his famous "padlock law" against subversive activities, Kon's Montreal office was raided and all documents seized. No charges were laid, no arrests made; Kon simply moved to a new address, opened for business and awaited the next onslaught. In all there were twelve such raids and lockouts under the direction of the Provincial Attorney General's department; one of them, as reported in the Legislature, yielded a file containing evidence that Kon kept an account in a Moscow savings bank; another padlocking later on was found necessary because the premises were being used for a "Communist school."

Kon died in 1956. When and if his bizarre life story is told, there should be a place in it for the name of John Bayne Maclean, the man who had the first doubt and at a time when Canada's No. 1 Communist propagandist was public relations expert for Canada's biggest capitalist.

In the Colonel's quest of revolutionaries and radicals—a self-imposed mission which would continue through the remainder of his active days—he drew a careful distinction between those dangerous types and the Socialists. The latter, he insisted, were merely misinformed, and they could be put right with the proper guidance. Perhaps that explains the volume of lively correspondence exchanged between him and Miss Agnes Macphail, first woman to be elected to the House of Commons, a vigorous but warmhearted Socialist, and frequently a thorn in the side of Canada's businessmen.

It was routine for Maclean to drop her a note of congratulation following any of her speeches, in Parliament or on the hustings. As her fiery comments and long-term aims were well removed from his political philosophy, the only assumption possible is that the Colonel approved of anyone who had been well brought up on an Ontario farm, as she had, who had done a conscientious stint at country schoolteaching, and who bore the good, dependable name of Macphail. The Colonel's father had been helped by a Macphail family when he was opening up his parish in Canada West; much later another Macphail—eventually Sir Andrew, and head of McGill's School of Medicine—had been a hard-working "stringer" for *Canadian Grocer*'s early issues, earning money to finance his university course. These little bits-and-pieces from the past could never be forgotten, as indicated in a letter from the Colonel to Agnes in 1941: "Keep up the good work you are doing. Based on your ancestry, representative of character, imagination and vision, I always felt you would grow from the babyhood of Socialism, through experience and observation, into a safe and sane public leader."

But the doughty Agnes, M.P., wanted no praise of that type. She replied: "So you think I *was* a Socialist and that I am becoming safe and sane. That worries me a little. The next stage after that is stagnation. Just see where safe and sane leadership is getting Canada."

Another contact with the left-of-center ranks developed in the Colonel's later years, when he deliberately sought out and made friends with the Reverend James G. Endicott, son of a former Moderator of the United Church of Canada. Endicott, Jr., had been a soldier in World War I, later a missionary in China, and following his return to Canada, had drifted into Communist-front groups active among young people. He was frequently in attendance at international Communist gatherings in Moscow. In 1944, after listening to an Endicott address over the radio, the Colonel invited him to lunch, at which other guests were the company's president, Horace T. Hunter, and two senior editors. Endicott, good-looking, well-mannered, convincing in conversation, declared he was a Socialist, not a Communist. The Colonel, true to form, was happily reassured; his intuition had been proved right; now he could persuade this charming, knowledgeable young man of the cloth to approach socio-economic facts from the proper, realistic angle; and meantime, on his return to the University Avenue office, he would draft a letter thanking Endicott for the radio message which had been, as he was to express it, "an accurate and honest review of the world situation."

The Colonel was never one to quit, whether the goal was damnation or salvation.

# CHAPTER XXII

## THE COLONEL AND HIS EDITORS

"The duty of the press is to comfort the
afflicted and afflict the comfortable."
*Finley Peter Dunne*

THE COLONEL loved controversy, not because he was a quarrelsome
person, but because he believed he had a responsibility to expose
the failings, intrigues and possible malfeasance of men in public life,
and also because, like any good journalist, he was aware that one
well-aimed rousing attack would attract more readers than a dozen
bland, factual articles.

But there were two kinds of controversy: the deliberate challenge
carefully planned and presented with full calculation of the risks;
and the other kind, where, through editorial misjudgment, carelessness
or just happenstance, a magazine suddenly found itself condemned
for offending its own public. In 1923, *Maclean's* would have that
dismaying experience, one which the Colonel was never to forget.

The editor, J. Vernon Mackenzie, had been assistant to Costain;
after the latter's departure he had moved up and continued the policy
of publishing articles and fiction by the leading Canadian writers of
the day. "Mac" (the signature often used for his chatty column on
the contents page) had little perceptive, analytical capacity; he was
a bluff, hearty individual who reinforced his strength hour by hour
with a chew of candy or gum from the top drawer of his desk.

Shortly after taking over, Mackenzie proposed that *Maclean's* promote a competition for an original Canadian novel. The Colonel
approved, and so, in association with the English book firm of Hodder
& Stoughton, the announcement was made and immediately caught
the attention of the writing fraternity, coast to coast. The prize of
$2500 was an impressive lure, at a time when first-rights short stories

brought little more than $100–$150 apiece. The judges, all of them well known, were recruited from areas outside the sponsors' staffs.

Some 250 manuscripts were received. To everyone's delight, it was an unknown author, Gordon Hill Grahame, war veteran, still in his twenties and then living in Ontario's Kawartha country, who captured the prize with his novel *The Bond Triumphant*. *Maclean's* editor, after a careful reading, split the script into five sections for serializing, and then handed them on for suitable illustration by Charles W. Jefferys—the ideal choice for a story out of Canada's far past.

The setting was French Canada in 1661. Although Etienne, the young hero, and his newfound love, both fictional, provided ample romantic interest, certain actual figures from history were given prominent roles in the plot development. Among these was none other than Bishop Laval, Vicar-Apostolic in Canada, revered by generations of French-speaking Canadians, and regarded by historians as one of the true moulders of Canada. But Grahame offered his own interpretation of Laval, presenting him as kind and gentle in personal matters, yet at the same time an overly strict and pious bigot, constantly at loggerheads with the secular authorities who should, he insisted, always be subject to the guidance of the Pope and his representative.

As soon as the July 1, 1923, issue was in the mails and on the newsstands, protests began to arrive. Catholic readers, both French and English, churchmen and laymen alike, wrote bitter letters; within a few days Catholic publications denounced *Maclean's* and the prize novel as another contemptible example of Protestant ignorance. Although today the book would hardly be regarded by French Catholics as offensive, the situation in the early twenties was sufficiently delicate to make any such story theme by an English-speaking writer in an English-language magazine highly suspect.

Another criticism, seldom particularized at the time but frequently discussed later, had to do with one of the illustrations. Jefferys had shown the two young characters seated on a bench, the girl smiling, eyes modestly downcast, as Etienne, with left arm about her shoulders, and the other clasping her hand, seeks to draw her into an embrace. The shock element derived from her costume: *she wore a nun's habit.* A quick reading of the adjacent text would have disspelled any alarm, however, for "Sister Jacqueline" had taken no vows but was merely serving as a volunteer lay-sister in the nuns' hospital during the

*"There is nothing to forgive, you foolish boy," said Jacqueline.*

current smallpox epidemic. Indeed, Etienne too is relieved, and his
ardor unleashed, when he hears from her own lips—right there in
the first installment—that she is "as free as you are."

Within a few hours after the deluge of protests began, the Colonel
requested a complete set of galley proofs so that he might read the
story to its conclusion. When he finished, he was not convinced that
the novel was either anti-Catholic or anti-French-Canadian, yet the
fact that those two groups for whom he had long held respect thought
so—in some cases going so far as to allege a deliberate plan on the
part of *Maclean's* to stir up religious and racial bias—urged him to a
decision. He ordered that the serial be dropped.

Mackenzie and his staff were staggered. This was an unheard-of
action by a great magazine in any country; the whole nation would
be witness to the *débacle* involving one of the finest Canadian
novels of all time, the long-awaited prize-winner in which so much
time and money had been invested. But the Colonel was adamant,
and *Maclean's* readers got just the first installment. Their July 15
issue listed *The Bond Triumphant* in the table of contents, in a section

which had been printed prior to the decision, but the pages specified contained a fiction piece by Archie P. McKishnie instead.

No explanation was offered until the August 15 issue. A brief statement affirmed that: "The story was taken entirely on the judgment of, and awarded first prize by, a committee of literary experts outside our organization. It is absolutely contrary to the principles and policies upon which *Maclean's Magazine* has been built up to publish partisan material which would hurt any reputable body of citizens in the Dominion." A final sentence sums up the objectives of the publication: "A Canadian magazine, the contents of which will be welcomed cordially in every real Canadian home, regardless of religion or race; and will further the development of goodwill and understanding through the interpretation of the sections and divisions of our people, each to the other, for the purpose of building up Canadian nationhood."

It sounds a little like the Colonel himself—and indeed he had been busy with the same sort of explanatory messages and apologies to scores of his Catholic and French-speaking friends. They in turn wrote him letters of gratitude and praise for his brave action in withdrawing the serial.

Nevertheless *The Bond Triumphant* did reach the public in other ways, and, because of the wide publicity attending the magazine incident, found an eager audience. The Toronto *Telegram,* strongly Protestant "Orange" at that period, bought serial rights and shared publication of the novel with several other dailies. In due course, Hodder & Stoughton brought out the book which sold well. All in all, the Colonel's stern ruling of the previous midsummer may even have advanced the cause of Canadian literature.

John Bayne Maclean was an active force in the editing of his namesake publication during Vernon Mackenzie's tenure. In 1921, he had opened its pages to a highly flattering article concerning the man he had so violently disliked on a certain Montreal occasion years before: Winston Churchill. The author bore a famous name too: General Sir Ian Hamilton—and the story behind his *Maclean's* story had its interesting moments and long-term results.

The friendship between the Canadian publisher and the British general had flourished since their meeting during the Diamond Jubilee events, and especially after Hamilton's first visit to Canada early in the new century. He had happened to mention his plans for proceeding to Washington where he hoped it just might be possible to meet a soldier he admired very much: President "Teddy" Roosevelt. Immediately the Colonel set wheels in motion. He did not know the President, but Mrs. Maclean's family and the Roosevelts were long-standing friends. When Hamilton left Toronto, he had Anna Slade Maclean's letter of introduction to "Mr. President," who was pleased to receive him. Hamilton valued both the occasion and the enabling courtesy.

Now began a steady flow of correspondence between the militia colonel and the professional soldier, with full exchange of confidences on both sides. One of Sir Ian's special undertakings was to win over the Colonel to a higher opinion of Churchill, whose presence and exploits added zest to the general's memories of operations in India, Egypt and South Africa and founded a lifelong friendship. The Colonel listened respectfully, but it was some years before he showed signs of yielding. By then, Hamilton's distinguished career was clouded by the World War I disaster of Gallipoli, which he had been commanding general. On his return to a civilian existence in Britain, he found himself the popular "goat" for that campaign and its appalling losses; by 1920, the publication of his impressive *Gallipoli Diary* in two volumes seemed merely to confirm the suspicions among top military echelons, "for," they now reasoned, "nobody could turn out literature like that and still be a real soldier!"

The Colonel did not agree. He had read the book, sent to him with greetings from the author, and he gave it full marks on every count: fine writing, honest reporting, and illuminated at every turn by expert military knowledge. The *Diary* was a classic of its kind and the Colonel recognized it as such.

Hamilton could be an outstanding addition to *Maclean's* galaxy of authors—and what more appealing assignment than an article on that favorite subject, Churchill? So off went the Colonel's request, suggesting a very personal appraisal of the young man whom Hamilton had encountered on far frontiers, and who in his forties looked like a rising political star, having just been made Colonial Secretary. The old soldier responded enthusiastically, and the June 15, 1921, issue's special feature headed "The Right Honourable Winston Spencer Churchill, by Gen. Sir Ian Hamilton, G.C.B., D.S.O." gave John Bayne Maclean, the instigator, a justifiable flush of pride. It was an adventure story that left Alger and Henty, and even Kipling, far behind, and it was all true.

Hamilton had first met Churchill, "an eager, chubby-faced boy," on a ship crossing the Indian Ocean in 1897; a year later the lieutenant reported for duty at the general's headquarters, recently set up to render support for the loyal Sikhs of the Malakand. Hamilton was rather surprised at the sudden reappearance, but he was quick to perceive that this young man, scion of the great Marlborough family, was possessed of boldness and determination to a marked degree. Churchill insisted on seeing military action; so, quite naturally, he went where the action was. "All day he was out stalking the enemy snipers or relieving some picket whose position seemed to open an opportunity for bloodshed," Hamilton records, probably with an indulgent smile on his face. "At night, he wrote copiously"—for, even then, Churchill was bent on sharing his experiences through correspondence for the London papers.

By September 1898, when Hamilton had returned to England, his erstwhile lieutenant wrote a long letter to "My dear General" from the Sudan; there, it seems, action had been available in abundance during the previous weeks. Hamilton's quoted extract of some 1500 words from the letter includes a vivid description of Churchill's mounted detachment's unexpected confrontation with thousands of enemy dervishes—and this time they were not spearmen, but "armed with rifles." It was a harrowing half-hour or so, and the aftermath would continue to be a somber memory, but Churchill wound up his private report with the words, "I am glad to have added the experience of a cavalry charge to my military repertoire." Another paragraph mentions a small sortie into territory known to be highly dangerous. Churchill wrote: "I informed the attached officers on the way up that there was only one part of the despatch in which they could hope to be mentioned. They asked what part. I replied, 'The casualty list.'" A fairly accurate forecast, as out of eight (including the officer-correspondent) the casualties were one killed and two badly wounded.

But Hamilton indicates that Churchill's most dangerous enemies were not among the dervishes but, rather, in the top British command. His name "was to be written down in Lord Kitchener's blackest books"—an attitude based on prejudice, and nurtured in the "special preserve" atmosphere of the great "K's" long-time headquarters in Khartoum. It was well known, Hamilton states frankly, that Churchill had been invited by Kitchener "to stay away."

Hamilton's story then moves on to the South African War, and his own delight in another reunion with his irrepressible young friend, who one day turned up, this time accompanied by his cousin, the

Duke, and begged to report for duty, any duty which the good General thought fit to assign. Churchill was immediately taken on staff, and, over the next grinding months that were to involve many critical maneuvers including the British march from Bloemfontein to Pretoria, he proved himself "quick, audacious, decisive in big things or little"—indeed, an officer capable of "flashlight decision." "He had a great eye for country, and danger made no odds to him at all," declares Hamilton. And as to character: "Whatever Churchill's faults, he is affectionate in his friendships, enduring in his gratitude, loyal in his *camaraderie*, punctilious in his execution of an agreement, and, above everything, first class company in a tiger shoot."

So, in that summer of 1921, at least one constant reader of *Maclean's Magazine* found himself persuaded to relent a little in his long-standing antagonism to Winston Churchill. Not only did the Colonel publish the article and give it full play with picture layouts, but he took the rather unusual action of sending advance proofs to Munsey, with the suggestion that this might make an interesting feature for his U.S. newspapers. Munsey accepted with thanks.

The Colonial Secretary was pleased too, and soon the Colonel received a cordial invitation to visit the Churchills in the South of France. On Maclean's next trip abroad he was happy to put Cannes on the itinerary, but by the time of arrival he was informed that his host had been called back to London, and thus their first meeting was to be delayed until 1925 when they found themselves seated side by side at a luncheon at the Ritz in Paris.

However, the earlier engagement had had its special compensation: the Colonel became acquainted with Mrs. Churchill, and he was immediately magnetized. "She is one of the most charming women I have ever met!" he wrote a Canadian friend. She was well-informed and had understanding in depth concerning the important topics of the day; at the first luncheon, she and the Colonel enjoyed discussing the rivalry between her husband and Sir Robert Horne for the Conservative leadership. As a result of the visit, the Colonel added her name to his list of treasured friends the world over; it was a delight to write to her on any propitious occasion, and to forward copies of his *Maclean's* articles. Each brought a polite note of acknowledgment, and occasionally a promise to show Winston the enclosure. Once or twice in the interest of better international relations, the Colonel arranged an introduction for certain friends. After dining with the William Randolph Hearsts in New York, and learning of their early departure for England, Maclean dispatched a note to Sir Ian Hamilton, asking his help in ensuring "some flattering attention during their visit." Hamilton put the suggestion to Churchill, who not only entertained the Hearsts but saw to it that they met other leaders of state and society.

The subject of the Colonel's special editorial project had been made happy by the experience; so, too, the author. Sir Ian now came forward with dozens of ideas for *Maclean's* features, including a finished manuscript discussing "Belted Guernseys," which he was now raising in Scotland. These, he maintained, would be ideal for Canada, as "they would milk copiously and cut up well in the Hudson's Bay territory." Most of the suggested topics were of the same far-out type, and when Vernon Mackenzie protested, the Colonel wrote a nicely diplomatic letter to his friend, explaining that the magazine now found it necessary to confine its attention to Canadian articles.

In 1930, at the age of seventy-seven, Sir Ian visited Canada again. The Colonel arranged a special calendar of events, including formal dinners and an evening inspection of the 48th Highlanders, of which Hamilton was Honorary Colonel. The old soldier found every little detail a new experience. He had never before drunk the King's health immediately after the soup (still a general custom in heavy-smoking Canada); never before been on his feet making a speech while the main course was passed; never before appeared in full evening dress to inspect a battalion. His later letters constantly referred to the delights of the visit—and by then, it seems, he had quite forgotten his dreams of herds of Belted Guernseys growing fat on the green pastures around Hudson's Bay.

Aside from the Hamilton-Churchill triumph, most of the Colonel's efforts on behalf of *Maclean's* at that period continued to be of the watchdog variety—a situation forced on him by what he considered a near-crisis in 1921.

Hugh Eayrs of Macmillan's (the same Hugh Eayrs we met a few chapters back) had commissioned Augustus Bridle, well-known columnist and author of *Sons of Canada,* to write a book of brief, witty biographies drawn from the contemporary political scene. The title would be *Masques of Ottawa,* and to add a touch of mystery—and boost the sales—the author would be identified only by the pseudonym, "Domino." Vernon Mackenzie bounced into the act by buying the magazine rights, planning to present one chapter per issue, and for his own reasons changing the byline to "The Make-up Man." The articles were quite innocuous, certainly when compared with any good profile appearing in today's leading periodicals. Bridle made up for lack of research by squeezing every drop of juice from minor foibles and then attempting to serve up each dish with a twist of Chestertonian paradox. The public could take it or leave it, but the men subjected to the treatment, such as Sir William Mackenzie, the railway magnate, and Sir Henry Drayton, Minister of Finance, lost no time in complaining to the Colonel. Nothing could be done about the pieces already in print, but he decided he must see the remainder of the script. To his amazement, he discovered a section wholly devoted to "Colonel J. B. Maclean." Within a few days, the sheaf went back to Mackenzie, along with a sharp memo ordering the series to be abandoned immediately, but the real surprise for Mackenzie was the vacuum where the chapter on the Colonel had been. The editor took the hint and asked no questions. Even Eayrs offered no comment when the original script minus one profile was duly returned to him. The book eventually came out, but John Bayne Maclean did not appear in its cast of characters.

Certainly this bit of pilferage could be understood so far as his own magazine was concerned, but only extreme sensitivity and wounded pride must have dictated the decision as to book use. Was it the "light touch" that bothered him? The original manuscript is still in the Colonel's files. Here's how the first paragraph opens: "In the back drop of Canada's Stage, there has been for some years—how many we scarcely know—the figure of a man who wants to step into the show: a man who has made a phenomenal success of his own business and in his later life thinks he has time and talent for the business of other people; who from as many angles as he owns trade papers—and one magazine not so classified—has for the whole of this century so far been engaged in odd jobs of plumbing in the house called Canada."

Very few people knew much about this man, Colonel Maclean; "even his face is unfamiliar," and Bridle does his best to describe it . . . "truly remarkable," especially the head "which comes to a peculiar apex without a dome." The face gave little indication of the personality behind it; indeed, the author goes on, "In all the numerous times I have seen this man in various relations to other people, I have never seen him smile. His smiles are probably sub-conscious, or reserved for rare occasions when, if I were a confederate of his, I should expect something either portentous or villainous."

The article takes pleasant glances at the Colonel's history, business success, and his recent vigorous campaign against the Canadian Manufacturers' Association, which earns the comment, "Courage has many varieties. This is one of them." Schwab and Munsey are mentioned, and on the last page the sentence, "When the Colonel comes back from abroad ten chances to one he will write a series of articles describing his experiences in Europe with Celebrities such as one seldom expects to meet except at Monte Carlo," drew his penciled comment in the Colonel's hand, "Have never at any time done so— not even once."

Anyway, from Mackenzie's point of view, the man who hated censors was clearly proving how well he knew their ways. When another "mystery" about Ottawa personalities, this time a novel entitled *The Land of Afternoon*, with no author's name revealed, was offered to *Maclean's*, the editor took the precaution of passing the manuscript along to the Colonel for an opinion. At the latter's request, he made an attempt to establish the identity of the leading characters: Dilling and wife were former Prime Minister Meighen and Mrs. Meighen; Sir Eric Demby could be none other than the veteran bearded Tory, Sir George Foster; certain ladies in the gossipy pages might be wives of M.P.s on either side of the House.

The Colonel's final verdict on possible serialization was "No," supported with the following explanation by memo: "We must on no account publish matter that would hurt any person's feelings for the sake of creating a sensation. It is only when the interests of the country are involved that we should hurt anyone's feelings. It has never been my policy to create a sensation and get talked about. I want to get our publications recommended by readers primarily because of their value and interest and their reliability and fearlessness. There are plenty of sensational stories available that would cause the magazine to be talked about as *Jack Canuck* [a wild and earthy weekly] is talked about, but unless there is some principle at stake, unless it is for the good of the country, I would not think of using these. When a publication is fighting its way for public recognition, it would be justified in a policy of sound, accurate sensationalism. We have got beyond that stage."

By 1926 Mackenzie had had enough. He resigned and after a short term as Canadian government trade commissioner in Glasgow, he became dean of the School of Journalism at the University of Washington. He was succeeded at *Maclean's* by H. Napier Moore, former New York special correspondent for the Montreal *Star*, and a popular contributor to the magazine since 1922, when his byline appeared on a short story. Moore, a first-rate journalist, early demonstrated his capacity as an editor. Although more cautious than Mackenzie, he had excellent judgment, and at all times remained fully aware of what Canadians wanted to read about themselves. He got, and deserved, the complete confidence of Maclean, Hunter and Tyrrell, and after editing *Maclean's* for twenty years, moved on to become the editorial director of the company as a whole.

Perhaps this is the place for a footnote of the "might-have-been" variety concerning the magazine's days between the two Great Wars. If a certain dashing Britisher named Major Francis Yeats-Brown had been able to get the job he wanted, it just might have come to pass that he would one day have occupied the editor's chair. In 1923, this thirty-seven-year-old veteran of soldiering in India, France and Mesopotamia arrived in Toronto on the last leg of a lecture tour. He was anxious to find steady employment, and his manager, a former employee at Maclean Publishing, brought him to see the Colonel. Questions and answers flew back and forth, Yeats-Brown insisting he could write the same sort of articles which he had read in *Maclean's*. No opening was available, however. A year later, the Colonel gave the same answer to further enquiries by mail. Eventually, Yeats-Brown seemed to have settled down as polo correspondent for the London *Times* and the New York *Herald Tribune,* and now the Colonel was besieged with special articles on the sport. They were returned, of course, with the gentle explanation that Canadians had never quite developed an interest in chukkers. But, said the Colonel, "why don't you write about your own experiences as a professional soldier, especially about those seven years served in India?" Yeats-Brown took up the suggestion; thus was born the well-known autobiography, and Hollywood movie, *Lives of a Bengal Lancer.* Yeats-Brown had at last found his *métier.*

The Colonel believed that every reputable publication should have well-defined policies, which would provide a strong guideline in every editorial decision. There should be no deviation from basic principles, regardless of pressures or their source. Any attempt by advertisers to influence or dictate, either by spending money in the publication or refusing to, must be resisted. (In fact, the Colonel became almost gleeful on several occasions when he heard of the cancellation of advertising contracts as a result of his own campaigning pieces; such action showed he was on the right track.) A paper or magazine must win the enduring loyalty of its readers by adhering to the standards it had laid down; with that condition achieved and maintained, it automatically became an important advertising medium. The experience of the Toronto *Star,* in the days of the battling left-winger, Joseph E. Atkinson, proved the point. Many businessmen condemned the paper as "subversive"; occasionally an outraged client would declare a boycott—but not for long. "Holy Joe's" service to his readers had drawn a very large audience with immense buying power which no advertiser could overlook, regardless of the paper's anticapitalist slant.

Any editor worth his salt was bound to agree with the Colonel's publishing doctrine. Certainly when this author took over as editor of *The Financial Post,* all those basic principles were accepted and kept constantly in mind. Nevertheless, experience showed that a few firm safeguards were needed for their better protection. "Campaigning" through a massive editorial effort to correct a great injustice or to achieve an important national objective had a legitimate place in the *Post's* service—yet surely all points of view were entitled to fair coverage in the news columns! (The Colonel regarded the publication of views contrary to his own as "propaganda.") And when a campaign had been fully won, or even partially, as often happens in an imperfect world, surely it should be dropped, for no reader wants to be bored with the same old arguments week by week.

Quietly, then, over the next few months, there was a tapering off in the Colonel's appearances in *The Financial Post;* readers were allowed a little change from the unceasing and unchanging broadsides against the CMA and Beck of the Hydro. The Colonel was at first nonplused, and later indignant. The *Post* had been his favorite medium, through which he spoke directly to the captains of industry and the financial elite; and under previous editors it had stayed wide open for anything he wanted to contribute. "After all," they argued, "he owns the paper, doesn't he?" Yet didn't the Colonel's own set of editorial ethics stipulate service to readers—not to the publisher—as the major responsibility?

Finally, the conflict was resolved by a simple announcement by the new editor to the Colonel. He could write any editorials he liked. If they carried the editor's judgment, they would be rewritten by him and published without byline as the views of the paper. If, on the other hand, they were not clear and lucid, if they were unfair or otherwise objectionable to the editor, they would be published somewhere in the paper, but not on the editorial page, and they would be clearly labeled, "by John Bayne Maclean," to advise all readers

that this was an individual, and not necessarily the *Post,* giving forth.
If the Colonel did not accept this arrangement, he could get himself
a new editor.

Perhaps it was a case of fools (especially that young one) rushing
in where old-timers (angels or otherwise) had feared to tread. Yet for
the sake of the paper, some measure of control had to be exercised
over the owner, even as with any other contributor.

The Colonel accepted the ruling but not exactly with good grace.
He tried to circumvent it in devious ways, even to delivering his
"copy" direct to the composing room, in the hope that this latest
smashing attack on an Ottawa bigwig, etc., would somehow get into
the paper without the editor's knowledge. Even when a piece was
properly channeled, there were headaches, for the Colonel had never
learned the discipline of deadlines. The *Post's* editorial page was "put
to bed" on Tuesday; he seldom came through with his big idea of
the week until 11 A.M., Wednesday—just one hour before the closing
of the last-minute news page, which happened to be the front one.
(The mechanical routine had to be unvarying in order to meet the
mailing schedule.) If the subject matter truly rated a position in the
paper, there would be a hectic skirmish to do the necessary rewriting
within the single, precious hour before that week's edition went on
the press.

Out of those regular crises would develop a *Post* feature which,
even after forty years, can still claim to be one of the most widely
read and influential departments in the paper. A double-column space,
headed "The Nation's Business," was reserved on the front page.
Each week the editor wrote his own copy and had it typeset well
in advance, ready to go. If the Colonel managed to come through
with a worthwhile contribution, capable of being quickly rewritten,
the original feature was lifted and his piece substituted.

In spite of the unhappy moments suffered by both parties at the
outset of the original plan, it was soon obvious that the Colonel
liked to have an editor who would stand up to him. The more the
two battled and outsmarted each other in the office, the closer their
personal relationship seemed to become. After a hectic Wednesday
closing, the editor and his wife would be invited to have dinner the
next evening at the Maclean residence. If there were other guests
present, they would listen to the Colonel's recounting, in terms of
mock censure, of the difficulties he was having with his young editor,
"but probably he will learn in time."

# CHAPTER XXIII

# FRIENDS, REGAL AND OTHERWISE

"The ornament of a house is the
friends who visit it"
*Emerson*

THE NEW assistant editor on the trade paper hurried along the corridor, rounded the jog toward the elevator and ran smack into the Colonel, just stepping off. He looked very fit, the bristling mustache white and gleaming against the Florida tan.

"Good morning. You're Edwards on *Men's Wear,* aren't you?"

"Yes, sir. Glad to see you back, sir. Was it a fine holiday?"

A slight clearing of the throat, and then the patient answer: "Young man, I never take holidays. When I go south or overseas, I keep in touch with the office and I do my regular office work. The reason I travel is to meet important people and dig up the news before it happens. I hope all of you boys will be able to do this one day."

This was the Colonel's standard reply to the normal greeting on his return from a long trip. It was heard in brief or detailed versions by some two generations of employees; after the first experience, however, they tried to remember to rephrase their welcome. For example, "I'm sure you've had a very busy time, Colonel," showed a proper empathy and staved off the sermon.

John Bayne Maclean actually did work hard during his travels. His month or more in Palm Beach each year yielded innumerable notes, sometimes two or three a day, to individual colleagues in Toronto. He reported on various encounters and conversations, passed along newly discovered diet routines, criticized the last issue of one of the publications, and invariably stressed the fact that he was terribly, terribly busy. Several times a week, he sent a long, general memorandum for circulation to twenty or more executives and senior staff. From February 21 to April 7, 1938, a period of forty-six days including Saturdays and Sundays, his round-robin dispatches alone contained a total of 32,940 words—all written by hand and retyped by his secretary.

The subjects were far-ranging, one of the shortest of the memos including these: a visit from Arthur William Brown, famous illustrator for *The Saturday Evening Post,* who discussed "what was happening on that magazine" . . . Didn't all serious-minded people feel that, basically, Hitler's aims for Germany's domestic success were the same as what they believed in for their own country? . . . The Joseph P. Kennedys (recently installed at the U. S. Embassy in London) were in Palm Beach and when they had a special party for their big family "gave instructions that their dinner table should be placed next to ours." . . . There was a story going around that Anthony Eden was a brother-in-law of Litvinoff . . . The Japanese were creating prosperity and happiness in Manchukuo . . . "Recently we were at dinner with Lord Iliffe on his yacht here, when the discussion turned to mining in Canada and Jules Bache mentioned that the Dome prospect had been first brought to him by Ambrose Monel"; Bache's associate was Bernard Baruch, and indeed the latter "told me three or four years ago that he was the second largest stockholder." . . . Rackets flourished in Florida; cooks and butlers were bribed with "a retaining fee, plus up to 10%" on all orders placed with supply firms for liquors, foodstuffs, etc. . . . "I see a reference to the late Father Duffy. We used to meet here on the beach, in our bathing suits. Governor Al Smith often said to us, 'When these two Canadians get together no one else has any chance to talk to them.'" . . . (And for general guidance in business or private life) "If a person prove himself unreliable once, watch him; if a second time, never again trust him."

A few years later, these regular reports to home-office of what the Colonel regarded as "news" even increased in number and length, following the Colonel's new routine of having his secretary, Miss Dove, accompany the party, which always included Ritchie, the chauffeur, and Mrs. Maclean's personal maid. The group's headquarters was a "cottage" named The Surf, a pleasant house with shingled exterior, delightfully situated in the grounds of The Breakers. The Macleans' allegiance to that hotel never faltered; when it burned down in 1925, they had escaped with little more than the clothes they were wearing; on the next visit the Colonel, worried about his wife's immobility, decided in favor of the separate, single-story residence.

Much of his entertaining and "news-gathering" took place at the Everglades Club, of which he had been a member ever since architect Mizner had completed the transformation of a military hospital into this sumptuous, neo-Spanish masterpiece. At the height of the season, the Colonel could be sure of meeting an impressive representation from American Who's Who and Debrett's during the noonday buffets; very quickly he realized his Toronto *confrères* would benefit from such opportunities, and he decided to invite, in rotation, executives and editors, with their wives, to join him for a Florida fortnight—at company expense.

A worthy idea, yes, but not many of those tentatively listed got to go. Horace Hunter tried Palm Beach once but found it too hot and humid; thereafter Pinehurst, N.C., would be his farthest-south destination. Others had to cancel the trip because of special business or family emergencies. More often, their respective superiors balked at the expense. The author of this book counted himself fortunate to manage two visits. At an Everglades luncheon given by the Colonel the guests included, among others, Replogle (Republic Steel); Bache, New York broker (chief shareholder in Walter Chrysler's automobile company, and still doing nicely with Canada's Dome Mine); Shepherd, the New England radio network owner; and Woolworth. The sole non-millionaire present went brazenly around the table asking each person's age; most of them were over eighty and the only guest under seventy-five was the interloper just arrived from Toronto.

But Palm Beach attracted others besides the rich industrialists and bankers. By 1939, it had become the winter playground for a well-to-do, leftish, smart set from Washington, enthusiastic backers of Roosevelt's New Deal, and quite as pro-Russian and anti-British as they were anti-Fascist. This was predominantly the audience that confronted *The Financial Post* editor when he accepted, at the Colonel's urging, an invitation to speak at the Palm Beach Round Table, which turned out to be a semi-serious, semi-social afternoon affair. The committee had suggested the subject, viz., a Canadian's interpretation of Neville Chamberlain's policies toward Hitler. Well, it had to be done. And there were one or two points worth emphasizing: that the Munich "peace"—while nothing to be proud of or contented with— had at least given Britain a vital extension of time, time for the gearing of industry and preparation for the war which was certain to come.

Almost from the outset, the speaker felt a great gulf fixed between

him and the circle of listeners. They had obviously expected a denunciation of Britain, in the manner of most of their other visitors, both
Old Country and Canadian; they wanted to have their own theories
upheld, i.e., that Britain had gone soft, that she should make it her
primary responsibility to keep the peace in Europe, and that she was
letting down the world by not stopping Hitler. It was the time when
American liberals decried in the same breath British Imperialism and
British unwillingness to carry the world's burdens. They were all for
American—but not British—isolationism. At no point in the ensuing
general discussion did any group member suggest that the United States
might be willing to share the burden of holding Hitler in check.
Mercifully, the meeting adjourned, to be followed by a cocktail bash
in which everyone joined, especially the speaker, who badly needed
a drink.

The Colonel himself quite missed the antagonism in the atmosphere; it was, he declared, "a worthwhile session," and his visitor had
"done well."

The Colonel's European jaunts, too, took on something of a repeat
pattern year by year, even though the geographical coverage might
range from the Mediterranean to the Scottish Highlands. So long as
Aunt Elise lived, a visit to her chalet northwest of Lisbon was
virtually a ritual of the totally ecstatic kind for a man who loved kings
and crowns and ancient bloodlines.

Just when the Colonel was first presented to the Countess d'Edla as
a new member of her family circle cannot be established with exactitude now. If the Macleans started their Portuguese pilgrimages in early
married life, it is quite likely they made formal bows to King Charles
I, who reigned until 1908, when he and his heir apparent were as-
sassinated. For the next two years Manuel II occupied the throne;
after a revolution forced his abdication (and quick withdrawal to a life
of luxury in England) Portugal became a republic. Royal palaces would
soon lose their sentry squads and open their gates to sightseers. Titled
personages and even princes, so long as they represented no threat
to the new state, were permitted to lead the same gay, unhurried lives
as in the past, and spend their remaining years discussing bygones.

With Anna's husband as an audience, the Countess could reminisce
to her heart's desire. Undoubtedly he heard from her own lips the
correct version of the story that used to amuse nineteenth-century
European courts—about Portugal's "two kings, one reigning, one

ruling." Translated, that meant Luiz, the very young heir to the throne, and his father, King Consort Ferdinand, who shouldered the serious responsibilities of the monarchy. The pair insisted on a protocol that amounted to simultaneous precedence. Each would enter the great reception hall at precisely the same moment but by opposite doors. Each moved slowly forward and, when they came face to face, the boy made a low bow to his father and kissed his hand, to be followed by the same formality on Fernando's part. Then, side by side, the two mounted the dais to receive their visitors.

Don Luiz and Don Fernando—as they were known to the Portuguese—spent much of their time at the fabulous Pena Palace in Sintra. The Countess's private residence was situated halfway down the nearby slope: none other than the chalet the Macleans were to visit in after years, and which still remains a special attraction for visitors to Portugal. By now Sintra's tourist guides have their own version of the old king's romance and they proffer it with full exotic impact. "Those windows up there—see?—belonged to Don Fernando's private suite. Now—see?—he could look down the hillside to the chalet where lived his mistress, the opera singer." The uninterrupted view also made possible a signal system; as dusk fell, a lighted candelabra behind the panes far above served to inform Elise that she would have a royal caller within the hour.

Mayhap there was an early phase involving these informal arrangements, yet it is a fact that the marriage took place in 1869, just eight years after Luiz began his reign; indeed, the young king himself sanctioned his father's wish that a title be bestowed on the bride. Like a certain famous lady from Baltimore in a later era, she was not allowed to become a Queen, but she did achieve the rank of Countess —and her husband continued with his duties to the nation.

Elise was constantly discussed, frequently criticized, sometimes disdained by the Old Guard who believed morganatic marriage a shameful business, yet the Macleans of Toronto were her devoted admirers and exceedingly proud of the connection. Other people's ignorance of this "royal" relationship could lead to an occasional embarrassing contretemps, as happened with one of the company editors during a dinner party at Austin Terrace.

Mrs. Maclean happened to ask, in her gracious hostess way, "What have you been reading lately?"

The guest replied, "Over the weekend, I read The Vanished Pomps of Yesterday, by Lord Frederick Hamilton."

"Oh," she exclaimed, her eyes flashing above the ropes of pearls, "that terrible man! He wrote those awful lies about my aunt." This is how "that terrible man" had dealt with the Countess:

Don Fernando had married morganatically, as his second wife, a dancer of American origin. This lady had a remarkably strident voice, and was much to the fore on the fortnightly afternoons when Don Fernando received the men of the Corps Diplomatique. For some reason or other, the ladies of the Diplomatic Body always found themselves unable to attend these gatherings. The courteous, genial old King would move about, smiling, dispensing his truly admirable cigars, and brimful of anecdotes and jokelets. The nasal, raucous tones of the ex-dancer, always known as the Countess, would summon him in English, "Say, King! You just hurry up with those cigars. They are badly wanted here."

I imagine that in the days of her successes on the stage the lady's outline must have been less voluminous than it was when I first made her acquaintance.

Even today, Lord Frederick's attempt at a quick impression has a rather false sound. No wonder the Colonel dismissed all that author's works as sheer impertinence "based on obvious ignorance."

Through Aunt Elise and her hospitality, John Bayne Maclean was brought into touch with various members of the European nobility; through his own perseverance, such pleasant first contacts often developed into firm friendships—as with the Duke of Alba. In September 1924 a special welcome to Toronto for the Duke and party was organized by the Colonel, who wrote to Honorable Harry Cockshutt, Ontario's Lieutenant-Governor, suggesting, if convenient, a tea at Government House, and requesting the pleasure of the Cockshutts' company for dinner with the same visitors at Austin Terrace. "The d'Albas are one of the richest families in Spain," he wrote, "I have known him . . . for a number of years. The remainder of their party, I am sure, will stand equally well." There is a persuasive footnote, to the effect that d'Alba is of Highland-Scotch ancestry, too. ("He comes of the Royal Stuart line," Maclean once explained to another friend. "I always tell him he's just good plain Jimmy Stuart to me.") The visiting group lived up to the Colonel's expectations, it seems, for the newspapers' report listed seven impressive names, five of them titled.

Strange little echoes of the Countess d'Edla saga reverberated now and then on the local scene. One morning, the editor and staff of

*Canadian Homes and Gardens,* the company's monthly "class magazine," covering architecture, decoration, landscaping, received a memo from the Colonel requesting pictures, clippings, descriptive material of "mid-18th Century Spanish or Portuguese bedrooms"; this material was needed at the earliest possible moment. After a frantic scurry through old magazine files and batches of reference books, the staff managed to produce a neat, well-documented presentation and forward it to his office downstairs. But the reason for this sudden interest in the sleeping habits of the Iberian Peninsula had to wait for a later flash by grapevine, to the effect that the Colonel's wife had recently received a magnificent antique bed from the estate of her aunt, who had died in Lisbon in 1929. Quite possibly, an overnight guest at Austin Terrace would have the thrill of seeing, even using, a king's bed, but, alas, none of the regulars for dinner or tea occasions could study it, because that would be an invasion of second-floor territory.

A Countess d'Edla souvenir with four centuries of history turned up at the sale of some Maclean family possessions after the Colonel's death. Ex-King Ferdinand II had presented to wife Elise a curious little, rectangular writing-box, richly carved. It was the wood itself which made the piece authentically venerable, for this came from Shakespeare's famous mulberry tree, planted by him after his move to New Place in Stratford-on-Avon, and destined to grow to immense size. Well over a century later, the occupant of the house, Reverend Dr. Gastrell, became so annoyed with the throngs of Shakespearean pilgrims who invaded his garden to see the tree that he ordered it chopped down. The indignant citizens salvaged the wood and various objects were fashioned from it. The writing-box had been commissioned as a gift to David Garrick, following his special Shakespeare Jubilee at Stratford in the year 1769. Eventually, the piece journeyed to the chalet in Portugal, then to the house on Toronto's "hill," and was finally bought for $6 at the auction sale by a local lady who still has it.

Although the Colonel's European travels never equalled the Palm Beach visits in memo output, they did add up to plenty of the same type of "hard work" on the ground, and especially when Munsey was along. Those two friends made a strong assault team. Both had the same restless craving to meet and move among the great, both loved pedigrees (the American at one time employed genealogists to trace his own ancestry, hopefully), both insisted on traveling in the grand manner, were past masters in the niceties of international etiquette (formal jacket, black tie at dinner—in Munsey's case, even when quite alone at home), and decried looseness of behavior or speech. Both liked to write and see themselves in print, hence they shared the conviction that, as journalist-publishers, their sojourns in Europe were an essential part of the year's hard labor. Both, indeed, cherished illusions which might today rate them as "eccentric," but that was an acceptable condition in the day of self-made millionaires, especially in the publishing field. Munsey was described by S. S. Mc-Clure, his friend and competitor, as "a little bit crazy," and at just about the same time, Munsey summed up McClure in precisely the same words.

On the Continent, Maclean and Munsey were constantly opening doors for each other to new experiences. Through Munsey's insistence, his Canadian friend met Count Zeppelin in 1909—the occasion being a gala dinner party in Mentz, Germany, following the airship pioneer's first great flight. That was to become a high point in the Colonel's reminiscences, principally because his pleasant chat with the guest of honor yielded the information that the Countess Zeppelin was a Canadian. Later researches in Toronto established her as a Mc-Garvey, a native of the Colonel's own county of Wellington.

At the Carlsbad spa, Maclean and Munsey became well-known figures over the years, and in turn they were delighted to note a lengthening list of famous names on their roster. It just might have included a reigning monarch, except for the unfortunate circumstances surrounding the first meeting. The custom at Carlsbad was to assign each patron of the mineral baths a special cubicle for regular use at fixed hours. One morning, the Colonel turned up promptly to keep his appointment with health, but on opening the door found the tub occupied by a complete stranger, and the entire cubicle splashed and disheveled. "You are in my bath, sir!" he said. "I must ask you to leave at once." The unknown left quickly, offering no argument. The horror of the Colonel's discovery, a few hours later, that he had thrown out King Ferdinand of Bulgaria, one of the Saxe-Coburg-Gotha princes, blood relation to dear Aunt Elise's husband, is, even at this far-on date, too shattering to contemplate. But it actually happened, and the Colonel did not mind telling the story to the folks back home. After all, very few men can boast of seeing royalty actually in the flesh.

Munsey had his encounters with kings, too. Alphonso XIII of Spain was a friend and admirer, and generally managed to see the American publisher on his visits. Years later, in a letter to Sir Frederick Williams-Taylor, the Colonel wrote: "I never knew anyone who was more sought after in the world's highest political and social circles than the late Frank Munsey. I remember in 1925, at San Sebastian, the King of Spain motored several hours up and back to spend an hour with us. I once asked Frank how he did it. He replied, 'With good manners and a little money, you can get anywhere in the world.'"

At one point, Munsey found himself in an embarrassing predicament involving the King of England, but his friend Maclean was able to come brilliantly to the rescue. The pair had planned a special travel program that would open in France; sailing date, reservations were settled. Suddenly, Munsey received a cabled invitation from the U. S. Ambassador in London for a dinner in honor of George V. But as this would snarl the arrangements with Jack, only one reply seemed possible: regrets. Next day came an angry cable from one of the Vanderbilt ladies, advising him that he dare not turn down a royal occasion. When the Colonel arrived in New York, ready to board ship, Frank made a clean breast of the whole matter, saying, "What can I do? It would be impolite to leave you." Nonsense, replied the Colonel, "you must cable your acceptance; you can leave the boat on arrival at Southampton; I'll go on to Paris and wait for you there." And by the skin of his teeth, plus transport by a fast naval craft sent to meet the ship in the Channel, and a special train to London, Munsey made it. "After dinner," according to the Colonel's story later, "the King asked him to sit on the sofa while His Majesty himself sat, half-standing on the arm and gossiped with him, as Frank said, 'Just like a couple of farmers sitting on a log whittling a stick in Maine.'"

Munsey had a high regard for the Colonel's advice on publishing decisions, and vice versa. Round about 1920, the American's intricate transactions for more New York newspapers had landed him with the famous *Paris Herald,* which he didn't want. He offered it as a free gift to Jack, who said, "No, you keep it." A little later the question of a good editor for the paper was put to Jack. He thought he knew exactly the right man, Honorable Rodolphe Lemieux, distinguished, polished French-Canadian, former Speaker of the House of Commons and cabinet minister, a person perfectly at home in both languages. "Try to get him for me," said Munsey. Lemieux answered the Colonel: "At first I was somewhat surprised and expressed my doubts as regards my ability to take the editorial management of such an important paper. Your suggestion is most flattering to me. I shall pause and ponder for a while and then will let you know if I can expatriate myself." But as he pondered, there was a change of plan in New York, Munsey deciding that importation of an editor from North America might disturb the French government.

After one of their stops in London, Maclean egged on his friend to consider purchase of the *Morning Post*. Munsey started exploratory moves, but then asked the inevitable question: Who could run it for him? Maclean wrote back: "Hold the appointment open until I hear from a man to whom I have written today—R. B. Bennett, K.C., late M.P. for Calgary . . . one of the Prime Minister's right-hand men . . . has unusually good business, financial and social connections in London . . . quite well off, likes public life . . . (has) a superior personality that will carry him into any circle." Bennett was not interested, nor did Munsey get the *Morning Post*. He had negotiated through a third party, not revealing his interest to the owner, Lord Glenesk, who had suspected the plan originated with his old enemy, Northcliffe. "Lord Glenesk told me that he would rather kill the *Morning Post* than ever allow it to get into Northcliffe's hands," Maclean reported to Munsey. "If he had known that you were interested, he would have taken up the matter at once and probably favorably."

At one point, Munsey was searching for an editor for his top paper, the New York *Sun*. Maclean, always ready, suggested Stephen Leacock. "Excellent!" was the reply. "Talk to him." Leacock rather liked the idea and offered to go to New York to meet Munsey. In the meantime, the Colonel had started some inquiries among the staff at *Maclean's Magazine,* which regularly presented the wit and drollery of McGill's favorite professor. His working habits, it seemed, were inclined to be less than ideal. Reluctantly, the Colonel reported to Munsey: "He is not dependable in work or correspondence. We have to write and telegraph several times to get copy of promised articles." The McGill campus was in luck, and Munsey had to look elsewhere.

## CHAPTER XXIV

# SUNDRY PRIME MINISTERS

"When a man assumes a public trust, he should
consider himself as public property"
*Thomas Jefferson*

_____

JOHN BAYNE MACLEAN was always ready to declare his political
allegiance. In printed articles and conversations, he would gladly state,
"I am a Conservative by birth and tradition," or, if in an impish mood,
"For census purposes, put me down as a Conservative."

Yet he was never a party stalwart; he eschewed active connection
with political organizations and had no interest in seeking office. In
1913, when Prime Minister Robert Borden dispatched Honorable
Frank Cochrane, Minister of Railways and Canals, to offer the Colonel
a seat in the Senate, the reply was firm and immediate: No. Maclean
believed his duty to Canada could be best done by staying outside the
political sphere, clear of any debt which might hamper freedom of expression by himself or his publications. And how could he keep an eye
on the world scene if he were to exchange Palm Beach and Europe
for months of slow sessions in Ottawa?

Nevertheless, he made it a point to visit the capital frequently, covering "the beat" in his own way, and over the years building up an association with several of Canada's Prime Ministers. He called on them,
dined with them, listened carefully to their important plans and hopes,
and, as always, followed up each contact with correspondence, often in
congratulatory vein. That sort of cultivation by the country's leading
national publisher was flattering to the head of government; it could
also be misleading. Two Conservative Prime Ministers, Meighen and
Bennett, as well as the Liberals' long-time leader, W. L. Mackenzie
King, interpreted the Colonel's developing friendship as unquestioning
support; each in turn was destined to have a rude awakening.

Of all the political figures whom the Colonel studied and knew, just three were to be granted his unswerving confidence. The first, of course, was "Sir John A.," who never fell from his pedestal. The other two were to play their major roles as premiers of Ontario— and both, interestingly enough, had been well established as writers for *Maclean's Magazine* years prior to their entry into politics. Honorable George A. Drew, who won his first seat in 1939, after being named leader of Ontario's Conservatives, had been a close associate of the Colonel's since 1928—and that story with its later developments deserves full telling farther along.

The third man who, in the Colonel's eyes, could do no wrong was, as indicated earlier, Honorable E. C. Drury, head of the Farmer government from 1919 to 1923. Their mutual trust and friendship remained intact at all times; even the sudden *exposé* of a major scandal in the Drury cabinet did not inspire the Colonel to sharpen his pencil. The *Financial Post* gave objective news coverage, plus brief editorial comment, during the weeks of public inquiry into the situation, but John Bayne Maclean's byline was mysteriously absent. The case eventually led to court action, in which Honorable Peter Smith, the government's treasurer, and Aemilius Jarvis, a Toronto financier, were tried on a charge of conspiracy to defraud the province. Smith got a three-year term in the penitentiary, Jarvis six months in jail, and there was a joint fine of $600,000.

The details have faded into minor historical importance, but the crux of the affair may be summed up briefly. Jarvis had developed a plan to buy up provincial, succession-duty-free bonds in London and refinance them at a saving. The province made some $4,000,000 profit on the deal, Jarvis about $400,000 gross in commissions. Somewhere along the line, a $7500 payment was deposited to the Provincial Treasurer's bank account. That Smith, in the confusion of handling a vast financial operation, understood what had happened, or that Jarvis personally had any knowledge of the alleged "bribe" is most doubtful. Smith was the victim of his own inexperience; Jarvis held a respected place in Toronto society, an honorable, if irascible fox-hunting gentleman of the old school.

The Colonel may have withheld comment while the case occupied newspaper headlines, but it seems he was merely biding his time. Six or seven years later he decided there must be a careful, detailed review of the whole sorry affair and done by one who had lived with it, day by day. That meant Drury, now retired from politics and enjoying his rustic life. So, in *Maclean's Magazine* for September 15, 1933, appeared the first installment of a three-part feature under the title, "Have We a Canadian Dreyfus?" signed by Ontario's former premier, who left no doubt of his answer in the affirmative, especially concerning the charges against Jarvis, and with complete exoneration for both men.

Maclean never succeeded in establishing any intimacy with Sir Wilfrid Laurier, the graceful, polished leader of Canada's Liberal government from 1896 to 1911. True, a call at the Prime Minister's office in 1909 had gone off quite smoothly, the publisher making a specific request for closer relations between business newspapers and those Cabinet ministers directly involved with the economic life of the country. More news should be made available from such departments as Trade & Commerce, Fisheries, etc., to publications serving those fields, and particularly in view of the scant attention given at that time by the daily press and wire services to business news. Later, the Colonel sent Laurier a copy of the U.S. management journal, *System,* which, in presenting a specially prepared statement by new President Taft to the nation's business leaders, seemed to be a convincing example of such *liaison.* Nowadays, there is the closest possible news relationship between Cabinet ministers and departmental heads on the one hand and business papers on the other. But to Laurier such a proposal had no appeal and, for some reason, he chose to misinterpret the Colonel's suggestion. "The object of your communication, I understand, is that we should exclusively deal with the papers you control," he wrote. "I hardly believe that would be advisable." The Colonel was shocked by both the interpretation of his effort and the rude brush-off; all contact with Laurier ceased.

Sir Robert Borden, the Conservative leader who took over after Laurier, won the Colonel's admiration for his statesman's skill and businesslike administration. The two maintained a friendly relationship, but it was largely conducted *in absentia,* often through the various Cabinet ministers with whom the Colonel had many conversations, especially during the war years. Borden wrote pleasant letters acknowledging the suggestions or comments passed along, and invariably concluding with best wishes and the hope that "you and I will be able to get together soon." Yet he seemed to be unavailable on most occasions when the Colonel wanted to call.

By the opening of the 1920s, both major parties in the House of Commons had new leaders. Borden's retirement had brought forward

Arthur Meighen as Prime Minister, and across the dividing strip
of red carpet he was confronted by the squat figure and watchful eyes
of the Liberals' recently chosen top man, W. L. Mackenzie King.
Their politics were markedly different but their positions were rather
similar: each in an unfamiliar role at the age of forty-six, each trying
to cope with the maze of Canada's postwar problems, and, of a certainty,
each needing friends in or out of Parliament. John Bayne Maclean, the
publisher who had direct lines to the whole nation, was—each hoped—
to be an important influence in their futures.

At that moment, the Colonel liked both men and for his own special
reasons. The King family had been Maclean's friends for many years.
Back in the '90s he had attended Bible class under John King,
Mackenzie's father, at St. Andrew's, King Street, Toronto. As a
lawyer and an expert on libel (author of two books on the subject),
John became the ideal choice for the publisher's legal adviser. "We
never lost a case," the Colonel proudly recalled later. The fact that
John King failed to manage his own business affairs, or that he was
frequently hounded by creditors, may not have been known to the
client. But Maclean did regret his inability to help at a certain point
in the lawyer's career. In 1902, John King had hoped he might be
appointed to fill a vacancy on the bench; his friend, who could have
put in a good word, was in Atlantic City, convalescing from the
typhoid fever, and King's request got no follow-up. The close association continued, however, and on several occasions, the Colonel sought
the medical advice of Dr. D. Macdougall King, "Max," the lawyer's
second son.

"Willie" King—later to be known to his intimates as "Rex"—had
been under careful observation for some time. His record as Deputy
Minister in the Department of Labor had won approval; subsequent
expanding activities, especially his association with the Rockefeller
Foundation in the U.S., had been noted and found all to the good.

Admittedly, the Colonel was a little shaken when King edged out
the experienced Honorable W. S. Fielding in the race for the Liberal
leadership after Laurier's death. The Colonel did not realize that, at
seventy-one, Fielding was hardly fit for stiff parliamentary combat,
especially after losing Quebec support by voting for Borden's conscription measure in 1917. However, once the party had made its
final decision, the Colonel dropped all reservations and sent his hearty
congratulations to King. "Willie" responded with an invitation to lunch
in Ottawa; soon after that occasion he was a guest of the Macleans in

Toronto; and thus began a new friendly fraternizing with the late John King's clever boy.

Nonetheless, John Bayne Maclean was still a Conservative "by birth and tradition," and he stood ready to give Prime Minister Meighen support. The new Tory leader's background had its special appeal; born on an Ontario farm, brought up in strict Calvinistic tradition, poor and struggling through all his early years of a rural education, school-teaching and eventually the study of law. Maclean could only admire the forthright character, honest, industrious and sober, which had emerged.

What bothered him was Meighen's far-out brilliance, his range of knowledge and stunning performance in debate. By the time the Colonel heard the much-quoted comment of Grattan O'Leary, Ottawa *Journal*'s political analyst and a contributor to *Maclean's*, that "Meighen has become the first citizen of Canada by divine right of intellect," his needling suspicion changed to a state of alarm. No such "right" existed in Maclean's point of view. He distrusted erudition and the dizzy heights of learning; intellectuality was too often something quite different from sound common sense. Once he was inspired to toss off a little memo to the staff on the subject: "I think there is a really good story in the prize pupil. I have written on it myself and have drawn attention to it in little talks to the effect that the head boys seldom ever get anywhere in life, are never heard of again. Of Upper Canada head boys, whose names you will find printed in gold on the walls of the assembly room, only one was ever heard of again to any extent . . . [Edward Blake] . . . and he was best known for his failures."

There was, then, a wariness in the Colonel's acceptance of his party's leader, even though a succession of congratulatory notes on speeches and policies sped from University Avenue to the Prime Minister's office, and several friendly calls in Ottawa had been followed up by dinner parties for the Meighens at Austin Terrace.

But "the first citizen of Canada" did not hold office long. In December 1921 Mackenzie King's Liberals were elected to govern and Meighen now found himself on the opposition side of the House. The Colonel wrote him a not very helpful letter of sympathy. He had been defeated, the Colonel explained, because he had "lost touch with the masses of the people." It was an unhelpful comment and Meighen's reply indicated considerable bafflement. Of course, members of any government "lost touch with the people in the personal sense. . . .

The weight of governmental responsibilities in these years has been no ordinary weight, and the members of the government were not super-human." But he refused to admit that he or the Cabinet had been out of touch with public opinion.

Maclean continued to wrestle with the problem of Meighen and the masses. At last a great light dawned: Meighen should join his editorial staff! That way, he would come close to the people of Canada and get to know what they were thinking. Off went a letter setting forth the plan, urging full consideration of its potential. "A few years here would be the very best training for future usefulness and success in public life," and the writer virtually promised the Right Honourable leader of the opposition that, by getting in touch with public opinion in some such way, "he could, in five years, sweep the country."

Meighen's brief reply, promising "to keep it in mind," and thanking the Colonel for his interest, seems to have brought the idea to a full stop. Undoubtedly, it was a hare-brained proposition to make to a middle-aged man who had been active in politics for more than a decade and whose brilliant capacities in ministerial posts and complex legislation (e.g., merging several railways to create the Canadian National) had been thoroughly demonstrated. Within the Colonel's prom-ised span of "five years," Meighen had abandoned notions of sweeping the country; instead, he had entered a Toronto financial firm, Canadian General Securities, organized by a friend from Western Canada, W. Watson Evans, and was well on his way toward becoming a millionaire several times over. Meighen liked the security that money provided and he enjoyed even more the leisure time that enabled him to play bridge endlessly, with a few old college chums.

Meantime, the Colonel continued in pursuit with other ideas, most of them less specific than the first. What the Conservative party needed was a "constructive program," he said—and so often that Meighen finally demanded exactly what he meant by the phrase. Promptly the answer came back: the first step in a constructive program was to re-duce taxation.

Meighen's rejoinder sounded tired, though still patient. "In nine out of ten of the many speeches I have made in the last six months, I have concentrated on the overwhelming necessity of a large curtail-ment of expenditures and the withdrawal of taxation. . . . None, however, who have not had part in an administration can conceive of the obstacles that are thrown in the path of one who seeks to effect real economy in public administration."

But in another month or two, the patience was wearing thin. He answered the Colonel's latest blast thus: "How can reduced taxation honestly be called a policy? Who is not in favor of reduced taxation? To keep proclaiming oneself in favor of reduced taxation is to my mind just talking hollow platitudes. In promises of this kind, no one can ever compete with Mr. King anyway."

John Bayne Maclean was already deep in a missionary drive to help Mr. King become a good Prime Minister, even if a Liberal. Early on, the new government's difficulty in organizing a Cabinet had opened the way for presentation of one of the Colonel's pet schemes, viz., that the custom of choosing ministers from elected M.P.s only should be abandoned. He had discussed the idea in numerous articles and correspondence, always stressing the point that the U. S. President enjoyed a special advantage in being free to range over the entire nation in search of the best man for each cabinet job, regardless of his status as politician, Congressman, or plain private citizen.

There were several Maclean-King letters back and forth on the subject. Early in 1922, the Colonel wrote: "I discussed it with Mr. Meighen last May. He said he had been looking into it and felt that, while it was legally possible for a Dominion Premier to select a Cabinet from outside the House, he thought it was not constitutionally permissible at present. I gathered that he was quite favorable. Why should you not look carefully into the matter and take steps that would enable you to call to your Cabinet the best people in the country?"

King was not prepared to take so bold a step. He proceeded with the fine-combing of his recently elected ranks and eventually announced his Cabinet appointments. That was the practice prevailing in British Parliaments, where responsible governments had an entity, as opposed to the division of legislative and executive functions inherent in the U.S. system. In a letter to Maclean he explained his views:

> I should like to discuss with you the relative merits of the American and British systems of Cabinet relationship to the legislative branch of government; the subject, however, is too large a one to attempt by correspondence. Each system has its distinct advantage and disadvantages. As your letter indicates, we are at a disadvantage as regards the freedom of choice in the selection of the executive; the Americans are distinctly handicapped by having no place for the members of their executive on the floor of Congress.

It may be that constitutional development in both countries may yet work out a method whereby we each may gain from the other some of the advantages in our respective systems which at present they lack.

Probably there were some further discussions on the matter over the years, but the Colonel would never budge an inch from his original position. Three years later, he brought up the subject with Calvin Coolidge during a conversation in the White House. The President did not agree that his powers to choose Cabinet material were as great as the Colonel believed, and, he continued with a thin smile, "Your Prime Minister does not have the Senate to contend with." (Just recently, the Senate had turned down the President's selection of an Attorney-General because the man had at one time acted as counsel for large corporations.) "However, I think our system has great advantages," Coolidge was glad to admit. "It happens at the moment I am looking for a Secretary of Agriculture and I have a list of about a hundred outstanding men across the States. I hope to be able to induce one of them to join me in serving the country." (The final choice was William M. Jardine who held the post from 1925 to 1929.) At dinner that evening, the Colonel met Herbert Hoover, Coolidge's Secretary of Commerce and eventual successor in the White House; from his point of view, there could be no possible question of the superiority of the American method of Cabinet structure and operation.

What the Colonel found ludicrous in the Canadian system was the necessity to consider representation from every province, every economic activity and if possible, every religion; that sort of cross-sectioning became the paramount concern, and individual ability was a secondary matter. Writing on the subject in *The Financial Post* in 1935, he recalled that "It is not so many years since great consternation prevailed at the first Cabinet council of a new government on discovering that there was not a Presbyterian among them. Fortunately, politicians have learned to be accommodating and instantly two of the Cabinet, a North Irish Methodist and a Scotch Anglican, found it quite easy to revert to the religion of their ancestors."

Colonel Maclean was proud to proclaim himself an Imperialist —a term which, in his private lexicon, meant a supporter of commercial expansion throughout the Empire. In a memo to one of his editors he stated: "From our earliest newspaper days as a reporter and writing on business topics, I realized very definitely that our great market was our Mother Country and the Empire. First, through preferences leading eventually to free trade within the United Kingdom, the British Dominions and Colonies. And, as we progressed, my own policy and the policy of my papers was to gradually bring the United States in on similar lines until we had a British Empire–United States free trade union. . . . When all this was established on a sound basis, we might then make deals with Germany, which was our next most promising customer. Incidentally, I had a long chat with the late President Coolidge on this . . . and found him in entire agreement."

The Colonel could give his hearty approval to extensions of trade with the Mother Country, but British foreign policy was a rather different matter. He had little faith in the leaders of the period, such as Lloyd George, and Curzon; he was still cautious concerning Churchill. The ways and means of the Colonial and Foreign Offices were frequently suspect. Canadian statesmen should "be on their guard," he said, when visiting London; they should be aware that the lavish entertainment offered was part of the softening-up process for Downing Street schemes—and such projects were too often based on the long-held British prejudice against both the industrial development of Canada and the country's adoption of it's own commercial and diplomatic policies.

His suspicions reached their peak at the time of what came to be known as the Chanak crisis in the autumn of 1922—and that little chapter of history, with its swift tangling of events in Asia Minor, London, Ottawa, to be followed up by a torrent of verbiage from the Colonel, would have important results in his relations with both Prime Minister King and Right Honorable Arthur Meighen.

Chanak had been an untidy situation ever since the defeat of Turkey, Germany's ally, in 1918. Greece had troops in occupation of much of the area and wanted them to stay; British soldiers policed a "neutral" strip along the Dardanelles. Suddenly Turkey's rising young leader, Kemal Pasha, determined to lead his secretly trained army against the hated Greeks and drive them out of Asia. There were hideous massacres on both sides—and trapped in the middle, almost forgotten by the outside world, was the small British garrison. Prime Minister Lloyd George decided on a show of strength by sending reinforcements which would include contingents from the Dominions. He asked Churchill to obtain the views of Canada, South Africa,

Australia and New Zealand. The cablegrams sent off suggested a certain bellicose gusto hovering over the Colonial Office.

In Ottawa messages of the kind had at that time to pass through several hands (including the Governor-General's) before final delivery. Thus it happened that the first news of the "crisis" was received by the government and the public through the daily papers. King, on a visit to his North York riding near Toronto, read the Associated Press dispatch, quoting Churchill's announcement of Britain's request, and was roused to a state of astonishment and wrath. He had never been warned of any threatening situation around the Dardanelles; he was as uninformed as any other newspaper reader that day. And immediately he had to come to grips with the dismaying feature of the whole matter, which was that Lloyd George and Churchill, by their early disclosure to world press services, were attempting to sway public opinion throughout the Empire and, as a result, force the Dominions back into colonial status. He wrote in his diary: "It is drafted designedly to play the Imperial game, to test out centralization vs. autonomy as regards European wars."

Australia and New Zealand answered the appeal with favorable replies; South Africa wanted more information; Prime Minister King asked briefly and in diplomatic language what all the proposed shooting was about.

The English-language press in Canada to a large extent—a notable exception being John W. Dafoe's Winnipeg *Free Press*—praised Australia and deplored the unpatriotic, ungenerous attitude of Ottawa. But that sort of knuckling-under was not for the Colonel. In his *Financial Post* piece, under the heading, "Canada Imperialistic But Refuses to Be Stampeded," he backed the Prime Minister and reiterated the warning that the sinister group of powerful political and financial interests operating through the British cabinet must be carefully watched. He wrote several letters to King urging him to stand pat.

The Chanak crisis subsided quickly, once Lloyd George realized he had little more support at home than in Canada; within a few weeks he retired from office and let Bonar Law take over.

But Chanak was to become a landmark in ending Britain's traditional role of policymaker for the Empire, and setting Canada on the road to complete and final independence in her relations with other nations. King, adroit and perceptive as always, had realized its constitutional significance at once; not so, John Bayne Maclean. That the Colonel was right at the time cannot now be challenged, but he was right for the wrong reasons.

To him it was a point at which Canada had to act firmly against the continuing intrigue of groups who sought to make governments and leaders their pawns. He had been forewarned by European friends about the rise of the energetic young Kemal Pasha, whose objective was to modernize Turkey, and who was the avowed enemy of the international narcotics ring which wanted to preserve control of the poppy-growing lands and opium factories of Asia Minor.

Once or twice, in private letters, the Colonel went so far as to identify the head of the narcotics smuggling trade, (it would not be fair to mention the name here) who was known to be a friend of Lloyd George and Churchill—although the Colonel maintained they were merely innocent dupes. For a good many years Maclean held a private watching-brief on the ringleader, reporting frequently to Admiral Richard P. Hobson, president of the World Narcotic Defense Association, the international body set up to combat illegal commerce in opium.

Thus, with all this undercover information in his files, it was only logical that the Colonel should come forward to give valiant support to Prime Minister King because (a) international opium-smuggling was bad, (b) Kemal Pasha, who felt the same way, should be allowed to clean up Turkey and force out the Greeks, (c) the British government was under the influence of unsavory, powerful political and financial interests—"Lloyd George is their chief agent and for several years they have been preparing Winston Churchill to succeed him"—and (d) certainly Canada should not get involved in a war that would only serve to protect international gangs and the opium traffic.

In the Colonel's hands the plot thickened, obviously. Not all of these revelations got into print, although there were mysterious hints now and then, especially in his 5000-word article for *Maclean's,* where he attempted to analyze the whole Chanak event from the standpoint of the Canadian people. Under the title, "Did Canada Stop Near East War?" he led the reader down many garden paths and bypaths; a clear, direct answer to the question was hard to discover; nevertheless, references to Ottawa's "refusal to take precipitous action" were presented with a strong tone of approval.

Prime Minister King was effusively appreciative. Within a few days of the magazine's appearance, he wrote to thank the Colonel for his "remarkable article" on the Near East situation and expressing "feelings of gratitude and admiration for what you have written."

All the Colonel's pieces at the time of Chanak were valuable to Mr. King who wanted Canadians to believe that it was through his decision that he had saved the nation, indeed the Empire, from another world conflict. Too shrewd to make the claim outright, he could, and did, resort to frequent quotations from Colonel Maclean's articles. Even six years later, when the Tories' Richard Bedford Bennett in the House of Commons derided King's role in the Chanak affair, the Prime Minister reached for his precious folder of clippings from the *Post* and *Maclean's* and read aloud the parts most apt in the argument. A day or so later when the *London Times'* Ottawa correspondent in a much condensed report implied that the Canadian Prime Minister claimed credit for preventing the Near East War, a further Bennett-King storm broke out. Pages of Hansard were to be filled with violent accusations by the former and long-winded denials by the latter, who insisted he had never at any time gone beyond quoting John Bayne Maclean as giving the Canadian government credit.

An absurd and arid debate—yet from the Colonel's point of view it was a triumph, for had he not caused Canada's two leading statesmen to read hundreds of words of his articles into the public record?

Chanak had been the beginning of many things. For Opposition leader Meighen it was to mark the beginning of the end, both as to his public career and the Colonel's sympathetic interest. During the two or three days of the crisis, while Mr. King pondered his final reply to Downing Street, Meighen stepped forward with the pronouncement that Canada's answer to any such request from Britain should be "Ready, aye ready!" Thus he alienated half the people of Canada. Three years later that damage he sought to repair in a speech insisting Canada should never send troops anywhere outside the country without first holding a national plebiscite. This alienated the other half. And each time, the Colonel found himself, no doubt a little sadly, having to side with the opponents of the Conservative leader.

Probably each of the two men welcomed the peace and quiet after Meighen left the public limelight and entered the Toronto financial arena. But the end was not yet—far from it! In 1932 Meighen accepted appointment from Prime Minister Bennett as Conservative head man in the Senate; by 1941, when the party was desperately casting about for an effective House of Commons leader, one equal

A big moment in the history of the Colonel and his company: the sod-turning ceremony for the new printing plant at Willowdale, north of Toronto, with a throng of employees in attendance. At right: Hunter, Maclean's successor in top command; at left, Chalmers, who became the third president in 1950

John Bayne Maclean's birthplace, as it looked a half-century later when he made his first trip back to Crieff. The house was derelict, having been unoccupied for many years

After the Colonel's careful renovation and additions, the old manse emerged as a picturesque country retreat. The wing in the foreground, containing his private apartment with spacious library, took shape over the core of the old driving shed, moved from the rear of the lot

The brothers, Hugh C. and John Bayne Maclean, guests of honor at a church anniversary occasion in Crieff. The tablet on the cemetery wall was erected by the congregation in 1934 in grateful appreciation of all that Lieutenant Colonel J. B. Maclean, V.D., LL.D., had done for the community

# KING or

## The Next Five Y

### This election is the
CANADA

## YOU

This election will decide YOUR future a
future of CANADA — YOUR happiness a
prosperity of Canada. Make no mistake abo
and make no mistake when you cast your
You will do one of two things.  You will
strengthen the hands of a democratic gove
and place it in a position to carry through leg
that will lead us up the hill to prosperity.

## WHI

Five years of unstable and autocratic governme
split what was a happy and united people into
factions — West against East, class against cla
Tory against Tory. It has brought us, as a people
face with stagnation and ruin amid the fragm
unkept promises now being renewed on a gran
with a supreme belief in our continued gullibility

RT. HON. MACKENZIE KING

## What the Liberal P

The Rt. Hon. Mackenzie King, in speeches inaugurating this campaign, showed that the policies and pledges of the Liberal Party are not the promises of one man and subject to his whims or well-being. These pledges have been endorsed by all Liberal members of Parliament, by the National Liberal Federation and all Liberal organizations from coast to coast. The elector is thereby assured that they will be carried out irrespective of the fortunes of one man.

#### THE LIBERAL PARTY PLEDGES ITSELF —

To regard unemployment as Canada's most urgent problem and through the agency of a representative national commission to co-operate with the provinces and municipalities in the

administration of unemployment relief and in an en
to provide work.

To the enactment of a constitutionally valid sys
unemployment insurance and as rapidly as poss
extension into a general scheme of social insurance in
health insurance, as well as old age pensions.

To policies that will liberate and expand external tra
which depends our recovery.

To end artificial price control and price fixing which
trade internally.

To the development of primary industries by the redu
the costs of instruments of production.

When you cast your vote, consider what a government with a strong majority can do for you
and for Canada. Compare it with a hodge-podge of minority groups — each group impotent in
itself and all pulling against each other. Consider the national policy that is best for Canada and

## VOTE LIBERAL AND CUT THE

# CHAOS

e in Your Hands

tant to YOU and to
r history

## TURE

will elect a number of minority parties that
ean impotence of Parliament. We have
sed in other countries various groups vying
uence by bartering and trading of principles.
ment by groups, each impotent in itself, leads
chaos.

## RTY?

confusion that prevails there is only one party —
beral Party — which remains true to the ideals
nocratic Government by Parliament — only one
which is strong, united and abundantly supplied
perienced and tested leadership. That Canadians
ning once more to this party to lead us out of the
ness — just as we have in every similar period
t being disappointed—is evidenced by the sweeping
ial victories of recent months.

There can be but one road.

## will do for Canada

eduction in the cost of living by substantially reducing
ies on the necessaries of life, and by exempting from the
ax many articles of domestic consumption.

te assistance in the marketing of natural products.

restoration of control by the state over currency and

establishment of an investment control board.

maintenance of the integrity of the Canadian National
ays as a publicly owned and controlled utility.

democratization of industry.

restoration of responsible government.

To the re-assertion of personal liberty and the right of free
speech and free association.

To a balanced budget.

To retrenchment of public expenditures.

To reduction of the principal and interest on the public debt.

To inquire into federal, provincial and municipal costs of
government.

To a more equitable distribution of wealth to the furtherance
of social justice and the promotion of the common good.

To the furtherance of international peace.

then help put the party with that policy in a position of strength sufficient to do things for you
and Canada. Your vote for the Liberal Party is a vote for Unity, Renewal of Trade and a Return
to Prosperity under an experienced administration of proven ability.

## RDS THAT STRANGLE CANADA

Published by National Liberal Federation, Ottawa

The slogan that won the 1935 election for Mackenzie King was dreamed
up by two members of *Maclean's Magazine* advertising staff under the
Colonel's prodding. Weeks before the issue with this double-page ad
was in the hands of the public, "King or Chaos," had been jubilantly
adopted by the Liberal party for billboards, newspapers, etc., coast to
coast

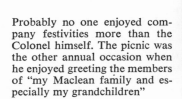

The Colonel welcoming employees and families at the annual Christmas Tree in 1939 when the audience numbered over a thousand

Probably no one enjoyed company festivities more than the Colonel himself. The picnic was the other annual occasion when he enjoyed greeting the members of "my Maclean family and especially my grandchildren"

It's still University Avenue, the headquarters site chosen by the founder in 1910, but today's Maclean-Hunter building occupies the whole city block. From this executive-editorial centre the lines of communication stretch to branches and other publishing offices in Canada, the United States, the United Kingdom, and Europe

The printing plant, located in Willowdale north of Toronto, encloses 200,000 square feet of space—over four and a half acres under one roof. It was opened in 1948, and a few months later the Colonel received the Governor-General, Viscount Alexander of Tunis, for a conducted tour of the building

Karsh's portrait of John Bayne Maclean at his office desk—against the arch of the fireplace and
with his favorite quote by friend Munsey shown in its frame at left

to the double challenge of Mr. King and the inevitable escalation of World War II, there seemed just one proper choice: Meighen again.

So the Colonel took up battle position once more in the columns of *The Financial Post*. He was convinced that the "draft Meighen" campaign had been "engineered and executed by a well-organized group who in the past have been notoriously more selfish than statesman-like," and went on to quote from the Toronto *Telegram* which had named General D. M. Hogarth, wealthy mining magnate, as its prime mover. "It is now clearly up to Mr. Meighen to demonstrate that he can rise above the rather sinister implications of his 'machine' support," the Colonel declared.

Next week's *Post* published Meighen's brief rejoinder: "I am not clear how it can be that the fact that a mining man, whoever he may be, is credited with holding 'the view that I am necessary in the House to spur on the war effort' can carry with it 'sinister implications.'"

That was merely the opening of the petty, back-and-forth argument which would continue in print or on platforms during the next two months as Meighen, now resigned from the Senate, electioneered for the South York seat in Parliament. Few careful observers were surprised when he was beaten by a large majority. The successful candidate, J. W. Noseworthy, of the socialist CCF party, had been aided by the Liberals on the quiet instructions of Prime Minister King, who feared Meighen's return to the house as a fate worse than death, knowing that it would immediately resurrect the vexed question of conscription for the armed services.

So Meighen's doom was sealed and he said his final farewell to politics. But he could neither forget nor forgive the Colonel and his comments. Following the election a Meighen letter to Maclean refers to the "harm" done by the line taken by *The Financial Post* immediately following his appointment. "The Western press used it as an admission from within that I am a stool pigeon of wealth and was put over on the Conservative party by a clique in Toronto. It is likely, of course, I would have been defeated in any event in South York. The damage done has been in giving the enemy the very tools they wanted and they will never cease to use them."

One puzzling detail in this small, bitter, intra-party wrangle still remains. The Conservative conference which had voted unanimously for Meighen's return as House leader was attended by some two hundred delegates from across the country—including John Bayne

Maclean of Toronto. Yet at no point in the *Post* pieces concerning the scheming of Hogarth, *et al,* did the Colonel bother to mention that fact. Was it merely an oversight? Well, Mr. Meighen was not slow to remind him. In a long, caustic letter he reviewed the events of that day in Ottawa:

"I had done everything which I thought a man could honorably do to avoid being put in the position in which I was ultimately placed. I had told the Conference that I would not accept the leadership, and when asked just before leaving if I would do so in the event of the request being made unanimous I answered that the same reasons I had then given would still prevail . . . The meeting however continued, and in the middle of the afternoon . . . a unanimous resolution was passed, urging upon me to accept the leadership and thereupon the Conference dissolved and the delegates prepared to return. I was advised of this action just as I was boarding the train for Toronto. Under these circumstances the pressure commenced and I can definitely say that no one was more urgent than yourself . . . Under the circumstances I yielded but never did I undertake anything more against my personal inclinations . . . I may add here that prior to the Conference no pressure was brought on me at all by any group of rich people in Toronto, or by any group of any kind except some members of the House of Commons."

After referring to *The Financial Post* comments and his realization that its stand "would be the groundwork for a ruthless and dishonest campaign all through Canada," he expresses "bitter disappointment and indeed astonishment" at such treatment. "This is because of the fact that the pressure to accept this task was exercised in no more forceful form by anyone than by yourself."

The Colonel's reply, delayed for almost a month, offered little but vaguenesses, along with formal best wishes. He may have realized that the weak spot in his argument had at last been pierced by his former friend, a man with a clear, logical mind, who demanded full loyalty from anyone calling himself a friend.

# CHAPTER XXV

# MORE FIGHTS WITH OTTAWA

"That solitary figure toiling up the
heights is R. B. Bennett."
*Bob Edwards in* The Calgary Eye Opener

RICHARD BEDFORD BENNETT was a prime ministerial horse of a different
color. He needed no stable mates, he fought free of any harnessing
to traditional party policies, and wanted only to be allowed to gallop
full tilt ahead without let, hindrance or criticism. It was inevitable that
there should be a collision with John Bayne Maclean who was also
given to fast action, free of any check-rein.

The Colonel had been watching the able young lawyer from Calgary
for some years—and liked what he saw. Bennett's furious energy
and habit of complete immersion in any job had marked him out during
his years as a member of Parliament under Borden; he was a man with
a future, certainly, and even if the Colonel had not succeeded in
interesting him in an overseas newspaper career, a big opportunity was
bound to seek him out eventually. The setback of a defeat at the polls,
shortly after he had been named to Meighen's short-lived Cabinet
in 1921, could be written off as valuable experience.

Another important item on the asset side of the ledger was the fact
of Bennett's wealth. In the political arena this could be of favorable
significance in the days before it was routine to turn the rather harsh
public spotlight on a man's private fortune. The backroom boys,
the groups of powerful financial interests intent on swaying, even
"buying," a government for their own ends, would be given short
shrift by a leader already rich. The Colonel could find nothing but
approval for the pleasantly romantic story behind the Bennett millions.

"R.B." had been born to a pioneer United Empire Loyalist family
in New Brunswick and strictly brought up; as a shcoolteacher he

saved enough money to study for the bar; around 1890 he joined a law firm in Chatham, N.B. Here he met the girl who would influence the far-off future, Jennie Shirreff. Within a few years she had finished her nurse's training and begun her career in the Ottawa-Hull district. She was engaged to nurse the ailing, elderly E. B. Eddy, whose name on boxed kitchen matches had become a household symbol throughout Canada. She married him in 1894 and, upon his death, she inherited the majority interest in the E. B. Eddy Co. of Hull.

As soon as Bennett appeared in Ottawa as a member of Parliament, the old friendship blossomed afresh; indeed, Jennie had sought his business advice many times throughout her widowed years, and when she died in 1921 few people in the know were surprised that "R.B." had been named her heir to the Eddy empire, now comprising forest rights, pulp mills and paper plants, match factories. It is only fair to point out that he had quite adequate financial resources of his own as well, having been long established as a top legal light in the province of Alberta.

In 1927 Bennett became leader of the Conservative party—and the Colonel was one of his heartiest supporters from the sidelines. Was there now a chance that the Eddy company might be put up for sale, to make way for this new political responsibility? It seemed the Colonel thought so, for within a month of the Tory convention's decision he was writing a long, rambling letter to Bennett, hinting at the possibility of the Maclean company's purchase of the Hull outfit. (The Colonel was a long-standing customer for its printing paper.) R.B.'s reply, dated November 25, was more crisply explicit: "I am not at the moment making any disposition of my shares in the Eddy company but I have received two offers and the sale price would run into several millions of dollars. I do not think this business would suit your requirements." The Colonel shelved the idea.

Nevertheless, he kept his editorial binoculars trained on Bennett in the House and looked forward eagerly to "the next election." Mackenzie King and his Liberals had been too long in office, he believed; taxation was still rising, and, as constantly reiterated in his *Financial Post* pieces, there had been no proper effort to control waste in government expenditure. With Bennett as Prime Minister, supported by a clear majority of Tory seats, things would be different.

And they were—with total, tragic unexpectedness. When Bennett and his triumphant Tories took up position on the government benches, the time was summer's end, 1930, and the Great Depression hung like poisonous smog over the nation. The stock market crash of the previous October–November had wiped out businesses and private savings; industries closed down and laid off their help; the prairies were a continuing problem—first because of drought, and later because of larger yields but no market. It was R.B.'s unhappy destiny to be in charge during his country's lowest, blackest five years in peacetime history.

The Colonel showed understanding and sympathy during the first months of the new regime. A memo to Horace Hunter and a few senior editors stated: "I think the work that Bennett is doing, and doing it thoroughly and conscientiously in the public interest—working under excessive pressure—might be commented on favorably and sympathetically."

But this feeling of hopeful confidence did not, could not, last long. A few weeks later *The Financial Post*'s regular editorial page had to speak out plainly: "Mr. Bennett has yet to establish his capacity for national leadership by successfully general-managing Canada." (In addition to the Premiership, he had assumed two other Cabinet posts: Minister of Finance and Minister of External Affairs.) "He is making many mistakes and apparently has some bad advisers. Some of his policies are very unjust to established Canadian interests. He is finding many conditions are not what he thought they were. But he is learning —getting a broader education than he has ever had in his whole previous, rather narrow career."

The *Post,* as it soon discovered, was naïvely wrong about his "advisers." Bennett brushed aside any such assistance, even from his own devoted *confrères.* As to advice from outside, especially the Colonel's kind, in print and bolstered with criticisms direct or implied, the Prime Minister regarded that as little short of heresy. Yet he had only himself to blame, for seldom before had any government leader advanced so many hasty schemes, only to alter or withdraw them with equal speed, leaving industry, business and the general public to wander and flounder, uninformed, rudderless and hopeless. The *Post*—and other publications, including the leading dailies—felt obliged to point out that the Bennett plan to create jobs by government-paid public works had proved "an utter failure"; that the pre-election promise to use the tariffs "to blast a way into the markets" hitherto closed to Canada was still merely a promise; that "every one of his schemes to restore the dollar has fallen through," and at the present (October 1931) rate of 87 cents, the additional premium required for millions of dollars' worth of Canadian securities about to mature in the New York market would be another drastic drain on Ottawa's wobbling finances.

A somber barrage, indeed, to hurl at this "one-man government" (so defined by Mackenzie King, sitting contentedly across the way as leader of the opposition), and Bennett finally reached the explosion point.

What set him off was an article which the Colonel knew nothing about, never saw until it was in print: a *Financial Post* dispatch from Ottawa by the able, invariably accurate Grant Dexter, who reported that Bennett, recently returned from a visit to New York bankers, had been bluntly turned down for a new government loan; a Canadian bond issue would be unwelcome in the U.S. "until Canada came to grips with its costly railway problem."

The day Bennett received that copy of the *Post,* he was confined to his bed in the Château Laurier Hotel, a man far from well, running a high temperature, yet still trying to cope with a hundred problems. With a monumental heave he tossed everything to one side to deal with this latest assault. He sent secretaries on the double for law books; two hours later he was deep in drafting and dictating "a case" under Section 136 of the Criminal Code (now incorporated in Section 166) which would fill several long pages of foolscap.

Bennett's brief for the prosecution cited many cases from English history, all based on the statute *De Scandalis Magnatum,* passed in the reign of Edward I, and which declared that none should be "so hardy to tell or publish any false news or tales whereby discord or occasion of discord or slander may grow between the King and his people, and the great men of the realm." As no action had been taken under this statute or its successors for 221 years, and the statutes themselves had been repealed in Britain in 1888, Bennett had to strengthen his case by citation of other decrees and precedents down the centuries.

Having dictated his indictment, he summoned Honorable Hugh Guthrie, Minister of Justice. "Take this, read it, and act on it," he thundered. "I have stood enough from John Bayne Maclean."

Guthrie telephoned Toronto only to learn that the Colonel was out of town. What next? he asked Bennett. "Get hold of Chalmers then, and don't permit any delay."

So, on a Sunday afternoon the present author answered the phone to receive instructions to appear at the Minister of Justice's office in Ottawa next morning at ten o'clock. But couldn't the meeting be delayed until Tuesday? Surely Mr. Guthrie would allow the editor to keep certain appointments he had made in Toronto. "I'm sorry," Guthrie replied. "Unless you give me your word right now that you will be here tomorrow morning I shall instruct the law officers of the Crown to have you *brought*."

The next morning Guthrie, sitting behind his desk and a long row of law books sent over by Bennett, was more apologetic than brusque. The Prime Minister's instructions had been precise, and it was necessary that he should act accordingly. But he did not relish his task. He picked up the foolscap pages covered with typewriting and proceeded to read. Although in the form of a letter from Bennett addressed to the Colonel, it was actually a weighty legal document. To achieve those liberally annotated references to cases by British parliaments over the centuries must have involved at least ten hours of concentrated work— by the busiest man in Canada and one of the sickest.

At the end of the reading there was the natural question: "What is it you want, Mr. Guthrie?"

"The Prime Minister demands that you publish a complete retraction and correction."

The only answer could be a refusal. Reports of the conversations between Bennett and the New York bankers had already appeared on the Dow-Jones service and in *The Wall Street Journal;* there had also been comment on the situation by *The Times* of London. Dexter's report had merely rounded up information that was the subject of public discussion; in fact, some of his special angles had been supplied by Bennett himself on returning from New York. All this was presented to Guthrie, along with the suggestion that surely, at this critical period, the Canadian people were entitled to know how the railway *débâcle* was affecting their country's credit.

Guthrie looked worried. "I'd better talk to the P.M.," he said, reaching for the phone. There was a delay at the other end; Mr. Bennett was very ill with a temperature of 103 degrees; the doctor at his bedside had forbidden all calls. But the patient, overhearing the conversation, insisted on having Guthrie's report.

When the Minister got off the line, the frown on his face was still there. "He says I am to lock you up in the tower."

Well, certainly towers had been mentioned in Bennett's citations from history, and England seemed well provided with such. But did we have a tower in Canada?

"There's always the Tower of Parliament," said Guthrie. "I guess we could lock you up there." The Minister of Justice was beginning to see a certain wry humor in the situation. A normally cheerful type, he obviously wanted to terminate the whole business quickly.

Finally, the visitor offered an alternative plan. *The Financial Post* would publish any statement the Prime Minister wished to make, would even regard it as a news scoop worthy of speedy and complete presentation, but there could be no retraction of the earlier story. Guthrie said he would have another talk with Bennett. No more was heard of the incident. The Tower of Parliament remained untenanted.

The next week, the *Post* gave front-page space to Bennett's view of the episode with the New York bankers, the sequence of events leading up to it and its cabled leap around the world. Everything was clearly explained from the standpoint of Ottawa, and everything was attributed to "the highest possible source," since Bennett had decided that he would not be personally quoted. If the Prime Minister felt grateful, he gave no sign.

The letter itself never reached the Colonel, nor was this author allowed the copy he requested. A diligent search of various files at Ottawa has failed to turn it up.

In due course Bennett recovered his health and vigor and was again ready to take on all feuds and foes, real or imagined, single-handed. He could never forgive the Colonel or *The Financial Post;* indeed, in his mind, owner and paper were one and the same, and any printed comment, report, forecast, etc., touching even remotely on government policy or personnel was immediately attributed to the enmity of John Bayne Maclean. The Colonel remained calm and detached most of the time—even during a directors' luncheon at the Canadian National Exhibition in 1932, when he, as a guest, had to listen to the speech from the head table where the Prime Minister berated him publicly by name, and declared *The Financial Post* "the most inaccurate paper in Canada," incapable of printing a good or honest word about the government or its leader.

Bennett's problem, obvious throughout his political life, was personal and psychological. In his frenzied drive toward each new goal there was no time to pause, consult, or understand any other point of view. This could result in serious mistakes, even when he had deliberately set out to be helpful. At one point he slapped a tax on all United States magazines coming into Canada; that, surely, would please Maclean and the other publishers north of the border! Not so—and the Colonel spoke out in condemnation of the move. He opposed any such direct tax which would raise the price of individual copies for Canadian readers. The better way to promote national periodical literature would be to relieve Canadian publications of duties and taxes on their raw materials, such as paper, artwork, engravings, electrotypes, etc. American publishers were free of such extras, and if Ottawa could remove the burden, Canadian periodicals would be able to compete equitably with the imported "finished product." Yet to Hunter and Tyrrell, more directly concerned with the immediate financial problems of Canadian magazines, the Bennett tax was not unwelcome. In fact, it gave *Maclean's* a large circulation boost that further strengthened its claim to be "Canada's national magazine."

By the end of Bennett's tour of duty, the Colonel was totally disillusioned, and a little sad as well. In May 1935 he was asked by his friend, Admiral Hobson, to sound out the Canadian Prime Minister on the possibility of speaking at the great New York rally of the World Narcotics Defense Association. If Mr. Bennett would accept, the U. S. Secretary of State Cordell Hull promised to attend to welcome "the distinguished neighbor." The Colonel's reply holds out little hope for the plan: "The fact is that Mr. Bennett is a lonely man—takes no one in his confidence unless it is perhaps his brother-in-law, Herridge, the Minister at Washington." Farther along, "I could not approach him (Bennett) myself. We are not on friendly terms" . . . and, after some disconnected explanations for that state of affairs, the Colonel remarks that this is the first Prime Minister in many years "with whom I have not been at all times on more or less intimate terms."

By that time the Colonel was again looking forward to "the next election," and his decision had been made. In a letter to one of his favorite correspondents, Sir David Gordon, former President of the Legislative Council of South Australia, whom he had met in Geneva, he discusses Bennett: "the greatest failure in the history of the country; a vainglorious dictator . . . (of) no administrative capacity," a leader who had actually caused rifts in his own party which in turn were resulting in splinter groups. So, though heretofore a Conservative, the Colonel declares himself to be "quietly supporting the Liberals. The leader, former Prime Minister Mackenzie King, is a very old friend of mine . . . and although sometimes quite strongly opposed, we have always been more or less intimate, and I have helped him when he has been in a national political hole. I am doing so now."

As luck would have it, the Colonel and his publishing organization were to play an unexpected part in the Liberals' victory in 1935. From University Avenue headquarters would emerge the slogan which sparked the campaign from coast to coast, summed up the issue at stake, and captured popular imagination with just three little words.

Early in September—a few weeks before polling day—two young men of *Maclean's Magazine* advertising staff were deep in a plan to sell a double-page spread to Liberal headquarters for a rousing pre-election message. Speed was of the essence because of the early closing date of the October 15 issue. One of the salesmen, L. C. West, rushed back and forth to Vincent Massey, president of the National Liberal Federation, to learn first that a double spread was out of the question though a single page just might be considered, and to be told later that even this possibility must be vetoed owing to the depleted condition of party funds. "Unless," added Massey, "your Colonel Maclean, who has frequently supported Mr. King, would care to donate the space." Young West promptly reported the suggestion to the Colonel, only to have it just as swiftly turned down. But the latter, wise in the ways of publishing, had a second thought: "Why don't you give them something concrete to consider? Draw up a rough layout for a double spread, having a strong message to show the public the danger of voting for these noisy new parties. Massey and his people might find the money then."

West dashed back to his office and went into a huddle with his friend at the next desk, E. C. Calder.

"Sounds so easy," West said, "but where are we going to get that kind of copy on such short notice?"

"Write it ourselves! In the first place you need a heading that will tell the whole story," and Calder reached for a sheet of paper and started to scribble, "—something like 'It's King or' . . ."

"King or Chaos!" West shouted happily.

Massey bought the ad. Within twenty-four hours he and his committee had abstracted the headline for use on billboards and other advertising-media which would reach the public several weeks before *Maclean's* was on the newsstands. But West and Calder didn't mind; they had sold their double page spread ad, complete with the original layout of Mackenzie King's picture on one side, a cartoon on the other showing the voter wisely taking the right road to prosperity and spurning the signposts marked, "C.C.F.," "Social Credit," "Reconstruction," "Conservative."

The Colonel was happy, too. He decided to help the Liberal campaign financially. In a private discussion with Mr. Massey he stressed that this was to be considered his own personal contribution, with absolutely no involvement of his company which had never given money to any political party and never would. The amount of the donation happened to be $2100—exactly the cost of the advertisement in *Maclean's*.

The news of this confidential understanding with the Federation president leaked out to other top Liberals. One of them, John F. Mackay, suggested that the Colonel should be rewarded. Would he, for instance, consider going to Washington as Canada's minister? (The post was first held by Vincent Massey, 1926–30.) The Colonel besought him to discard any such notions. "In all my life," he wrote, "I have asked only once for a position; that was in 1885 when I asked Sir John Macdonald to appoint me as Inspector in the Northwest Mounted Police. He was much wiser than I. He refused, and instead offered me a lieutenancy in the permanent Corps, the Royal Canadian Dragoons at Quebec, which I luckily refused. Twice, in 1912 and 1913, I refused appointments to the Senate because I could not afford the time, it being much more important for the readers I serve to travel abroad and get the news affecting Canada." At no point in this leisurely comment did the Colonel mention the possible handicap of his age, which in 1935 was seventy-three.

The Colonel's active aid in the Liberal party's victory was gratefully acknowledged in several letters and long-distance calls by the new Prime Minister; the situation seemed to augur well for a freer, deeper community of interests between the two in the future. Yet the Colonel remained wary; after all, Mr. King was a politician and, as such, must be watched; moreover, he had little understanding of the problems of businessmen.

The Colonel had tried to explain that last point in a letter to his friend several years before—a letter painstakingly rewritten half a dozen times. The effort had been inspired by a chat they had managed to have during a smart wedding reception in Toronto; the Prime Minister (it was the year 1928) mildly complained that the Maclean publications were unfriendly to his administration; the Colonel came back with the charge that Mr. King had been "hearing stories," and by believing them had been led into an antagonistic position concerning the publishing industry in Canada. (There had been difficulties at the time over matters of postage rates and duties on paper.)

"I would very much prefer to find myself heartily back of you in your public career," the letter had begun. "But this is not to be expected. Though racially and by birth we have much in common, we have grown up in two entirely different atmospheres. You have been brought up in the academic world. You have lived in a higher latitude where ideals, theories and debates govern. Your way has been made smooth from childhood. I had a very great advantage of being born in the Manse and with a Tory father and a wonderful mother of a violently Highland Scotch Grit family. George Brown's sister was her most intimate friend. The congregation was 99 percent Liberal. I was brought up with the masses, the pioneer Highland Scotch families of the congregation. Then I was sent away to school with the sons of farmers and workers. As a reporter I grew up with the same classes, all of us fighting our way, earning little and saving much. These children of the masses, who were able to stand the pace of hard work and strenuous living, became strenuous employers, men who were willing to risk their savings and accept the worries of business in strongly competitive fields. Then, theories were based on experience and were tested in practice and not in debate.

"The differences in our two careers and therefore in our attitudes toward life and the world were brought out clearly, I recall, when I read your excellent book *Industry and Humanity*. You were at a disadvantage by not having to make your own way in the world, of not being an employer of labor, of not being an owner-executive, of not having built up a business of your own.

"Added to this is the fact that to hold your place, to hold your Party in power, you may feel it incumbent upon you at times to abandon ideals and principles."

Having reached that point in his analysis of the Prime Minister's background, training and character, Maclean probably decided he had gone too far. He never finished the letter, never sent it—but the several versions and careful rewrites were to occupy a special folder in his files, no doubt ready for instant reference and moral support in case the winds from Ottawa blew cold.

Certainly Mr. King in his first two terms of office had done nothing to recognize or remove the handicaps under which the Canadian periodical press labored. It was only after his defeat in 1930 that he showed a readiness to study the publishing situation. In January 1931 he wrote the Colonel, asking for a detailed review, plus specific recommendations for improvement. The Colonel's reply was lengthy, yet precise. He asked for no tax on imported magazines; rather, he requested that Canadian publications be allowed equality of opportunity with those from abroad, and to achieve this there should be (a) exemption of duties on magazine paper, ink and machinery, and (b) freedom from the sales taxes charged against the national journals but not against their foreign competitors.

The letter was businesslike and carefully objective, stressing that these moves were in the interests of all Canadian periodical publishers. (In avoiding examples from his own company's experience, he may have lost some pungency of argument—of the kind he had presented in 1927 in a letter to R. B. Bennett, when he wrote: "If I were conducting my business this year just across the line in Niagara Falls [New York] it would cost me $250,000 less; that is, I would have that much more to spend on my publications and giving better service to Canadian readers.")

The special problems of the periodical publishing industry continued to be disregarded, let alone unsolved, year by year. As a matter of fact the situation had worsened after King repealed Bennett's taxes on imported magazines. But he obviously hoped to retain Maclean's affection and even support. One of his most cordial letters, seemingly written in an expansive, unhurried mood (it filled four pages) is dated March 27, 1936. He was grateful for the Colonel's recent note; he harked back to his friend's special article in *The Financial Post* a few months before, under the title of "Role of the Church," which extolled the service of such pioneer men-of-God as Reverend Dr. John Bayne. "He lives again in that sympathetic presentation," the Prime Minister declared. "Any reader, and particularly one who was fortunate enough to have known in childhood men of the generation that had come directly under Dr. Bayne's influence, can understand how great a part he played in shaping the character and the standards and the way of life of the whole community. It was a rich land they settled in, but, without good stock and good leadership, it would never have taken the striking place in Canadian life which you rightly attribute to it."

The next paragraph turns again to the recent election campaign and the Colonel's support, which "was all the more effective because it came from one who was known by everyone to hold views . . .

widely differing from those of the (Liberal) party." He promised
to understand if the Colonel opposed some of the new government's
policies in the future. "You remember Sir John Macdonald's remark
that he wasn't concerned about support when he was right; what
he really appreciated was support when he was wrong. There was
a real understanding of human nature and human needs in that
remark; but I wholly agree with you that, if we are to rise to the
great tasks that challenge us all, we must not let our personal feelings
blind us to public danger."

The Prime Minister went on to refer to the "extraordinary difficulty of government at the best of times in this half-continent, with
its diversity of economic and racial ambition, and all the commitments
of youthful ambition which we have inherited, and particularly in
times of depression. We are trying," he said, in rather more official
tones, "to keep this country united and on a level keel." He knew
he could count on the Colonel's "discriminating and sympathetic support." He reminded his friend of the early links between their two
families. "You know how greatly my father appreciated his association
with you. I hope to continue to enjoy a similar friendship."

The Colonel's first reaction was similar to that in the old story
of the psychiatrist who, with a friend, was walking down the street
when he met an acquaintance who proffered a "Good morning!"
The psychiatrist nodded and continued walking. Two or three steps
later he stopped, turned to his friend and said, "I wonder what
he meant by that?" The Colonel sent the letter on to Horace Hunter
with an attached memo, commenting "Wonder what started King to
write me. Have we been stirring him up?"

The answer must have been "Yes!"—for the Colonel's associates
and fellow members of the Periodical Press Association (it was known
by another name at that time) had been pounding on cabinet doors
in Ottawa, asking for the same tax exemption enjoyed by U.S. publications. Gradually, under Honorable Charles A. Dunning, the new
Minister of Finance, concessions were introduced; first a 50 percent
drawback on imported paper, later raised to 75 percent; then removal
of duty on electrotypes—although engravings had to wait for some
years for free entry.

It was a slow process, and the Colonel's indignation stayed at the
simmer. His files are bulky with bitter, almost vituperative letters
to the Prime Minister; most of their final drafts, fortunately, were
to be toned down into more reasonable, diplomatic language after

discussions with Hunter and Tyrrell and deft editing by Napier Moore.

The King-Maclean friendship languished on other counts as well. The Colonel felt that the Prime Minister was looking more and more toward the United States and less and less to the Mother Country in important policies. True, the famous Statute of Westminster, introduced at the 1926 Imperial Conference where Mackenzie King had been a major force, recognized the autonomy of all the British Dominions—but was it necessary for Canada to proclaim her independence of Britain at every point, governmental or sentimental? The Colonel thought not. He had serious reservations, too, about the constantly expanding Canadian diplomatic service; wasn't this another dangerous tinkering with the ties of the Empire? And why suddenly, should the Sovereign whom Canadians held in respect and affection, be denied the traditional prerogative to bestow knighthoods and baronetcies on the nation's distinguished citizens?

In short, the Colonel had lost confidence in Mr. W. L. Mackenzie King; the break was inevitable, and there would never be a *rapprochement* from either side.

Thus the Colonel had given three successive Prime Ministers similar treatment; first, encouragement and later cold criticism which all found disillusioning. Yet there was still to be another political figure who, like Ontario's Premier Drury, could in the Colonel's eyes do no wrong.

# CHAPTER XXVI

## ANOTHER FIGHTING COLONEL

"He (King) dislikes being bothered by
people who want things done."
*R.T.L.* (*Charles Vining*) *in "Bigwigs"*

IT WAS FATE of the happy, fortuitous kind which first brought George
A. Drew and the Colonel face to face. To begin with, the Macleans
had decided to stay close to their home base in the summer of
1928 because of certain interesting programs in their engagement book.
There had been the impressive day in London at the convocation
of the University of Western Ontario when John Bayne Maclean
stepped forward to receive the honorary degree of Doctor of Laws,
given in recognition of his services to Canadian periodical literature.
At Austin Terrace, Mrs. Maclean was inaugurating a series of Sunday
garden teas for various staff groups, such as Bindery, Stenographic
Department, etc. The Colonel's annual picnic for all employees and
their families took place at Centre Island on schedule and drew the
largest crowd ever—almost seven hundred. And a few days later
at company headquarters, steam shovels started their big dig on a
100-foot-square section of the vacant lot where the new nine-story
building would rise, providing three floors for urgently required expansion of the mechanical departments, with modern offices above.

All of these were to make agreeable landmarks in the Colonel's
history, yet from the standpoint of a totally fresh, wholly unanticipated
interest, destined to retain its stimulus and personal satisfaction for
the rest of his life, the best was still to come—via the July 1
issue of *Maclean's Magazine,* brought warm from the press to his
desk. He opened it to glance at the first feature which bore the
heading, "The Truth about the War," by George A. Drew, and
for the next hour he remained engrossed in what he regarded as
the finest article he had ever read. Here was a writer who marshaled

all the facts and knew how to use them, here was a mastery of the exacting art which the Colonel enjoyed above all others: international controversy.

Immediately he dictated a memo to the editor: "Who is George A. Drew?" To ensure a complete answer, Napier Moore brought the two men together, and from that moment a relationship of special significance for both was solidly established.

Drew had many marks in his favor. He hailed from Guelph, not many miles from the old Maclean manse at Crieff. His grandfather had been a member of Canada's first Confederation Cabinet and later a judge; both George and his father practiced law in Guelph. George himself had been somewhat delayed in entering the profession, for the important reason of his service in the Great War. In 1914, at the age of twenty, he enlisted in the artillery, went overseas as a lieutenant; was wounded in France two years later and invalided home in 1917. He recovered sufficiently to take command of a training battery in Guelph, but the injured left arm necessitated an early return to hospital. As soon as the doctors permitted, he was studying for the bar in Toronto and commuting regularly to his home town for parade nights with the gunners of the 16th Field Battery—most of them veterans like himself, who wanted to continue the drill and comradeship of army life in the peacetime militia. He quickly rose to the rank of major in command. He was elected Mayor of Guelph, the youngest head of civic government in Canada in the year 1925. Twelve months later he went to Toronto to take over new duties as Assistant Master of the Supreme Court of Ontario and eventually succeeded to the full mastership.

These were the biographical facts, all of them to the Colonel's taste, certainly; yet there was much more to claim the older man's affection. Drew was a Conservative, born and bred and unalterable; an Imperialist, dedicated to the throne and the Union Jack; and, as a descendant of United Empire Loyalists who had left New England to stay under British rule, it came naturally that he should form a one-man resistance movement to the Americanizing of Canada. He hated Communism with the same passion as the Colonel did. And he had just recently discovered that writing could be a profitable sideline to his rather routine Court duties which were not too onerous; extra income was useful in his regular contributions to the support of his widowed mother and younger sisters in Guelph.

The Colonel had found the ideal collaborator. Drew had acquired a sponsor and champion who would make his name famous throughout Canada.

Drew's debut with "The Truth about the War" was the result of his violent reaction to a sudden wave of articles in United States publications which claimed that the Americans had won the war. *The Saturday Evening Post*'s Garet Garrett had stated that eighteen months after the declaration of war the U.S. had more men on the front facing Germany than any other nation except France. Brigadier General Henry J. Reilly, U. S. Army (Ret.), signed an article in *Liberty* making a similar claim; his views were further elaborated in a series he wrote for *Cosmopolitan* under the standing title, "Who Won the War?" Reilly denounced Britain's "lackluster" effort in 1918 when that ally, he said, failed to throw its own troops into action against the enemy.

As American magazines dominated Canadian newsstands—and, just as significantly, Hollywood's current spate of war movies attracted line-ups outside every local cinema—Drew was deeply disturbed. Exposed to this distortion of history, the Canadian public, and particularly the young people with no memory of the real facts, would be brainwashed into believing that Britain's war effort had been mediocre and uninspiring, and that it was left to the Americans to go in and end the war by a prodigious act of unselfish sacrifice.

Drew made it clear at the outset of his article that he had no intention to disparage the splendid contribution of the U.S. armed services in the recent European conflict. He wished only to set the record straight, and to do that he brought forth all the official statistics from British, French, German and American files, which could not but lead to the clear conclusion that the "facts" as presented by Reilly and Garrett were "absolutely false." U.S. war records showed 4,165,483 as the total American troops mobilized, while the British Empire total was 8,654,280; total casualties were 360,263 for the U.S. and 3,679,264 for the British; divisions in action during September 1918 totaled 25 U.S. confronting 14 enemy divisions, while the Empire had 62 facing the enemy's 76. The table listings included all spheres of operation—merchant shipping, anti-submarine service, even air photography groupings, etc.—and in each case the British Empire's total involvement exceeded the figures shown in the U.S. official records.

This was strong meat indeed, and it seemed just what Canadians needed at that moment to invigorate them and stiffen their pride. The issue sold out on the newsstands within a few days; the clamor for more copies was so insistent that pamphlet reprints of the article were published and offered at a small charge; two months later the full run of half a million had been exhausted.

*Maclean's* sought out Brigadier General Reilly and gave him the chance, plus a proper fee, to reply. Thus, the November 1 issue carried the American's article and his picture on the left-hand page, and Drew's "Rebuttal" on the right. Reilly's attempt was weak in that it consisted chiefly of personal opinions; Drew mercilessly assailed him with still more facts, most of them drawn from U. S. Army official documents. There could be no doubt as to who won the debate. Drew's articles were polemic journalism on the highest level.

The logical next step, as pointed out by *Maclean's* readers in a flood of letters, was a review of Canada's own participation in the war—and this required a two-part presentation, even at that tightly condensed. Also, wouldn't Canadians like to have a close-up of the war in the air, and get to know their own heroes better? They would, and did—through Drew's series entitled "Canada's Fighting Airmen," which gathered together the amazing records of Bishop, Collishaw, Barker, McLeod and others who flew the 1914 "crates" in the Royal Flying Corps. The seventeen separate articles later appeared in book form, to become a best seller.

By that time Drew was dividing his schedule between writing assignments for *Maclean's,* his voluntary militia duties with the crack 11th Field Brigade of which he had been made officer commanding with the rank of Lieutenant Colonel, and a new job as chairman of the Ontario Securities Commission, recently set up by the provincial government. There, his special achievement was the merger of the Toronto Stock Exchange and the old Standard Stock & Mining Exchange, a shotgun wedding which Drew believed would improve the ethics of mining brokers through their contact with the more conservative trading houses. There were repercussions, of course, for by then everyone knew Drew as a stubborn, uncompromising fighter—a "hell-raiser," as Toronto newspapermen described him—the kind that automatically caused onlookers to split into two groups, positively "for," or firmly "against." Maclean never budged from his position in the "for" line-up; indeed, he engaged Drew as his personal lawyer as

soon as the latter had left the Securities Commission hotbed to return
to law practice.

They met frequently, often in the Colonel's office, sometimes for
lunch across the street at the Canadian Military Institute, the officers'
club of which both were members and where bachelor Drew was a
resident. A casual observer might have wondered at the close friendship and animated conversations of the two Colonels—one just half
the age of the other, and handsome, tall, dominating. But neither of
them seemed conscious of any disparity, and they enjoyed their team-
work.

In this atmosphere of complete confidence and understanding, it
was natural that other ideas for controversial articles should be hatched.
There had been nasty outcries against Britain in recent Congress sessions and American magazine commentaries which demanded that the
United States be repaid in cash for the loans made to each of the
Allies in the Great War. The fact that efforts to collect reparations from
Germany and settle the war debts had already plunged the world into a
serious economic depression was quite overlooked, either deliberately
or from ignorance. Drew took on the subject and came forth with
*The Truth about the War Debts,* which, like his introductory article
some years earlier, was a masterpiece of hard-hitting analysis, broad-
based on detailed research.

Still more successful was the Maclean-Drew collaboration which
brought off the *exposé* of Sir Basil Zaharoff and other armament
makers.

Drew had stumbled on the Zaharoff trail in 1917. On leave in
London between sessions in military hospital, he had taken a room at
the Carlton Hotel, and one day he passed David Lloyd George hurry-
ing along the corridor. His curiosity was aroused: Who could be so
important during this serious phase of the war as to necessitate a
private call by the Prime Minister of Britain? It was Zaharoff, according to the guests' register—and next came the inevitable question:
Who was he? Drew determined to find out, even if it took years,
which it did. He discovered that Zaharoff, born in 1849, an obscure
Greek, was the chief owner of Vickers, the great British arms corporation, and of Schneider-Creuzot in France, and, rather more significantly, one of the powers behind both the Skoda works and the
Krupps domain in Germany. Piece by piece the young Canadian
lawyer fitted the evidence together, watching the emergence of a
startling picture of one man's multi-million-dollar fortune achieved

through control of Europe's armament industries and sales to a long list of governments in peace or war.

"That's what I have up to now," said Drew during an afternoon chat in the Colonel's office. "I still lack proof for some of the connections, and I'm not quite sure where to look for it."

"Perhaps I can help," said Maclean. He stood up, crossed the floor, pressed a button that opened one of the squares in the oak paneling, and reached in for a sheaf of intelligence reports from British and American sources concerning Zaharoff and his henchmen. "That so-called 'mystery man of Europe' is no mystery to me. I've had my eye on him for years. Take this file, and when you've digested the new material, come back and we'll draw up a plan for the article."

In August 1931 Lieutenant Colonel George A. Drew's feature, "Salesmen of Death," created a sensation. He did not describe his early suspicions from the time of the Carlton Hotel encounter (indeed, Drew seldom used first-person-singular reminiscences) but he spoke out firmly against Lloyd George who had allowed himself to be "used" by Zaharoff and "the armament industry which makes wars to make money . . . this Frankenstein monster which must be smashed or it will smash civilization." He presented the full story of Sir Basil (knighted by George V for services to the Allies), listed his holdings in armament industries and their subsidiaries, analyzed their annual balance sheets and net profits. All such details were carefully brought together in a final, sobering challenge to the statesmen and nations who would participate in the World Disarmament Conference, to be held in February 1932. This forthcoming gathering, Drew insisted, must not end in the fiasco of the 1927 Naval Disarmament meeting, where one of Zaharoff's on-the-spot agents, the American Dr. William B. Shearer, had actually "prevented any results." Drew told that story too: how the Doctor came to public notice after suing Bethlehem Steel and two other U.S. companies for $255,000, the balance still owing for his services; and right there in Colonel Maclean's own publication, old friend Charles M. Schwab was to be identified in plain print as an associate of Shearer's, while the Bethlehem Board chairman lamely explained that the man had been sent to the Naval Disarmament talks "simply as an observer." Letting Drew point the finger at Charlie Schwab was powerful proof of the Colonel's absolute faith in his young associate.

Today there is still a bit of interesting addenda discernible in faded penciled scribbles by the Colonel on the pages of the article in the bound volume reposing in the company's library. Re Shearer: "I met him in 1924 or 1925 at the Ritz in Paris . . . He admitted to me quite frankly he was in Zaharoff's employ." At another spot along the margin, the Colonel noted that back in 1897 he had been approached in London for a possible job by a daily paper editor who was a retired naval officer. "He was disgusted" with his present position, as the paper had been started by one of the British steel combines to agitate "for more battleships."

Drew's "Salesmen of Death" piece went round the world via translations by the League of Nations into thirty languages for pamphlet distribution. Probably even the aging Zaharoff spent a quiet afternoon over it, at whichever of his secret residences throughout Europe he was currently using. But, true to style, he uttered no sound, offered no argument. He was to die in 1936, unsung, unhonored and not unremembered.

Of course, Drew was not alone in his campaign against the "war makers" and their world-wide combines. Periodicals in various countries, chiefly organs of the peace groups, sometimes leftish, otherwise "liberal," were denouncing the builders of bombers and guns, and it would be foolish to deny that this concerted effort had much to do with the unpreparedness of nations which would eventually have to face Hitler's totally armed Germany. Thus Drew and the Colonel contributing in their own way to the cause of the peace-lovers—the real ones, the phony ones and those who were merely mixed-up—delayed the steps which certain pessimistic realists, with their eyes on Germany and Italy, knew were inevitable.

By 1936 Drew of his own volition decided to look into the European situation, and submitted an article under the statement "Germany Prepares for Conquest." Napier Moore toned down the title to "Tear up the Treaties." Nevertheless, despite the heading first suggested, Drew was not entirely convinced that war with Germany was unavoidable. When Beverley Baxter, regular contributor of *Maclean's* popular "London Letter," reported on his 1938 visit to Germany and noted the underlying hatred of Britain among the population, Drew took pen in hand to reply. Hitler, he declared, was a dangerous man, but the mass of the German people did not hate the British. Hitler could be held in check if Britain and the other Empire countries would assure Germany of "access to supplies of certain raw materials in exchange for finished goods which Germany can make so well." A few years later, when the war was on, Drew's political opponents quoted the article as proof that he was pro-Hitler.

Certainly on the surface there was some ambivalence in Drew's attitude. In a 1936 article discussing "Our Bow and Arrow Army," he had pointed out that Canada's fighting men had no modern equipment. Still he did not urge increased expenditure for defense, though he declared that, if Canada was to continue to support its fighting services, nothing less than up-to-date methods and *matériel* should be countenanced. At that point, however, he argued against arms contracts to private firms; defense supplies should be provided on a non-profit basis by government-owned arsenals.

It was that last recommendation which would be quite ignored by the powers-that-be in Ottawa when they finally got around to taking his advice (and many other people's) about modern equipment. Drew, critic-extraordinary, could not himself endure criticism, real or implied; to see his non-profit plan totally dismissed was tantamount to a public challenge. When the government announced the awarding of contract to a manufacturer with no previous experience in the armament business that was all the inspiration he needed for the next big onslaught in *Maclean's*. The famous Bren gun controversy was on.

Napier Moore and Drew—close friends always—became the investigating team, with the Colonel standing by to render aid if necessary. Moore was convinced the scheme was improvident, that the public treasury was being raided to make a huge fortune for Major James E. Hahn, an industrial entrepreneur (radio sets being his specialty) with good political connections, who did not have to pull too many wires to get the contract out of the then Minister of Defense, Honorable Ian Mackenzie—the same "professional" Scot whom the Colonel had tried so hard to like.

Drew's article, forceful, factual, appeared under the title, "Canada's Armament Mystery," in September 1, 1938, *Maclean's*. His chief complaints related to: the manner in which Hahn acquired the "broken-down boiler factory" where the guns would be manufactured; the cost plus 10 percent feature of the price; the lack of public tenders; the government's delay of one month between the signing of the contract and announcement of the arrangement to Parliament; certain activities of M.P.s and other politicians in the matter; and the over-all switching of policy from government arsenal production to a privately operated plant.

A first-rate political scandal erupted. Prime Minister Mackenzie

King had no alternative but to appoint a Royal Commission under
Mr. Justice H. H. Davis to investigate. The final report gave basic
confirmation to Drew's criticisms, challenging very few of his facts.
The Commission chairman stayed carefully away from comment that
might have been embarrassing to any party of the contract; he was
content to leave the moral conclusions to Parliament. His single firm
recommendation, for a Defense Purchasing Board to assume charge
of all orders for military supplies, was accepted by the government;
when war came the Board expanded into an efficient Department of
Munitions and Supply, under the energetic, imaginative if unconven-
tional Honorable Clarence Decatur Howe. There were other beneficial
results following Parliament's study of the report. Ian Mackenzie and
his deputy were quietly side-tracked. The Bren gun contract was rewritten to eliminate the cost-plus features. And under Hahn's continuing management, his company chalked up a notable contribution
to Canada's rapidly accelerating wartime production, which involved
the nation's whole industrial establishment.

Following analysis of the Davis report, the Ottawa *Journal* concluded its leading editorial in these words: "Summed up, this investigation in its outcome is all to the good. Those responsible for it—
*Maclean's Magazine* and Colonel George A. Drew—did a good job
for this country."

Yet a few questions may still be raised. Wouldn't Howe's smooth
departmental machine for war orders have had to be created, even
without the Commission's recommendation, let alone Drew's Bren
gun revelations? The answer may be that the article, plus a series in
*The Financial Post* dissecting various examples of imprudent government contracting, stirred Ottawa to action early, certainly saving precious time, along with probably hundreds of millions of dollars for the
taxpayers. And, journalistically, one may ask if it was wise to let
Drew, by now a politician himself, write and sign such an article? He
had become the Tories' new hope in Ontario, soon to win a seat in the
Legislature, eventually to become Premier of the province, until, in
1948, he would be persuaded to transfer his interests to Ottawa where
he would lead the Conservative Opposition for several years. His
name on an inflammatory *exposé* of a Liberal government's action on
the vitally needed Bren gun equipment was bound to bring political
partisanship to the boil-over point. Had Napier Moore or his managing
editor, W. Arthur Irwin, prepared and bylined the article, the national

significance of the disclosures, and the objective, non-political motives necessitating them, would have been more clearly apparent.

Drew's writing association with *Maclean's* reached its *finale* in December 1941, when his forty-first contribution, a fine, patriotic call for attack on the Continent, attack with surprise, force and united effort, was presented under the heading, "Beat Hitler at His Own Game." The readers gave their hearty assent, and not a single argumentative voice was raised.

In spite of his new political activities, Drew kept in close touch with the Colonel. There were frequent letters back and forth; occasionally the Macleans would stage a foursome dinner party, where the two ladies would enjoy exchanging reiminiscences of old Portugal. Mrs. Drew, a most attractive brunette, was the daughter of Edward Johnson, famous tenor hailing from Guelph, one-time general manager of New York's Metropolitan Opera, and in later years chairman of the board of Toronto's Royal Conservatory of Music; his wife had been born a Portuguese *contessa* and Fiorenza Drew could remember a happy childhood among her continental relatives. She and George were married in 1936.

The two Colonels never lacked important public issues to discuss, and they were to take action, each in his separate capacity, following the Hong Kong tragedy of 1941. Drew, still in the Ontario arena, openly criticized Ottawa—as had Opposition members in the House of Commons—for the emergency dispatching of two army battalions to reinforce the little British island's garrison against the new enemy, Japan. On Christmas Eve, after constant air bombings, the colony surrendered, with more than a quarter of the Canadian contingent killed and the remainder taken prisoner. Canada reeled with shock and sorrow; George Drew was more than saddened, he was bitterly angry. In full, clear voice he accused the Canadian government of sending troops who were both untrained and ill-equipped.

Prime Minister King appointed a Royal Commission to examine the charges. Four counsel were selected to serve, one of them Colonel Drew, under the chairmanship of Chief Justice Sir Lyman Duff, who himself drafted the final report. It was a whitewash affair, with only selected portions of the evidence included, and the most damning facts carefully withheld "for reasons of wartime security." Drew felt obliged to speak out in dissent, whereat the Ottawa government decided to take action against him for statements "prejudicial to recruiting." Somebody

of normal common sense persuaded the Cabinet to stop this childish
and foolish move against a man who had amply proved his loyalty in
times of war and peace.

But Mackenzie King did not give in easily. He refused to publish
Drew's letter to him, setting forth the inaccuracies and incomplete-
ness of the Duff report. In fact, as late as 1948, Mr. King refused to
table it in the House. Finally, Drew, from his place across the floor
as Conservative leader in the Commons, read his copy of the letter into
Hansard. That Drew was right and Duff wrong, about the whole matter
of Hong Kong, has become firmly established over the years as all
the details have been brought forward for careful study.

And what was Colonel Maclean's part in this unhappy Hong Kong
business? It had to do with money. Three of the four counsel serving
the Commission were paid for their services; Drew refused any fee. As
soon as the Colonel got wind of that decision he made out his personal
cheque for $5000 and mailed it to the friend who had been his mainstay
through so many years.

Drew valued and enjoyed the association too. "I was very fond of
John Bayne Maclean; in fact, I had a deep affection as well as admiration for him," he remarked on more than one occasion. He admitted
that the Colonel was not an easy man to talk to; the tendency to
wander off the main subject had to be dealt with . . . "You had
to bring him back to the theme in hand." Sometimes, Drew said, the
Colonel made statements that seemed preposterous at the moment. "But
I cannot recall any statement he ever made to me in the course of the
long hours when, together, we gathered material for my articles, that
turned out to be inaccurate. His brain was a storehouse of information."

Theirs was a private working partnership with obvious mutual
benefits. Through the Colonel's unflagging support and encouragement,
Drew rose to the position of a national figure. And because of his
willingness to listen and to accept an older man's co-operation, Drew
contributed vitality and a sense of accomplishment to the Colonel's final
years.

# CHAPTER XXVII

# PIONEER VILLAGE

"Most people think of a small community as being a sort of
Utopia . . . actually that isn't a true picture."
*Kate Aitken in* Never a Day So Bright

---

THE RETURN of the native to Crieff was rather different from other
millionaires' back-to-the-land movement. For John Bayne Maclean
there had been no nostalgic dream awaiting the right time for fulfillment, no tired city man's urge to get away from it all and discover
the joys of Nature or prize cattle. The Colonel was no romantic, a
point that stands forth clearly in the story of his sudden reacquaintance
with the little crossroads hamlet where he had been born. Quite
simply he found—or thought he found—there was a job to be done,
and he assumed it with enthusiasm, unsparing of both time and money.
That the completion of the project would mark the beginning of a new
private career, filled with fascinating interests, was a development
quite unforeseen—by him at any rate, although the record of his
whole life contains instances of one thing leading to another.

When his mother died in 1916 he and brother Hugh had taken her
to Crieff for burial beside the Reverend Andrew. On this, the first visit
in more than forty years, the Colonel was shocked by the neglected
condition of the churchyard and general surroundings. A year or two
later he made a more leisurely trip, chiefly for the purpose of deciding on a suitable monument for his parents' graves, and hoping that
his earlier impression of the place would be proved wrong. Not so;
the weeds were hip-high, it was dangerous to walk about because
of the bumps and hollows in the ground; tombstones leaned drunkenly
or lay in pieces, and whatever vestiges of fencing remained could
not keep out the wandering cows.

By the time he climbed back into the car, which Ritchie had waiting
in the rutted gravel lane, the Colonel's original plan had been

considerably extended. As a memorial to his parents and also to their friends and fellow worshipers buried here—the Galloways, Stewarts, McDonalds and others—and as a gift to the community, he would undertake the complete renovation of the area and make provision for its future upkeep. He must engage the best professional designers available—and that meant Messrs. Olmsted Brothers, recognized as North America's leading landscape architects.

If some people thought he was aiming too high, going too far both in geography and investment, he took no notice. The old Boston firm had achieved impressive results in such developments as New York's Central Park and Montreal's Mount Royal; the same high standards were required for Crieff's little cemetery and church lot, comprising hardly more than an acre. Here, too, was another opportunity to prove his long-held theory that whenever Canada imported an international architect, or editorial consultant or operatic director, some young Canadians would benefit from their association with the masters. Thus, far from denying Canadians a job, he felt he was helping them, in turn, to reach the top.

On Canada's Thanksgiving Day, 1924, people from nearby cities and towns gathered with the local folk to admire the results of Olmsted Brothers' work, join in the dedication service, and express their appreciation to Colonel John Bayne Maclean in person.

He was a happy man that afternoon, delighted to conduct the little groups about, sharing the landscaping lore acquired during his project, explaining the why's of this shrubbery corner, that choice of tree, the height and thickness of the graveyard's stone enclosure, and in turn enjoying the others' family recollections as they stood respectfully in front of the massive gray granite monument bearing the brief histories of his parents.

There were old local tales to be exchanged, and the Colonel never tired of hearing them, or saving them for a playback on his return to Toronto. One of his favorites had to do with a certain Scot who had settled in Crieff equipped with little more than an *expertise* in distilling. Yet from a modest shanty hideaway north of the village he rapidly became a business success, supplying the needs of the whole township with a new brand of whiskey yclept "Kilrae." It was powerful stuff, as indicated by the leading Crieff storekeeper who, after sustaining a nasty fall in his cellarway, answered a customer's solicitous inquiry with the honest statement, " 'Twas no accident, mon; 'twas Kilrae did it."

Those had been the "boom" days for the area, the '70s of the Colonel's childhood, when Crieff was a crossroads village. Many changes had occurred in later years; fires had demolished various log or frame structures; the old church and school attended by Maclean had been replaced by buildings erected some time after the family moved to Chatsworth. One familiar place remained: the manse, his birthplace, its silhouette still the same staid, squarish bulk with center doorway, steeply sloping roof over the upper bedrooms, twin chimneys at either end, and the kitchen wing projecting toward the rear. The old driving shed at the bottom of the vegetable garden had also managed to survive. But it was obvious the property had lost any reason for being; no minister had been in residence for years; here stood merely a sad, dilapidated reminder of another century, another way of living and serving, and the end was inevitable.

So it must have seemed to the Colonel—yet the good folks of the Presbyterian congregation were deep in a plan which would abruptly change the course of his thinking. In 1925 they presented to him and his Maclean descendants the manse and its half-acre lot, in grateful recognition of his zeal and generosity.

What a surprise! What a pleasure! Quite aside from the sentimental associations involved, here was a completely new experience for John Bayne Maclean, in that he had never before received a gift of "real property" by deed or inheritance. (In fact, this would be the single such occasion of his lifetime—for even Munsey, who died in that important Crieff year, 1925, had no thought for him in a will disposing of many millions, the bulk of which went to the Metropolitan Museum in New York. "All that money—and he didn't even leave Jack a pair of cuff-links," as Mrs. Maclean tartly remarked. The Colonel paid little heed to such comments; loyalty to his friend could not be shaken. He made his own private reply to William Allen White, the Kansas editor, who concluded his famous summing-up of the American publisher thus: "Frank Munsey contributed to the journalism of his day the talent of a meat packer, the morals of a money-changer and the manners of an undertaker. He and his kind have about succeeded in transforming a once-noble profession into an 8 per cent security. May he rest in trust." The Colonel's files still contain that clipping, and along the margin there is a penciled comment in the familiar hand: "White was a dirty skunk." Those words were probably the strongest ever used by John Bayne Maclean.)

Soon the new Crieff program was nicely under way. Architects took charge of a careful restoration scheme which would retain the original character and plan of the manse as closely as possible, while adding all the comforts of modern living, and finally achieving a spanking-white Colonial clapboard house, snug and serene among its new lawns and gardens. Year by year, further improvements were made, the most ambitious being the moving forward of the old carriage-house to a situation where it could be linked with the main dwelling by means of a roofed patio. Thus the cavernous place where the Reverend Andrew had kept his horse, buggy and cutter became the nucleus for the Colonel's spacious private retreat, laid out exactly as he designated, with large, airy library paneled in pine, amply windowed and having a handsome fireplace, and with plenty of space remaining for a big bedroom, bathroom and entrance hall.

The acreage expanded too. Those constantly watchful eyes of the new country gentleman had noted the absence of beneficial bird life— the hawks and owls which kept rodents in check, the many sparrow types which lived on weed seeds, the others which pursued bothersome insects—and the reason was clear: the natural woodland habitat had long ago disappeared, leveled for crops or pasture. So, when a farm next to the manse became available, the Colonel purchased it and started a reforestation project. As other neighboring properties came on the market, he acquired them, winding up with a total holding of more than 300 acres. His idea now was to establish alongside his new wood-lots a modern (he avoided the term "model," as too suggestive of theoretical agriculture only) working farm, which would become a source of information and inspiration in the best practical methods for the whole district.

Again, Olmsteds were consulted and layouts for the most efficient and attractive development prepared. At this point the Colonel decided he must have an expert on such matters close at hand—and, of course, he had already picked him out. Gordon Culham, a talented young Canadian, was a member of the Boston firm's staff; he had graduated from Ontario Agricultural College at Guelph, later from Harvard, and was now specializing in estate design. On a trip to Olmsted's headquarters the Colonel met Culham and urged him to return to Canada to carve out a career in a field which was so far sparsely served. "In fact," he said, "I will promise you enough work to make the move worthwhile."

It was a deal, and from his new office in Toronto Culham moved about, supervising the many projects at Crieff—the access lanes, enclosures on the expanded farm, carefully interpreting the Colonel's later ideas, as when he decided to remodel the local school grounds for play area and neat landscaping—also redesigning the surroundings of the Austin Terrace house, and doing the permanent ground-and-garden plan for the Tyrrell's new country place northwest of the city. The Colonel was indefatigable in living up to his promise. Sometimes he had to admit defeat, as when his efforts to have Culham engaged as consultant for the Niagara Parks Commission petered out; nevertheless the Colonel's own project for the beautification of the grounds of the University of Western Ontario which Culham carried out, made significant compensation for such setbacks.

At that period few universities engaged land engineers or area architects to plan for future growth, and such agglomerations of mixed styles and patchwork placing of buildings as seen at Toronto and McGill campuses were the result. Maclean was determined that "Western" would be different, and the president and board of governors, in accepting the offer of his rather untraditional gift, were happy to promise their full support. Together, the Colonel and Culham visualized an over-all scheme that would isolate the grounds from encroachment of the urban influences which were bound to grow along with the city. The approaches, paths, driveways, as well as the lots specifically assigned for building expansion, must be sited in a manner to ensure beauty, dignity and peace, as well as service, for the foreseeable future. That meant the drawing-up of a twenty-five-year program at the outset, and the careful detailing and supervision of each phase of the basic construction work. Culham took on the job enthusiastically and the Colonel kept him in funds for the Western undertaking over the next five years. The long-range planning made possible by John Bayne Maclean, LL.D., is still being admired in London, Ontario, today. And the Colonel would have rejoiced to learn that in 1966 his brilliant collaborator, Gordon Culham, received the honorary degree in recognition of his services over many years as "a partner in the development of Western."

Fresh contacts and friendships developed, inevitably, from these special Maclean ventures. J. Sterling Morton, founder of Arbor Day and its ritual of tree-planting for American communities, especially through the schools, became a regular correspondent. In the Colonel's files is a first day cover of the U.S. stamp issued on the first Arbor

Day, and sent to him by friend Morton. Later, son Joy Morton, the salt king ("It never rains but it pours") continued the happy relationship, and, after he had built an arboretum near Chicago in memory of his father, frequently sent specimen saplings across the border for use in Crieff. On a visit to the younger Morton the Colonel was delighted to discover that his friend had attended London's Hellmuth College, the predecessor of Western. He suggested to the university authorities that Morton be given an honorary degree, and the idea was promptly approved. Unfortunately Joy Morton died a few days before Convocation, and it was left to the Colonel to come forward to accept the posthumous award of citation and hood, for later delivery to the family.

The Crieff activities multiplied. During the restoration of the manse and the three old fieldstone houses belonging to the contiguous farms, numerous quaint artifacts from pioneer days came to light in sheds, basements and attics. "These things must be saved," the Colonel declared, viewing the collection of Gaelic psalm books, legal documents, coins, tin-type portraits, school readers, and larger items such as primitive farm tools and household furnishings. Some of the last-mentioned—spool-legged tables and stands, several sturdy chests of drawers, etc.—were carefully refinished and took their place in the country-style decorating scheme of the manse. For the remaining miscellany the Colonel set aside a small building as a museum where all members of the community, and especially the young people, he hoped, would visit and study these symbols of the busy life of their forefathers. To round out the display he engaged Captain John Gilchrist, something of a local historian and certainly a skilled artisan, to fashion small-scale models of early farm implements, housekeeping aids, plus carefully detailed reproductions of the important buildings in old Puslinch, including the first church at Crieff. As the collection grew— frequently added to by well-wishing neighbors—the Colonel announced that he would erect a special fireproof building to house it.

World War II forced abandonment of that plan; indeed, there was to be little further development of the Maclean interests at Crieff. Shortage of help slowed the activities at his "demonstration" farm, and the pure-bred Ayrshire herd, comprising up to thirty head of cattle, including two bulls famous for their prize ribbons, had to be dispersed.

The Colonel probably saw Crieff for the last time in the spring of 1950. If he could visit it today he would feel sad about the changes which time and the pressures of highly specialized agriculture have wrought. Some of the farmers have moved away to more productive areas; houses are boarded up; the school has been closed for several years, with resulting disintegration of the property.

The Colonel's residence and adjacent acreage, willed to his nephew, was bought by the Danish Association of New Canadians and operates as a social and vacation resort. All remaining lands and buildings were bequeathed to the Presbyterian Church in Canada, but meantime three of the Colonel's faithful associates have rent-free occupancy of them for life, under his explicit arrangements.

Miss Dove, long-time secretary, spends her summers in one of the fieldstone houses, the farm manager and his family live in another, and the gardener, who supervises maintenance of church and cemetery, etc., occupies the third. The reforested section has flourished, and a good deal of cutting goes on, especially for the Christmas tree trade. The greater part of the pioneer collection was turned over to the Wellington County Historical and Research Society for permanent display in the Elora museum, some miles distant.

The present panorama at Crieff falls sadly short of the Colonel's vision. Yet who would be so coldly pragmatic as to dismiss the whole effort as wasted? In his sixties, when most executives are forced to consider retirement, John Bayne Maclean entered buoyantly on a totally new adventure of study, planning, rescuing, building. For the next twenty years and more, he was the visiting squire, the local benefactor, yes, but, more importantly, a man busy with a dozen decisions, all leading toward an avowed purpose. He was no farmer, he made many expensive mistakes; nonetheless, he labored unstintingly to bring rural renewal to a played-out stretch of Ontario countryside. What he actually achieved was a second great personal heyday, constantly stimulating, wholly satisfying for himself.

Only a few people in Toronto had any inkling of the extent of the Crieff development. At long intervals the Hunters and Tyrrells might drive out for Sunday tea in the manse—and on the return trip deplore among themselves the cost of the new concrete piggery or the latest notion in sanitary poultry-houses—on wheels. One of the most frequent visitors, of necessity, was the internal auditor from the company's business office; assigned to the job of keeping the farm books, he wrestled valiantly with inventories, assessments, taxes, staff lists, wages, and at a certain point found himself forced to probe the mysteries of butterfat content in milk. "The Colonel was sure his herd's production rated the best price going," Ed Paterson recently recalled. "Yet the dairy he shipped to constantly produced records showing the milk lacked the proper butterfat ratio. I even went to the plant to watch the lab tests. Neither the Colonel nor I could get to the root of the problem. Then one Monday morning he came back from Crieff in a state of glee. 'Paterson, I've solved it!' he said. 'I dropped by at the herdsman's house; there was no one around, so I went in—and what do you think I found in the cellar? A separator, and three full pails of cream! I want you to fire the thief at once.'"

No other friends or associates, however, reached that degree of confidential exchange concerning Crieff. Mrs. Maclean did not like the place. On her first visit she had been horrified by the proximity of the cemetery to the main floor bedroom furnished expressly for her. Unable to move about easily she could find no pleasure in shady walks and woods full of wild flowers. Her friends were not available for teas and dinners. Although relenting sufficiently to make one or two more excursions, each as unnerving as the first, she showed little interest.

So, lacking a hostess in residence, the Colonel set aside any thoughts of special parties or weekend guests, and most of his friends had to be content with the vague rumor that "he seems to own a farm somewhere." And, just as inevitably, his wife was to endure many lonely days, sitting in her wheelchair at Austin Terrace. Rather than face an argument, the Colonel would say to Ritchie, "Run along the hall and tell Madam we are leaving for Crieff at ten o'clock." Immediately "Madam" would call back on the intercom phone to protest. But the Colonel had made up his mind, and, as he had never learned to drive, it was essential to have the chauffeur along. The two men became familiar figures in the village neighborhood, both of them fond of walking and ready to take off across the fields to call on one of the "Mac" families, and both turning up regularly for Sunday service at the church—a routine which the Colonel followed only in Crieff.

# CHAPTER XXVIII

## *SHARING THE WEALTH*

"Not what we give, but what we share."
*James Russell Lowell*

JOHN BAYNE MACLEAN was no financial wizard. Corporate matters, complex fiscal affairs, even the more or less routine disclosures of balance sheets were beyond his grasp—as he readily admitted. At the annual meeting of the company in 1935 he opened his speech by recalling how Sir John A. Macdonald had once wound up an excellent address on national problems with the remark: "Now, coming to the question of finance, I will have to confess that I do not know that subject, and that is why I have Foster here," pointing to his Minister of Finance. "Frankly," said the Colonel, "I think perhaps I am worse than Sir John because I cannot add up a column of figures and be sure the result is correct."

His lack of corporate management skill never worried him. His philosophy was that if the company served the country well, the profits would follow. Out of the profits earned, the proprietors should draw only the amounts necessary to live on; the rest should remain in the business for improvement of its service. Besides, by the time his company had grown to be large and complex, he knew he possessed an astute, careful administrator in vice-president Horace T. Hunter. Thus, for well over half the long span of the Colonel's publishing career, he found himself happily free from major financial decisions.

Managing his personal business affairs was a rather different matter —pleasurably exciting at many points because of the friendships involved, nicely rewarding through his ready access to some of the world's most expert advice. Thanks to Schwab, Baruch, Bache and others headquartered in New York, the Colonel was spared any major setback in his investments. His purchases of Canadian shares—profitably guided in former years by Montrealers Shaughnessy and Hosmer

—had ceased immediately following the founding of *The Financial Post*. To free the paper from any possible suspicion or charge of manipulation of news for the owner's benefit, Maclean laid down a rule that henceforth he would buy no Canadian stocks.

One minor disappointment in money matters arose from his inability to establish a claim, on behalf of his mother, to a certain Scottish estate amounting to £57,000. "The Mackillican Estate" identifies a thick file in the Colonel's personal archives; to open it is to be confronted with a miscellany of letters, tombstone inscriptions, parochial records, genealogical tables going back as far as the year 1630, newspaper clippings, lawyers' reports and, of course, Maclean's own penciled memos to himself. The case came to public attention in 1913 following the death of William Mackillican of Nairnshire, who had made his success in the tea business in India and then retired to Scotland. The heirs named in the will had predeceased him, and there were no near relatives extant; hence the courts must review all claims and determine the closest kinship for distribution of the estate.

Here was a project bound to excite the Colonel, with his predilection for bloodlines and old Highland lore; also, from the standpoint of any self-respecting Scot, the prospect of acquiring, by dint of a little careful research, a fortune for family sharing could not be lightly passed over. His mother (still alive at ninety or more, but invalided and beset by failing memory) was a Mackillican on her mother's side; the place with the odd name, Tirfogrein, sprang to her son's mind from conversations a half-century ago; he must start delving.

Soon most of the Colonel's Scottish contacts, in Canada, the U.S. and overseas, found themselves on his active correspondence list. Indeed, he had received the first news of the undisposed estate in a letter from a Glasgow lawyer, a distant cousin named Maclean, and so proud of the connection that he invariably opened with the salutation, "Dear Clansman." The Toronto *Telegram*'s John Ross Robertson, a loyal Hielan' man albeit Canadian-born, had some interesting suggestions from his own family files for the Colonel; so, too, a Mackillican descendant in Michigan, another, a Holstein breeder, in Ontario, a third in Winnipeg, and so on. By the time the Macleans packed their bags for Europe in the summer of 1914, a goodly bundle of Mackillican-Cameron references was ready to travel, too.

But of course that was the year the Kaiser's war erupted, sending the visitors scurrying back to England. Of the missing baggage, the case containing the documents was among the last lot returned to

Toronto, well over a year later. Although the Colonel cabled his lawyers in Scotland, "Enter Mother's Claim Mackillican Estate, Family Papers Held in Germany," a detailed submission could not be prepared before the mills of the gods and the Lord Justice in Edinburgh started their grinding as scheduled. If it afforded any consolation the Colonel learned that he did not lose solely by default, for the Court's findings, announced in March 1916, recognized only the Mackillicans of Piperhill to be blood relations, and therefore heirs, of the late tea-planter; the Mackillicans of Tirfogrein, from whom the Colonel had painstakingly traced his own descent, were not connected.

Anyway, a nice try, and—to use a phrase foreign to the Colonel— fun while it lasted.

The wildest financial scheme ever to come within tempting range of John Bayne Maclean had to do with the purchase of a million acres of land in the Austrian Tyrol region. This vast domain had belonged to Archduke Frederick, wealthiest of the Hapsburgs; after World War I and the Peace of Versailles, it underwent drastic carving-up and confiscation by several countries—Austria, Czechoslovakia, even Poland. The old empire of Franz Josef had crumbled, but these miles of picturesque terrain remained quite unspoiled. Just to look at them could start a man to dreaming—or, in the case of an active acquirer such as Frank Munsey, to planning.

He would buy up the estate, holus-bolus, and then carefully divide for highly profitable resale. Meantime he invited a few friends to participate in the enterprise, and among them, naturally, the Colonel, whose enthusiastic response was a foregone conclusion. Together the two visited the area, drove through the rich grazing lands, paused to enjoy the quaint charm of the villages, which numbered more than a hundred, and argued the architectural merits and present-day value of the castles—several dozens—which dominated the most dramatic vistas. This remote heartland of Europe could offer the ultimate in experience for tired Wall Streeters who were perhaps bored with the hotel routine in Florida or the hunt club set in Virginia. Why, with the purchase of a couple of medieval hamlets, a little lake, a skyline of mountains, and a castle with walls three feet thick, a man could live like a king!

But the plan died a-borning. None of the governments in control would agree to de-confiscation; there could be no transfer of title, regardless of the multimillions of dollars stalled and waiting for investment. Munsey returned quietly to his old stamping-ground and bought, merged or killed off a few newspapers. Maclean was back at the University Avenue office, intent on another slash at Ottawa for initiating schemes which any sane, practical businessman could recognize as "crazy."

If the Tyrol real estate deal had gone through, the Colonel just might one day have found himself open to the charge which he continued to make against this or that person, near or far—i.e., that he was a member of "an international group," bent on exploitation. Mercifully, the collapse of the Munsey dream saved him from any taint of belonging to those foreign financial cliques which he believed constituted the greatest evil of the modern world.

Maclean had little understanding of international finance or central banking; thus he was all too ready to believe that a group of piratical types juggled exchanges and influenced fiscal policies for their own financial aggrandizement. When Prime Minister Bennett established Canada's central bank, the Colonel was sure it would become a tool of "Austrian, German, Dutch, or Greek-born financiers," who were known to be "the world's greatest profiteers."

In his driving desire for more information and lively debate, he carried on correspondence with an assortment of monetary cranks, including Arthur Kitson, the English scientist who in later life became a mystic about money, and the author of many pamphlets and books on the subject. He had been co-inventor with Thomas A. Edison in the electric light field, and collaborator with Alexander Graham Bell. Kitson with his Banking & Currency Reform League campaigned against the "disease of world finance," with its "unscientific" currency and banking laws, and maintained that the gold standard "enriches the rich and destroys the small producer." In an early letter to the Colonel, he mentioned having delivered a series of lectures under the chairmanship of Ramsay MacDonald who later said: "Stay with me; one day I will be Prime Minister and I will make you my Chancellor of the Exchequer." MacDonald was right in his first prediction, but Kitson stayed a pamphleteer. He made many converts, ranging from the Australian Prime Minister, Sir William Hughes, to Charlie Chaplin, whose unorthodox views on money, as set forth in his autobiography, are a reflection of Kitson's preachments.

The Colonel studied the theories and occasionally borrowed from them for his own articles, especially during the bad times of the early 1930s. But Kitson's claim that "the Jews"—particularly the Rothschilds and the Warburgs—were behind international monetary machinations, found no acceptance. The Colonel's old friends, Baruch, Bache and the Speyer brothers, were Jews; he also had personal acquaintance with other wealthy Jews, some of them international bankers, in both Europe and America; he was prepared to stand firm against the rising storm of hints, suspicions or castigations which he believed were based largely on prejudice. He wrote Kitson: "I would not damn the Jews any more than I would damn the Conservatives who gouged the public through the mining brokers." In short, there were good Jews and bad Jews, just as there were good Tories and bad ones.

And whether the "international clique" whom he mistrusted comprised Jewish—as Kitson insisted—or non-Jewish operators, as the Colonel maintained, the fact of their ancestry was as nothing compared to their evil intentions, their deliberate exploitation of national treasuries and gullible investors. He went even further: certain sinister banker groups had been the secret financiers of the Bolshevist revolution. Surely any reasoning observer could see why! International Communism had, as its primary objective, the destruction of democratic and social values in Western countries. International bankers had a similar goal, since they hoped to buy cheaply in a disturbed global investment market and then, in due course, unload on the public at high prices. As with the old problem of the chicken and the egg, and which came first, the Colonel never quite clarified the point of the original responsibility, nor settled the matter of whether the money-men were using the Communists as agents of destruction, or vice-versa. What he did assert constantly was that they worked together, and for the undoing of the decent world.

The conspiring financiers were, admittedly, hard to track down. He suspected certain leading New York banking firms, and said as much on many occasions, although avoiding any identification. But in the same breath he was careful to exclude from any shadow of doubt those other companies, which he gladly named, and which were not and could not possibly be involved—for the overwhelming reason that they belonged to his friends, who were above suspicion.

Europe, too, had plenty of financial wheeler-dealers. In 1923 the Colonel had success of a sort when he happened on confirmation of suspicions which had been bothering him for some time. A routine newspaper announcement reported the formation of a new company, the United European Investors Limited, incorporated under the laws of Canada but managed from a New York address. A group of the promoters called on the Colonel to enlist his support.

In copious memos and frequent conversations later, the Colonel identified the group as Andrew Haydon of Ottawa, Martin Nordegg and Grigory Zinovieff. Haydon, a lawyer, was chief organizer for the Liberal party; he would soon be rewarded by a seat in the Senate. Nordegg, German-born, had first appeared in Canada in 1906, going to Alberta where he developed a coal mine and had a new town named after him. He fled the country in World War I, his enterprises were seized by the custodian of alien property, and the community of Nordegg was rechristened Brazeau. A few years after the Armistice he returned to Canada, sought out Haydon and worked with him for the restoration of German-owned properties. Zinovieff was none other than the erstwhile associate of Lenin and Trotsky, a character so unsavory that both the Bolshevik leaders fought him, yet at the same time so powerful that he warranted such top appointments as co-editor of *Pravda,* and by 1921 the presidency of the Communist International. (His chief contributions to today's history books derive, first, from the notorious "Zinovieff letter," which, with its detailed instructions for a Communist uprising in England, influenced the overthrow of the British Labour Government in 1924; and, second, from Stalin's final denunciation of him as a traitor, with its inevitable follow-up in front of a firing squad in 1936.)

Whether or not Zinovieff was actually a member of a trio who called at University Avenue is still a question. It is true that, as head of the Comintern, he did make various plotting trips outside of Russia at that period, yet there is no public record of his ever having been to Canada. Would a man deeply embroiled in the high councils of the new Soviet Russia, constantly greedy for more power therein, have taken time out to visit Toronto for the promotion of a rickety financial experiment? The answer is obvious. Perhaps the Colonel was merely indulging in the familiar sport of leaping to conclusions; the Zinovieff he met may have hailed from New Jersey.

Aside from the syndicate's personnel, the scheme itself had fantastic angles. United European Investors planned to sell 60,000 shares of stock, each priced at 10,000 German marks. Although the mark was shortly to become worthless through the postwar inflation in Germany, there were still people in 1922 who thought it was a good gamble. So, the new company would accept marks in exchange for shares; in turn it would use the marks to buy up industries and real estate in Germany. The scheme was bound to fail, as no sane German citizen would be likely to part with a tangible asset in exchange for a steadily falling currency. Within a few months of the incorporation date, the whole 600,000,000 marks of the company's capitalization—enough to fill a laundry basket—would have bought no more than a couple of loaves of bread.

The reason for the threesome's visit to the Colonel was, of course, not an unusual one: it would be nice if *The Financial Post* would "write up" the project in an early issue. The Colonel, an old expert at such overtures, gave no promise, but said he would discuss the matter with Tyson, the editor. Next morning, the latter received an interoffice memo from his chief urging that the *Post* take vigorous action to warn Canadians against gambling in German marks. The United European Investors' prospectus was passed along too—and, from the standpoint of later world developments, its most interesting information was the name of the president: Honorable Franklin D. Roosevelt, former state senator in New York, former Undersecretary of the Navy, although the listing referred to him merely as "Vice-President, Fidelity & Deposit Co. of Maryland."

---

*NEW ISSUE*

# 600,000,000 German Marks

Divided into 60,000 Common Shares, par value 10,000 Marks each
Application will be made to increase the Common Share Capital of this company.

## UNITED EUROPEAN INVESTORS, LIMITED

(Incorporated under Charter of the Dominion of Canada)

**PRESIDENT**
Hon. Franklin D. Roosevelt
Vice-President, Fidelity & Deposit Co. of Maryland

**VICE-PRESIDENT & CHAIRMAN EXECUTIVE COMMITTEE**
William Schall
William Schall & Co., Bankers, New York

| TREASURER | | SECRETARY |
|---|---|---|
| August Scherer | | A. R. Roberts |
| 45 William St., New York | | 7 Pine Street, New York |

**DIRECTORS**

| | Hon. Franklin D. Roosevelt | |
|---|---|---|
| William Schall | Almet F. Jenks, New York | Andrew Haydon, Ottawa, Canada |

**ADVISORY BOARD IN GERMANY**
Senator August Lattmann
Former partner, G. Amsinck & Co., New York

| Senator John von Berenberg Gossler | | Alfred Arnthal |
|---|---|---|
| Partner, John von Berenberg Gossler & Co., Hamburg | | Hamburg |

**BANKERS AND DEPOSITORS**

| Deutsche Bank, Hamburg | William Schall & Co., New York | Norddeutsche Bank, Hamburg |
|---|---|---|

**TRANSFER AGENTS**
The Bank of America, New York

The purpose of this company is to exchange its shares for German marks held by American investors, and to invest these marks in actual values in Germany. Carefully selected investments will be made in real estate, mortgages, securities and participation in Industrial and Commercial enterprises.

The company's facilities and connections enable it to secure attractive and sound investments; the directors will take advantage of the present money stringency in Germany and of the purchasing power of the mark, which is far greater than is reflected by exchange quotations.

By 1936 there had been a great change. Roosevelt and Zinovieff were headline names: the former as the hard-hitting man in the White House, the other as the leading figure in Stalin's murderous party purge in Moscow. Once again the Colonel took pen in hand, this time to tell the story of the three callers he had received some fourteen years ago, identifying the trio, sketching their separate careers and with all the colorful details intact, quoting from the prospectus and, of course, stressing the name of the company's president. Under the arrangement then in operation—that the Colonel's "reminiscent" material, which depended largely on memory and could thus be uncertain as to facts, must always appear under his own name—the article was accepted for *The Financial Post*. The reaction was unexpected, even to the writer of this book. The revelations "by Lieut.-Col. John Bayne Maclean, as in the recent *Financial Post* of Canada," were widely quoted in the anti-FDR press throughout the United States. The paper giving it the greatest prominence with the blackest headlines was the Chicago *Tribune*—probably because its publisher, Colonel Robert Mc-Cormick, like his friend in Toronto, believed the woods were full of international schemers.

The Colonel became a millionaire. He could easily have become a multi-millionaire—and the fact that he did not brings into clear focus the two principles governing his career. First, he was more concerned with editing and publishing as a national service than with a merely money-making business. Second, he believed profoundly in sharing with the senior associates who had contributed importantly to the firm's success.

So it came about that when he died in 1950 his estate was valued at $1,039,802, and included only a tiny minority shareholding in the company of which he had been sole owner twenty years before. Individual fortunes as large as and in some cases much greater than his own were to be amassed by one or two others within the Maclean-Hunter executive group—a fact which would have pleased him, for he had planned it that way.

True, there was no family heir with any earned right to his publishing business. Brother Hugh C. had broken away before the turn of the century and built up his own prosperous line of publications. Had Hector lived, he would undoubtedly have been the largest beneficiary of his father's publishing success, even if the lad's inclinations had taken him into quite different fields of activity.

Yet long before Hector's death the Colonel had been pondering various forms of employee ownership, as indicated in his discussions with Hunter and Tyrrell in 1911 and earlier. Shared responsibility should bring shared returns—as stressed in chats with A. W. Shaw of *System,* the business monthly which had done pioneer campaigning on the subject, and with publisher Cyrus H. K. Curtis in Philadelphia, who felt the plan was not only fair to senior staffers but good for the business as well. "It keeps them in your employ," as Mr. Curtis put it.

For a man with little taste or talent for corporate financing, the problem of how to go about the project was undoubtedly one of the knottiest ever to be faced. It beset the Colonel's waking hours for years, and not until after World War I and the recapitalization of the company would he have the satisfaction of formulating a practical plan and seeing it function.

The task facing Maclean's accountants, auditors and legal advisers during the recapitalization process was formidable. Like little Topsy, his company "just growed," and by 1919 it was indeed high time to bring it under corporate discipline.

As described in earlier chapters, *Canadian Grocer,* the first publication, was started in 1887 with a capital investment of $3000, of which approximately two-thirds was Maclean's and the remainder made up of small investments from his hired printer and a few friends. The little firm was known sometimes as the J. B. McLean Company, and just as often as the Grocer Publishing Co.; the owner himself used the names interchangeably. Within two or three years the modest profits enabled him to buy out his partners. By 1891–92 there were five papers, two shareholders—"Jack" and brother Hugh, just recently recruited—and the first formal organizing move had been made by the incorporation of the J. B. McLean Publishing Company, Limited, through letters patent.

Each paper managed to stay in the black, and the firm's total profits grew, steadily if not spectacularly, ranging anywhere from $4000 to as much as $10,000 per year. Maclean drew very modest sums, occasionally as salary, often as expenses. No dividends were paid; all surpluses remained in the business; hence by 1899 when Hugh pulled out, the company had sufficient resources to justify the price of $50,000 agreed upon for his one-third share—which, his brother reminded him, had been a gift from the outset.

During World War I the Colonel's wholly-owned publications numbered a dozen, including *Maclean's Magazine* and *Farmer's,* as well as the expanded trade and technical groups; total annual profits amounted to as much as $40,000.

The Colonel was definitely the sole owner, yet there were fiscal difficulties due to the laxity that had existed. *Canadian Grocer* remained the property of the J. B. McLean Company, but for some curious reason all other publications, all real estate, buildings and printing plant appeared in the ledgers as belonging to the Colonel *personally.* The business office and the auditor—dour John MacKay—had frequently muttered, not always politely, about this state of affairs, but John Bayne Maclean had paid little heed. He owned the company and all the other assets; what difference did it make where the legal title rested? He had earlier agreed to a loose form of contract which gave the company the right to administer the enterprise as a single entity; thus all publications were handled uniformly as company property. If the accountants had trouble with their bookkeeping—well, that was their worry and not his.

*The Financial Post* had stayed in its own separate category over the years, with the Colonel holding two-thirds of the stock and Mrs. Stewart Houston, widow of the co-founder, retaining one-third. As she had agreed to the senior partner's plan for reinvesting profits in the *Post,* there had been no distribution of income. One of the first moves, therefore, in Maclean's recapitalization program was to tidy up that situation: first, by dividing the accumulated profits of $41,000—two-thirds to the Colonel, one-third to Mrs. Houston—and next, by buying out her interest for $38,500 worth of the new 7 percent preferred stock in the reorganized Maclean company. And that profit split with the lady was to mark something of a milestone in the Colonel's business history, as these preferred dividends to Mrs. Houston were actually the first dividends ever taken out of the enterprise in 32 years.

The 1919 streamlining accomplished several important purposes. The name was fixed: The Maclean Publishing Company Limited. (True enough, everyone knew it as such, for the Colonel had casually, and without such bureaucratic frills as supplementary letters patent, dropped the "J.B." from the original incorporated title some years earlier.) The formation of the new company necessitated proper evaluation and transfer of all assets. His personal holdings of the University Avenue block of land, the buildings, machinery, the *Post* and the dozen other publications were bought by the company for $944,906.22. In payment he was to receive $250,000 of preferred shares, $164,500 of bonds and $33,406.22 in cash, plus all the common stock. After some reflection he decided against taking any cash, preferring to leave the $33,000 in the company as the nucleus of a general reserve fund. (Note: At that time it was a recognized practice for the major owner of a business to let profits build up and then, through recapitalization, to draw out a portion, as desired, free of income tax. No illegality or impropriety was involved. Today, after the tightening up of corporate and income tax laws under successive governments, such transactions would not be possible.)

The reorganization now enabled the Colonel to proceed with his long-deferred plan to share the wealth. He could set his own price, too. In 1920 he sold 30 percent of the common shares to Hunter for $50,000, and 10 percent to Tyrrell for $12,500.

The company moved ahead rapidly, due to the thrust given its policies by the aggressive Hunter-Tyrrell management, and perhaps also by the admitted rivalry, always respectful, between the two. Maclean's hopes had been realized, perhaps left far behind, as the annual profits rose to more than $100,000. All surpluses after operating expenses and dividends remained in the business to finance further expansion. The common stock did not pay dividends until 1927 when the rather grudging rate of 6 percent was announced. This required just $30,000 annually and was continued, with a modest lift to 8 percent, until after World War II.

Meantime, gross revenues grew apace, reaching $3,000,000 for the first time in 1928. That was the year the Colonel at the annual meeting protested, while smiling: "Will our expenditures on better and better service never cease?" The financial statement had delighted him, and he was an enthusiastic listener and participant in the discussions concerning reinvestment of accumulated profits—in additional real estate, office building expansion, better machinery.

And, of course, new publications, especially the spectacular, fast-rising star of that year, *Chatelaine,* the magazine for Canadian women. The name was selected through a coast-to-coast contest which drew over 75,000 entries; hundreds of ladies had decided this was the ideal title because, as one of them explained, "it has the same distinctive, gracious meaning in both the French and English languages." The grand prize-winner—Mrs. Hilda Pain, rancher's wife of Eburne, British Columbia—was chosen on the basis of having been the first to mail her entry, according to the postal date on the envelope.

Indeed, the Colonel could look around him and see progress at every point. Believing, as he did, that one-man leadership *cum* responsibility was the correct course, particularly to ensure independence from political and commercial pressures, he initiated an arrangement whereby Hunter could eventually acquire, from the Maclean estate, enough shares to represent full voting control. At the same time small lots were made available to twenty or so other executives, managers, editors and secretaries, who were allowed ten years to pay his asking price of $120 per share. (They paid no interest and their dividends covered two-thirds of the annual installment.) By 1968 that stock— split 800 to 1—was selling on the exchanges at the equivalent of $12,000 a share.

Financial and publishing interests turned covetous eyes on Maclean's company from time to time, and the Colonel was at least willing to listen to their proposals. The U.S. *Dry Goods Economist* came quite close to buying *Dry Goods Review* in 1901. An offer of $200,000 for the machinery papers was duly considered in 1911—and on this occasion the owner consulted John A. Hill, whose own publications after his death were to be joined with those of James H. McGraw to form the McGraw-Hill organization. The Colonel went so far as to indicate that he might just consider that price for the machinery group, but only if Hill was the buyer.

Hill answered in robust style. "I note that you have been approached with an indecent proposition. I have also been tempted but am too old to fall for anything like this. Unless they cut me off a very large piece of the sub-treasury they will not get any of my papers . . . I note your offer to sell your machinery group and do not believe anyone on this side could run them as well as you do. Mormon as I am, I have wives enough, and do not want any more publications. Our circle is complete, we have enough for any one institution to carry, we have them paid for, thank God, and I am going to play more golf and hunt more fish than I have ever before. . . ."

Hill's stand helped stiffen the Colonel's own resistance to further overtures. One of the most persuasive in terms of backers' names and apparently unlimited money reserves came via Sir Robert Donald, a leading British periodical owner, who visited Maclean in 1929. Supported by a group of English financiers, he had formed a company to buy up newspapers and publishing properties throughout the world; he was prepared to make an offer for the Colonel's complete organization. Maclean and Hunter responded with a polite refusal, of course, but the Colonel found the suggestion flattering because he was sure Lord Rothermere was the instigator. Over the years the two had met and chatted, and on more than one occasion the newspaper peer had urged him to move to England where there was "a

huge magazine market within a few miles of the great core of London"
—so different from the situation in Canada where publishing service
must be spread across thousands of miles of sparsely settled country.

In conversations later the Colonel even went so far as to intimate
that Donald had been authorized by Rothermere to offer the presidency of the new global publishing outfit to their Canadian *confrère*.
It seems hardly likely—not merely from the standpoint of his advancing age, but because an operation of such magnitude would most
certainly have required a financial genius to head it. And that Maclean
was not, as proved by his desperate wrestling with the routine matter
of his own income tax.

The Colonel's attitude to income tax was similar to that of the man
who, after listening to a careful explanation of its workings, remarked:
"Thank you very much, but I don't think I want to join."

John Bayne Maclean had never paid himself a high salary. His top
figure, $15,000, was reached in the year 1919; before that, he had
simply drawn various modest amounts as required. His expense accounts were never excessive, despite his regular shuttling back and
forth to Florida and Europe. In 1919 they added up to about $3000.

In order to break free from the bother of income tax on his $15,000
salary, he made a special arrangement with his Board in the mid-
1920s. He refunded to the company all salary received from 1922 to
1925, and in lieu of this fixed income he would accept total payment
of his travel expenses. (The highest figure would be reached in 1926
when he received $21,500; after that there was a gradual decline until
in time he no longer troubled to submit expense accounts.) The directors duly passed a by-law confirming that their president was to
serve the company, that he was to receive no salary but was to be paid
expenses for traveling to make contact with world leaders in government and finance and to induce industrialists to establish plants in
Canada. A copy of the Minute was filed with the Commissioner of
Income Tax who apparently found it satisfactory.

But those dividends which he had been forced to inaugurate and
accept, willy-nilly, on his shares were to cause considerable confusion,
especially in his own mind.

For several years the Colonel's tax report blandly ignored them,
although all other income was carefully recorded. When the tax officers
called attention to the omission, he argued that he was not drawing the

dividends for personal use but merely to finance expenditures on behalf of the company.

In a lengthy memorandum to the Commissioner he stated that during the 1919 reorganization he had considered taking his stock in the form of a non-dividend-paying preferred, letting his new partners draw the profits. But this had proved a difficult system to set up, and he had accepted the regular shares. Actually for several years he did not collect any dividends but was finally persuaded to take them when the company's auditor voiced objection to a liability for undisposed dividends having to appear in the company's accounts. But he assured the tax authorities that he spent the money entirely in the company's interest.

The ordinary newspaper man, the Colonel went on to explain, found that the great mass of his news was made easily available to him through coverage of a routine beat. But the reporter who gradually worked up to the higher fields of journalism, commerce, finance and higher politics, faced a different situation. "He is only successful when he builds up, throughout the years, important connections. To make and maintain these connections in newspapers like mine involves especially heavy expenses," which meant gifts and entertainment for people who were important sources of information, club memberships and traveling (although neither Palm Beach winters nor overseas jaunts were specified). To prove his points the Colonel went on to list many of his journalistic successes, such as the *exposé* of the German marks gamble, and to show how his private advice on investments in Canada had been requested and adopted by the world's leading financial men—each of them named.

Why, then, should he pay income tax on dividends that were entirely devoted to public service?

It was a remarkable document but somehow the income tax people were not impressed. He had to pay.

The Colonel's will, disposing of his million-dollar estate, reflected the philosophy that had guided him throughout his lifetime. First, he took generous forethought for his secretary, chauffeur and servants of long-standing. No cash was left to any relative, but Hugh C.'s son Andrew received the valuable real estate of 7 Austin Terrace, plus the Colonel's residence and 50 acres of land at Crieff. The sum of $100,000 went to the University of Western Ontario to establish the Bishop M. F. Fallon Chair in Medicine. Upper Canada College received $10,000 in memory of Hector Andrew Fitzroy Maclean, and for the purpose of providing an endowment to further the instruction of pupils in matters of "good health, good morals, and fair play, earning a good living, saving money and rendering public service." The residue of the estate, including the remainder of the Crieff property, went to the Presbyterian Church in Canada as an endowment for various specified purposes, such as augmenting the stipend of the minister at Crieff, assisting the schools in the neighborhood, providing young men and women of the area with bursaries to finance their courses at University of Western Ontario or at Ontario Agricultural College. The will paid a special tribute to his father and recalled the happy relations between Gaelic-speaking Catholics and Protestants during the long-ago days when the Macleans occupied the manse.

Certain of the will's provisions in reference to Crieff were hardly feasible for implementation, owing to the changing character of the locale. Fortunately, perhaps on the insistence of his long-sighted lawyer, the Colonel had provided that any surplus income could be used for the general purposes of the Presbyterian Church in Canada. The church, too, became the recipient of some 60 shares—1.2 percent of the outstanding total—of company stock, which turned up unexpectedly, probably quite forgotten, in the Colonel's strongboxes.

Compared with the multi-million-dollar fortunes his various friends left for the business historians to analyze, John Bayne Maclean's personal financial record is modest indeed. Yet he was a shrewd investor in that he had made enough money "in the market," as he often liked to recall, to support his high standard of living, while permitting profits from his own company to remain intact for corporate expansion. He became a rich man whose wealth was much less than it should have been. If he had set himself a goal for multimillions, he could undoubtedly have made it, but it is a question if he would have been happier. A scribbled note, found in his files, reads:

"My desire has always been to earn a living and save enough to take care of myself and dependents in our latter years. I have never had any ambition to build a fortune and to leave one to relatives unaccustomed to the trusteeship of great wealth or wealth which experience in Canada particularly shows to be the worst possible inheritance for young people. It is the ruin of young people. You have only to look about you to see abundant proofs of this. Good character and a capacity for hard work are the very best inheritance that any of us can give to our families and employees."

# CHAPTER XXIX

## *THE SOCIAL NICETIES*

"It is for superfluous things
for which men sweat."
*Seneca*

IT WAS RATHER too bad that Anna Maclean had cut herself off from
the new contacts that Crieff might have established. People, their
conversations and experiences, were as important to her as to her
husband, and at Austin Terrace the occasions when dinner was laid
for only two were probably a little dull. These didn't happen frequently,
however, for the Colonel, entrepreneur-extraordinary in the host department as in some others, constantly sought out interesting new visitors
in town, especially if he had heard of them through mutual friends.
"Bread-and-butter" letters bulk large in his correspondence file. One
of them, dated 1925, written on orchid stationery which still retains
a hint of matching perfume, is a charming expression of thanks from
Baroness Orczy, author of *The Scarlet Pimpernel* and other novels.
Apparently her recent visit to Canada had included a dinner party at
the Macleans' and, through the Colonel's follow-up, special attentions
in Montreal. "My husband and I think and talk so much of our
lovely time," she wrote from Monte Carlo, "and of all the kindness
to us there. The whole trip now seems like a beautiful dream."

For many years the Colonel had admired from afar the career of
Emmeline Pankhurst, Britain's pioneer suffragette. When she moved
to Toronto in the early '20s he lost no time in seeking an introduction,
and very soon the great battler for women's rights was in the guest
of honor's place at his table. Both the Macleans were delighted—his
wife for the happy discovery that here indeed was a lady of quiet
modesty and charm, and the Colonel for her readiness to answer his
queries concerning the organization she had designed to harass the
Houses of Parliament.

Eventually he got round to the matter of her life story: had she ever thought of writing it? Her answer by letter admitted she was constantly being asked that question, "an evidence, I suppose, that people think I have reached a time of life when most people think of the past rather than of the future. Seriously, however, your question has set me thinking how I could weave into a personal story something that would make people realize the great revolution that has taken place in the political, legal, industrial and social position of women during the last fifty or sixty years. There is an entirely new world for women . . . the public has recently been reading memoirs that reveal the weak and foolish side of great men and women. I would like to tell them the story of what I have seen of high purpose and noble endeavor."

Alas, the idea seemed to stall at that point—perhaps for the reason that Mrs. Pankhurst, whose financial resources were very limited, accepted a paid engagement with the Society for the Prevention of Venereal Disease, with the understanding that all her platform speeches and written messages to the Canadian public must mesh with that organization's information campaign. The arrangement became rather tedious, especially when she so often heard herself presented at fluttery women's club teas in such words as, "And now it is my pleasure to introduce the great Mrs. Pankhurst who represents venereal disease." After a couple of years she returned to England, where the Colonel's notes and gifts faithfully followed her. No one was more pleased than he when she won a seat in the House of Commons.

Owing to her crippled condition, perhaps also because she was a hostess in the grand manner, with a competent staff behind the scenes, Mrs. Maclean stayed remote from the actualities of cooking and housekeeping. The Colonel, perfectionist, careful of details, may have brooded on this situation; at any rate, he knew precisely where to turn for help within his own company.

The Chatelaine Institute test center for foods, cookery equipment, methods, etc., hummed with activity in a well-planned suite in the Dundas Street extension, and expert advice would be forthcoming there.

The Colonel dropped in on Helen G. Campbell, the Institute Director, and asked if she would inspect the Austin Terrace kitchen, pantries and all equipment to make a confidential report and suggest improvements. "I'll be glad to, of course," said Helen, and in the next breath, after he had gone, muttered to her assistants, "So there's

all of tomorrow shot! We'll have to leave the decorating of the Easter
hams until the next day."

It was entirely in keeping with her hearty, forthright character that
on returning from the Maclean residence the following afternoon she
should explode indignantly with the remark, "Why—can you believe
it?—there isn't *one* decent mixing bowl in that kitchen!"

Nevertheless, her report struck a nice balance between conscientious
advice and studied diplomacy; after all, three pairs of eyes would be
scanning it, including the cook's. Whether it inspired positive action
was never revealed; the Macleans took off shortly for Florida, and
the Institute experts could give full attention to their Easter creations—
with a dozen mixing bowls standing by.

The Institute's magazine, *Chatelaine,* received less of the Colonel's
critical appraisal than any other of his publications. The reason may
have been its healthy progress, quality appearance, early use of color
in dramatic layouts, and so on; or perhaps he withheld judgment simply
because a woman's magazine was rather outside his sphere. Mrs.
Maclean became an interested reader early-on, and that was as it
should be. Her interests were entirely feminine; she enjoyed lively
profiles of women in the news, celebrities' memoirs, the latest word on
beauty routines, and, most of all, fashions. One morning she was moved
to telephone the editor and offer congratulations on the new cover
featuring a hat—described inside as "a rapturous throwback to Ed-
wardian days." Mrs. Maclean thought it the loveliest thing ever. "If I
were twenty years younger, I would be ordering that hat right now,"
she declared. "Thank you so much for just letting me look at it."
She was then approaching her seventy-ninth birthday.

In mentality, temperament, training, Anna Maclean proved a strong
courageous partner for her husband. She had patience with him
and his countless repetitions of past successes in debates and exposés;
only occasionally would she yield to the impulse to remind him firmly,
"Jack, our guests heard that story the last time they were here," or,
again, to try to keep him on the main track. She had the same gracious
impersonal manner with all his friends and business associates, whatever their rank; "playing favorites" would have been totally reprehensi-
ble to her. Loyalty to her husband's firm remained unshakeable—
to the point where she steadfastly refused to recognize its new name.
The switchboard operators, answering incoming calls with "Maclean-
Hunter," got used to her little lecture, delivered with some asperity,
"I am not calling Maclean-Hunter. I am calling the Maclean Pub-

lishing Company." In private tête-a-têtes with wives of rising executives she was always willing to discuss their future social responsibilities and offer encouragement. She viewed Mrs. Horace T. Hunter as
the perfect hostess. "You will have to entertain a great deal," Mrs.
Maclean said to the wife of the new executive vice-president. "Watch
what Mrs. Hunter does and pattern everything you do after her."

Pride in her own Slade family was a continuing interest with Mrs.
Maclean—and understandably, for the various brothers and sisters
and their spouses formed a quite colorful collection. Consider, for
example, Conrad Slade, a talented artist who, going to Paris as a
young man, became one of the exclusive group around Renoir and a
familiar figure in the great painter's household. Eventually he married
Gabrielle, the most famous of Renoir's models, whose devotion to the
family has been set forth so tenderly in Jean Renoir's biography of his
father. Slade and his wife escaped from Nazi-occupied France in
1941 and settled in Los Angeles. A few years later the present author,
planning a business trip to California, was to have the unique experience of meeting Gabrielle, already so well known in face and form—
oh, those lovely, lyrical lines of nudity in its innocence—from Renoir's
masterpieces.

"You must take a parcel to Conrad," Mrs. Maclean had said, on
hearing of the expedition. "I have some family jewels that belong to
him." It could be dangerous, trying to smuggle a fortune in gems across
the international border, but the errand had to be done, and the little
box was duly wrapped in a pair of pyjamas and packed. Mercifully,
the customs men were too busy to ask awkward questions, and, as
it turned out, the parcel contained trinkets, worth little more than the
half-hour taxi ride from the hotel to the Slade *ménage*. But Gabrielle,
then almost seventy, and speaking only her native French, was a delight worth a treasury of precious stones.

Mrs. Maclean's will, disposing of an estate valued at $84,907 after
her death in December 1949, took thought for all surviving Slades. The
only Canadian beneficiary was Upper Canada College, which received
$10,000 as a trust fund for a mathematics scholarship "in memoriam
of my dear son, Hector." The remaining monies, specified household
effects and personal property were carefully distributed among the older
and younger generations of the Boston family—and the many hand-
written codicils, bearing dates ranging over some twenty years show
how frequently the testatrix changed her mind! Sometimes it was neces-

sary, because of a relative's removal by death; other alterations are not so easily explained. In 1928 Anna Maclean stipulated payment of $200 a month for life to Gabrielle; ten years later this had been nullified, and in the final distribution of the estate the French sister-in-law received several jewelry items including "the gold-braided Lisbon bracelet," and certain antique furniture such as "two Lisbon chairs."

Perhaps in the meantime Anna had discovered that Conrad had managed to retain his share of the Slade family wealth and, like herself, arrive at a position of independent means. Although working diligently at his easel for many years, he refused all overtures from art galleries or dealers. "He was even proud of not having ever sold one of his works," Jean Renoir told this author. "Conrad Slade was a pure artist, following his own inspiration without compromising." It is doubtful if any Conrad creation came into the Macleans' possession. Yet one of his gifts to them was a painting, highly prized and always on view in their drawing room; a portrait of Louis XIV by Hyacinthe Rigaud, the contemporary court painter (1659–1743). Conrad had bought the picture at an auction; his knowledge and constant study of French art underwrote its authenticity. At the final sale of the Macleans' household goods somebody picked it up for $30—perhaps little knowing that this was a companion piece to a famous Rigaud group reverently displayed in the Louvre.

The arts never entered conspicuously into the Colonel's pattern of living. He was never to make any sizable investment in fine art. The great surge forward in Canadian painting missed him entirely; people who sought his reaction to the Group of Seven and its leader, Lawren Harris, could find themselves having to listen to revelations about that artist's financial status through the accident of birth within the Massey-Harris (farm implements) connection.

Musical events had little appeal, unless the occasion promised a turnout of special friends—as at Palm Beach in 1936 when the Colonel reported: "Madame Alda. At Mrs. Dillman's she sang marvelously. We talked over old days with Louise Homer."

New books might be taken in small, well-spaced doses, except when the author happened to be a friend, such as Costain, or perhaps a dangerous politico who had to be read in order to be exposed. Literature as a daily need was quite unknown to John Bayne Maclean and his wife. They attended the theatre infrequently, although they treasured their personal encounters in New York and Florida with such stars as the Barrymores and Marie Dressler; the latter's comeback in middle age with the *Tugboat Annie* film role drew warmest congratulations from the Colonel.

On the other hand, the Colonel had genuine pleasure in design and craftsmanship, as exemplified in architecture, and in antique furniture and *objets d'art*. Was it because these had a positive, recognized value the world over, as contrasted with the other art forms which, after all, challenged one's own individual opinion and level of culture?

His University Avenue office suite reflected his interest in the old and fine. The Tudor paneling and fireplace had been imported from an authentic period house (circa 1630) in Clovelly, Devonshire, and carefully installed in the original dimensions to make a spacious oblong office. The small outer room used by his secretary was of the same period and came from Wingerworth Hall near Chesterfield, Derbyshire. The two rooms, laid down and set in place, cost $14,000. A Toronto architect designed the richly moulded plaster ceilings, but the windows were "original," in that they consisted of tiny panes of old glass salvaged from various dismantled buildings in Britain; some of the little sections were stained, though there was no continuous pattern.

(While deep in these decisions as to background, the Colonel had found cause for another journalistic campaign. British landlords and families of dwindling resources were ordering in the wreckers, after discovering a brisk market among Americans for any salvageable item, whether a carved overmantel or a heraldic plaque. Such pieces entered the U.S. duty-free as antiques. Was it fair that Canadians had to pay a full duty on like imports? Certainly not! Thus began a series of unsigned editorials in *The Financial Post,* and an article in *Canadian Homes and Gardens,* backed up by personal letters to the Minister of Finance, demanding duty-free entry into Canada of any object more than one hundred years old. It took time; there was hedging in Ottawa, and Honorable James A. Robb wrote in reply that he himself had visited shops in England where workmen were busy turning out entirely new "antique" furniture; nevertheless the Colonel persisted, and about ten years later the duty was removed by another Finance Minister, Honorable Charles A. Dunning.)

The furnishings for his office were selected without stint, as proved by the invoice still existing. Six high-backed chairs of the seventeenth century cost £65 apiece; a William and Mary settee rated £450; a period screen, £75, and so on. A gentlemanly argument with the

London suppliers met with their final agreement to pay the duty which, as they were at pains to point out, gave the purchaser in effect a 20 percent discount on their original quotation.

Other furnishings included one or two chairs of red velvet, brocaded in gold; across each of these stretched a white braided cord, museum-style, to discourage use. The Colonel's desk was actually a large Louis XV table with black morocco leather top.

The room was gloomy, but the dark sheen of the aged paneling could not fail to impress visitors. It remained an uninterrupted expanse—except for three items. One was a Georgian gilt sunburst clock. The second looked, from a distance, like an early Victorian framed motto; on closer inspection it gave forth with Frank Munsey's famous thesis: "You cannot get out of a man what God Almighty did not put in him. You have to suit the man to the job and not the job to the man." And the third hanging piece was the 1897 letter from Honorable (Sir) Frederick W. Borden, Minister of Militia, offering Maclean the command of the contingent of Canadian troops going to Britain for the Queen's Jubilee.

The place where the Colonel sat in baronial splendor (the only jarring notes the telephone and dictaphone) has long disappeared. Most of the furnishings were auctioned off at rummage-sale prices. The two paneled rooms found no bidder, and they were finally given away to a woman who gladly accepted the responsibility and cost of removal—just before the whole building was torn down and the present structure begun.

The Colonel, of course, was never a man to be tied down to one fixed location. Within his almost complete city block of office buildings and plant, he was the perambulating president, dropping in unannounced here and there as the whim seized him, sometimes just to see if all those electric lights were actually needed, or, again, to have a chat with a staff member.

J. Herbert Hodgins, editor of *Canadian Homes and Gardens* and *Mayfair,* was frequently on the visiting list. Both those class magazines came within the Colonel's very special purview; their avowed purpose was to serve the top layer of Canadian society, the people concerned with their individual environment in all its details, and equally avid to follow the social doings of their sisters and brothers under-the-skin across the whole Dominion. Hodgins, a small-town boy from Picton, Ontario, and proud of the fact, had come to the job from a trade paper and later *Maclean's Magazine* editorial staff; he was a productive writer, a hard worker able to handle a dozen chores, including that of layout chief for both publications. Sometimes, as a result, he didn't have quite enough time to think things through—and such little lapses had their inevitable follow-up.

"I hear you have taken pictures of Tyrrell's new garden," said the presidential visitor one day. "Culham has done very well, especially on that difficult terrain, with the ravine so near." Enthusiastic agreement from Hodgins, and then the quiet voice resumed. "Of course you will not be mentioning the owner's name in the magazine. As you know, it has always been a rule with me—and with Mr. Hunter too—that no publicity of the personal kind should ever be used in either *Canadian Homes* or *Mayfair*. Well, I must run along now . . ."

Poor Hodgins. Which boss should he please? Tyrrell, his immediate superior, terrible of temper now and then, socially ambitious, enormously proud of his new country estate? Or the man at the top? A decision was further complicated by the fact that Tyrrell had been given the complete set of page proofs the day before. "You might like to take them home to show Mrs. Tyrrell," Hodgins had blithely suggested. The afternoon wore on, along with the nervous indigestion which he was subject to. Just before quitting time the phone rang. "Thanks for the proofs," said Tyrrell. "The photographs are quite good. But I would like to see the captions rewritten. Take out my name and just talk about the garden. As you know, it has always been a rule with the Colonel—and with Mr. Hunter and myself—that no publicity of the personal kind should ever be used," etc., etc.

The dear old Colonel had obviously made one more call to good purpose that afternoon.

*Mayfair,* through the month-by-month coverage of big weddings, horse shows, club galas, debutantes' parties and so on, naturally claimed a large share of the Colonel's attention. He was proud of "the magazine that holds a mirror up to Society," as its subtitle read, delighted with the rapid growth to 150-page issues within two years of the first number, and no doubt happy to take a bow after the Vancouver *Sun* opened a congratulatory editorial with these lines: "The Canadian public should feel grateful to Colonel Maclean for the *Mayfair Magazine*. Until the appearance of *Mayfair* there was no class magazine through which Canadians could express their social personality."

But only the right type of Canadians should be allowed that privilege, as the Colonel constantly emphasized. "People of questionable reputation must be kept out of our pages; we don't want their pictures or

their names." Hodgins' attitude was that people who rated sufficiently
to participate in the big occasions must surely be considered legitimate
material for *Mayfair*. Probably a showdown was inevitable—and it
occurred one morning when the Colonel appeared at the editor's desk
with the new issue opened at a splashy spread of groups in the members' enclosure during the Woodbine spring race-meet.

"Hodgins, this is disgraceful!" he said, pointing to a picture.

"But I can't see anything wrong with it," replied the defendant. "I
know she's awfully fat, but they have lots of money, her husband's
a K.C.—we say so in the caption—and, as you can see, he's quite
good-looking, well turned out with gray cutaway and topper."

The Colonel measured out the horrible truth carefully. "It is clear
that you are not familiar with the Toronto background. Why Jim
married her, no one has ever understood. But by doing so he ostracized
himself from decent society. That woman used to keep a House!"

The interesting question of how the Colonel knew was left quite
up in the air. Hodgins subsided meekly, and within a few weeks the
editorial staff was increased by the appointment of a society editor
experience in her local Who's Who and Why Not.

*Mayfair* even managed a one-shot campaign at the Colonel's prodding. Both he and the editor had attended the New Year's Day reception at Government House—the all-male ritual for the respectful exchange of greetings with the sovereign's representative. Next morning
Hodgins looked up to see the familiar figure in the office doorway.
"Something must be done to inform Canadian men about proper dress
for an occasion like that," said the Colonel.

Together they talked over the points to be covered, and so in the
February 1929 issue an up-front page featured a vigorous scolding
piece by "York," the editor's pseudonym. "There is scant excuse for
men of affairs presenting themselves before the Lieutenant-Governor
of the Province and his lady in their every-day business suits—less
excuse for a man who will don a morning coat and with it wear a
printed foulard tie in shades of pink, as actually happened on New
Year's Day." The correct outfit was morning coat with silk topper,
"although, in this country of concessions to dress, I am willing to concede the bowler on occasions." Anyway, it was disturbing to realize
that the recent New Year's receptions in all provincial capitals, as well
as the Governor-General's levee in Ottawa, showed "probably the
same haphazard manner of dress" . . . Canadian men "for formal
occasions have much to learn in the manner of the clothes they wear."

Another *contretemps* with the Colonel on men's clothes gave Hodgins a chuckle that went on reverberating down the years. This time the president had dropped by to deplore the lack of fine custom-tailoring in Toronto. In the course of the chat, he reached out and fingered the buttonholes on the editor's jacket. "It's little things like this that distinguish British tailoring," said the Colonel. "One touch and you know: hand-made buttonholes, perfectly finished." True, they had been subject to a certain amount of needlecraft, for just the previous evening Mrs. Hodgins had reworked the ragged edges on that $29.95 suit, bought three years before from Eaton's racks. "At least my wife will be flattered," said the editor, summing up the incident for his staff later.

# CHAPTER XXX

## A KINDLY MAN

"giving and keeping require brains."
*Cervantes*

---

THE COLONEL had his parsimonious habits, especially where small sums were involved. In certain areas this may have reflected a lack of discrimination in his own taste—as in the matter of cigars. Although he enjoyed an occasional smoke, he had never learned the difference between a dime stogie and a Corona Corona; consequently the cigars passed with the coffee following a champagne dinner at Austin Terrace were apt to be the ten-cent variety. In other directions penny-pinching was a deliberate enterprise, conscientiously pursued. He would argue with the cashier in the company cafeteria as to whether the items on his tray added up to thirty-five cents, as she made it, or thirty cents according to his mathematics. But on visits to Montreal he would invite several of the local staff with their wives to dinner in the hotel and command the personal services of the head waiter in searching out the most exotic and costly courses on the menu. Summer by summer his gardener earned reprimands for letting the hose run too long— "and with city water rates as they are!"—but when the Colonel took up the cultivation of melons (having firmly set aside his earlier prejudices against them), seeds were imported, a special glass structure was built to protect the vines, and in a good year he might harvest up to a dozen edible specimens—at a cost of several hundred dollars.

Nothing quite equaled his private, life-long paper-saving campaign. It was amazing how many sources existed for paper scrap and how handy the stuff could be, as demonstrated at a little conference in 1934. The Colonel and the present writer were calling on Sir Joseph Flavelle to sound him out on one of his favorite and carefully studied subjects: the pressing problem of Canada's railways. There had been no intention of taking notes—indeed, that little routine often defeated the purpose of such meetings—but as Sir Joseph, pacing up and down, his head high, eyes closed, hands clasped behind his back, warmed to the subject, the *Post's* editor felt moved to jot down a few questions for presenting after the monologue. The pencil was poised, but what about paper? The Colonel saw the predicament, and, with no words exchanged, reached toward his vest and brought out the stub of a chequebook.

Next morning this author found it in his pocket. The cheque stubs, neatly filled out, were dated 1912. One recorded "White Star Line for Suite B—$1600"; another "The Breakers, for petty cash—$250"; a third, "Mrs. Maclean, for tips—$300." In brief, hundreds of dollars for elegant living, and less than a cent's worth of used paper saved for twenty-two years!

Yet the Colonel was a generous man in many ways, and especially to his faithful servitors. He insisted that the chauffeur, on travels abroad with the Macleans, always have first-class accommodations on ocean liners and in hotels. In 1966 Ritchie enjoyed harking back to his first long-distance trip, when he had submitted a bill of ten cents for breakfast. "What did you have?" asked the Colonel. "Toast and coffee," was the reply. His employer was shocked. "I will not have you doing 150 miles on toast and coffee," he said. "Always have bacon and eggs."

If Mrs. Maclean sometimes felt like interposing with a few rules, her husband would apply his own veto, diplomatically. On a train trip to Florida, she had consulted the dining car menu and prices, and then instructed Ritchie and her maid not to order a meal above a certain figure. A few minutes later the Colonel drew them both aside and said, "Order anything you want and let me have the bill. But don't tell Madam." In 1927 the Colonel took the chauffeur to England to pick up the family's second Rolls-Royce—a $17,400 made-to-order limousine, with special features for Mrs. Maclean's convenience (the car that was to clock 190,000 miles without a repair bill). That bit of business concluded, Ritchie was sent off for a week's visit with his mother in Scotland, all expenses paid of course, and an extra $50 earmarked for the good lady and her special efforts on behalf of the reunion.

Members of the company staffs now and then had pleasant experiences of the Colonel's thoughtfulness. Kenneth R. Wilson, brilliant young writer on the *Post,* suffered from uncertain health; he was

"ordered" to drop all routine and have a month's rest at Crieff, free of
any charges or encumbrances. When another staffer and his wife
made their first trip overseas, the company paid the cost, and the
Colonel presented the happy young lady with a green morocco overnight case, fitted with sterling silver. On several occasions editors and
wives were entertained in Palm Beach, quartered in furnished apart-
ments provided by the Colonel who also had ready his cheque to cover
meals and other expenses.

Sometimes there could be an unforeseen hazard for an employee-
guest, as one of the company editors discovered during a year-end
Caribbean cruise on the luxurious *Empress of Britain*. On New Year's
Eve the Colonel, then almost seventy, blithely announced that he
would stay up to see the old year out, whereupon his young companion got busy and rounded up a little group of the ship's professional
entertainers—a concert singer, a "blues" expert and a cowboy guitarist
from Calgary. A few other passengers stopped by, and all the ingredients of a gay party were present, except for the liquid refreshment. No one seemed ready to venture the first move, either out of
deference to the oldest gentleman present or because, in that time
of depression, only he could afford it. But the Colonel, deep in animated conversation on the sidelines was quite unaware of the crisis.
Finally the editor ordered up a round of drinks, followed by a couple
of magnums of champagne. There were toasts to the New Year,
everybody had a good time including the Colonel, and the editor decided it had been worth the bad news that would await him on the bar-
bill. But at the end of the cruise when he went to the purser to settle,
he found the Colonel had got there first.

The Colonel was a very temperate man in the matter of food and
drink, as his straight, slim figure indicated. One cocktail and perhaps
one glass of wine represented an ample daily ration; not until his
seventies did he bother with whiskey, and then only on the suggestion
of his doctor, who thought an ounce or so in plenty of water might
relax him before dinner. He had been a cigarette smoker in his
twenties, abandoned the habit throughout his busy middle years but returned to it later on, as an occasional treat, and generally with the
help of a long holder. Never at any time did he develop a smoker's
dexterity; people watching him as he thrust out his lips, flailed lighter or
match uncertainly through the air and only after two or three tries

got the cigarette alight, might easily have thought this his first experiment.

His gourmet interests ranged over cheese, honey, vegetables, fruits, breads—a simple-sounding list, yet each had to meet precise standards. One time after returning from Europe he paid a call on his *Canadian Hotel Review* editor and held forth on his recent dining adventures. Eggplant, the way the good Italian chefs prepared it, deserved to be better known in Canada. "What's their secret?" asked the editor, always a keen culinary researcher. The answer was the recipe itself, delivered then and there from memory. Here it is as the editor wrote it down:

Cut the eggplant in very thin slices (quarter-inch), remove the purple skin and soak the slices in cold salted water for three or four hours. Drain and pat dry. Dip the slices in beaten raw egg, well seasoned, then roll them in crushed soda biscuits. Fry in small amount of sizzling hot bacon fat in an iron frying pan. Serve hot, right from the pan.

(This recipe may safely be tried. The director of the Chatelaine Institute tested it before its publication here.)

Honey, the Colonel insisted, should be No. 1 White, and just as the bees made it, i.e. non-pasteurized. B. T. Huston, editor of *Canadian Grocer,* had a standing brief to watch for the prize-winners in this category at the Canadian National Exhibition and Royal Winter Fair. With cheese there was more latitude as to type; here flavor, texture, age became the important factors.

His annual investments in the pick of Canada's apple crop may have been stimulated early-on by Aunt Elise in Portugal. Throughout her life the ex-King's widow retained a nostalgic interest in the fruits she had enjoyed in her New England youth: the blueberries from the woods and the hard cooking apples that made the world's best pie. In fact, for several years she was busily involved in pomological techniques for the establishing of these favorites at various points around Lisbon; nursery experts on both sides of the Atlantic were regularly consulted and their recommendations as to seedling stock followed up with sizable imports. The project had to be abandoned when soil and climate proved too stubbornly exotic. Nevertheless the Countess d'Edla in her old age could indulge her fancy for apple desserts through the Colonel's regular shipments of prize Greenings from Ontario orchards.

For many years his discoveries of "the best" in apples or other
fruits, honey and cheese were shared with friends throughout the
world, at Christmastime or any other time the spirit moved him. Invariably a personal note went forward simultaneously, stating the name
of the variety, the circumstances under which it had merited selection
or blue ribbons, and so on. In June 1925 U. S. Postmaster-General
Harry S. New and his wife (both meriting a place on the Colonel's
list, he because of his solid newspaper career, she as a former Prince
Edward Island girl) were forewarned of the arrival of a Canadian
Stilton cheese . . . "all duty and other charges prepaid . . . made
from spring grass milk in June 1923, and just reaching the prime of
condition in its mild, delicate flavor." Instructions for storing, turning,
cutting were explicit. During Britain's stringent rationing in World
War II, the Colonel's frequent boxes of honey to overseas friends, Lord
Queenborough, Chairman of the Royal Society of St. George, for one,
drew letters of deep-felt gratitude.

It was through the pursuit of a very special gift that Maclean became responsible for the inauguration of an important export business
for Canada—important in prestige and publicity, if not dollars.

A titled lady in Paris had recently entertained him; a present wholly
Canadian yet with a touch of novelty would be the ideal choice.
Flowers? Of course—and nothing else but the magnificent roses produced by Dale Estate nurseries in Brampton, Ontario. Their managers were bowled over by the suggestion, and even the normally
co-operative CPR steamships people said it just couldn't be done. The
Colonel persisted, going to great pains in the preparation of time
schedules for freight consignments from Brampton to Montreal docks,
to coolroom storage on shipboard, and prompt delivery in Paris or
London. Probably in the hope of proving him wrong, the two groups
agreed to a test run. It worked! Shipping Canadian roses to Europe
became a successful enterprise. For many years thereafter no CPR
vessel left Montreal without a huge cargo of fresh roses from Brampton—and the Colonel could henceforth extend his favorite gift selections for overseas destinations.

Presents of straight cash to any person, however deserving, had little
place in his generosities; indeed the type of rich man who "threw money
around" was an object of scorn. Friends or former employees in need
could, he maintained, be helped much more effectively by sympathetic
study of the whole situation and a positive, directing hand toward get-

ting them back on the path of self-sufficiency, whether by means of a new job or a guaranteed bank loan.

One of his few money gifts was made entirely "for auld acquaintance." After his beloved friend, Sir Fitzroy Maclean, Chief of the Clan, died in 1936, aged 101, the eldest grandson, Charles H. F. Maclean, inherited the headship, and a year later, on his twenty-first birthday, there were gala celebrations at Duart Castle on the Isle of Mull. The Colonel, regretting his inability to attend and remembering his happy encounters with the lad in London or Scotland, decided to send a very special "Maclean" token, consisting of five shares of company stock. When Sir Charles sold the holding in 1965 he received the going market price of $18,000. (If he had waited another two years, he would have realized $60,000.)

The Colonel would have been pleased—although perhaps even that pleasure might rate second place to one other arising out of the Maclean kinship. Sir Charles made a trip to Canada in 1950 and visited the Colonel in hospital during his last illness. In a recent letter to the author of this book, the Chief wrote: "When I entered his room I was immediately struck by the almost complete likeness of him as an old man to that of my Grandfather. We in the Clan Maclean have always said there are certain features amongst the members of the Clan, and if this ever needed to be proved, it was done so on the occasion of my final meeting with J.B."

# CHAPTER XXXI

## *LOVABLE GIANT*

"A dwarf is not tall, though he stands on a mountaintop;
a giant keeps his height though he stands in a well."
*Seneca.*

THE YEAR 1949 opened on an anxious note and was to close with a
solemn ritual, yet the summer in between must be recorded as one of
the happier seasons for Anna and John Bayne Maclean. Was it
because each voluntarily moved out of the rut of fixed habit? Perhaps
—and there is the possibility that those separate decisions reflected a
sudden flash of consciousness that time was getting short and it should
be utilized and savored to the full.

The Colonel's heart attack toward the end of the winter had
necessitated weeks in bed with nursing care, but, by the time the
Austin Terrace gardens were in bud with lilacs and tulips, he was
pronounced well enough to get up and enjoy the sunshine. But, said
the doctor, it would be wise to drop the daily downtown routine.

Both suggestions added up to just one thought: Crieff—and this
time he would go with a sense of release, free of any arrangement as
to a return date. The office could wait—and, as things turned out, he
was never again to enter 481 University Avenue.

Within a week or so, the carefully planned removal and installation
had been accomplished; although Ritchie was sent back to town to
stand by for Mrs. Maclean's requirements, the Colonel had an efficient valet-nurse with him, and the farm staff made sure that meals,
housekeeping and other maintenance went forward smoothly. His daily
reports to Anna by phone had only good news to convey, but this year
more than ever he regretted the separation, for she too had been
housebound for months, receiving no visitors, and under the constant
strain of watching over a sick-room. "If only you could be here with
me," he would say—repeating it so often that on the morning when

she made her important announcement, "I've decided to join you tomorrow," he was probably stunned as well as jubilant.

Anna's reconciliation with Crieff was total, with no reservations. The place had been improved and groomed to a state of perfection since her last visit; the new sweep of lawn at the back, ending in a brilliant rock garden on a natural slope that descended from the thick woods, became her favorite vista; also, it was fully within range of her wheelchair position on the patio. Occasionally there were leisurely drives around the countryside; sometimes guests arrived for lunch or afternoon tea—the local minister and his wife, the Colonel's doctor from the city—and neighbors from the farms roundabout dropped in now and then with greetings and county news. It was a month of quiet rural pleasure for both the Macleans, and it was to be the last of their many holidays together.

A few weeks after the return to town, Anna became ill. The chief trouble was diagnosed as a slight heart condition which complete rest in bed could probably halt. Yet in spite of solicitous care there was a gradual decline, and on Thursday, December 15, Anna Slade Maclean died, at the age of eighty-two. The Colonel's big annual event, the Christmas tree party for employees and their families, had long before been scheduled for the following Saturday; several company executives thought there should be a postponement, but the host himself anticipated the problem and telephoned to say there must be no change in the plan; he hoped everything would be done to ensure a happy gathering. "My wife would have wanted it that way."

There were sad and lonely hours facing the Colonel, but there were also the salutary pressures of tasks needing attention. The flood of letters must be answered, carefully one by one, with the aid of his secretary. He could help the executors of his wife's will by gathering and identifying the bequeathed jewels and *objets d'art*. The household staff deserved a rest; he drew up a holiday schedule. By March these immediate duties were finished and he was on his way to Palm Beach, this time by air, and taking Charles, the houseman, along. It was just fifty years since he had first set eyes on those palms and beaches and fallen in love with Munsey's friend from Boston. The place had changed yet the memories hadn't; they continued to be happy ones.

Crieff, of course, was his summer goal. But there, early in August, he suffered a collapse necessitating a trip by ambulance to Toronto. "Leukemia," the doctors said, and hospitalization was required. After a fortnight in Toronto General Hospital he showed remarkable im-

provement and was permitted to go home—and Austin Terrace had
its interesting diversions if only through the pile of correspondence
awaiting him. The company's quarterly profit and loss statement was
well worth a leisurely study, although there could be no question about
its favorable news. One of his major efforts must be the composition
of a suitable letter to the sister of former Prime Minister W. L.
Mackenzie King, whose death had recently occurred. After several
penciled starts he felt ready to begin dictation with his secretary; but
the project was never to be completed. Later that week a severe
stroke incapacitated him, and on September 25, 1950—just one day
short of his eighty-eighth birthday—John Bayne Maclean died.

On Wednesday, September 27, the Colonel went by his office for
the last time, as the funeral procession drove slowly up University
Avenue, on its way to Mount Pleasant Cemetery and the new grave
beside his wife and son.

The service in St. Andrew's Presbyterian Church had been attended by a throng of public dignitaries, friends, associates, employees, neighbors—indeed, a congregation that bore impressive testi-
mony to one man's life and contacts. Ontario's Lieutenant-Governor
and Quebec's Chief Justice were present; university presidents, sena-
tors, embassy officials, chiefs of voluntary organizations, representatives of various publishing groups filled the pews, along with the
many others who came to pay their last respects as plain individuals
with their own personal recollections of a good friend. The masses of
floral tributes included a spray with a card written in a shaky hand,
"From Comrades of the old Royal Grenadiers—five veterans of 1885,"
and those five attended the obsequies. Farmers from Crieff made the
trip down with their families, and the chief address from the pulpit
was delivered by the minister of the late Reverend Andrew Maclean's little church at the old crossroads in West Puslinch.

Only one painted portrait of the Colonel exists, and that was done
months after his death: a study in oils skillfully achieved by Kenneth
Forbes from photographs in the company's library, plus many consul-
tations with the subject's associates as to the important small details.
Like so many other men of decision in the business world, the Colonel
had regularly brushed aside all suggestions on this matter through
his active years. Eventually he agreed to sit for Karsh's camera, but
the results, excellent as they were, depict an old gentleman.

For many people, of course, a pictorial reference is quite unnecessary; his features, figure and bearing survive as a lively memory, giving flesh-and-blood reality to the countless stories and scenes centering on the Colonel. The legend that grew with him refuses to die.

As an employer, he is remembered with affection and esteem, especially for those little extracurricular activities of man-to-man generosity and sympathetic interest.

However, there are still others who do not look back entirely in kindness. Those, in large part, were the young men, many of them brilliant, who thirty or forty years ago abruptly resigned from the staff rather than endure his petty criticism; they had no time to probe behind that nagging habit and discover a personality constantly hoping for and delighting in an argument. Such ex-Macleanites, including others who were attracted by better salaries than the Colonel offered, were to form a vast alumni in the publishing and advertising fields throughout Canada, and even abroad; their influence has been impressive in many spheres—and who can doubt that some of their first principles were learned on University Avenue?

As a publisher and journalist, the Colonel was a staunch conservative, yet such was his passion for truth and integrity and public service that he constantly infuriated the "establishment." Sometimes his campaigns in print were ill-judged and impractical; quite frequently they were repetitious and boring; almost always they were wandering in theme and style; yet these weaknesses must not obscure the high batting average he was to achieve in his avowed purpose of enlightening public opinion and influencing governments.

The final judgment of the Colonel and his career must rest upon the institution he founded and which he developed through its first sixty years. Today, it publishes periodicals in Canada, the United States, France, England, Germany and Italy. It owns radio and TV stations, operates trade and industrial shows, and has ventured into several other service fields. John Bayne Maclean could not have built the complex as it now operates, but he provided the strong base, the leadership and inspiration, along with the diversified capacities of executives of his own choosing.

The Colonel lived in the great age of journalistic giants—of Northcliffe in England, of Pulitzer, Hearst, Munsey and McCormick in the United States. By the standards of his time, by the strength of the institution he designed, John Bayne Maclean deserves a place among the giants.

And, no matter how varied today's communications are, the power of the printed word continues. As Ralph Allen, editor of *Maclean's*, wrote in his next issue following the Colonel's funeral:

"It's our feeling . . . that the magazine to which he gave his name cannot, in simple reality, concede the death of John Bayne Maclean. For as we mourned him, the parts of him that lived were as close and challenging as tomorrow's deadline or the next stack of proofs." Allen went on to list the current editorial activities, finding all of them due directly to the courage and enterprise of the publication's founder. "Over the long haul he sought to prove or disprove nothing except that understanding comes with knowledge. That is why, as we honor him and mourn him, we cannot quite bring ourselves to believe that he is dead. Perhaps somewhere in this issue of the magazine there will be a sentence or a phrase that will cause some young man or woman to believe that Canada is a better or more interesting place than he or she had realized, or that something is amiss in Canada that he or she must try to fix. Perhaps in time some small new better thing will come of that small new stirring of awareness. And John Bayne Maclean . . . will be embarked on the 89th year of a valiant and fruitful life."

# ACKNOWLEDGMENTS

A great many kind people who came to my aid during the past several years of research into the life and times of Colonel Maclean are going to be hurt (and justly so) because I do not mention them here. I failed to establish a proper, tidy file of names at the outset, and now I must depend upon my memory which is not unfailing.

There were, of course, numerous former employees of the Colonel who recalled interesting little incidents that helped to make the story come alive. His secretary, Miss I. Ethel Dove, and her predecessor, Mrs. George Allingham, produced many letters and notes. The late James Ritchie, chauffeur, contributed valuable sidelights, especially concerning travels. B. T. Huston and other old associates of the publisher's earlier days gladly answered questions or wrote memos. W. Arthur Irwin, now of Victoria, B.C., filled in details surrounding the Bren Gun revelations.

I owe a special debt to the late W. Arnot Craick, who supplied a copy of his own 200-page typewritten memoirs of his relations with John Bayne Maclean. The distinguished novelist, Thomas B. Costain, gave me two highly rewarding days with him in New York just shortly before his death.

Members of the Maclean and Slade connections have been very helpful. Special mention should be made of Andrew Dyas MacLean, of Toronto, the Colonel's nephew, Mrs. Charles (Frances) McGoughran, of Norfolk, Connecticut, the late Mrs. Geoffrey (Louise) McDougall, of Montreal, a niece of Mrs. John Bayne Maclean, and Mrs. Henry D. Warner, of Boston, a sister.

Colonel George A. Drew, one of the Colonel's closest friends, had many specific facts and memories to draw upon—and share. Professor and Mrs. Gilbert Bagnani (she was formerly Miss Mary Stewart Houston) contributed importantly to the complete picture of the Macleans' home life.

To librarians any biographer owes a debt that can never be adequately acknowledged. Mrs. Jean Reid MacKay, Maclean-Hunter librarian, has been a patient, diligent expert in information retrieval over these several years. The Toronto Central Reference Library, the Toronto *Star*'s and the Montreal *Star*'s libraries have been mines of facts as recorded in newspaper items; similarly, the files of the Palm Beach *News* were valuable in tracing the Colonel's activities in that "winter news capital of the world." The libraries of Victoria University and Knox College produced interesting material concerning the nineteenth-century Presbyterian community and its church periodicals. The well-preserved bound volumes of the *Canadian Military Gazette* were made readily available for study through the courtesy of the archivist at the Canadian Military Institute. Harvard University supplied material on Professor Slade, the father of Mrs. Maclean. The New York Public Library helped out on Frank A. Munsey and various members of the Colonel's group of friends.

I am particularly indebted to Dr. W. Kaye Lamb, National Librarian and Archivist, Ottawa, for very detailed searches through the Sir John A. Macdonald and other papers. The military historians of the Department of National Defense, particularly Lieutenant Colonel H. F. Wood, traced many important facts, such as dates, records of service, medals, etc. The Chief of the Clan, Sir Charles H. F. Maclean of Duart Castle, Isle of Mull, checked references to a previous chief.

My wife, Jean A. Chalmers, endowed with a memory that approaches total recall, has helped to keep me on a straight course through the confusing multiplicity of events, places and personalities. To her, I owe the descriptive notes about furniture, Mrs. Maclean's clothes, jewels and table settings—matters which I would seldom have noticed.

The Academy of Medicine, Toronto, supplied a photograph of 13 Queen's Park Crescent.

The main source of information has been the Colonel's files, which remained as he left them—stuffed with thousands of letters and a few million (so it seemed) scraps of notes written to himself in his own hand. Here the problem was one of selection.

On the general structure and style of the book, I early consulted more experienced writers, including Eric Hutton and the late Ralph Allen and Ian Maclure Sclanders. The last-named prepared a sample chapter, of such quality that I asked him to take over all my material and write the book himself. His untimely death defeated that project.

When I was about two-thirds of the way through the undertaking I accepted an "outside" job which consumed a great deal of time and threatened to delay unduly my researches into the Colonel's many activities. At that point, Mary-Etta Macpherson, an experienced and devoted editor, came to my assistance, rechecking many sources, digging new material out of the bound volumes of the Colonel's publications, applying her highly professional blue pencil to my script and in general rounding out some elements of the story. She supplied some revealing personal recollections of the Colonel and Mrs. Maclean, both of whom she knew. Without her research work, the book would not have been finished for another two or three years.

My associate, Donald F. Hunter, president of Maclean-Hunter Limited, read all the chapters and caught many discrepancies. He made no effort to edit, in any way, my story of his father's relations with the Colonel.

My secretary, Mrs. Kathleen T. Mainprice, deciphered and copied many hundreds of pages of untidy manuscript and retyped several versions of rewriting. I apologize to her for my handwriting and thank her for her devoted effort.

In the final analysis, it is only fair to state that I relied chiefly upon personal research and my own memory; therefore, any errors of commission or omission are my own.

*FSC*

# APPENDIX

## THE HOUSE THAT J.B.M. BUILT

This book is the personal story of one man. It was never intended to be a corporate history of the publishing house founded by John Bayne Maclean. But someone has suggested that a brief record of how the company developed, both in the Colonel's lifetime and to the present day, would add additional historical value.

Here, then, is a condensed chronology of Maclean-Hunter.

### The First Thirteen Years

The first publications were *Canadian Grocer,* 1887; *Hardware and Metal* (now *Hardware Merchandising*), 1888; *Dry Goods Review* (now *Style*), also 1888; *Books and Notions* (which amoebalike separated into several publications over the years and itself disappeared), 1890; *Canadian Printer and Publisher,* 1892.

During most of this period, the Colonel's partner (with a one-third interest) was his brother, Hugh Cameron MacLean. The brothers parted company at the end of the century and the Colonel took in no other partner until 1919.

### 1901–10

Five more business publications were added. But the chief events were the founding of *Maclean's Magazine* in 1905, when it was known as the *Busy Man's Magazine,* and *The Financial Post* in 1907. The company bought land on the then rather remote University Avenue and built its first major building. It installed a modern printing plant and launched a large commercial printing business. The Canadian Press Clipping Service came into being.

A farm periodical (*Farmer's Magazine*) was founded in 1910; it never made a profit and was eventually suspended in 1922.

## 1911–20

World War I hampered developments but the office buildings and printing plant were expanded; circulations soared; good profits were made. Four trade papers were added to the list, bringing the total number of publications to sixteen.

Horace T. Hunter, who had joined the staff in 1903 as an advertising salesman, emerged as Maclean's chief lieutenant. On reorganization of the corporate structure in 1919, he was able to buy a large block of stock. This led him to the presidency and ultimately to his personal control of the company on Maclean's death.

## 1921–30

The company extended its magazine operations, buying *Canadian Homes and Gardens* in 1925 and establishing *Mayfair* in 1927. These magazines attracted much attention but were financially successful for only a comparatively short period. In 1955 *Mayfair* was sold and in 1962 *Canadian Homes and Gardens* was sold.

In 1927 the company moved into the United States with the purchase of its first two trade papers in that country.

In 1928, what was to become Canada's major magazine for women was launched, *Chatelaine,* a bold venture indeed.

In 1930 the company acquired its first United Kingdom publication, *British Printer,* and, as in the United States, laid the foundations of a very successful trade publishing enterprise.

In the same year, the company moved into French-language publishing in Quebec Province with the acquisition of *Le Prix Courant.* This was but the first of a very substantial group of publications in the French language.

During the decade four trade papers in all were added, bringing the company's total number of publications to twenty-six.

But dark clouds were looming on the business horizon and the company's profits were to be seriously affected by the rapidly developing world depression.

## 1931-40

These were difficult years. Colonel Maclean felt the need of strong and active leadership. He became chairman of the board in 1933 and appointed Horace T. Hunter as president.

Four more trade publications brought the company's publishing roster to thirty-two.

## 1941-50

The line of succession in the company was established when vice-president and general manager, H. Victor Tyrrell, died in 1942 and Maclean and Hunter agreed on the choice of Floyd S. Chalmers, then editor of *The Financial Post,* as executive vice-president.

In 1945, Maclean Publishing Company became Maclean-Hunter to recognize the contribution of Horace T. Hunter to its growth.

Five more business publications brought the net total of periodicals (after a couple of unprofitable papers were dropped) to thirty-four.

## 1951-60

John Bayne Maclean had become a less frequent visitor to the office and his influence waned. Hunter was firmly in control but more and more of the planning and management were assigned to Chalmers.

In 1950 Maclean died, and in 1952, Hunter, after forty-nine years with the company, became chairman of the board and chose Chalmers to succeed him as president.

*Chatelaine* launched a French-language edition in 1960.

Canada was prospering. It was a decade of vigorous growth in the business paper fields in Canada, U.S.A. and U.K. and the decade ended with a total roster of fifty-one publications.

## 1961-

In 1961, a French edition of *Maclean's* was established under the name of *Le Magazine Maclean.*

In the same year, the company entered the European field. It had started to publish an advertising rate and data paper in France under the name *Tarif Media.* This was followed by similar publications in Germany (*Media Daten*) and Italy (*Dati e Tariffe Pubblicitarie*). But Standard Rate & Data Service, of Chicago, also had its eyes on the European market. Obviously only one such publication was needed in any country and M-H and SRDS agreed to share ownership of the three European publications on a 50/50 basis.

The company had been looking at broadcasting, wondering if it should not have entered the field earlier. By this time, Donald F. Hunter was vice-president and managing director (appointed 1952) and he and Chalmers felt the move should be made.

The first purchase was a half interest in Radio Station CFCO, Chatham. Later CKEY, Toronto, was purchased and CHYM, Kitchener, and CFOR, Orillia, added. The first three are now owned outright but the interest in CFOR is fifty per cent.

Radio led to television and in 1964 a minority interest in CFCH, Halifax—operating both radio and television—was acquired. But later in 1966, an opportunity to buy the pioneer radio station CFCN, Calgary, presented itself, along with TV station, CFCN, Calgary. Due to limitations on multiple ownership of stations on the private network, the Halifax interests had to be sold.

By early 1969, the company owned outright four radio stations and half interest in another. It owned outright the television station in Calgary.

When cable television, sometimes known as Community Antenna TV came along, the company moved quickly into systems in some 15 cities.

During the years from 1961 on, expansion took place in other areas of communication. The long-established Fraser's Trade Directories were acquired; also National Market Reports, producing in the U.S.A. and Canada car valuation handbooks. Some twenty trade and industrial shows were initiated, including one in Great Britain. Design Craft Limited, designers and manufacturers of displays, interiors, etc., was bought and expanded.

A translation service and a Direct Mail Division were set up.

In 1965 the first public issue of shares was made and the shares were listed on Toronto and Montreal Stock Exchanges.

In 1964, Chalmers became chairman of the board and Donald F. Hunter became president.

During the period to December 31, 1968, twenty-nine new trade papers and three new magazines were established or acquired, bringing the total number of publications to eighty-seven.

And finally, in 1968, to mark the broader range of the company's activities, the company's name in Canada was simplified to Maclean-Hunter Limited.

# INDEX

Academy of Medicine (Toronto), 348
*Acadian,* 30
Addison, W. H. F., 140
*Advertiser* (London), 30
Aitken, Kate, "Never a Day So Bright," 303
Aitken, Max. *See* Beaverbrook, Lord
Alba, Duke of, 260
Albani, Madame (Marie Louise Lajeunesse), 80
Alda, Madame, as singer, 330
Alger, Horatio, 246
Allen, Ralph, 346, 349
Allingham, Priscilla Forbes, as Maclean's secretary, 43–44, 66, 67, 140, 144, 217, 347
Allison, J. Wesley, 207
Alma-Tadema, Sir Lawrence, 65
Alphonso XIII, King of Spain, 261–62
*American Illustrated,* 151
American Iron and Steel Association, 127
Amery, Leopold S., 58
Appleton, John, 164
*Arena,* 151
*Argosy,* Munsey and, 101, 102
Argyll, Duke of, 60
*Art of Conversation, The,* 37
*Art Weekly*
    W. J. Douglas and, 64, 66
    T. W. Dyas and, 63–64, 66
    Maclean's management of, 63–67, 69, 79, 93, 100
    Toronto *Mail* and, 66
Associated Press, 171
Astor, John Jacob, IV, 135
Astor, Lady, 104
Atkinson, Joseph E.

anti-Maclean editorial by, 236–37, 253
    as *Daily Star* owner, 53, 170, 172, 236–37
    as *Globe* reporter, 52
    marriage of, 52
    politics of, 253
Atkinson, Madge Merton, 52
Atwill, Lionel, 134

Bache, Jules, Maclean and, 256, 257, 315
    advice of, 128, 311
Baden-Powell, Sir Robert
    Boy Scouts and, 86, 230
    British Intelligence Service and, 230
    *My Adventures as a Spy,* 230
Bagnani, Gilbert, 348
Bagnani, Mary, 348
Banking & Currency Reform League, 314
Barker, Lt. Col. William George, 295
Barrie, Sir James, 68
    *Little White Bird,* 138
Barrymores, the, 331
Baruch, Bernard M.
    advice of, 128, 311
    Maclean and, 256, 315
Baxter, Arthur Beverley, 119, 193, 298
Bayne, Rev. John
    as Canadian minister, 2–5
    death of, 7
    influence of, 289
    Rev. Andrew Maclean and, 3–5, 7, 10
    as substitute minister, 2–3

Beatty, Edward R., 55, 56, 129
Beaverbrook, Lord (Max William Aitken)
Costain and, 213
Ministry of Aircraft and, 53
as writer, 193–94
Beck, Sir Adam, 222
Maclean's battle with, 226–29, 239, 253
in *Maclean's Magazine*, 186
Bell, Alexander Graham, 314
Belleville *Intelligencer*, 82
Bengough, J. W., cartoons of, 49, 193
Bennett, Richard Bedford, x, 264, 276
*Financial Post* and, 282–84
Herridge and, 285
as prime minister, 265, 279–85, 289, 314
youth of, 279–80
Bernhardt, Sarah, 43
Bethlehem Steel, 125, 152, 297
Bishop, Air Marshal W. A., 295
Black, Robson, 205
Blake, Edward, 31, 269
Blake, William, 63
Bolshevism, 230–41, 315–16
Trotsky and, 212, 230–34
universities and, 222, 235–37
Bonar, Rev. John, 3–4
*Bond Triumphant, The* (Grahame), 243–45
*Bookseller and Stationer (Books and Notions)*, 47–48, 149, 350
customs, 48
editors, 53, 54, 137
"The Fire," 145
first issues, 47
profits, 111
reviews, 120, 137–38
textbook campaign, 47–48, 112
Borden, Sir Frederick, 202
as Minister of Militia, 73, 76–77, 136, 208, 332
St. John's Ambulance Brigade and, 45
Borden, Sir Robert
*Mail and Empire* and, 167–68
as prime minister, 202, 233, 265, 267–68, 279
Boston Opera Company, 116
Boston *Sunday Globe*, 106
Boswell, James, *Tour of the Hebrides*, 224
Boswell, Sir Mackenzie, 81–82
Boy Scouts, founder of, 86, 230
Bradley, Col. Edward R., 104

Brantford *Expositor*, 191
Bridle, Augustus ("Domino"), 151–52
*Masques of Ottawa*, 249–51
Sons of Canada, 152, 222, 249
Brigden, Fred, 36
Brigden, Fred H., 36
Brigden, George, 36
British American Assurance Company, 30, 34
*British Printer*, 351
Brock, W. R.
as dry goods wholesaler, 38, 110
as *Empire* president, 38, 59
Brown, Arthur William, 256
Brown, George, 288
as Liberal leader, 14
murder of, 21
as Toronto *Globe* founder, 14, 18
Bryan, William Jennings, silver "panic" and, 64
Bryant & Gibson, 30
Bunting, as Toronto *Mail* editor, 130
Burns, Capt., as business manager, 140
Burrell, Martin, as Ottawa's Secretary of State, 233–34
*Busy Man's Magazine. See Maclean's Magazine*
Butler, Ellis Parker, 151
Butler, Nicholas Murray, 237
Byng, Julian Hedworth George (1st Viscount Byng of Vimy), 128

Calder, E. C., 286
"Calgary Eye Opener, The" (Edwards), 279
Cameron, D. R., 73
Cameron, Rev. James (uncle)
*Canada Christian Monthly* and, 18–19
home of, 13–15, 92
Cameron, John (uncle), 94, 95
Cameron family, 15, 59, 227
Campbell, Helen G., 327–28
*Canada Christian Monthly*, Rev. Cameron and, 18–19
Canadian Armored Corps, 90
Canadian Bank of Commerce, 236
Canadian Club, 126, 134
*Canadian Courier*, 53
Canadian Daily Newspaper Association, 174
Canadian General Securities, 270
*Canadian Grocer*, 82, 227, 241
campaigns in, 112–13
contents of, 49, 140, 149

founding of, 29–30, 32, 34–37, 39,
  166, 319, 350
E. Cora Hind and, 123–24
B. T. Huston and, 339
Hugh MacLean and, 40–41, 43, 97
profits from, 47, 111, 138, 319,
  320
*Canadian Home Journal,* 149
*Canadian Homes and Gardens,* 261,
  331–33, 351
*Canadian Hotel Review,* 339
*Canadian Machinery and Manufactur-
  ing news*
early issues of, 147–49
World War I and, 201–2
*Canadian Magazine*
Hugh MacLean and, 92, 149
as national magazine, 149
Canadian Manufacturers' Association,
  146
Maclean's attack on, 225–26, 228,
  251, 253
*Canadian Military Gazette,* 81, 103, 348
campaigns of, 72–77, 207–8
as *Illustrated War News,* 71–72
Maclean's purchase of, 71–73, 94
naming of, 99
sale of, 78
Canadian Pacific Railway, 12, 35, 79,
  128, 152
Canadian Packers' Association, 41
Canadian Press, founding of, 171
Canadian Press Association, Maclean's
  membership and, 49, 170–74, 202
*Canadian Printer and Publisher* and,
  51–52
disintegration of, 172–74
Canadian Press Clipping Service, 140,
  351
*Canadian Printer and Publisher,* 140
campaigns of, 173
editors of, 53–54
first issues of, 51–52, 350
*Canadian Sportsman,* 161
Carman, Bliss, 32
Carnegie, Andrew, 125, 126, 138, 152
Carroll, Lewis, 119
Cartwright, Sir Richard, 155
*Cassel's,* 151
*Century,* 193
Cervantes, Miguel de, 335
Chalmers, Floyd S.
as executive vice-president, 352, 353
as *Financial Post* editor, 239, 282–
  84
first meeting of Maclean and, vii-
  viii

Chalmers, Jean A., 348
Chalmers, Rev. Thomas, vii, 10
Chamberlain, Joseph, 39–40
Chamberlain, Neville, 257
Chambers, E. J., 72–74
Chambers, Col. Ernest, as chief cen-
  sor, 210–12
Chanak, crisis at, 273–76
Chaplin, Charlie, 314
Chapman, Frank M., 227
Charles I, King of Portugal, 258
*Chatelaine*
contents of, 321, 328
founding of, 321, 351
French-language edition of, 352
Chatelaine Institute, 327, 339
Chicago *Tribune,* 28, 318
Chilton, Mary, 107
Choate, Arthur P., 53–54
*Christian Guardian,* 30
Christie family, residence of, 110
*Chronicle* (Halifax), 141
Chrysler, Walter, 257
Churchill, Lady Randolph, 43
Churchill, Lord Randolph, 43, 121
Churchill, Lady (Mrs. Winston Chur-
  chill), 122, 125, 248
Churchill, Sir Winston, 273–75
Canadian visit of, ix, 120–22
exploits of, 246–48
*From London to Ladysmith via
  Pretoria,* 120
Maclean's dislike of, 122, 124, 245–
  49
World War I and, 198, 209
Clan Maclean Society of America,
  79
Clark, Gregory, 53
Clark, Joseph, 53
Clarke, Richard, 107–8
Clouston, Edward S., 121
Cochrane, Frank, 265
Cockshutt, Harry, 260
*Collier's Weekly,* 186
Collishaw, Air Vice Marshal Ray-
  mond, 295
Colquhoun, Dr. A. H. U.
as Deputy Minister of Education,
  17, 54
as editor, 54
*Empire* and, 38
Communism. *See* Bolshevism
Connor, Ralph, *Glengarry School Days,*
  138
Consumers Gas Company, 29
Coolidge, Calvin, 58, 84, 222, 272,
  273

Cooper, Col. Ernest, career of, 53
Cooper, John A.
as editor, 53
Red Cross and, 53
Corelli, Marie, 138
Cornell University, 31
*Cosmopolitan*, 294
Costain, Ida Spragge, 195
Costain, Thomas Bertram, 347
books of, 330
as editor, 190–95, 208–9, 211–12, 223
Lord Beaverbrook and, 213
*Maclean's Magazine* and, 191–95, 211–13
Cox, Herbert C., 110
Coxey, Jacob Sechler, 64
Craick, William Arnot
as editor, 137, 151, 187
first meeting of Maclean and, 113–16
memoirs of, 347
resignation of, 187–88
Creighton, David
as *Empire*'s manager, 38, 39, 55
Macdonald biography by, 60–61
Cromwell, James H. R., 134
Cromwell, Louise, 134
Crowell Publishing Company, 150
Culham, Gordon, 306–7, 333
Currie, Sir Arthur, 235
Curtis, Cyrus H. K., 101, 104, 329
Curtis Publishing Company, failure of, 165
Curzon, Lord, 273

Dafoe, John W., 124, 274
*Daily Mail* (Toronto)
*Art Weekly* and, 66
employees of, 29, 53, 54, 63, 64, 66, 130
founding of, 22
Sir John Macdonald and, 22, 26, 37, 59
Maclean at, 22–29, 39, 59, 130
merger of *Empire* with, 60
value of, 169
(*see also* Mail and Empire)
Daily Mail Publishing Company (Montreal) 174
*Daily News* (Yarmouth), 97–98
*Daily Star* (Toronto), 53, 168, 170, 172, 228, 229, 236, 253, 348
Dale Estate nurseries, 340
Danish Association of New Canadians, 309
*Dati e Tariffe Pubblicitarie*, 352–53
Davies, Rev., at Toronto Normal School, 17

Davis, H. H., 300
d'Edla, Countess (Elise Hensler, sister-in-law)
death of, 261
Ferdinand II and
first meeting of, 116–17
morganatic marriage of, 117–18, 259–60
as Maclean's hostess, 108, 118, 258–60, 339
as singer, 116
DeLamatter, as head master, 15
Denison, Gen. Daniel, 107
Denison, Col. George Taylor, 137, 196
British Empire League and, 84
as magistrate, 21
in 13th Hamilton Regiment, 73
Dennis Col. John S., 231–32
de Pencier, Nina Wells, 177
Depression, 280–81, 351
Desbarats, Edward, 72, 73
Design Craft Limited, 353
Devonshire, Duke of, 127
Dewey, Adm. George, 104
Dexter, Grant, 282, 283
Diamond Jubilee of Queen Victoria, 73–74, 83
Dillman, Mrs., as hostess, 330
Dingman, R. G., 164
Dixon, Maj. F. S., 74–76
"Domino,". *See* Bridle, Augustus
Donald, Sir Robert, 322–23
Doria, Marquis of, 155
Douglas, W. J.
*Art Weekly* and, 64, 66
*Mail* and, 25, 29
Douglas family, *Mail* and, 169
Dove, I. Ethel, as Maclean's secretary, 223, 256, 309, 347
Dowler, W. A., 237
Doyle, Arthur Conan, 68
*Dramatic World and Sporting Record*, 31
Drayton, Sir Henry, 250
Dressler, Marie, 331
Drew, Fiorenza Johnson, 301
Drew, George A., 266
as anti-"war maker," 296–98
background of, 293
Maclean and, 292–302, 347–48
marriage of, 301
political activities of, 300–2
*The Truth about the War Debts*, 296
Dreyfus, Alfred, 267
Drummond, Sir George, 121
Drummond, Dr. William Henry, 80–81

Drury, Charles, 227
Drury, Ernest C.
  as political writer, 227, 266–67
  as prime minister, 127, 227–28, 291
*Dry Goods Economist* (U.S.), 322
*Dry Goods Review* (*Style*)
  contents of, 50–51, 111, 136, 138–39, 145
  editors of, 53, 54
  founding of, 50, 350
  *Men's Wear Review* and, 180
  possible sale of, 322
  revenue from, 111, 138
Duff, Sir Lyman, 301–2
Dufferin, Lord, 21
Duffy, Father Francis Patrick, 256
Duke, Doris, 134
Duke of York's Royal Canadian Hussars
  Duke of York's visit to, 89
  history of, 86
  Maclean and, 86–90, 106, 142–44
  Montreal Cotton Mills' strike and, 88–89
  World War II and, 90
Dundas, Lord, 2
Dunne, Finley Peter, 242
Dunning, Charles A., 290, 331
Duplessis, Maurice LeNoblet, as Premier, 240
Dyas, T. W., 29
  *Art Weekly* and, 63–64, 66
  *Mail* and, 29, 63

Eaton, John Craig, 158, 178
Eaton, Lady, 179
Eaton, Timothy, 28, 64
Eaton's (store), 114
Eayrs, Hugh, 223, 249–50
Eddy, E. B., 280
Eddy, Jennie Shirreff, 280
Eden, Anthony, 256
Edison, Thomas A., 19, 314
Edmonds, W. L., 70, 139, 146, 181
Edward, Bob, "The Calgary Eye Opener," 279
Edward VII, King of England, 80
Edwards, of *Men's Wear*, 255
*Elementary Arithmetic for Canadian Schools* (Smith and McMurchy), 14–15
11th Field Brigade, 295
Elliott, Madge Merton, 52
Elora Museum, 309
Emerson, Ralph Waldo, 255
*Empire* (Toronto), 160
  advertising solicitation for, 55
  contents of, 42, 43, 49
  founding of, 38–43
  Macdonald and, 37–40, 42–43, 55–62
  Maclean and, 38–43, 49, 55–60, 105–6, 135, 160, 163
  *Mail* merger with, 60
  See also *Mail and Empire*
Endicott, Rev. James G., 241
Evans, W. Watson, 270
Everglades Club, 257
*Examiner* (San Francisco), 67
*Expositor* (Brantford), 191

Falconer, Sir Robert, 236, 237
Fallis, W. S., 226
Fallon, Bishop, 127, 237, 324
*Farm and Fireside*, 150
*Farmer's Advocate*, 30
*Farmer's Magazine*, 180–81, 319, 351
*Farmer's Sun*, 32
Farrell, Maj. R. B., 78
Ferdinand II, King of Portugal, Countess d'Edla and
  first meeting of, 116–17
  morganatic marriage of, 117–18, 259–60
Ferdinand, Duke of Saxe-Coburg-Gotha, 117
Ferdinand, King of Bulgaria, 262
Fielding, William S., 58, 83, 171, 268
*Financial Chronicle*, 161
*Financial Post, The*, 188, 190, 272, 289, 337
  Bennett and, 282–84
  campaigns of, 174, 209–10, 222–27, 253–54, 266, 274, 276–78, 281, 300, 317, 318, 331
  Chalmers and, vii–viii, 352
  contents of, 56, 58
  editors of, 160–64, 239, 253, 257, 282–84
  founding of, 159–63, 312
  Houston and, 160–63
  stock of, 320
1st Prince of Wales Regiment, 85–86
Flagg, Elisha, II, 106
Flagler, Henry M., 100, 103–4, 132, 133
Flavelle, Sir Joseph, 336–37
Forbes, Kenneth, 344
Forbes, Priscilla (Allingham), as Maclean's secretary, 43–44, 66, 67, 140, 144, 217, 347
Ford, Arthur, 55
Foster, Sir George, 72, 251, 311
Franz Ferdinand, Archduke of Austria, 196
Fraser's Trade Directories, 353

Frederick, Archduke of Austria, 313
Free Church, 3
*Free Press* (London), 55
*Free Press* (Winnipeg), 123, 124, 274
French, Sir John, 84, 86, 201
Frick, Henry Clay, 135
*From London to Ladysmith via Pretoria* (Churchill), 120
Fulford, George, 151
Furness, Sir Christopher, 155

Gabrielle. *See* Slade, Gabrielle
Gaelic Society, 37
*Gallipoli Diary* (Hamilton), 246
Galloway family, 304
Garrett, Garet, 294
Garrick, David, 261
Gary, Elbert H., 103, 129, 135
Gastrell, Rev., 261
Gates, John W., 135, 156–57
*Gazette* (Montreal), 38, 77, 82, 166
*General Commerce*, 161
George, David Lloyd. See Lloyd George, David
George V, King of England, 86, 263, 297
Gibson, Charles Dana, 104
Gibson, Mrs. Charles, as "Gibson Girl," 104
Gibson, J. M., 72–73
Gilchrist, Capt. John, 308
Gilchrist family, 4
Glasgow *Herald*, 60
*Glengarry School Days* (Connor), 138
Glenesk, Lord, 85, 161, 264
*Globe* (Toronto)
  J. E. Atkinson of, 52–53
  founder of, 14, 18, 21
  Maclean and, 21, 199
  political position of, 37, 228
Glyn, Elinor, 100, 105
Gompers, Samuel, 237
Good, Harry J. P., 38–39, 130
Goodhugh & Company, W. S., 35
Gordon, Sir David, 285
Gouin, Lomer, 187
Grahame, Gordon Hill, *The Bond Triumphant*, 243–45
*Grand*, 151
Grocer Publishing Company, 34
Guelph *Mercury*, 191
Guidi, Signor, 116
Guthrie, Hugh, 282–84
Gwatkin, Gen. William G., 231

Haggard, H. Rider, 68
Hahn, Emmanuel, 229

Hahn, Maj. James E., 299–300
Haldenby & Mathers, 179
Halifax *Chronicle*, 141
Hambly, W. J., 28
Hamilton, Sir Ian, 84, 122
  Churchill and, 245–49
  *Gallipoli Diary*, 246
Hamilton, Lord, *The Vanished Pomps of Yesterday*, 259–60
Hamilton *Spectator*, Southam and, 27
Hanbourg, Mark, 163
Hanlan, Ned, 33, 39
Harding, Warren G., 127, 222
*Hardware and Metal (Hardware Merchandising)*, 70, 147
  campaigns of, 113
  contents of, 49, 139
  founding of, 49, 97, 350
  H. T. Hunter and, 141–42, 191
*Harper's*, 193
Harriman, Edward Henry, 129
Harris, Lawren, 330
Harris, Sam, 225
Harvard University, 348
Haughton, M. G., Jr., 106
Hawk Bay Company, 95
Haydon, Andrew, 316
Hearst, William Randolph, vii, 345
  anti-Bolshevism of, 235
  anti-Canadian feelings of, 209–11
  Churchill and, 248–49
  Maclean and, 67, 166
Heming, Arthur, 193
Henry, George Alfred, 246
Henry, O., 188
Hensler, Elise. *See* d'Edla, Countess
Hensler, Mina Louise (mother-in-law), 116
*Herald* (Glasgow), 60
*Herald* (Montreal), 93
*Herald Tribune* (New York), 252
Herbert, George, 110
Herridge
  Richard Bennett and, 285
Hewett, Arthur, 29
Hill, J. J., 129–30
Hill, John A., 322
Hind, E. Cora, in *Canadian Grocer*, 123–24
Hitler, Adolph, 256–58, 298–99, 301
Hobson, Adm. Richard P., 275, 285
Hodder & Stoughton, 242, 245
Hodgins, J. Herbert, as editor of *Mayfair*, 332–35
Hodgins, Mrs. J. Herbert, 335
Hogarth, Gen. D. M., 277, 278
Holmes, Oliver Wendell, 108

Holt, Sir Herbert S., 169, 238–39
*Home & Foreign Record,* 13
Homer, Louise, 330
Hoover, Herbert, 58, 84, 222, 272
Horne, Sir Robert, 248
Hosmer, Charles R., 82, 128, 166, 311
Houston, Stewart, 120
  death of, 163
  *The Financial Post* and, 160–63
Houston, Mrs. Stewart, 164, 218, 320
Howe, Clarence Decatur, 300
Hugh C. MacLean Publishing Co., 98–99, 318
Hughes, Gen. Sir Sam, 196, 202–8
Hughes, Sir William, 314
Hull, Cordell, 285
Hunter, Donald F., 349, 353
Hunter, Horace T., 149, 218, 252, 257, 281, 285, 290, 291, 309, 319, 333
  advancement of, 181–85, 208, 311, 321–22, 351, 352
  *Hardware and Metal* and, 141–42, 191
  as president, 241, 352
  tuberculosis of, 182–83, 199
Hunter, Mrs. Horace T., 329
Hussars Cavalry Brigade, 86
Huston, B. T., 347
  as editor of *Canadian Grocer,* 339
Hutton, Gen. Edward, 75
Hutton, Eric, 349

Iliffe, Lord, 256
*Illustrated War News. See Canadian Militia Gazette*
Imperial Federation League, 37
*Industrial Canada,* 188
*Industry and Humanity* (King), 288
*Insurance Chronicle, Monetary Times and,* 31
*Intelligencer* (Belleville), 82
International Nickel Company, 125
  founding of Canadian, 148
Irwin, W. Arthur, 300, 347

*Jack Canuck,* 251
Jardine, William M., 272
Jarvis, Aemilius, 266–67
Jefferson, Joseph, 104
Jefferson, Thomas, 165, 265
Jefferys, Charles W., 193, 243
Johnson, Edward, 301
Johnson, Pauline, 32
Johnson, Samuel, 18, 224
*Journal* (Ottawa), 25, 269, 300

Karsh, Yousuf, 344
Kemal Pasha (Kemal Atatürk), 273, 275
Kemp, Albert Edward, 167, 168
Kemp, Sir Edward, 323
Kennedy, Joseph P., 256
Kerensky, Alexander, 232–33
King, D. Macdougall, 268
King, John, 170, 268, 269
King, W. L. Mackenzie
  death of, 344
  as Deputy Minister of Labor, 88–89, 186, 268
  *Industry and Humanity,* 288
  as leader of opposition, 282
  as prime minister, x, 170, 222, 238, 240
    Maclean and, 265, 268–69, 271–77, 280, 285–91, 299–302
  Progressive Party and, 222
  at Valleyfield incident, 88–89
Kipling, Rudyard, 68, 246
Kitchener, Lord, of Khartoum, 137, 205, 206, 247
Kitson, Arthur, economic theories of, 314–15
Knox Church, 2
Knox College library, 348
Kon, Louis, 238–40

Labelle, Maj., of 65th Regiment, 73
*Labour Gazette,* 235
*Ladies' Journal,* 31
Lajeunesse, Marie Louise (Albani), 80
Lamb, W. Kaye, 348
Lampman, Archibald, 32
*Land of Afternoon, The,* 251
Lash, Zebulon A., 96
Laurier, Sir Wilfrid
  defeat of, 204, 208, 267
  Imperial preference scheme of, 58
  as prime minister, 73, 75, 76, 83, 137, 203, 208
Laval, Bishop, 243
Law, Andrew Bonar, 274
Lawrence of Arabia (T. E. Lawrence), 159
Leacock, Stephen, 127–28, 194, 264
*Leisure,* 151
*Le Magazine Maclean,* 352
Lemieux, Rodolphe, 263–64
Lenin, Vladimir Ilyich, 159, 212, 230, 316
Lennox, E. J., 178
*Le Prix Courant,* 351
*Liberty,* 294

Light Brigade, charge of, 86
*Little White Bird* (Barrie), 138
Litvinoff, Maxim Maximovich, 256
*Lives of a Bengal Lancer* (Yeats-Brown), 252
Lloyd George, David (1st Earl Lloyd-George of Dwyfor), as prime minister
  Maclean's dislike of, 209, 273–74
  Trotsky and, 233
  Zaharoff and, 296, 297
London, Jack, 194
London *Advertiser,* 30
*London Free Press,* 55
*London Magazine,* 151
*London Morning Post,* 85, 161, 264
London *Times,* 252, 276, 283
Lorimer, George Horace, 213
Lowell, James Russell, 311
Luiz, King of Portugal, 259–60
Luke, Lord, of Pavenham, 36
Lvov, Prince, 232
Lyle, John M., 178

MacArthur, Gen. Douglas, 134
McBean family, 4
McCall Corporation, 165
McCarthy, D'Alton, 38, 55, 56
McClure, S. S., 68–69, 101, 262
*McClure's Magazine,* 68, 186
McCormick, Col. Robert, vii, 166, 318, 345
McDonald, Donald, 60–61
McDonald, Helen Shaw, 60–61
McDonald, Hugh, 60–61
McDonald, James, 60–61
Macdonald, John, 62
Macdonald, Sir John A.
  birthplace of, 60–62
  Conservative Party and, 290
    plan for Canada of, 14, 37–40, 48, 57–58
    rally for, 26
  death of, 59–60
  knighthood of, 202
  Maclean's first meeting with, 14
  Maclean's friendship with, 58–59, 266, 287
  newspaper support of
    *Empire* and, 37–40, 42–43, 55–62
    *Mail* and, 22, 26, 37, 59
  papers of, 348
MacDonald, Ramsay, 314
Macdonald, William, 187
Macdonald family, 9, 304
Macdonnell, James S., 75–77
McDougall, Louise, 347

McGarvey, Countess Zeppelin as, 262
McGoughran, Frances, 347
McGraw, James H., 322
McGraw-Hill, 165, 322
MacKay, Alexander Grant, 148
MacKay, Jean Reid, 348
MacKay, John F., 287, 320
Mackenzie, Alexander, 14
Mackenzie, Ian, 124–25, 299, 300
Mackenzie, J. Vernon, 242, 244–46, 249–52
Mackenzie, Sir William, 12, 250
Mackenzie King. *See* King, W. L. Mackenzie
Mackillican, William, 312
McKim, J. Meredith, 140
McKishnie, Archie P., 187, 245
Maclean, Rev. Andrew (father), 92, 98–99, 152, 306, 344
  ancestors of, 9–10
  as clergyman, 1, 3–9, 11–12
  death of, 13, 303
  library of, vii
  marriage of, 8
  as student, 5–6
  as teacher, 6
MacLean, Andrew Dyas (nephew), 98, 334, 347
Maclean, Anna Denison Slade (wife), 115, 137, 196–201, 259–71, 305
  ancestors of, 107–8, 116–18
  appearance of, 107
  courtship of, ix, 63, 105–9
  Crieff and, 310, 343
  death of, 343
  marriage of, 328–29
  Munsey and, ix, 105, 108–9
  paralysis of, 178–79, 256
  Roosevelts and, 246
  social life of, 110–11, 131, 154, 166, 178, 214, 218–21, 292, 325, 327
  son's death and, 217–19
  will of, 329–30
MacLean, Bessie Dyas (sister-in-law), 98
Maclean, Catherine Cameron (mother), 40–41, 94, 96, 106
  ancestors of, 8, 10, 312
  death of, 303
  husband's death and, 13
  marriage of, 8
Maclean, Sir Charles H. F., 204–5, 341, 348
Maclean, Lt. C. W. Weldon (cousin), 106
Maclean, Evan (grandfather), 5

Maclean, Sir Fitzroy, 341
Maclean, Hector Andrew Fitzroy
     (son), birth of, 139, 142
  childhood of, 144, 166, 196–201
  death of, viii, 216–19, 318, 324,
     329
  illness of, 139, 214
  teen years of, 214–16
MacLean, Hugh Cameron (brother),
     40, 106, 303, 324
  birth of, 9
  *Canadian Magazine*, 92, 149
  education of, 13
  family of, 98
  Hugh C. MacLean Publishing Com-
     pany, 98–99, 318
  partnership of, John and, 50, 51,
     64, 91–97, 319, 350
     *Art Weekly*, 69–70, 93
     *Canadian Grocer*, 40–41, 43, 97
     dissolution of, 95–97, 142, 318,
        358
  personality of, 93
  as printer, 33, 40, 69
  recreation of, 33, 34
Maclean, Jimmie, 21
Maclean, John, 21
Maclean, Col. John Bayne
  ancestors of, 8–10, 98, 312
  appearance of
     as child, 9
     as publisher, 250
     as reporter, 27, 56
  arts and, 330
  as *Art Weekly* manager, 63–67, 69,
     79, 93, 100
  Bache and, 256, 257, 315
     advice of, 128, 311
  Baruch and, 256, 315
     advice of, 128, 311
  Beck and, 182, 226–29, 239, 253
  birth of, 1, 8, 98
  childhood of, 8–10, 288
     discipline of, 12
     as student, 10, 13–16
  as crusader, ix–x, 222–41, 345
     advertising cancellation, 252
     anti-Bolshevism, 212, 222, 230–
        41, 315–16
     anti-Canadian Manufacturers' As-
        sociation, 225–26, 228, 251, 253
     anti-Canadian-U.S. union, 34–35
     breeder-shippers, 24–25
     crop conditions, 35
     duties, 48, 284–85, 288–90
     fire insurance, 145–46
     military, 74–77, 223
     price-fixing, 112

  prime ministers, x, 265–304 (*see
     also* specific prime ministers)
  public power development, 226–
     29, 253
  Royal Military College, 73
  school textbooks, 47–48, 112
  telephone companies, 113
  trade periodicals, 48, 284–85, 288–
     90
  trading stamps, 113
  U.S. companies, 148, 171
  death of, viii, 318, 341–44, 346
  education of, 10, 13–17
  foods and, 338–39
     diets of, 132
  *Empire* and, 38–43, 49, 55–60, 160
  *Mail and Empire* (Toronto) and,
     60, 105–6, 135, 160, 163
  marriage of, ix, 63, 105–9, 328–29
  militia and, 103
     Canadian Military Gazette, 71–78
     as career, 15, 85–86
     devotion to, viii, 90
     Diamond Jubilee, 83–84
     Duke of York's Royal Canadian
        Hussars, 86–90, 106, 142–44
     1st Prince of Wales Regiment,
        85–86
     need for advancement, 71
     Owen Sound Militia, 17, 23, 45,
        85
     retirement, 142–44
     Royal Military College, 15, 73
     Royal School of Gunnery, 16
     St. John's Ambulance Brigade,
        45, 77, 79, 80
     6th Fusiliers, 72, 79, 85
     10th Royal Genadiers, 45–47, 71,
        344
     World War I, 204–9, 223–24
  money of, 63, 65, 311–25
     company stock, 319–24
     economic theories, 314
     estates, 305, 312–13
     income tax, 323–24
     investments, 29–30, 34, 71, 111,
        125–26, 128, 311–13
     speculations, 314–18
     will, 324
  Munsey and, 125, 212–13, 248, 251,
     348
     advice, 167, 171–72, 192, 263–64,
        332
     *Busy Man*, 152–53
     death of, 305
     first meeting, 67
     other friends and, 135, 261–63

speculations, 313–14
travels, 100–6, 108–9, 132–33, 149, 153, 166, 197–99, 261–63
partnership of Hugh and. *See* Mac-Lean, Hugh Cameron
personality of, 93, 102–3, 250
boldness, 9
fault-finding, 145, 184, 187, 345
individuality, vii
interest in people, vii–x, 99, 119–22
thriftiness, 144, 336–37
women and, 122–23
pets of, 27–28
radio and television stations of, 353
reading of, 138, 330
religion of, 1, 124, 144, 268
as reporter, viii–ix, 17–28
as freelancer, 22, 30, 43
Toronto's *Daily Mail,* 22–29, 39, 59, 130
Toronto's *World,* 20–22
publishing empire of, vii–ix, 24, 111, 350–53
banquet for, 146–47
Canadian Press Clipping Service, 140, 351
daily newspapers and, 165–74
expansion of, 353
first magazine of, 148–53
at 481 University Avenue, 175–77, 180
residences of
Chatsworth, 13–15, 305
Crieff, 8–14, 303–10
Durham, 16
Montreal, 70–97, 106
New York City, 64–71, 97
Owen Sound, 15–16
Rolls-Royce motorcar and, 156–59
Schwab and, 125–28, 148, 152, 156, 166, 251, 297
advice of, 103, 125–26, 182
as teacher, 16–17
World War I and, 196–202, 204–12, 214, 223–24, 230–33
World War II and, 209
*See also Bookseller and Stationer* (*Books and Notions*); *Books and News; British Printer; Canadian Grocer; Canadian Homes and Gardens; Canadian Hotel Review; Canadian Machinery and Manufacturing; Canadian Magazine; Canadian Military Gazette; Canadian Printer and Publisher; Chatelaine; Dati e*

*Tariffe Pubblicitarie; Dry Goods Review (Style); Farmer's Magazine; The Financial Post; Hardware and Metal (Hardware Merchandising); Le Magazine Maclean; Le Prix Courant; Maclean's Magazine (Busy Man's Magazine); Maclean's Weekly; Mayfair; Media Daten; Men's Wear Review; Metropolitan; Monthly Bulletin; Plumber and Steamfitter; Power House; Printer and Publisher; Tarif Media*
Maclean, Katharine Fraser (grandmother), 5
Maclean, W. F. ("Billy"), 21, 99, 129
Maclean-Hunter, chronology of, 350–53
*Maclean's Magazine (Busy Man's Magazine),* 269, 285, 319, 332
campaigns of, 209, 211–12, 222–23, 233, 234, 266–67, 275–76, 286–87, 292, 298–300
contents of, 150–53, 186–95, 205–6, 227, 242, 295, 346
contest in, 242–45
Costain and, 190–95, 211–13
first issues of, 150–53, 166, 350
Mackenzie and, 242–45, 249–51
Moore and, 251–52
name of, 99, 150, 186
*Maclean's Weekly,* 196, 200, 216, 217
McLeod (Canadian airman), 295
Macmillan's of Canada, 223, 249
McMurchy, *Elementary Arithmetic for Canadian Schools,* 14–15
Macphail, Agnes, 240–41
Macphail, Sir Andrew, 241
Macpherson, Hugh, 10
Macpherson, Mary-Etta, 249
Magor, Robert J., 129
*Mail and Empire* (Toronto)
Borden and, 167–68
Houston and, 163
merger of, 60
possible sale of, 166–68
social column of, 105–6, 135
value of, 169
Mainprice, Kathleen T., 349
Mann, D. D., 152
Mann, Sir Donald, 12–13
Mann, Rev. Hugh, 12
Manuel II, King of Portugal, 258
Marconi, Marchese Guglielmo, 68
Maria II, Queen of Portugal, 117
Marlborough family, 247
*Marmion* (Scott), 21
Martin, Sgt., with 10th Royal Grenadiers, 46–47

Mary, Queen of England (wife of
    George V, formerly Duchess of
    York), 89, 132
*Masques of Ottawa* (Bridle), 249–51
Massey, Vincent, 286, 287
*Massey Report, The*, 186
Mathers & Haldenby, 179
Matthews, Andrew, 17
Mavor, James, 187
*Mayfair*
    founding of, 351
    Hodgins and, 332–35
*Media Daten*, 352–53
Medill, Joseph, 28
Meighen, Arthur
    intellectuality of, 269
    as opposition leader, 270–71
        273, 276
    as prime minister
        Maclean and, x, 127, 251, 265
            268–71, 273
    in retirement, 277–78
Meighen, Mrs. Arthur, 251
Meisonnier, Juste Aurèle, 65
Mellon, Andrew, 222
*Men's Wear Review*, 255
    campaigns of, 223
    first issues of, 180
*Merchant*, 22, 30
*Merchantman*, 31
*Mercury* (Guelph), 191
Meredith, Vincent, 79, 87
*Metropolitan*, 82–83
Middlemiss, Rev. James, 5, 6
Middleton, Gen., in Northwest Rebel-
    lion, 44
Military units
    Canadian Armored Corps, 90
    Duke of York's Royal Canadian Hus-
        sars
        Duke of York's visit to, 89
        history of, 86
        Maclean and, 86–90, 106, 142–44
        Montreal Cotton Mills' strike and,
            88–89
        World War II and, 90
    11th Field Brigade, 295
    1st Prince of Wales Regiment,
        85–86
    Hussars Cavalry Brigade, 86
    Owen Sound Militia, 17, 23, 45, 85
    Royal Flying Corps, 295
    Royal Horse Artillery, 106
    Royal Montreal Cavalry, 86
    Royal School of Gunnery, 16
    St. John's Ambulance Brigade, 45,
        77, 79, 80

6th Fusiliers, 72, 79, 85
65th Regiment, 73
10th Royal Grenadiers, 45–47, 71,
    344
3rd Canadian Infantry Division, 90
3rd Victoria Rifles, 72
13th Hamilton Regiment, 73
13th Hussars, 86
31st Greys, 15–16, 45
Minto, Earl of, 75, 121, 137
Mizner (architect), 257
Montreal *Herald*, 93
Mordore, defined, 50–51
Moffat, Christopher, 11
Moltke, Gen. Helmuth von, 199
Monel, Ambrose, 256
*Monetary Times*, 22, 30, 161
*Monetary Times and Insurance Chron-
    icle*, 31
Monk, F. B., 76
*Monthly Bulletin*, 146
Montreal Club, 80
Montreal *Gazette*, 38, 77, 82, 166
Montreal *Star*, 43, 53, 72, 251, 348
Moore, H. Napier, 251–52, 291, 293,
    298–300
Morang, George M., 164
Morgan, J. P., 35, 133, 135, 182
Morison, Charles, 53
*Morning Journal* (New York), 67
*Morning Post* (London), 85, 161,
    264
Morton, Joy, 308
Morton, J. Sterling, 307–8
Mount Royal Club, 121
Munro family, 9
Munsey, Frank A., 212–13
    Anna Slade Maclean and, ix, 105,
        108–9
    background of, 67, 100–1
    fortune of, 103
    Maclean and, 125, 212–13, 248,
        251, 348
        advice, 167, 171–72, 192, 263–
            64, 332
        *Busy Man*, 152–53
        death of, 305
        first meeting, 67
        other friends and, 135, 261–63
        speculations, 313–14
        travels, 100–6, 108–9, 132–33,
            149, 153, 166, 197–99, 261–63
    personality of, 100, 102
    as publisher, 67–68, 345
        *Argosy*, 101, 102
        *Munsey's Magazine*, 67, 68, 101,
            171, 186

*My Adventures as a Spy* (Baden-Powell), 230

*National Geographic,* 151
National Market Reports, 353
New, Harry S., 340
New, Mrs. Harry S., 340
Newfoundland, Canada and, 81–82
*News* (Toronto), 54
*News* (Palm Beach), 348
*News* (Yarmouth), 97–98
New York *Herald Tribune,* 252
New York *Morning Journal,* 67
New York Public Library, 348
New York *Sun,* 264
New York *World,* 152
Nietzsche, Friedrich Wilhelm, 1
Nixon, Lewis, 104
Nordegg, Martin, 316
Nordheimer family, 178
Northcliffe, Lord, vii, 85, 166, 264, 345
Northwest Mounted Police, 207
Noseworthy, J. W., 277
Nyberg, Sauteri (Nuorteva), 233

O'Leary, Grattan, 269
Olmsted brothers, 304, 306
Ontario Hydro-Electric Power Commission, Beck and, 226–28, 239, 253
Ontario Rifle Association, 33
Ontario Securities Commission, 295–96
Orczy, Baroness, *The Scarlet Pimpernel,* 326
Osler, B. B., 110
Osler, Edmund, 167, 168
Ottawa *Journal,* 25, 269, 300
Otter, Sir William, 46
Owen Sound Militia, 17, 23, 45, 85
Owen Sound *Times,* 19
Oxford University, 31

Pacific Railroad, 14
Paderewski, Ignace Jan, 104
Pain, Hilda, 321
*Pall Mall,* 151
Palm Beach *News,* 348
Pankhurst, Emmeline, 326–27
*Paris Herald,* 363
Parker, Sir Gilbert, 193
Parkman, Francis, 108
Parsons, S. R., 225
Paterson, Ed, 310
Pearson, Sir Arthur, 85
*Pearson's,* 151
Peel, Paul, 65

Pellatt, Sir Henry, 177–78
Pellatt & Pellatt, 22
Pennsylvania Iron and Steel Association, 127
Periodical Press Association, 174, 290
Periodicals
  in nineteenth-century Canada, 30–31, 37–38
  tax problems of, 48, 284–85, 288–89, 290
  *See also* specific periodicals
Perkins, George W., 182
Pickford, Mary, 192–93
Plowder, Pamela, 121
*Plumber and Steamfitter,* 176, 191
Pond, Maj. S. B., 120
Pope, Sir Joseph, 59, 60, 62
Port Hope *Times,* 115
*Power House,* 165
*Pravda,* 316
*Presbyterian, The,* 141
*Presbyterian Record,* 12
*Printer and Publisher. See Canadian Printer and Publisher*
*Proverbs,* 42
Pulitzer, Joseph, 345

Quebec Press Association, 171
Queenborough, Lord, 340

Read, Sir Hugh Gilzean, 155
Red Cross (Canadian), 79
  John Cooper and, 53
  founding of, 44–45
Reilly, Gen. Henry J., 294, 295
Renoir, Jean, 329, 330
Renoir, Pierre Auguste, 329
Replogle, J. Leonard, 257
Republic Steel, 257
Riel, Louis, 44, 72
Rigaud, Hyacinthe, 330
Riordon brothers, 167, 169
Ritchie, James, 219, 256, 303, 310, 337, 341, 347
Robb, James A., 238, 331
Roberts, Charles G. D., 32
Robertson, John Ross, 172, 174, 312
Robinson, Blackett, 29, 32
Robinson, "Blackjack," 172
Robinson, John Beverley, family of, 160
Rockefeller Foundation, 268
Rolls, Charles S.
  death of, 159
  Rolls-Royce and, 156–59
Rolph, Ernest, 66
Roosevelt, Franklin D., 134, 257, 317–18

Roosevelt, Theodore, 246
Root, Elihu, 237
Ross, P. D., 25
Ross rifle, controversy about, 207–8
Rothermere, Lord, 322–23
Rothschild family, 314–15
Royal Flying Corps, 295
Royal Horse Artillery, 106
Royal Military College (Kingston), 15, 73
Royal Montreal Cavalry, 86
Royal School of Gunnery (Kingston), 16
Royal Society of St. George, 340
Royce, Henry, 157, 159
Russell, T. A., 151
Ryerson, Rev. Egerton, 17
  Christian Guardian, 30
Ryerson, Gen. G. Sterling, 45

St. James's Club, 121
St. John's Ambulance Brigade, Maclean and, 77, 79, 80
  founding of, 45
St. Maurice Fishing Club, 81
St. Paul, Minneapolis & Manitoba Railway, 129–30
San Francisco Examiner, 67
Saturday Evening Post, The, 213, 256, 293
Saturday Night, 31, 53, 149
Saxe-Coburg-Gotha, Duke of. See Ferdinand, Duke of Saxe-Coburg-Gotha
Scarlet Pimpernel, The (Orczy), 326
Schwab, Charles M.
  career of, 125
  Maclean and, 125–28, 148, 152, 156, 166, 251, 297
  advice of, 103, 125–26, 182
Sclanders, Ian Maclure, 349
Scott, Sir Walter, Marmion, 21
Scribner's, 186
Seaboard Railway, 103
Seneca, 326, 342
Service, Robert W., 186, 188
Shakespeare, 144, 176, 214, 230, 261
Shaughnessy, Lord, 80, 128, 187, 311
Shaw, A. W., 319
Shearer, Dr. William B., 297, 298
Shepherd, Dr. Francis J., 122
Shepherd (radio network owner), 257
Shirreff, Jennie (Eddy), 280
Silver "panic," Bryan and, 64
Simcoe, John Graves, 19
6th Fusiliers, 72, 79, 85

65th Regiment (Montreal), 73
Slade, Anna. See Maclean, Anna Denison Slade
Slade, Conrad (brother-in-law), 106, 329, 330
Slade, Daniel Denison (father-in-law), 107–8, 348
Slade, Denison (brother-in-law), 106
Slade, Gabrielle (sister-in-law), 330
  as Renoir model, 329
Smith, Alfred, 256
Smith, Elementary Arithmetic for Canadian Schools, 14–15
Smith, Goldwin, 31–32, 84, 170
  The Week, 32
Smith, James, 17
Smith, Peter, 266–67
Society of Master Cutlers, 83
Sons of Canada (Bridle), 152, 222, 249
Southam, William, 27
Southam-MacLean Publications, 99
Southam's publishing house, 165, 174
Specator (Hamilton), Southam and, 27
Speyer, James, 128, 129, 197–98, 315
Sphinx Club, 67
Spragge, Ida, 195
Sproatt & Rolph, 66
Stalin, Joseph V., 316, 318
Standard Oil Company, 68
Standard Rate & Data Service, 352–53
Star (Montreal), 43, 53, 72, 251, 348
Star (Toronto), 53, 168, 170, 172, 228, 229, 236, 253, 348
Stevenson, Robert Louis, 68
Stewart family, 4, 9, 304
Stotesbury, E. T., 133–34
Stotesbury, Mrs. E. T., 133–34
Stoughton, Hodder &, 242, 245
Strathcona, Lord, 129–30, 137
Stringer, Arthur, 193
Style. See Dry Goods Review
Success, 151
Sullivan, Alan, 193
Sun (New York), 264
Sun (Vancouver), 333
Sunday Globe (Boston), 106
Sunday World (Toronto), 130, 151
Swiss Club, 37
System, 267, 319

Taft, William Howard, 267
Tarbell, Ida M., 68
Tarif Media, 352–53
Taylor, Sir Henry, 29

*Telegram* (Toronto), 172, 228, 229, 245, 277, 312
Temple, Sir William, 131
10th Royal Grenadiers, 45–47, 71, 344
Thaw family, 104
3rd Canadian Infantry Division, 90
3rd Victoria Rifles, 72
13th Hamilton Regiment, 73
13th Hussars, 86, 204–5
Thompson, Lt. Col. Andrew T., 78
Thompson, Coté, Burgess & Code, 78
Thomson, Lord, 169
Thomson publishing house, 165
Time Inc., 165
*Times* (London), 252, 276, 283
*Times* (Owen Sound), 19
*Times* (Port Hope), 115
Toronto's Arts and Letters Club, 193
Toronto Central Reference Library, 348
Toronto Club, 229
Toronto *Daily Mail*
  *Art Weekly* and, 66
  employees of, 29, 53, 54, 63, 64, 66, 130
  founding of, 22
  Sir John Macdonald and, 22, 26, 37, 59
  Maclean at, 22–29, 39, 59, 130
  merger of *Empire* with, 60
  value of, 169
  *See also* Toronto *Mail and Empire*
Toronto *Daily Star*, 53, 168, 170, 172, 228, 229, 238, 253, 348
Toronto *Empire*, 160
  advertising solicitation for, 55
  contents of, 42, 43, 49
  founding of, 38–43
  Macdonald and, 37–40, 42–43, 55–62
  Maclean and, 38–43, 49, 55–60, 105–6, 135, 160, 163
  *Mail* merger with, 60
  *See also* Toronto *Mail and Empire*
Toronto Fencing Club, 27, 33
Toronto *Globe*
  J. E. Atkinson of, 52–53
  founder of, 14, 18, 21
  Maclean and, 21, 199
  political position of, 37, 228
Toronto Hunt Club, 106
Toronto Land and Investment Cor-
poration, 30, 34
Toronto *Mail and Empire*
  Borden and, 167–68
  Houston and, 163
  merger of, 60
  possible sale of, 166–68
  social column of, 105–6, 135
  value of, 169
Toronto *News*, 54
Toronto *Sunday World*, 130, 151
Toronto *Telegram*, 172, 228, 229, 245, 277, 312
Toronto University, communism and, 236–37
Toronto *World*, 20–22, 54, 99, 130
  Maclean and, 20–22
*Tour of the Hebrides* (Boswell), 224
*Tribune* (Chicago), 28, 318
Trinity University, 160
Trotsky, Leon, 212, 230–34, 316
Trotsky, Mrs. Leon, 232
*Truth about the War Debts, The* (Drew), 296
Tudor, Frederic R., Jr., 106
Tupper, Sir Charles, 73, 188–89
Twain, Mark, 68, 104
Tyrell, Herbert Victor
  Company and, 201, 252, 285, 291, 309, 319, 323
  diligence of, 140, 183, 200
  stock and, 182, 213, 321
  as Vice-President, 140
  death of, 352
Tyrell, Mrs. Herbert Victor, 333
Tyson, J. W., 164, 317

United European Investors Limited, 315–17
University of Toronto, 12, 114
University of Western Ontario, 323
  grounds of, 307–8
Upper Canada College, 75, 241, 324, 329
U.S. Steel Corporation, 125

Van Blaricom, George, 187, 188
Vance, Arthur T., 149–50
Vancouver *Sun*, 333
Vanderbilt family, 104, 263
Van Horne, Lt. R. B., 106
Van Horne, Sir William, 188–90
*Vanished Pomps of Yesterday, The* (Hamilton), 259–60
Victoria, Queen of England, 15, 80, 117
  Diamond Jubilee of, 73–74, 83

Victoria University library, 348
Vining, Charles, "Bigwigs," 292
Vogts, Dr. A. S., 186

Waldorf, William, 135
Waldorf-Astoria, 135
Walker, Sir Edmund, 236, 237
*Wall Street Journal, The,* 283
Wanamaker, John, 104
Warburg family, 315
*Warder* (Lindsay), 202
Warner, Mrs. Henry D. (sister-in-law), 347
*Wealth of Nations, The* (Smith), 57
*Week, The,* 32
Wellington County Historical and Research Socity, 309
Wells, H. G., 194
West, L. C., 286
Wheelright, Arthur W., 106
White, R. S., 77
White, Sidney, 180
White, William Allen, 305
Whitehead, Col. E. A., 121
Whiteway, Sir William, 81–82
Whitney, James Pliny, 167
Wilcox, Ella Wheeler, 78
Wilhelm II, German Kaiser, 197–200, 312
Williams-Taylor, Sir Frederick, 79, 209, 263
Willison, Sir John, 54
Wilson, Kenneth R., 337–38
Winnipeg *Free Press,* 123, 124, 274

Winslow, Edward, 107
Wolfe, Elsie de, 180
*Women's Home Companion,* 149 150
Wonham, Walter C., 80
Wood, Lt. Col. H. F., 348
Woolworth, Frank Winfield, 133, 257
*World* (New York), 152
*World* (Toronto), 20–22, 54, 99, 130
  Maclean and, 20–22
World Narcotic Defense Association, 275, 285
World War I, 196–202, 204–12, 214, 223–24, 292–96, 312, 313, 351
  Bolshevik Revolution and, 230–34
World War II, 209, 302–3
  Duke of York's Royal Canadian Hussars in, 90
  *See also* Hitler, Adolph
Wright brothers, 159

Yarmouth *Daily News,* 97–98
Yeats-Brown, Maj. Francis
  *Lives of a Bengal Lancer,* 252
York, Duchess of. *See* Mary, Queen of England
York, Duke of. *See* George V, King of England

Zaharoff, Sir Basil, 296–98
Zeppelin, Count, 262
Zeppelin, Countess, 262
Zinovieff, Grigory, 316, 318

S0-BBZ-798

# THE ILLUSTRATED GUIDE TO
# PREGNANCY BABYCARE & BABY FOOD

## AN EXPERT VISUAL SOURCEBOOK ON ALL ASPECTS OF PREGNANCY AND CARING FOR YOUR NEW BABY

### Alison Mackonochie & Sara Lewis

southwater

A very special thank you to Robin for his unfailing support, to Lucy and Kate, without whom we would not have had Christmas, and to Dominic for just being himself. (AM)

This edition is published by Southwater

Southwater is an imprint of Anness Publishing Ltd
Hermes House, 88–89 Blackfriars Road, London SE1 8HA
tel. 020 7401 2077; fax 020 7633 9499
www.southwaterbooks.com; www.annesspublishing.com

If you like the images in this book and would like to investigate using them for publishing, promotions or advertising, please visit our website www.practicalpictures.com for more information.

© Anness Publishing Ltd 2003, 2006

UK agent: The Manning Partnership Ltd
6 The Old Dairy, Melcombe Road, Bath BA2 3LR; tel. 01225 478444
fax 01225 478440; sales@manning-partnership.co.uk

UK distributor: Grantham Book Services Ltd, Isaac Newton Way
Alma Park Industrial Estate, Grantham, Lincs NG31 9SD
tel. 01476 541080; fax 01476 541061; orders@gbs.tbs-ltd.co.uk

North American agent/distributor: National Book Network
4501 Forbes Boulevard, Suite 200, Lanham, MD 20706
tel. 301 459 3366; fax 301 429 5746; www.nbnbooks.com

Australian agent/distributor: Pan Macmillan Australia,
Level 18, St Martins Tower, 31 Market St, Sydney, NSW 2000
tel. 1300 135 113; fax 1300 135 103; customer.service@macmillan.com.au

New Zealand agent/distributor: David Bateman Ltd
30 Tarndale Grove, Off Bush Road, Albany, Auckland
tel. (09) 415 7664; fax (09) 415 8892

All rights reserved. No part of this publication may be reproduced, stored in a retrieval system or transmitted in any way or by any means, electronic, mechanical, photocopying, recording or otherwise, without the prior written permission of the copyright holder.

A CIP catalogue record is available from the British Library.

Publisher: Joanna Lorenz
Project Editors: Casey Horton, Nicky Thompson, Judith Simons, Emma Wish, Molly Perham
Editor: Elizabeth Longley
Designers: Bobbie Colgate Stone, Sue Storey
Special Photography: Alistair Hughes, John Freeman
Additional Photography: Carin Simon
Illustrations: Ian Sidaway
Home Economists: Sara Lewis, Jacqueline Clarke, Petra Jackson
Stylist: Judy Williams
Hair and Make-up: Bettina Graham

Previously published as The Practical Encyclopedia of Pregnancy, Babycare & Nutrition for Babies & Toddlers (updated for this edition)

10 9 8 7 6 5 4 3 2 1

**NOTES**
Terms in brackets are intended for American readers.
For all recipes, quantities are given in both metric and imperial measures and, where appropriate, measures are also given in standard cups and spoons. Follow one set, but not a mixture, because they are not interchangeable.
Standard spoon and cup measures are level.
1 tsp = 5ml, 1 tbsp = 15ml, 1 cup = 250ml/8fl oz
Australian standard tablespoons are 20ml. Australian readers should use 3 tsp in place of 1 tbsp for measuring small quantities of gelatine, flour, salt, etc.
Medium eggs (US large) are used unless otherwise stated.

# CONTENTS

| | |
|---|---|
| Introduction | 6 |
| **PART ONE: PREGNANCY** | **10** |
| Preparing for pregnancy | 12 |

**The first trimester**
| | |
|---|---|
| Weeks 1–4: Conception | 14 |
| Week 5: Confirming pregnancy | 16 |
| Week 6: Ante-natal choices | 18 |
| Week 7: Possible problems | 20 |
| Week 8: Booking in/Routine tests | 22 |
| Week 9: Special tests | 24 |
| Week 10: Hormones/Maternity record | 26 |
| Week 11: Common discomforts | 28 |
| Week 12: Healthy eating | 30 |
| Week 13: The health professionals | 32 |

**The second trimester**
| | |
|---|---|
| Week 14: Sex during pregnancy | 34 |
| Week 15: Health and safety | 36 |
| Week 16: Scans/twins | 38 |
| Week 17: Your pregnancy wardrobe | 40 |
| Week 18: Looking your best | 42 |
| Week 19: Exercise | 44 |
| Week 20: Skin care/Cravings | 46 |
| Week 21: Minor complaints | 48 |
| Week 22: Relaxation and massage | 50 |
| Week 23: Preparing the nursery | 52 |
| Week 24: Baby clothes and equipment | 54 |
| Week 25: Feeding choices | 56 |
| Week 26: Parentcraft classes | 58 |

**The third trimester**
| | |
|---|---|
| Week 27: Choices in childbirth | 60 |
| Week 28: The birthplan | 62 |
| Week 29: Special care | 64 |
| Week 30: Travel/Backache | 66 |
| Week 31: Dealing with discomfort | 68 |
| Week 32: Positions for labour | 70 |
| Week 33: Emotions in late pregnancy | 72 |
| Week 34: Older first-time mothers | 74 |
| Week 35: Final preparations | 76 |
| Week 36: Discomforts in late pregnancy | 78 |
| Week 37: As birth approaches | 80 |
| Week 38: Induction/Pain relief in labour | 82 |
| Week 39: Complications during birth | 84 |
| Week 40: Labour and birth | 86 |

## PART TWO: BABY CARE     90
Post-natal care     92
Caring for your newborn     98
Breast-feeding     104
Bottle-feeding     108
Introducing solids     112
Nappies     118
Dressing your baby     124
Bathing     130
Sleeping     134
Crying     136
Colic     138
Teeth     139
Immunization     142
Childhood illnesses     144
Childhood diseases     147
Learning with toys     150
Baby massage     154
Travelling with a baby     156
Keeping your child safe     158
First aid     162

## PART THREE: THE FIRST YEAR     168
Newborn     170
One month     174
Two months     178
Three months     182
Four months     186
Five months     190
Six months     194
Seven months     198
Eight months     202
Nine months     206
Ten months     210
Eleven months     214
Twelve months     218

### Understanding your child's development
Sight and vision     224
Hearing     228
Smell, taste, touch     230
Talking     234
Social behaviour     238
Mobility     242
Play     246

## PART FOUR: COOKING FOR BABIES AND TODDLERS     252
Introduction     254

### First foods     258
Weaning from milk feeds to solids     260
Introducing solid food     262
Sterilizing and food preparation     266
Reheating, freezing and using a microwave     270
Choosing a high-chair     272
Stage 1: First tastes – early weaning     274
The recipes     276
Stage 2: Around six to six-and-a-half months     278
Going vegetarian     280
The recipes     282
Stage 3: Seven to nine months     294
The recipes     296
Stage 4 : Nine to twelve months     308
I can feed myself!     310
Coping with a fussy eater     313
The importance of a varied diet     314
The recipes     316

### Food for toddlers     332
Coping with a fussy eater     334
A balanced and varied diet     338
Lunch specials     340
Going green     358
Quick meals     368
Toast toppers     384
Easy desserts     394
Quick cakes and bakes the kids can make     404

### Family meals     416
Eating together     418
Meaty main meals     422
Perfect poultry     442
Fish dinners     452
Vegetable feasts     462
Just desserts     474

Nutrition information     496
Glossary of pregnancy terms     500
Useful addresses     502
Index     504
Acknowledgements     512

# INTRODUCTION

BEING A PARENT is the most important and responsible role you will ever have. And it begins long before the birth of your child. By making sure that you and your partner are both healthy before conception, you will be giving your baby the best possible start in life. Once you have conceived, and your pregnancy is confirmed, you will want to do everything you can to ensure that you are doing the best for your developing baby.

Understanding what happens during your pregnancy and how your baby is developing will help you to cope with both the physical and emotional changes that you are likely to experience. Part One of this book guides you through your pregnancy. To keep things simple, a new topic is discussed for each week of your pregnancy. Do remember, though, that every pregnancy is different, and many of the topics mentioned will be relevant throughout the baby's development and not just for the week in question.

Thankfully the days when you had to give birth lying in bed, on your back, are gone. Today, you and your partner can usually choose where and how you give birth. Although this is good news, you may find it difficult to know what would be best for you. Once you know about the available options you can then make informed decisions.

As the end of the nine months draws near, it is natural to be concerned about the approaching birth. Sometimes fear about how you will cope can overshadow what is the most miraculous event you are likely ever to encounter. By preparing yourself for labour and understanding what will happen, both you and your partner will be able to make the most of this unique experience.

Once your baby is born, your role as a parent begins in earnest. You are responsible for the care and well-being of this person. This can seem rather daunting at first as your baby will expect you to be on call whenever he wakes. Coping with tiredness, a completely new routine and the demands of a new baby can be overwhelming, so it is most important that you look after yourself.

As time goes by, you will develop a routine that suits you both but at first you may need some help. Part Two guides you through the necessary daily babycare routines. So, whether you are concerned about feeding, bathing or nappy changing, you'll find help and practical advice in this section. Having a baby isn't all hard work and, if you use the time you spend each day on babycare to play and get to know your baby, you'll find that even the chores will be a pleasure!

Your baby's health and development are very important and as a parent you will be concerned about what to do if your child is ill or injured in any way. The chapters on first aid and illnesses are designed to be a quick and easy reference guide to help you to cope with emergencies and know when you should call the doctor.

When your baby celebrates his first birthday you will look back and marvel at how much he has learned in this first year. Part Three explains, month by month, how your baby will progress during the first twelve months. Do remember that this is only a guide and that every child develops at his own rate.

So that you will be able to help and encourage your child, the final chapters look in more detail at the development of your child's senses and explain how he learns to talk and walk. Play and social behaviour are also an integral part of your child's development.

As a mother of three children I know that, more than anything else, during my pregnancies and their babyhood, I wanted to be reassured that I was doing everything "right". I hope that you will get this reassurance from my book and that you will find it a helpful companion during your pregnancy and your child's first year.

*A toddler should still have about a pint of milk a day, but he is now grown up enough to drink from his own cup rather than a bottle.*

Part Two guides you through the necessary babycare routines. Whether you are concerned about feeding, bathing or nappy changing, you'll find help and practical advice in the section. A baby isn't all hard work and, if you use the time you spend each day on babycare to play with and to get to know your baby, you'll find even the chores can be a pleasure!

Your baby's health and development are extremely important and as a parent you will be concerned about what to do if your child is ill or injured in any way. The chapters on first aid and illness are designed to be a quick reference guide to help you cope with emergencies and know when you should call the doctor.

When your baby celebrates her first birthday you will look back and marvel at how much she has learned in this first year. Part Three explains, month by month, how your baby will progress during the first twelve months. Each month she will grow stronger, learn to control her

movements and start to understand the world around her. Do remember that this is only a guide and that every child develops at her own rate.

So that you will be able to help and encourage your child, the final chapters of this section look in more detail at the development of your child's senses and explain how she learns to walk and talk. Play and social behaviour are also an integral part of your child's development.

The right food is, of course, the basis of health, and providing a balanced diet can be one of the most challenging aspects of babycare. Nutritional needs change dramatically over the first couple of years, and you need to be aware of your baby's requirements – at every meal. Children eat four or five times a day, so Part Four takes a slightly different approach, focusing on the practical aspects of food.

It provides sound nutritional advice on what foods you should introduce at each stage of development, and which are best avoided. Time saving tips are included, along with guidance on common food problems: hygiene, fussy eating and going vegetarian.

*A bouncy chair will keep your baby safe while allowing him to see all of the activity going on around him.*

This section also provides over 200 recipes, each fully illustrated and set out in a step by step style. From first purées for a baby to fun meals for a fussy two-year-old, the recipes are easy to follow and perfectly designed to meet the nutritional needs of your child. There is also a special section on cooking for all the family, helping you to adapt a single recipe so that it can feed a baby, a toddler and their parents.

*Even when she is accepting solid foods, your baby still needs her bottle; settle down and enjoy this quiet time with her.*

Tips such as these help make life easier, taking the stress out of deciding what to eat, showing the simple steps required to prepare a meal and perhaps preventing food fads from becoming an overwhelming problem. They help you to concentrate on the important things in life: sharing a pleasant meal with your family and enjoying their company.

This book has been written by two experienced mothers, drawing on their own first-hand knowledge. The aim is to give you a comprehensive source of information and, most important of all, the reassurance that you are doing everything "right." We hope you find it a helpful companion during your pregnancy and your baby's first year.

*Above: Toddlers learn how to interact with others of their own age and build the basic skills for friendship.*
*Left: As you eat together, don't forget to praise your child for good behaviour. This forms the basis for good table manners later.*

## PART ONE

# PREGNANCY

PREGNANCY IS A VERY SPECIAL TIME for both you and your partner. Knowing what is happening to you and your growing baby during the weeks ahead will help you both to enjoy this exciting period in your lives. Starting with pre-conceptual care, this section explains how conception takes place and then looks at pregnancy and your baby's development week by week. Many of the issues raised will be relevant throughout your pregnancy and not just during the week in which they are first mentioned, so do read it all.

It is normal to experience some minor discomforts during pregnancy and you will want to know how to cope with them. More serious problems can occasionally occur, and it is important to recognize the symptoms so that you will know when immediate medical treatment is required. The birth is something you may feel anxious about and it will help if you understand the choices available in both ante-natal care and childbirth. By being informed you will be able to choose the type of care and birth that is right for you.

As your body adapts to the changes that pregnancy brings, you will begin to prepare yourself physically, emotionally and practically for parenthood. A well-balanced, healthy diet is essential for both your well-being and that of your baby. Exercise has an important part to play too, not just in keeping you fit but also in preparing your body for the birth. Looking good will help you to feel good, so you should take care of your physical appearance throughout your pregnancy. Knowing how to select the right clothes to suit your changing shape and how to use make-up to emphasize your best features will help you to feel confident and make your pregnancy an even more enjoyable experience.

# PREPARING FOR PREGNANCY

Once you have decided that you want to have a baby, you and your partner should concentrate on getting yourselves fit and healthy before you try to conceive. Ideally, you should begin preparing for pregnancy at least three months before conception so that you can be sure that your child will get the best possible start in life. If your pregnancy is unplanned, then start taking extra care of yourself as soon as you suspect that you might be pregnant. This may involve some basic changes in your lifestyle.

There is evidence that suggests that smoking by either partner can delay conception, so if you or your partner smoke you should stop now. In addition, smoking during pregnancy will put the baby at risk and can also affect your well-being; giving up before conception will benefit you and your child.

Alcohol can inhibit fertility, so both you and your partner should keep alcohol consumption to a minimum or avoid drinking altogether while trying to conceive. Once you are pregnant, alcohol, if taken in excess, can restrict fetal development and can even cause malformation. It is advisable to drink no more than one unit of alcohol a week during pregnancy.

## MEDICATION

Fertilization and early development of a baby are controlled by delicately balanced chemical processes in the body. Additional chemicals entering your body as medication can upset this development, so if possible you should avoid taking any medicines before conception and during pregnancy. If you are on long-term medication, you will need to talk to your doctor about your options. Medicines that are available over the counter, natural remedies and vitamin supplements should also be avoided, unless they have been recommended by your doctor.

Oral contraceptives rely on chemically-produced hormones to control fertility. If you are taking the pill, change to a barrier method, such as the condom or diaphragm, for three months before trying to conceive. This allows your body to clear itself of synthetic hormones and to re-establish its own cycle.

## IMMUNIZATIONS

An unborn baby exposed to rubella (German measles) during its early development can be born severely handicapped. Don't assume that because you were vaccinated in your teens, or you have had the infection,

*Before trying for a baby, both partners should get fit by walking and doing other exercise.*

*By doing regular stretching exercises at home, or at an organized class, you will strengthen yourself for pregnancy.*

*Salmon is ideal as part of a balanced diet, because it is low in fat but full of vitamins.*

that you are automatically immune. Ask your doctor to give you a blood test to check. If you are not immune you can be vaccinated, but you should not get pregnant until the vaccine virus has cleared from your blood, which takes about three months. If you have been given vaccines for tropical diseases, you should also wait for three months before getting pregnant.

### NUTRITION AND EXERCISE

A well-balanced and healthy diet is essential for both your well-being and that of your baby. Everything that you eat and drink will also become your unborn child's nourishment, and what you store before pregnancy is important for early fetal development when all the major organs are formed.

One of the B vitamins, folic acid, helps prevent neural tube defects (NTD), such as spina bifida, in unborn babies. It is recommended that all women planning a pregnancy should increase their average daily intake to 0.6 mg by taking a 0.4 mg supplement before attempting conception, and during the first 12 weeks of pregnancy. This is the time when your baby's organs and body systems are forming. If you are epileptic and take drugs to control your epilepsy you should consult your doctor before taking folic acid.

Regular exercise is important as it will help you get fit before conception and it will strengthen muscles in your lower back, stomach, and legs, which will help your body cope better with the demands of pregnancy.

*As your legs have to carry more weight during pregnancy, try to do regular daily exercises such as running on the spot to build them up.*

## THE FIRST TRIMESTER

# WEEKS 1–4: CONCEPTION

### You and your body

You won't be aware of the changes that are happening inside your body during these early weeks, although it is possible that you may experience very slight bleeding at the time when your next period would have been due. Usually the first indication that you are pregnant will be a missed period.

During the first half of the menstrual cycle two chemical substances called hormones are released from special glands into the bloodstream. One hormone stimulates the process that results in the production of an ovum, or ripe egg. The other hormone stimulates the endometrium, or lining of the uterus (womb), to thicken in readiness to receive a fertilized ovum. Midway through the menstrual cycle the work of the first hormone is completed and you ovulate; that is, a ripe ovum is released from one of your ovaries. Conception occurs if your partner's sperm fertilizes this ovum. This usually takes place in the Fallopian tube that connects the ovary to the uterus. The fertilized ovum completes its journey to the uterus, where it implants into the thickened uterine lining. Once this process occurs the cervix increases slightly in width and becomes softer, and a thick mucous plug seals off the uterus to protect it from infection. After two weeks, if there has been no conception, the thickened uterine lining is shed and menstruation takes place.

### AFTER FERTILIZATION

The fertilized single-cell egg multiplies into two, then four cells, and it carries on multiplying so that by about day seven, when it reaches the uterus, it has grown into a ball of over 100 cells with a fluid-filled cavity. This ball, called a blastocyst, has two layers: the outer one becomes the placenta, while the inner one forms the embryo, which develops into your baby. The embryo is made up of three layers of tissue, each of which forms separately. The outer layer develops into the nerves and skin; the middle layer forms the bones, cartilage, muscles, circulatory system, kidneys, and sex organs; and the inner layer becomes the respira- tory and digestive systems. The placenta is the unborn baby's life-support system. It is attached to the lining of the uterus and separates the developing baby's circulation from its mother's. It allows oxygen

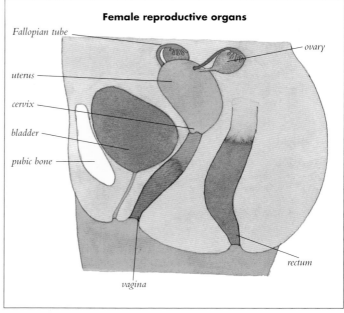

**Female reproductive organs**

*Fallopian tube*

*ovary*

*uterus*

*cervix*

*bladder*

*pubic bone*

*rectum*

*vagina*

*If an egg in the Fallopian tube is fertilized by a sperm, it will embed itself into the lining of the uterus. If not, it is shed down through the cervix and out through the vagina.*

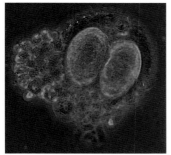

*This fertilized egg now has two cells called blastomeres and is the primitive embryo. It will multiply to over 100 cells.*

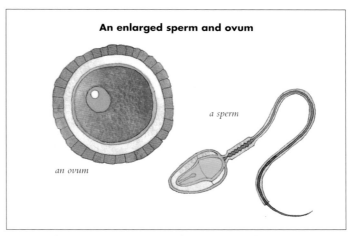

### An enlarged sperm and ovum

*a sperm*

*an ovum*

*A sperm and an ovum are tiny. A man ejaculates about 500 million sperm, while a woman usually produces one ovum halfway through her menstrual cycle.*

and food, as well as protective antibodies, to pass from the mother along the umbilical cord to the baby.

The placenta is fully formed at the end of the 12th week of pregnancy, and then it is able to take over the production of the pregnancy hormones, oestrogen and progesterone, from the ovaries. Within the uterus, the embryo is contained in the amniotic sac. This is filled with fluid in which the developing child will float until the actual birth. The amniotic fluid offers the embryo protection from external pressures.

### THE BABY'S SEX

A child's sex is determined by the father's sperm at the time of conception. Sperm carry either an X or Y chromosome while the egg has only an X chromosome. If a Y-chromosome sperm fertilizes the egg, the baby will be a boy. If the sperm carries an X chromosome, the baby will be a girl.

### Male reproductive organs

bladder

seminal vesicle

vas deferens

penis

rectum

foreskin

glans

scrotum    testis

*Sperm mature in both testes. When a man is sexually aroused, the penis becomes erect and the outlet from the bladder into the ejaculatory duct is closed leaving it free for sperm.*

### Trimesters

Pregnancy lasts approximately 40 weeks and is calculated from the first day of your last period, although conception will probably not have taken place until around two weeks after this. Pregnancy is divided into three parts known as trimesters. The first covers weeks 1–13, the second trimester weeks 14–26, and the third trimester week 27 until birth.

# WEEK 5: CONFIRMING PREGNANCY

### Your growing baby

Although the embryo is only just visible to the naked eye, the spinal column and brain have already begun to grow and a blood vessel has developed which will become the heart. The embryo is 4mm/⅙in long.

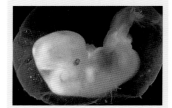

Pregnancy can be confirmed by means of a simple test that measures the levels of the pregnancy hormone, human chorionic gonadotrophin (HCG), that are present in your urine. The test can be carried out as soon as you reach the day that your next period should have started. Your doctor or Family Planning clinic may do the test free, or you can carry out a home test yourself using one of the pregnancy testing kits available from the pharmacist. Ensure that you choose one that will give an accurate result this early. Although many modern home-testing kits state that you can test your urine at any time, you may wish to use an early morning sample because this urine will contain the highest concentration of HCG.

If the result is positive, you must make an appointment to see your doctor so that he or she can make arrangements for your ante-natal care and the birth.

EARLY SYMPTOMS
Some women experience all the early symptoms of pregnancy, while others sail through the first weeks without any feelings of discomfort.
• Your body is having to work hard to adapt to the demands of pregnancy, so you may feel very tired. Try to get as much rest as possible. You will find that sitting with your feet up for even half an hour will help.
• Your breasts may tingle or feel tender, rather as they do before a period; your nipples will appear darker and more prominent and the veins will be more noticeable. You should wear a good support bra from now until after your baby is born.
• You may experience a strange metallic taste in the mouth, which

### You and your body

If you haven't been taking a folic acid supplement you should start now.

*If you're lucky, you'll experience no nausea in pregnancy and continue exercising as normal.*

*To confirm a pregnancy, you can do a test with a kit from a pharmacist, but ensure you choose one that is suitable to use for a test at five weeks.*

get up in the morning. Try eating six small high-carbohydrate meals, during the day, such as pasta, potato, and bread. Avoid rich or fatty foods.
• Finally, as the enlarging uterus presses on your bladder you may need to urinate more frequently.

## Dating the birth

Once your pregnancy is confirmed, you will want to know your baby's likely date of birth. You can calculate an estimated date of delivery (EDD) by counting 40 weeks from the first day of your last period. But you should remember that as you don't know the exact date of ovulation this EDD is approximate. At between 10 and 12 weeks you may be offered a scan to confirm your EDD.

can be accompanied by going off certain foods and tea and coffee.
• A feeling of nausea, or even actual physical sickness in the morning or at any time during the day, is quite usual. It is often worse when your stomach is empty, so have a plain biscuit and a cup of tea when you

## Estimated date of delivery

| Month | Days | Month |
|---|---|---|
| JANUARY | 1 2 3 4 5 6 7 8 9 10 11 12 13 14 15 16 17 18 19 20 21 22 23 24 25 26 27 28 29 30 31 | JANUARY |
| OCTOBER | 8 9 10 11 12 13 14 15 16 17 18 19 20 21 22 23 24 25 26 27 28 29 30 31 1 2 3 4 5 6 7 | NOVEMBER |
| FEBRUARY | 1 2 3 4 5 6 7 8 9 10 11 12 13 14 15 16 17 18 19 20 21 22 23 24 25 26 27 28 | FEBRUARY |
| NOVEMBER | 8 9 10 11 12 13 14 15 16 17 18 19 20 21 22 23 24 25 26 27 28 29 30 1 2 3 4 5 | DECEMBER |
| MARCH | 1 2 3 4 5 6 7 8 9 10 11 12 13 14 15 16 17 18 19 20 21 22 23 24 25 26 27 28 29 30 31 | MARCH |
| DECEMBER | 6 7 8 9 10 11 12 13 14 15 16 17 18 19 20 21 22 23 24 25 26 27 28 29 30 31 1 2 3 4 5 | JANUARY |
| APRIL | 1 2 3 4 5 6 7 8 9 10 11 12 13 14 15 16 17 18 19 20 21 22 23 24 25 26 27 28 29 30 | APRIL |
| JANUARY | 6 7 8 9 10 11 12 13 14 15 16 17 18 19 20 21 22 23 24 25 26 27 28 29 30 31 1 2 3 4 | FEBRUARY |
| MAY | 1 2 3 4 5 6 7 8 9 10 11 12 13 14 15 16 17 18 19 20 21 22 23 24 25 26 27 28 29 30 31 | MAY |
| FEBRUARY | 5 6 7 8 9 10 11 12 13 14 15 16 17 18 19 20 21 22 23 24 25 26 27 28 1 2 3 4 5 6 7 | MARCH |
| JUNE | 1 2 3 4 5 6 7 8 9 10 11 12 13 14 15 16 17 18 19 20 21 22 23 24 25 26 27 28 29 30 | JUNE |
| MARCH | 8 9 10 11 12 13 14 15 16 17 18 19 20 21 22 23 24 25 26 27 28 29 30 31 1 2 3 4 5 6 | APRIL |
| JULY | 1 2 3 4 5 6 7 8 9 10 11 12 13 14 15 16 17 18 19 20 21 22 23 24 25 26 27 28 29 30 31 | JULY |
| APRIL | 7 8 9 10 11 12 13 14 15 16 17 18 19 20 21 22 23 24 25 26 27 28 29 30 1 2 3 4 5 6 7 | MAY |
| AUGUST | 1 2 3 4 5 6 7 8 9 10 11 12 13 14 15 16 17 18 19 20 21 22 23 24 25 26 27 28 29 30 31 | AUGUST |
| MAY | 8 9 10 11 12 13 14 15 16 17 18 19 20 21 22 23 24 25 26 27 28 29 30 31 1 2 3 4 5 6 7 | JUNE |
| SEPTEMBER | 1 2 3 4 5 6 7 8 9 10 11 12 13 14 15 16 17 18 19 20 21 22 23 24 25 26 27 28 29 30 | SEPTEMBER |
| JUNE | 8 9 10 11 12 13 14 15 16 17 18 19 20 21 22 23 24 25 26 27 28 29 30 1 2 3 4 5 6 7 | JULY |
| OCTOBER | 1 2 3 4 5 6 7 8 9 10 11 12 13 14 15 16 17 18 19 20 21 22 23 24 25 26 27 28 29 30 31 | OCTOBER |
| JULY | 8 9 10 11 12 13 14 15 16 17 18 19 20 21 22 23 24 25 26 27 28 29 30 31 1 2 3 4 5 6 7 | AUGUST |
| NOVEMBER | 1 2 3 4 5 6 7 8 9 10 11 12 13 14 15 16 17 18 19 20 21 22 23 24 25 26 27 28 29 30 | NOVEMBER |
| AUGUST | 8 9 10 11 12 13 14 15 16 17 18 19 20 21 22 23 24 25 26 27 28 29 30 31 1 2 3 4 5 6 | SEPTEMBER |
| DECEMBER | 1 2 3 4 5 6 7 8 9 10 11 12 13 14 15 16 17 18 19 20 21 22 23 24 25 26 27 28 29 30 31 | DECEMBER |
| SEPTEMBER | 7 8 9 10 11 12 13 14 15 16 17 18 19 20 21 22 23 24 25 26 27 28 29 30 1 2 3 4 5 6 7 | OCTOBER |

*Find the first day of your last period on the white bands; the date on the tint band below is your EDD.*

# WEEK 6: ANTE-NATAL CHOICES

Who looks after you, and where your ante-natal care takes place, will depend a lot on the type of birth you want to have. If you decide on a home birth, the care will be carried out at home by a midwife and at your doctor's surgery. If you want a hospital birth your care will probably be shared between a midwife, your doctor and the hospital.

If you are not registered with a doctor, or you want a home birth but your particular doctor doesn't want to assist in the delivery, or you would rather be seen by a woman doctor and your doctor is a man,

you can go to see a different doctor just for your maternity care. The actual care you get will be similar wherever you receive it, because all ante-natal care is designed to ensure that you and your unborn baby remain healthy during pregnancy.

The best pattern of ante-natal care for a healthy first time mother is considered to be no more than 10 ante-natal appointments, and for subsequent pregnancies this is likely to be reduced to seven. If you have any concerns between these appointments, you can telephone your midwife or doctor for advice.

HOME BIRTH
A home birth means you give birth in the familiar surroundings of your home under the supervision of a midwife. If you want to deliver your baby in this way, you will need to talk to your doctor to see whether there are any medical reasons why this isn't advisable. It is also a good idea to contact the director of

## You and your body

If you are suffering from morning sickness, you may find that the smell of certain things, such as tobacco smoke or frying food, brings on the sickness or makes it worse. Your skin may become dry and flaky, or you may get spots. Now is the time to start thinking about your ante-natal care, and the type of birth you want.

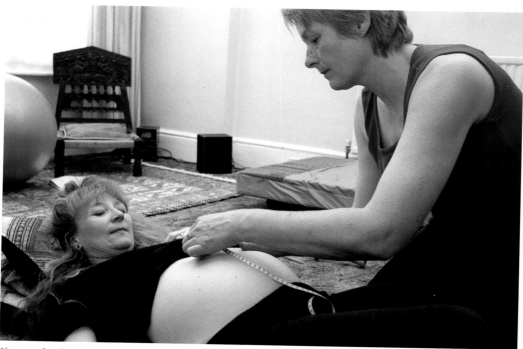

*If you opt for a home birth, care will be divided between your home and local surgery.*

maternity services (or supervisor of midwives) at your hospital in order to arrange for a midwife to visit you and discuss a home delivery in detail.

HOSPITAL BIRTH

Some women prefer a hospital birth because they feel safer knowing that there will be experts on hand to help if there are any complications. Also, if the baby needs special care this will be available almost immediately. Although hospitals try to cater for parents' wishes, not all of them are able to offer every type of birth. You will need to find out what facilities your local hospital offers. Before making your final decision talk to other mothers who have had their babies there recently. If you have any worries, discuss these with your doctor or community midwife.

There are a number of hospital birth schemes that involve your doctor and midwife to varying degrees:

**Midwife unit** This is usually based at the hospital and is run entirely by midwives who undertake ante-natal care, delivery and post-natal care for women having normal births. These units are not widely available throughout the country, so this may not be an option that is open to you.

**Domino scheme** The Domino scheme (Domiciliary In and Out) means that you are looked after by a team of community midwives throughout your pregnancy. Once you are in labour one of these midwives will come to your home and stay with you until you are ready to go into hospital. She then accompanies you to the hospital, where she delivers the baby. You can usually return home around six hours after the birth. The midwife then continues to look after you at

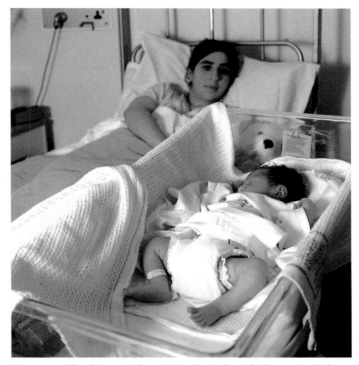

*You can spend from between six hours to three days in hospital when you give birth, depending on your delivery. After the birth you may keep your baby beside you.*

your home. Many women like the continuity this scheme gives them, but unfortunately it is only available in a few areas.

**Shared care** Your ante-natal care will be shared between your doctor and the community midwife and you may also see the obstetric consultant at the hospital where your baby is going to be born. The birth will take place in the maternity unit of the hospital.

PRIVATE CARE

If you can afford it, you may like to consider having a home birth with a private, or independent, midwife taking care of you. She will provide all your ante-natal and post-natal care and will also deliver your baby.

Alternatively, you can decide to have your baby in a private hospital or maternity home.

### Your growing baby

The heart has now formed in the chest cavity and is beginning to beat. By the end of this week the stalk connecting the embryo to the placenta will have begun to grow into the umbilical cord and blood vessels will have started to form. The embryo is now about the size of your little fingernail and its movements can be picked up by ultrasound scan. The head has the beginning of the eyes, ears, and mouth and there are tiny buds which will become arms and legs.

# WEEK 7: POSSIBLE PROBLEMS

Although most pregnancies go without a hitch, sometimes serious problems do occur and special care is needed. Complications can usually be resolved with monitoring, but occasionally the pregnancy comes to an end. Although the following conditions are not likely to affect you, you should be aware of their symptoms:

**Bleeding in early pregnancy**
Bleeding or spotting from the vagina is known as a threatened miscarriage. It is possible to bleed quite heavily and not miscarry or do any harm to the baby. All bleeding in pregnancy must be taken seriously, however, and you should report it to your doctor or midwife immediately. Your doctor is likely to carry out an internal pelvic examination and you may have an ultrasound scan to see whether the baby is developing normally, or a blood test to measure the levels of the pregnancy hormone human chorionic gondotropin (HGC). Providing everything is all right you will probably be told not to exert yourself until the bleeding has stopped.

**Ectopic pregnancy** This occurs when the fertilized egg implants itself in one of the Fallopian tubes rather than in the uterus. If it is undetected, the growing baby eventually ruptures the tube, which causes severe pain. Immediate surgery is required to terminate the pregnancy, and this often means losing the Fallopian tube as well. In extreme cases the ovary may also have to be removed. If the other ovary and Fallopian tube are healthy, there is no reason why another pregnancy should not take place. If the ectopic pregnancy is discovered early enough, a drug can be given that causes the embryo to be reabsorbed by the body; this prevents the Fallopian tube from bursting. Symptoms of an ectopic pregnancy include pain in the side of the abdomen, vaginal bleeding, and fainting.

**Miscarriage** The most common time for miscarriage is during the first three months of pregnancy, although losing a baby at any time before the 24th week is described as a miscarriage. Some miscarriages

**You and your body**
You may feel dizzy or even faint if you stand for too long or you are in a crowd. Overwhelming tiredness can also be a problem now, so make sure you get plenty of rest. If you don't feel like making love at the moment don't worry; this is quite normal and you may find that your sex life is better then ever in the second trimester.

*Regular blood pressure checks are essential at ante-natal clinics to detect pre-eclampsia.*

occur for no known reason. Known causes of miscarriage include hormonal problems, disease or infection, abnormalities of the uterus, or an incompetent cervix. This last condition can be dealt with by a simple surgical suture that will be removed shortly before the EDD.

Although it is unlikely that sexual intercourse will cause miscarriage, women who have experienced bleeding early in their pregnancy or who are known to have a tendency to miscarry are usually advised by doctors not to have intercourse for the first 12 weeks, until their pregnancy is well established.

**Pre-eclampsia** This is a high blood pressure condition that rarely occurs before 20 weeks. It is the most common complication of pregnancy with around one in 10 pregnancies affected. If left untreated it causes the blood vessels of the placenta to spasm, which reduces the oxygen flow to the baby and puts it at risk; the fetal growth rate may also be affected. Symptoms include high blood pressure, oedema causing swelling of the hands, feet, and

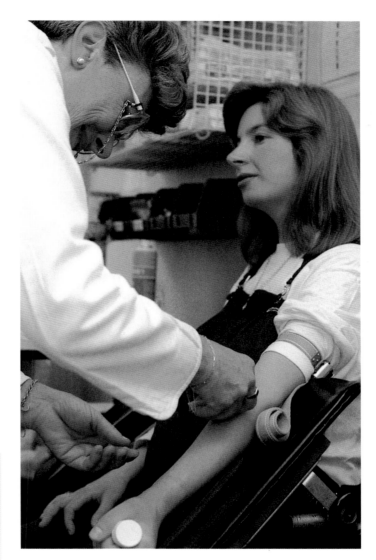

*At your first ante-natal check-up, a blood sample will be taken to find out your blood group and type, and to make sure you're not anaemic or carrying a virus such as hepatitis B. You will have blood tests regularly through your pregnancy.*

### Your growing baby

The unborn baby is now known as a fetus and is about 1.3cm/½in long. The nostrils, lips, tongue, and teeth are beginning to form and the arms and legs are growing. Lungs are beginning to develop and the intestines, spine, and brain are almost fully developed.

ankles, protein in the urine and a sudden increase in weight. In severe cases flashing lights, blurred vision or spots before the eyes may occur. You will be routinely tested for signs of pre-eclampsia at each ante-natal check. If you develop pre-eclampsia you and your baby will be closely monitored and you may need to go into hospital. If the condition becomes severe immediate delivery of the baby may be necessary.

# WEEK 8: BOOKING-IN/ROUTINE TESTS

Your first ante-natal check-up will take place between eight and 12 weeks, either at your doctor's surgery or at the hospital where you plan to give birth. This first visit is usually referred to as the booking clinic. You will be asked about your physical and mental health, family medical history and if there are areas where you need special support, such as domestic violence and sexual abuse. All this information is required to build up a picture of you and your pregnancy so that any potential risks can be spotted and help can be offered where needed.

If you have any questions or worries, this is a good time to discuss them. It's easy to forget to ask something important when there is so much to take in at one time, so it may help to write down things that you want to know about before you attend the clinic.

ROUTINE TESTS

Certain tests are carried out during pregnancy to ensure that both you and the baby are progressing well. Some of these will be repeated at each ante-natal visit; others are only carried out at the booking-in clinic.

**Blood pressure** This will be taken at each visit. Increased blood pressure could be a symptom of pre-eclampsia, which could endanger both you and the baby.

**Urine** You will be asked to bring a sample of urine with you to each ante-natal visit. This will be tested for bacteria, which could be a sign of a urinary tract infection which will require treatment, as well as for sugar and protein. Sugar in the urine could be a sign of gestational diabetes, a form of diabetes that only occurs in pregnancy which will need to be controlled, while protein may indicate the onset of pre-eclampsia.

### You and your body

The changes to your body are becoming more noticeable as your breasts and nipples enlarge and become sensitive. Your vagina changes from light to dark pink, and you may notice an increased vaginal discharge. It is time for regular monitoring of your pregnancy.

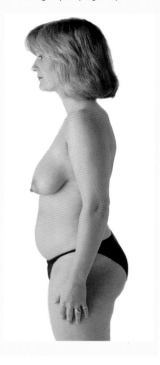

## Weight gain during pregnancy

Baby 39%

Blood 22%

Amniotic fluid 11%

Uterus 11%

Placenta 9%

Breasts 8%

Your weight increases by about ½–1 kg/1–2 lb weekly during months four to eight, with very little in the last month. As your breasts get larger, the uterus, placenta and baby develop, and the amniotic fluid increases, until they reach the percentages shown here.

*The amount of weight that you will gain during pregnancy varies, depending on your height and size, but can be as much as 20 kg/44 lb.*

**Height and weight** Your height and weight will be measured so that your body mass index (BMI) can be calculated (this is a medical classification system for your body weight). You are classed as underweight, normal weight and overweight or obese. If you are in the normal range your weight will probably not be checked again during pregnancy unless there are complications. If you are under- or

*Your weight and height will be measured at your first ante-natal check-up, so that your body mass index can be calculated.*

if you think you could be at risk, you can ask for a blood test. Other blood tests may also be carried out to detect any serious conditions that could affect your baby. If you are of Afro-Caribbean descent, they will test your blood for sickle-cell disease; if you are of a Mediterranean ethnic group you will be offered a test for thalassaemia.

**Wrists and ankles** These will be checked at each visit for swelling, or oedema, caused by fluid retention, since these signs could possibly indicate pre-eclampsia.

**Palpation** Your abdomen will be palpated (pressed), to feel the top of the uterus (fundus). The doctor or midwife will then feel down towards the pelvis to check the size of the fetus and the way it is lying. This will be done at every check up.

**Dating scan** You may be offered an appointment for a "dating" scan at between 10 and 12 weeks. This literally dates the pregnancy and confirms how many babies you are carrying.

### Your growing baby

The fetus is now about 2.5cm/ 1in long, which is 10,000 times bigger than at conception. All the major organs are present, although still developing. The ears and eyes have formed and the skin covering the eyes will eventually split to form the eyelids. The middle ear, which controls balance as well as hearing, is also developing. The heart is now pumping with a regular beat, and blood vessels can be seen. As the arms and legs grow longer, the fetus begins to move around and starts to kick, although it is still too small at this stage for you to be able to feel it.

overweight you may need specialist care. You can expect to gain anything from 10 kg to 20 kg/22 lb to 44 lb during your pregnancy, with most of this extra weight going on after the 20th week. A sudden increase in weight could be an indication of pre-eclampsia.

**Blood tests** You will be asked at your first appointment to give a blood sample to confirm your blood group and to find out if you are rhesus negative or positive.

Your blood will also be checked to see if you are anaemic and if you are immune to rubella (German measles). You may be offered HIV, hepatitis B and syphilis screening tests. Although you will not be routinely screened for toxoplasmosis,

# WEEK 9: SPECIAL TESTS

### Your growing baby

The face is now developing and the mouth and nose are clearly visible. The limbs continue to grow rapidly and the fetus now measures about 3cm/1¼in.

Your blood will be tested at your booking appointment to determine your blood group and to establish its rhesus (Rh) status. The rhesus status of your blood depends on whether or not it possesses the rhesus factor. If the factor is present, your blood is Rh-positive, and if it's absent, your blood is Rh-negative. Most people's blood is Rh-positive.

If both you and the baby's father are Rh-negative there is no problem. Complications will only occur when the father's blood is Rh-positive and yours is Rh-negative. The unborn baby may acquire the rhesus factor from its father, which can result in its blood being incompatible with yours. This can lead to a serious or even fatal illness for the baby before, or after its birth. Fortunately, this rarely affects a first pregnancy and it can be prevented in subsequent pregnancies by injections of Rh immunoglobulin (anti-D), an antibody given during pregnancy and again within 72 hours of a baby being delivered.

### SCREENING TESTS

These are given to assess the risk of the baby having a birth defect such as Down's syndrome or spina bifida. In the UK it is recommended that pregnant women should be offered one of three types of test: the nuchal translucency scan and blood test in weeks 11 to 14, the triple or quadruple tests in the 14 to 20 week period, or the serum integrated test which combines nuchal fold measurements taken in the first trimester with a blood test in the

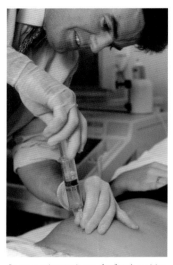

*In an amniocentesis test the fetus's position is checked by ultrasound, before amniotic fluid is taken by a needle from the uterus.*

second trimester. Most areas offer the triple test, although more centres now offer the nuchal translucency scan and blood test. The serum integrated test is not widely available and tends only to be offered in teaching hospitals or private clinics.

### You and your body

You will start putting on weight now so it is a good idea to keep a record of any weight gain yourself if your ante-natal care doesn't include regular weight checks. Your gums are becoming softer and thicker because of hormone changes so you will need to pay special attention to oral hygiene.

You should now familiarize yourself with some of the other ante-natal procedures and tests.

### Nuchal translucency screening

This is an ultrasound scan that measurers the clear (translucent) space in the tissue at the back of the baby's neck, known as the nuchal fold. Fluid retention in the nuchal fold during the 11 to 14 week widow may be a marker for Down's syndrome. When combined with blood tests this test has been shown to be 95 per cent accurate. If your hospital doesn't offer nuchal translucency screening you can arrange to have it done privately.

### Triple and quadruple tests

These are blood tests that measure the level of chemicals produced by the baby which are present in your blood stream. An usually high or low result could indicate that the baby has a birth defect. The triple test measurers three markers, while the quadruple test measurers four. Neither test can confirm that the

*Brush your teeth and gums regularly.*

baby is affected but it does indicate whether further diagnostic tests, such as amniocentesis, are required.

### DIAGNOSTIC TESTS

These are used to further investigate a positive screening test. Diagnostic tests will give a definitive answer because they involve analysing DNA taken from your baby's cells.

**Amniocentesis** If you have a family history of genetic abnormalities or your blood shows an exceptionally low or high AFP level, you will be offered an amniocentesis. This test is also offered to all women over 35 years as they have a higher risk of having a Down's syndrome baby. Guided by an ultrasound scan, a long hollow needle is inserted through the wall of the abdomen and the uterus to draw out a sample of amniotic fluid which is tested for abnormalities. The test is done between 16 and 20 weeks and carries a small risk of miscarriage.

**Chorionic villus sampling (CVS)** This is done at 11 weeks to test for Down's syndrome or other genetic or chromosomal abnormalities. A fine tube is passed into the uterus to remove some cells from the tissue that surrounds the baby. The cells are then tested and the results known within a couple of weeks. There is a slightly higher risk of miscarriage with CVS than with amniocentesis.

### GENETIC COUNSELLING

If you are worried about your baby inheriting a disease or handicap, a genetic counsellor will be able to explain the likelihood of a child being affected by the disorder and also about any tests that can be carried out. It is a good idea to have this discussion before attempting to get pregnant.

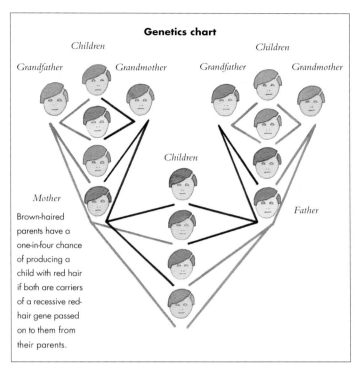

**Genetics chart**

Children

Grandfather　　Grandmother　　　　Grandfather　　　Grandmother

Children

Mother

Father

Brown-haired parents have a one-in-four chance of producing a child with red hair if both are carriers of a recessive red-hair gene passed on to them from their parents.

*This genetics chart shows how red hair that is inherited through a recessive gene can miss a generation, but has a high chance of re-appearing in the third generation. This can also apply to some inherited diseases.*

*If your family has a history of a genetic disorder, you can talk to a genetic counsellor who will discuss with you and your partner the likelihood of your baby having a problem.*

# WEEK 10: HORMONES/ MATERNITY RECORD

Hormones play an important part during pregnancy and labour. The prime source of the hormones related to pregnancy are the ovaries during the early stages, and then the placenta once it is established at around 12 weeks. These hormones dictate how fast the baby grows and are responsible for the changes in your breasts and body. They also ensure that your labour occurs at the right time.

High levels of the hormone called human chorionic gonadotrophin (HCG) circulate in your body during the first 12 weeks of pregnancy. They are responsible for any emotional changes, feeling tired, nausea, and vomiting.

HORMONES AND YOUR EMOTIONS
Pregnancy can produce a number of conflicting emotions, ranging from feelings of pure joy to bouts of black depression. It is quite natural to feel like this as you adjust to your changing role and come to terms with the fact that your life will never be quite the same again. You may

find that you start worrying about if you are ready for motherhood, or the effect that a new baby may have on your established relationship with your partner.

You may also find that mood swings, often brought on by the hormonal changes going on in your body, cause petty arguments between you. So it is most important

## You and your body

There is an increase in the amount of blood that is circulating in your body, which may cause you to feel warmer than usual. Your uterus is now the size of a large orange and your changing shape may mean that you are more comfortable in loose-fitting clothes that do not restrict you.

Other changes are also taking place in your body. Although these are not always physically obvious, they are in fact the result of shifts in your body's chemistry.

## Your growing baby

The external ears are now visible on the head, which is growing fast to make room for the brain. The fetal body is elongating and its fingers and toes are clearly defined but are still joined with webs of skin. At this stage of your pregnancy the fetus is now about 4.5cm/1¾in long and weighs around 5g/¼oz.

*As you experience hormonal changes in your body you may find you become irritable and anxious. Discuss any of your worries with your partner who can talk things through with you and reassure you.*

*As your emotions are probably mixed up at the moment, don't brood over rows with your partner, but apologize and make up.*

*If you find you're getting very tense, try practising relaxation techniques on your own, or some deep breathing exercises.*

### Terms and abbreviations

The following terms and abbreviations may appear on your maternity record.

**AFP:** Alpha-fetoprotein.

**BP:** Blood pressure.

**Cephalic:** Fetal head is nearest the cervix.

**Cx:** Cervix.

**EDD:** Estimated date of delivery.

**FHH:** Fetal heart heard.

**FMF:** Fetal movement felt.

**Height Fundus:** The distance from the pelvis to the top of the uterus is known as the fundus.

**LMP:** Last menstrual period. This is the date of the first day of your last period before pregnancy.

**NAD:** No abnormality detected.

**Oedema:** Swelling of hands and feet.

**Relation of PP to Brim:** The position of the baby's presenting part (PP), that is the part ready to be born first, in relation to the brim of the pelvis.

**Transverse lie.** The baby is lying across the uterus.

**Urine P G O:** Indicates whether your urine contains protein, glucose or anything else – other.

to make time to talk to each other so that you can both voice your feelings and share any worries or anxieties.

MATERNITY RECORD

You will be given your maternity record card at your booking-in clinic. It is used to record the results of the tests and examinations that are carried out during your pregnancy. You should keep it with you at all times, so that if you ever need medical attention when you are away from home all the information about your pregnancy is readily available to the medical staff.

# WEEK 11: COMMON DISCOMFORTS

As your body prepares itself for birth, you may experience some physical discomfort. This is perfectly normal, can usually be dealt with easily, and should not leave any long-lasting effects. Knowing the reason for a complaint can often help you cope better with it.

**Backache** This can occur at any time, but usually happens when you try to compensate for your baby's weight by leaning backwards which puts a strain on the lower back's muscles and joints. Try to avoid lifting heavy objects, when you bend down keep your knees bent, wear

your teeth, which can lead to bleeding gums. It is important to pay special attention to oral hygiene and to avoid snacking on sweets and sugary drinks. Dental treatment is free while you are pregnant so have at least two check-ups during this time.

**Cramp** You may experience a sudden sharp pain in your legs and feet, often at night. Try pulling your toes upwards towards your ankles and rub the affected muscles. Regular gentle exercise will help to prevent cramp.

**Constipation** Some of the extra hormones produced in pregnancy can cause the intestines to relax and become less efficient. Eating plenty of fruit, vegetables and fibre, and drinking water will help.

### You and your body

Any sickness should start to fade and you will begin to feel less tired. You should start to think seriously about ante-natal classes because private ones can get booked up quickly. Contact your hospital or the National Childbirth Trust, or ask at your doctor's surgery about local classes.

**Fainting** You may feel faint if you stand for too long or get up too quickly. This happens because not enough blood is getting to your brain. You can help prevent this by always rising slowly from either sitting or lying positions. If you feel faint sit down and lower your head towards your knees.

**Piles** Technically known as haemorrhoids, these are a form of varicose vein that appear around the back passage (anus). They can be very uncomfortable as they are itchy

*Your back is more vulnerable, so support it with a cushion when you sit down.*

low-heeled shoes, and sit with your back well supported.

**Bleeding gums** Hormonal changes can cause a build-up of plaque on

*Eating a high-fibre diet can help prevent painful constipation in pregnancy.*

### Your growing baby

Most of the major organs are formed, so the most vulnerable time will be over by the end of this week. The baby is now relatively safe from any congenital abnormalities and infections, excepting rubella.

The external genitals have formed, along with either ovaries or testicles. The heart is now pumping blood to all the major organs of the body. The baby weighs around 10g/½oz and is now about 5.5cm/2⅛in long.

*Although you may now be feeling less tired than in the early weeks, you should still rest as much as you can.*

and may even bleed. If left untreated they can become prolapsed, which means they protrude through the anus, causing a good deal of pain. Eating high-fibre foods will keep your stools soft so that you don't have to strain, which puts pressure on piles. An ice pack wrapped in a soft cloth, or a witch hazel compress, will bring relief, or you can buy a specially formulated haemorrhoid preparation from the pharmacist. Piles usually disappear within a couple of weeks of the birth.

**Vaginal discharge** An increase in vaginal discharge during pregnancy is quite normal as long as the discharge is clear and white. If it becomes coloured, smells, or makes you itchy, you may have developed an infection, such as thrush, which will need treatment.

*Take some gentle, regular exercise with your partner as this will help to prevent cramps and keep you feeling fit.*

# WEEK 12: HEALTHY EATING

Your baby gets all the nourishment he needs to grow from what you eat, so it is important to maintain a good diet throughout pregnancy. To achieve a healthy balanced diet you need to eat foods containing reasonable amounts of starchy carbohydrate, protein, fat, minerals, and vitamins each day. Starchy carbohydrates are found in bread, cereals, pasta, rice, and potatoes; they provide energy, vitamins, minerals, and fibre. Meat, fish, eggs, nuts, beans, peas, and lentils supply protein and minerals. Milk and dairy products such as hard cheese and yogurt will give you protein,

vitamins, and calcium. Fresh fruit and vegetables and washed salads are good sources of minerals and vitamins. Folic acid can be found, with other vitamins, in green leafy vegetables, fruit, nuts, bread, and rice.

If you are a vegetarian, you will need to increase your milk intake to at least 600 ml/1 pint a day of either pasteurized milk or fortified soya milk, or the equivalent in cheese, yogurt, and dairy products.

Vegans will need to discuss their diet with a qualified dietitian as they could be deficient in calcium, iron, and vitamin $B_{12}$, which is found in foods of animal origin. Try to avoid

**You and your body**

You can expect to put on about one-quarter of your pregnancy weight between now and week 20. You may be beginning to feel more energetic and generally better than during the past few weeks. You should consider telling your employer at this time that you are pregnant.

Meanwhile, look at your lifestyle and be sure that your diet includes a sensible range of foods – for you and the unborn baby.

eating sugary snacks and fizzy drinks and keep "junk" foods down to a minimum. Cut down on your caffeine intake from drinks like tea, coffee, chocolate and cola; try drinking bottled water and diluted fruit juices as alternatives.

*Eat plenty of fruit when pregnant as it is a good source of minerals and vitamins.*

*Cut down on your caffeine levels and drink more diluted fruit juices.*

*A grain salad will give you plenty of fibre.*

*Vegetables are important in your pregnancy diet as they are low in fat and contain minerals, vitamins and folic acid in leafy varieties.*

*Use olive and sunflower oils for cooking.*

### YOUR WEIGHT

Although you need extra energy during pregnancy to meet the needs of the developing fetus, and to store fat ready for breast-feeding later, you are not likely to need special energy foods. If you were an acceptable weight for your build before pregnancy, the only extra calories you should need are during the last three months when you eat around 200 extra calories a day. However, if you were overweight or underweight your weight gain will need monitoring, and a special diet may be necessary. Ask a professional for advice.

### Your growing baby

The baby's heart is beating at between 110 and 160 times a minute and its chest is beginning to rise and fall. It practises future breathing movements. Features are becoming more clearly defined and fingers and toes are now fully formed, with tiny nails beginning to grow. The baby can suck its thumb and it swallows amniotic fluid and passes it back as urine. The amniotic fluid is completely replaced every 24 hours. The baby is now about 6.5 cm/2½ in long and weighs 20 g/¾ oz.

# WEEK 13: THE HEALTH PROFESSIONALS

**You and your body**
Your uterus is enlarging at a noticeable rate and you will be able to see the first signs of a visible bump. Your nipples have become darker and the blue veins in your breasts are a lot more obvious.

Now that you have reached the end of the first trimester and your pregnancy is a visible state, you need to familiarize yourself with some of the professionals with whom you will regularly be interacting.

During pregnancy, and after the birth, a number of different people will be involved in your care. How many you see will depend on where you are having your baby and the kind of ante-natal care that is being offered. The type of professionals involved in your ante-natal and post-natal care will be the same wherever you are having your baby.
**Midwife** Your midwife has been trained to be an expert in pregnancy. A midwife will care for you from the time your pregnancy is confirmed until after the birth of your baby. She will be able to give you physical and psychological support and to help with any medical problems that arise during this time.

Building up a relationship with you and your family is an essential part of the midwife's job, so it is important to establish contact with her as soon after your pregnancy is confirmed as possible. In the UK the midwife will usually be found at your local health centre or your doctor's surgery, although it may also be possible to contact her direct through the Supervisor of Midwives at your local maternity unit. Your midwife will be able to help you make an informed choice about your right to have your baby where and how you wish. She will advise you on the most appropriate care for

your needs and, if specialist help is required, she will know the right person to contact.

In the UK the midwife will continue to look after you and your family until she hands over your care to a health visitor at between 10 and 28 days after the birth.
**General practitioner** This is your family doctor, who will probably have confirmed your pregnancy and who, along with the midwife, will help you plan your ante-natal care. He or she may be responsible for all or part of your ante-natal care and will work closely with your midwife. Some, but not all doctors are prepared to attend a home birth. If you think you would like to have your baby at home you will need to discuss this with your doctor.

Your family doctor will provide medical care for both you and your baby during and after pregnancy. You will need to register your baby with your doctor as soon after the birth as possible. You can contact your doctor at any time if either you or your baby are ill. Your doctor may have an arrangement where young babies are seen without making an appointment, possibly at the beginning or end of the surgery, or it may be possible to obtain some advice over the phone. surgery.
**Obstetrician** This is a doctor who specializes in the care of women throughout their pregnancy and

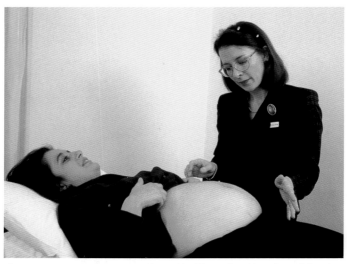

*As your pregnancy progresses you may be examined by an obstetrician who specializes in birth and child care. She will advise on your baby's development and discuss any problems.*

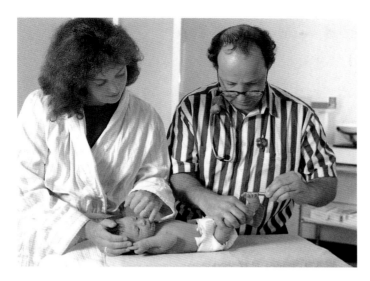

**Your growing baby**

The baby is now 7.5 cm/3 in long and weighs 30 g/1½ oz. The bone marrow, liver, and spleen have now taken over production of blood cells. The bones are developing and the teeth are in place. The baby may already be practising lip movements to develop the muscles needed for the sucking reflex after the birth.

*The pediatrician will perform several checks on your baby after birth. Here he is checking that the newborn's foot reflex works correctly.*

subsequent childbirth. If you are having a delivery in a hospital, the consultant you are under will be an obstetrician who is part of a special medical team.

**Anaesthetist** This is a specialist doctor responsible for providing pain relief. The anaesthetist can provide an epidural or spinal block during labour.If complications arise and a Caesarean becomes necessary the anaesthetist may need to administer a general anaesthetic.

**Pediatrician** This is a doctor who specializes in caring for babies and children. Your baby will be checked by a pediatrician after the birth.

**Health visitor** Your health visitor is a qualified nurse who has had extra training in caring for people in the community. Her role is to help families, especially those with young children. She will take over your care from the midwife and will visit you at home sometime after your baby is 10 days old. She can offer advice and give support if you have any worries about your baby or if you yourself have problems.

*Your health visitor will visit you after your baby's birth and check that the navel is healing.*

## THE SECOND TRIMESTER

# WEEK 14: SEX DURING PREGNANCY

For you to be able to enjoy sex it is important to know that making love cannot harm the developing baby. It is well protected in the uterus by the amniotic fluid and membranes, and the uterus itself is sealed with a plug of mucus, which stays in place until just before the birth. Even deep penetration is safe, but it should of course be gentle so that it doesn't cause discomfort.

Many women find that the middle months of pregnancy are a sensual and even erotic time. Physical changes, such as the increase in the size of your breasts, can actually serve to heighten your interest in sex, which in turn leads to an increase in sexual pleasure. Your genitals may also appear bigger and the pressure from the growing baby can actually make them more responsive. Some women find that they experience orgasm for the first time during pregnancy, while others come to orgasm much more quickly.

Experiencing orgasm is perfectly safe, in fact it can be considered to be beneficial since the uterus often remains hard and firm for several minutes afterwards. This is similar in effect to the Braxton Hicks, or practice contractions you experience towards the end of your pregnancy that prepare the uterus for the birth of your baby.

You may of course find that you feel a lessening of desire during pregnancy, or even a complete loss of interest in sex. These feelings are not uncommon, but they can cause unnecessary stress between you and your partner if they are not brought out into the open and discussed.

### You and your body

You are now beginning the second trimester when you should start experiencing what is known as mid-pregnancy bloom. You will be feeling better about everything; if your sex drive has diminished over the last few months it will probably return and sex may be better than ever.

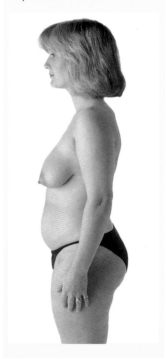

*If you don't feel much like making love in early pregnancy, still cuddle your partner and show him lots of affection.*

Your partner may feel that he is being rejected, so it is important to find alternative ways of giving each other love and reassurance.

DIFFERENT WAYS TO MAKE LOVE
It is important that you and your partner show each other physical affection during pregnancy, but this does not always have to involve sexual intercourse. You may find as your pregnancy progresses that you want lots of cuddles and other signs of affection from your partner without actually having sex. Men often find this hard to understand as they tend to link such physical contact with intercourse. Explain to your partner how you feel so that together you can find other ways of expressing your love for each other.

Try experimenting with forms of sex play that don't necessarily end in penetration, so that you can still make love even if you don't feel like intercourse. Take time to find out

*Often during the middle months of pregnancy, you can start to feel more sensual and show renewed interest in sex.*

### Your growing baby
The baby is beginning to look human as the chin, forehead, and nose become more clearly defined. It can now turn its head and even wrinkle its brow. The baby may even respond to external stimulus by actually moving away when the doctor or midwife feels your abdomen. The baby is now 9cm/3½in long and weighs about 60g/2oz.

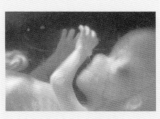

what you both enjoy and don't be afraid to tell your partner what you do and don't like. Stroking, massage, mutual masturbation, and oral sex are some alternative ways of making love which you can both enjoy and which may at times be more appropriate than full intercourse.

As you grow larger you'll find some positions for lovemaking more comfortable than others. Experiment with positions which keep your partner's weight off you.

USING SEX TO INDUCE LABOUR
Sex can sometimes be a way of inducing labour. Your partner's

semen contains a hormone called prostaglandin, which will help to soften the cervix in preparation for birth. Lovemaking will also stimulate the cells in the cervix to secrete their own prostaglandins; this too may help bring labour on.

Breast stimulation in late pregnancy sometimes produces quite strong contractions which are thought to help prepare the way for labour by softening and drawing up the cervix. It has been discovered that stimulating the nipples can reactivate a labour that has halted – something that your partner might like to remember.

# WEEK 15: HEALTH AND SAFETY

You may hear about risks during pregnancy. Some are valid, others are based on misinformation. If you work with dangerous substances such as chemicals, or in a job that requires you to do heavy lifting, you could be risking your health and that of your child, and your employer must offer you an alternative job. If you are concerned about risks at work talk to your doctor, your employer, or union representative.

One common concern is that sitting all day in front of a computer screen will harm the developing baby, but extensive research shows no evidence of this.

A more cautionary approach is suggested towards the use of mobile phones. Although there is no evidence that they can harm the baby. it is recommended that calls should be kept to a minimum during your pregnancy.

### You and your body

Your heart has enlarged to cope with the increased amount of blood circulating in your body and the baby's need for oxygen, and has increased its output by 20 per cent. You will be feeling more energetic than before and now is a good time to have a holiday before the birth.

HEALTH HAZARDS

While you are pregnant you should avoid eating unpasteurized milk and products made with unpasteurized milk; pâté made from meat, fish, or vegetables; soft and blue vein

*There is no evidence to show that there is any risk to the growing baby for women who regularly use computers, but use of a mobile phone should be kept to a minimum.*

**Your growing baby**
The fetal skeleton is developing and its legs are now longer than its arms. The hair on its head is becoming thicker and it has eyelashes as well as eyebrows. The baby can probably hear now and the amniotic fluid makes an excellent sound conductor, so it will be able to hear your stomach rumbling and your heart beating as well as the sound of your voice. The baby is 12cm/4¾in long and now weighs 100g/3½oz.

*Left: Make sure you only eat hard-boiled eggs and drink pasteurized milk to avoid* Listeria monocytogenes.

cheeses; soft-whip ice cream; pre-cooked poultry and cook-chill meals; and prepared salads (unless washed thoroughly) because of the risk of listeria.

*Listeria monocytogenes* is the bacterium which causes listeriosis in humans and animals. Animals that carry the bacterium are likely to infect the milk they produce and the meat that is produced from them. The bacterium is usually destroyed during the pasteurization of milk and milk products. However, if food is contaminated and then refrigerated the bacteria will continue to multiply. Listeriosis can also be spread through direct contact with animals that are infected.

Toxoplasmosis is a disease that occurs in both humans and animals. It can be extremely dangerous if it is contracted during pregnancy because it may cause miscarriage or severe fetal abnormality. The disease is spread to humans by eating undercooked or raw meat and through coming into contact with cat faeces. The

infection can also be caught from sheep at lambing time. It is possible to have the disease without knowing it, so you should have a blood test to find out whether or not you have immunity. If you are immune, you definitely cannot infect your baby.

If you find that you are not immune, you should take a number of precautions during pregnancy. Avoid meat that has not been cooked

thoroughly and wash your hands, cooking utensils, and surfaces after preparing raw meat. Wash fruit and vegetables to remove all traces of soil. Avoid unpasteurized goat's milk and goat's milk products. Finally, wear rubber gloves when gardening and wash your hands afterwards. Cover your children's sand boxes in the garden to prevent cats from using them as litter trays.

### Food safety

Avoid putting yourself at risk during pregnancy by taking the following precautions with food.
- Wash all fruit, vegetables, and salads, including any pre-packed salads, thoroughly.
- Don't eat raw or undercooked meat.
- Eggs must be well cooked and all dairy products should be pasteurized.
- Don't eat liver and liver products, such as pâté and liver sausage. They contain high levels of vitamin A, which is toxic in excess amounts.

- Avoid eating any soft, imported cheeses such as Brie and Camembert, blue-vein cheeses, and those that are made from goat's and sheep's milk because of the risk of listeria.
- Avoid cook-chill meals and shellfish.
- Keep your fridge below 5°C/41°F and don't refreeze any previously frozen foods.
- Pay special attention to hygiene in the kitchen.
- Don't eat food that is past its "sell by" or "best before" date.

# WEEK 16: SCANS/TWINS

A scan can be carried out at any stage of pregnancy (a dating scan may be offered as early as 10 weeks) to check on your baby's progress. The anomaly scan, which is a detailed check to see if your baby is developing normally, is usually offered between 16 and 20 weeks.

The procedure is completely painless. High-density sound waves are used to create a picture of your baby in the uterus, and you will be able to see this on a screen. The best pictures are obtained when you have a full bladder so you will be asked to drink a lot of fluid beforehand. You lie on a couch and your stomach is lubricated so that the person doing the scan can pull the scanner smoothly across it. The picture that appears on the screen may not be clear, so ask the radiographer to explain the images to you, if you are unsure of what you are seeing.

The baby's age can be determined from a scan; it also shows up most abnormalities of the head and spine that may have occurred and will detect the presence of twins. The exact position of the placenta and the baby can be seen, so if there are any problems, for example when the placenta is situated very low down, extra care will be taken throughout your pregnancy. You may also be given the opportunity to find out your baby's sex.

## TWINS
There is about a one in 80 chance that you and your partner will conceive twins. However, you are more likely to give birth to twins if

you have a history of them in your, or your partner's, family. Identical twins come from one egg which, once fertilized, then splits into two separate cells. Each of the cells then grows into a separate baby, but they usually share the same placenta. Because identical twins originally came from the same cells they are always the same sex and look like each other. Non-identical twins, or fraternal twins, are the result of two

### You and your body
You may feel your baby's first movements around this time. These early movements are like a fluttering, bubbling sensation. You may notice the beginning of *Linea nigra*, a dark line which appears down the centre of your abdomen. This will disappear after the birth.

eggs being fertilized by two different sperm at the same time. Each baby has its own placenta and the sex of the babies may differ. Fraternal twins usually don't look any more alike than other brothers and sisters.

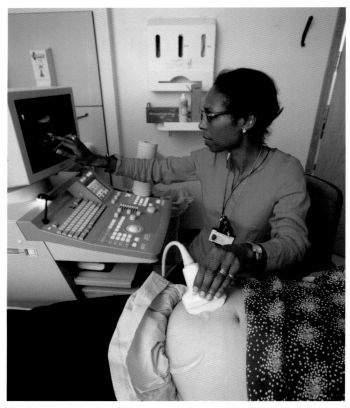

*An ultrasound scan will normally be carried out between 16 and 20 weeks of pregnancy. It will show up any abnormalities in your baby and also indicate the presence of twins.*

*The arrival of twins can come as rather a shock. Get your partner to help as much as he can and you will soon find that you both start bonding with them.*

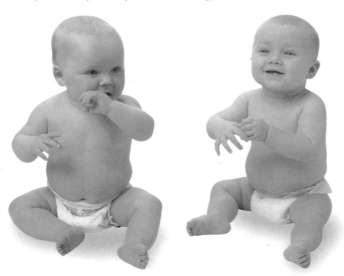

*The joy of having twins is that as they grow up they will learn to play with each other.*

### Your growing baby

The baby will be moving around frequently now, although you may have only just started to feel this. The body will become covered in a fine downy hair called lanugo, which is thought to maintain the right body temperature. It is possible to tell a baby's sex now through an ultrasound scan. The baby is 16cm/6¼in long and weighs 135g/5oz.

---

### Twins in the womb

Fraternal twins

Identical twins

# WEEK 17: YOUR PREGNANCY WARDROBE

You will find that ordinary clothes, in a bigger size if necessary, will see you through most of your pregnancy. A few basic garments that are interchangeable will help you achieve a variety of looks. Buy skirts and trousers with elasticated waists, and stretchy tops and T-shirts in natural fibres. Choose underwear with some cotton content for softness and absorbency and maternity tights or stockings to give your legs support. As your breasts are likely to increase in size rapidly during pregnancy, it makes sense to buy a well-fitting support bra as soon as your present bra feels tight. It is worth getting professionally measured so that you can be sure you are getting the correct size bra.

*Look smart in the office in skirts with elasticated waists and flattering tops.*

### You and your body

Your waistline will have completely disappeared and you may have begun to develop stretch marks. Bleeding gums may be a problem, so if you haven't had a dental check-up now is the time to go. If you work, you should start thinking about when you intend to leave and whether you will want to return.

### Your growing baby

Your baby's limbs are fully formed, as well as the skin and muscle. Its taste buds are beginning to develop so that it will be able to distinguish sweet from non-sweetened fluid. The baby is now about 18cm/7in long and weighs around 185g/6½oz.

### Maternity rights and benefits

Once your pregnancy is confirmed, you should make enquiries about your maternity rights and benefits. You will probably be entitled to some financial and/or medical benefits from the government. If you work you are entitled to maternity leave and you may qualify for statutory maternity pay or maternity allowance from your employer. You are entitled to take time off work to attend ante-natal clinics and parentcraft classes, so you may want to let your employer know that you are pregnant before booking your visit. You can get more information from your employer, trade union, local Jobcentre Plus or Social Security office.

*You can stay trendy in denim by wearing under-the-bump drawstring waist jeans or skirt.*

*Above: For formal occasions a little black dress with ruched sides, made from fabric that has plenty of stretch, will be perfect to wear throughout your pregnancy.*

*Far left: In summer stay cool by wearing cotton. A tiered dress will accommodate even the largest bump.*

*Left: There's no reason why you shouldn't wear shorts, matched with a pretty top.*

# WEEK 18: LOOKING YOUR BEST

You may find that your hair behaves in a rather unpredictable way while you are pregnant. Hormone changes mean that your hair may appear thicker than usual, or in some women the opposite happens and the hair loss increases so that the hair looks thinner. Dry hair may become even drier and oily hair more greasy. Whichever condition applies to you, just wash your hair using a mild shampoo. If your hair tends to be very dry, use a good conditioner after every wash and, if possible, allow it to dry naturally rather than using a hair dryer.

*Try using hypoallergenic skin-cleansing products on your skin as it will be particularly sensitive at this time.*

*Dry hair will need extra conditioning during your pregnancy because it becomes drier as your hormones change.*

Pregnancy hormones can affect the colour and texture of your skin. Uneven patches may appear and dark-skinned people sometimes get a butterfly-shaped patch of pigmentation across the face that is known as "the mask of pregnancy". Concealing foundation will help hide these marks and a UVA sun screen will prevent any further increase in pigmentation. Pregnancy "bloom", which is caused by an increase in the tiny blood vessels under the surface of the skin, can be toned down with green cream or powder. It is a good idea to use hypoallergenic skin-care products as your skin may be particularly sensitive at this time.

### FLUID RETENTION
Your body retains more water than usual during pregnancy, so your hands and feet may become slightly swollen and you may find that your eyes get puffy and your face looks fuller. The best solution is to get as much rest as possible, sitting with your feet higher than your heart, as this will help reduce the swelling in your feet and ankles. While you are resting, place some cottonwool pads soaked in witch hazel, or slices of cucumber, on your eyes. This will soothe them and reduce any puffiness. You can disguise a fuller face by applying blusher below the cheekbones and blending a darker shade of foundation along your jawline. Alternatively, you can draw attention away from your face by wearing a colourful scarf or a chunky necklace round your neck.

Try not to be too critical of your looks; many other people will consider that this new, softer look to your appearance makes you seem younger and healthier.

## You and your body
You should be able to feel the fetal movements quite clearly now. Your nose may become blocked as pregnancy causes the membranes inside the nasal passages to swell. You may also notice an increase in vaginal discharge. You will find that there are several physical changes besides the predictable weight gain.

## Your growing baby
The skin is still wrinkled because the baby hasn't started to gain body fat and is very active. It is becoming aware of sounds outside the uterus and you may be able to feel it jumping at unexpected noises. The baby is now around 21cm/8½in long and weighs about 235g/8oz.

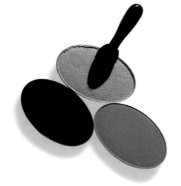

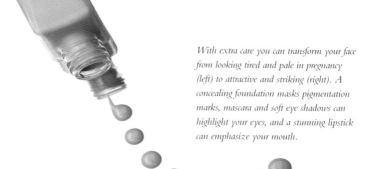

*With extra care you can transform your face from looking tired and pale in pregnancy (left) to attractive and striking (right). A concealing foundation masks pigmentation marks, mascara and soft eye shadows can highlight your eyes, and a stunning lipstick can emphasize your mouth.*

# WEEK 19: EXERCISE

Regular, gentle exercise has an important part to play in keeping you fit during pregnancy and will help you get back into shape after the birth. Remember, if you ever feel faint, light-headed or breathless while you are exercising you must stop immediately. If you haven't been taking regular exercise, start swimming, or take up yoga or walking, as they can all be done at a gentle, rhythmical pace that can be adapted to suit each stage of your pregnancy. If you find it easier to follow an exercise routine you can do at home, never include sit-ups or exercises that involve raising the legs when you are lying down as these could damage the abdominal muscles. It is important to stop and relax

**You and your body**

You have started to put weight on your bottom, hips, and thighs as well as your abdomen. Tiny veins may start appearing on your face. These are very small broken blood vessels which are caused by circulation changes. They will disappear after the birth.

between exercises and to make sure that your breathing always remains at a controlled rate.

## Toning your chest

**1** *Hold arms at breast level with hands loosely clasping opposite arm. Tighten grip and hold briefly, then relax.*

**2** *Still keeping your hands clasped, raise them to eye level and tighten your grip and hold, then relax.*

**3** *Lower your arms down to your waist, tighten and hold, then relax. Repeat this sequence several times.*

## Feet exercises

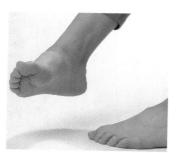

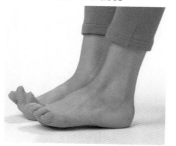

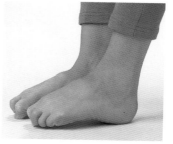

**1** *To loosen ankles, sit down with feet flat on the ground. Lift one foot at a time and circle ankle five times in both directions.*

**2** *To relax the feet, place your feet flat on the floor. Now lift your toes up as far as you can and hold briefly, then relax.*

**3** *Now clench your toes hard, hold for a few seconds, then relax again. Repeat this technique, and Step 2, 10 times.*

## Taylor sitting and squatting exercises

**1** *To loosen the groin and hips and stretch the inner thighs, sit with the soles of your feet together. Holding ankles, bring your pelvis and feet together by moving your hips towards your feet.*

**2** *This is a good position for labour. Squat down keeping a straight back; try to put your heels down keeping your weight even. Press your elbows against your thighs stretching the inner groin and thighs.*

## Tummy toning exercises

**1** *Put a folded towel or pillow under your head and lie with your knees bent and your feet flat on the floor. Tighten your tummy muscles so that your back is flat on the floor.*

**2** *Keeping your back pressed well down onto the floor, slowly extend both your legs in front of you until they are both completely straight.*

**3** *Draw one knee up and then the other, without lifting your back off the floor, then relax; repeat five times.*

### Your growing baby

The baby is starting to put on weight and its rapid rate of growth has begun to slow down. The milk teeth have developed in the gums and the buds for the permanent teeth are beginning to form. The baby is around 23cm/9in long and weighs about 285g/10oz.

# WEEK 20: SKIN CARE/CRAVINGS

Your breasts are likely to increase by as much as two bra sizes during pregnancy, so you will need to make sure that they are well supported so that they do not sag and become uncomfortable. Small bumps may appear in the skin around your nipples. These are sebaceous glands, which secrete sebum, a fatty lubricant. As your pregnancy progresses, your nipples grow softer and gentle massage will help make them supple and ready for breast-feeding. Your breasts may leak a yellow fluid called colostrum, which will form a crust on the nipples. You will need to wash and dry them gently and thoroughly at least twice a day.

Your nails are made of protein and are affected by the hormonal

*Check your bra size by measuring around your ribcage. For the cup size measure around your bust at its fullest.*

changes taking place in your body. Usually they grow longer and stronger during pregnancy, but occasionally pregnancy will cause them to split and break. If this happens, keep them short and protect them by wearing gloves when you are doing rough jobs or when you immerse your hands in water.

If the elasticity of your skin becomes overstretched as you put on

*Your nails may be brittle during pregnancy so keep them short to stop them splitting.*

*Paint on a nail strengthener to keep your nails strong at this time.*

### You and your body
Your uterus is enlarging quite rapidly now so that you look pregnant. Your navel may be flattened or pushed out and it will stay this way until after the birth. Heartburn may start to become a problem because the uterus is starting to push against your stomach.

weight, you may develop stretch marks. These usually appear on the breasts, stomach, and the tops of the thighs as thin, reddish lines. There is little you can do to avoid them, but keeping your skin well moisturized, and being careful not to put on too much extra weight, will help minimize them. Stretch marks fade to thin silvery lines after the birth.

Varicose veins can be caused by pregnancy hormones or, later in pregnancy, by the uterus pressing down and obstructing the flow of blood from the legs to the heart. Although not serious, they can lead to aching or sore legs. Try to avoid standing for long periods and put your feet up whenever possible to ease any discomfort. Walking will help the blood flow; put on support tights or stockings when you get out of bed in the morning to give your legs more support. Varicose veins usually disappear soon after the birth.

### CRAVINGS
No one is sure why some pregnant women have cravings while others don't. Doctors disagree about them; some are sympathetic, while others doubt that they actually exist. If you desire a certain food there is no reason why you shouldn't indulge yourself within reason, but make sure that you don't exclude other more nourishing foods as a result.

*Above: Your legs may ache more with the increased weight you're carrying, so try massaging them with a body lotion.*
*Right: You can't prevent stretch marks appearing on your stomach, but rubbing in moisturizing lotion may help.*

### Your growing baby

Vernix, a white greasy substance, is starting to form over the baby's skin to protect it from the amniotic fluid. This usually wears off before the birth, but sometimes traces of it can be seen. At this stage in your pregnancy the baby weighs around 340g/12oz and measures about 25.5cm/10in.

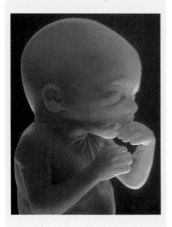

# WEEK 21: MINOR COMPLAINTS

By now you may be experiencing some of the minor problems that occur later in pregnancy. These include:

**Heartburn** This is a strong burning feeling in your chest that often happens during the last few months of pregnancy. It is usually worse when lying down. Hormones cause the valve at the top of your stomach to relax, which allows stomach acid to pass back into the gullet (oesophagus), causing a burning sensation. Avoid eating spicy and fatty foods. Eating small, but frequent meals will help reduce heartburn. Sleeping propped up at night and drinking a glass of milk before you go to bed will also help ease the discomfort.

tell the pharmacist that you are pregnant because some of the remedies that are available are not suitable for use during pregnancy or breast-feeding.

**You and your body**

You should be able to see your abdomen ripple as the baby moves. You may be feeling slightly breathless as your expanding ribcage pushes upwards, giving your lungs less room. You will probably be feeling energetic so now is the time to tackle things such as planning the nursery.

*Insomnia can be a problem in later pregnancy. If you can't sleep, try supporting your tummy on pillows to make yourself more comfortable.*

*If you are suffering from heartburn, try drinking a glass of milk before you go to sleep at night.*

Your doctor may prescribe an antacid if the problem frequently keeps you awake at night. If you buy an over-the-counter remedy always

**Insomnia** Sleeplessness is often a problem as your pregnancy progresses because you will find it difficult to get comfortable, and you have to make frequent trips to the toilet. Vivid dreams can also be a problem at this time. A bath followed by a warm drink at bedtime will help you relax. It is important to find restful sleeping positions, so use lots of pillows to support your abdomen when you lie on your side. You could also try practising some relaxation techniques.

**Itching** This often occurs on the areas of skin around the bump and is sometimes accompanied by a rash. Calamine lotion should help relieve the itching and since it is usually caused by sweating, wearing loose clothes made of natural fibres can help prevent it. Severe itching that occurs during the last three months of pregnancy could be a warning of pregnancy cholestasis – a rare but potentially dangerous liver disorder – and you should consult your doctor.

*It's important to get plenty of rest so take the opportunity to sit down and relax whenever you can.*

### Your growing baby

The baby is very active now and you will probably be able to feel it kicking quite easily. If this disturbs you at night, stroke your tummy and talk to the baby because it will be soothed by the sound of your voice. The baby is now around 28cm/11in long and weighs about 390g/14oz.

**Oedema** (swelling) This occurs in the feet and ankles, and sometimes the hands, because your body is holding more fluid than normal. By the end of the day this fluid tends to gather in your feet, especially if the weather has been hot or you have been doing a lot of standing. Try to sit with your feet up whenever you can, as this will help reduce the swelling. Wear support tights and comfortable shoes during the day and avoid standing for long periods. You should always tell your midwife or doctor about any swelling that you experience as it could be a sign of pre-eclampsia.

**Tiredness** The extra weight you carry during late pregnancy can make you feel more tired than usual. It is important to have regular rest periods when you can sit down with your feet up. If the tiredness you are experiencing feels excessive, you may be suffering from anaemia. Make sure you are getting plenty of iron in your diet by eating lean red meat, whole grains, dark green leafy vegetables, nuts, and pulses. If the feeling still persists consult your midwife or doctor.

*Swimming is an ideal exercise as the water supports the extra weight.*

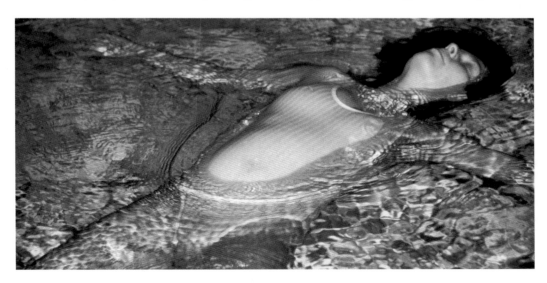

# WEEK 22: RELAXATION AND MASSAGE

It is important to be able to relax, both mentally and physically, during pregnancy because this will help you to rest. Knowing how to make your body relax during labour will allow you to work with the contractions rather than against them.

**Physical relaxation**
Start by getting comfortable and make sure that every part of your body is supported.

Concentrate on tensing and relaxing individual parts of your body. Start at your toes and work gradually upwards to your head and then back down to your toes again. By the time you have finished this exercise you should be feeling nice and floppy.

**Mental relaxation**  This requires deep concentration, so you need to be comfortable and in a quiet place where no one will disturb you. Empty your mind and concentrate on your breathing. Breathe in and hold your breath for a few seconds before letting it out slowly.

### You and your body
Your lower ribs are starting to cause you pain as they get pushed outwards by your growing baby and your expanding uterus. Your ribcage rises by a small amount as it is pushed upward. To minimize the discomfort, try sitting up as straight as you can or lifting your arms above your head. This is an ideal time to investigate the different methods that you can use to ease discomfort now and during labour and birth.

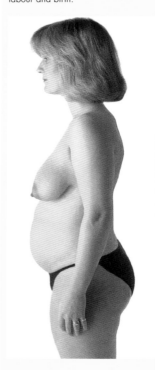

Once you have established a steady pattern of breathing, make sure all your muscles are relaxed, then allow your mind to float away. One way to do this is to imagine that you are floating on calm water under a clear blue sky, in tranquil surroundings.

OTHER TECHNIQUES

Massage is an excellent way of relieving tension. It is best done on bare skin, but if you find your skin is particularly sensitive, it can be carried out through a thin cotton nightdress. Massage strokes should be firm, smooth, and rhythmical.

Aromatherapy massage uses essential oils that are added to a carrier oil before being applied to your skin. Certain essential oils can be dangerous during pregnancy because they may trigger uterine contractions, so you must always get qualified professional advice. Many aromatherapists will not treat a pregnant woman at all. Most of those who will treat expectant mothers will do so only after the sixth month of pregnancy. One effective blend is mandarin oil well diluted (i.e. a maximum solution of one per cent: no more than 10 drops of oil to 50 ml carrier oil) in a sweet almond carrier oil. A well-diluted solution of true lavender, jasmine, and rose in sweet almond oil is also thought to be beneficial during labour and birth.

In acupuncture tiny needles are used to stimulate meridian points on the body's energy lines with the aim of rebalancing the energy flow. The treatment can help backache, but some points on the body are thought to stimulate uterine contractions, so it is important to let the practitioner know that you are pregnant.

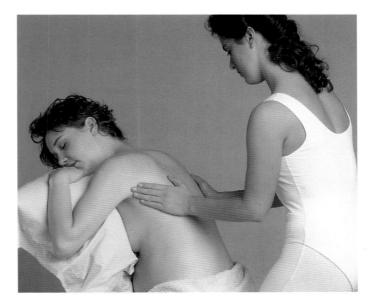

*Above: If you are suffering regularly from backache, having a soothing massage from a qualified practitioner can help. With an aromatherapy massage, make sure she chooses oils that will not affect the baby.*
*Below: Regular massage on your legs will help to relieve any aches and pains that you are experiencing.*

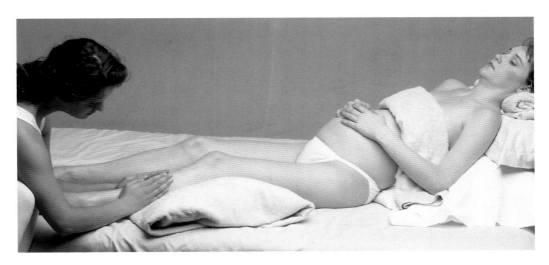

# WEEK 23: PREPARING THE NURSERY

**You and your body**

The baby can be felt through your abdominal wall and the midwife or doctor will palpate your abdomen to see how the baby is lying. You may occasionally feel a pain rather like a stitch down the side of your stomach. This is the uterine muscle stretching and it will go away after you have had a rest.

This is a good time to think of practical things like planning the baby's nursery. Whether you have a spare room which you are going to turn into a nursery, or you intend to make a nursery corner in your own bedroom, you should start getting it ready now while you have the energy.

Before you begin you will need to take into consideration the shape and size of the area so you can work out how much furniture and baby equipment will comfortably fit into it. You should also check whether there are enough electrical sockets; that there is sufficient heating; and that the ceiling or wall lights are where you want them. Major changes such as rewiring or putting in another radiator are better done before you start to decorate or carpet the nursery.

Babies enjoy looking at bright, primary colours and big, bold patterns, so choose a colourful paint and paper; washable materials will make it easier to keep the walls looking bright and fresh. Transfers, borders, pictures and mobiles can be used effectively to brighten up a plain background if you are reluctant to commit yourself to a colour scheme until you know your baby's sex.

Rugs and polished floors look nice but are unsuitable because of the risk of you slipping on them while holding the baby. Any flooring needs to be warm underfoot and non-slip. Sealed cork tiles are ideal because they are warm and any spills can be wiped up without damage to the floor. Fitted carpets and carpet tiles are suitable alternatives, but don't buy expensive carpet because it will probably need replacing after a relatively short time.

An overhead light with a dimmer switch or a specially designed nursery light is very useful for night feeds as it gives out a soft comforting glow that won't startle either of you too much in the middle of the night. A plug or cot light will provide enough illumination for you to check on your sleeping baby, but you will need a brighter light for nappy changing and general care. Avoid any lamps with trailing flexes that you could trip over, and fit all unused electrical sockets with a safety cover.

FINISHING TOUCHES

The room where the baby sleeps must be draught-proof, so cover any windows with thick, lined curtains. These will not only keep out any draughts, but will also keep the morning light from waking your baby during the summer. Windows need to be fitted with childproof

*Planning the nursery for your baby can be enjoyable. You can start to buy some outfits in advance, but remember that you will often be given baby clothes when your baby is born.*

*A cot will be necessary by the time your baby is three moths old. If you choose a secondhand one, it's a good idea to buy a new mattress. Make sure that the mattress is firm and fits snugly into the base of the cot.*

locks and the curtains should be out of reach of the cot. Never place the cot or crib under a window or near radiators. Young babies cannot regulate their temperature, so they need to be kept in a comfortably warm environment at around 18ºC/65ºF. A special nursery thermometer or a thermostat fitted to the radiator will help ensure that you maintain the correct room temperature.

Babies actually require very little in the way of furniture. Somewhere to sleep, a cupboard or chest to keep clothes in, and somewhere for changing and storing toiletries and nappies, as well as a chair for you to sit in while you are feeding or rocking the baby, is all that you really need for the first few months. All nursery furniture should be sturdy enough that it can't be pulled over when babies are older and using it for support as they begin to pull

themselves up on to their feet. If you buy secondhand furniture, make sure that any paint or varnish is non-toxic and lead-free. If you are in any doubt, get someone to rub it down for you so you can repaint with safe materials. Also check that there are no broken bits that could harm your baby.

### Your growing baby

The baby is beginning to look as it will at birth, with the head more in proportion to the body. In a boy, the scrotum is now well developed and in a girl the ovaries already contain several million eggs. (These will reduce to around two million at birth and will carry on decreasing until puberty.) The baby is around 31cm/12¼in long and weighs approximately 440g/15½oz.

*A dresser is useful for organizing all your baby's essentials in one place, and includes a changing mat on top.*

*A Moses basket can by kept by or near your bed, and your baby can sleep in it for up to three months.*

# WEEK 24: BABY CLOTHES AND EQUIPMENT

### You and your body

You will noticeably be putting on weight, perhaps as much as 0.5kg/1lb per week. Your feet and legs may start to feel the strain of carrying this extra weight, so make sure that you wear comfortable shoes and that you get plenty of rest.

Start planning what you need to buy for your baby so that by the time you give birth you will at least have purchased the major items. If you leave everything until the end of the pregnancy, you may be too tired to enjoy shopping for your baby.

Only buy a few basic first size or newborn garments as your baby will probably rapidly outgrow these. Also, most baby clothes are sized by the approximate age and height of

the child and you won't know the size of your child until she is born. Choose well-designed baby clothes, which will make your life easier and allow you to dress and undress your baby with the minimum of time and fuss. Clothes with envelope necks or a shoulder fastening will let you slip clothes over the baby's head easily, and poppers up the inside of legs of rompers or all-in-one suits will help twith regular nappy changing.

Your new baby will probably get through as many as three changes of clothes a day, so it is a good idea to check the washing instructions on any garment before you buy. These instructions will tell you how best to care for each garment so that you can see whether it is easy-care, or if it will require a lot of attention.

**Baby transport**

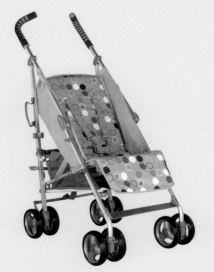

*A pram that converts to a pushchair is suitable from birth to the toddler years.*

A traditional pram is sturdy with plenty of space for shopping, and it will take a toddler seat. It is probably the best option if you are planning to have another child fairly quickly.

*A fold-flat buggy with a parcel tray is useful for shopping. Choose one that is light enough to carry on public transport.*

Generally, prams are unsuitable for cars unless they have a detachable body. A 3-in-1 combination converts from pram to pushchair and has a separate baby carrier or carry cot.

*A car seat carrier is easily transported and can be bought in different sizes to suit the age of your baby.*

## BABY'S TRANSPORT

Before you decide on a pram, buggy, or combination, you need to consider your lifestyle and the various methods of transport you will be using regularly. You also need to think about where it will be stored when not in use. Once you have selected the type most suitable to your needs, ask the shop you order it from to keep it for you until after the baby is born.

Your baby should always be in a car seat when travelling in the car. The seat must be suitable for your child's weight rather than age. Always buy new and make sure it complies with the relevant safety standard. Before placing your child's car seat in the front of the car make sure that the airbag has been disabled.

## EQUIPMENT

Whether you buy a cot, Moses basket, or carrycot will probably depend on where your baby is going

### Your growing baby

Vigorous movements followed by periods of quiet will start to occur as the baby develops its own waking and resting periods. The pattern that develops now may well continue after the birth so it's a good idea to monitor it for a few days to see how it compares with the sleep pattern once the baby is born. The heartbeat can be heard with an ordinary stethoscope and the baby can hear you clearly when you speak. It is now around 33cm/13in long and weighs about 0.5kg/1lb.

to sleep and how much space you have. If the baby is going to sleep in your room at first and you haven't much space, think about buying a cot later.

You need to have at least six sheets and several lightweight cot blankets for the cot and another six sheets and at least three more pram blankets for your chosen pram.

*A twin stroller with adjustable backrests is desgined to last from birth through to the toddler years. It is also suitable for two children of different ages.*

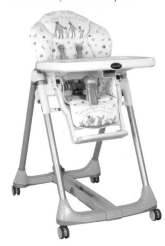

*A two-level high-chair can be used in the higher position when your baby is young and in the lower position when he is older.*

# WEEK 25: FEEDING CHOICES

**You and your body**
You should be looking rosy-cheeked and healthy because of the increase in blood circulation under the skin. Pressure from the growing uterus on the bladder means that you need to make frequent trips to the lavatory. Cramp, heartburn and backache are often problems now.

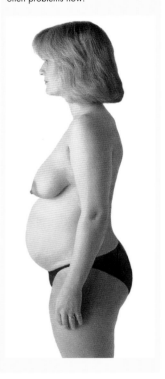

Now is the time to start thinking about how you are going to feed your baby. Whether to breast- or bottle-feed is a personal and emotional decision and one that you need to feel completely happy about. Before you make up your mind talk it over with your partner and your midwife, and get some first-hand experiences from other mothers.

BREAST-FEEDING
Breast milk is the best food for your baby because it contains everything he or she needs in the right proportions, and it changes as the baby grows. It contains antibodies, which will help protect the baby, and it is easily digestible so less likely to cause stomach upsets. Breast-fed babies are also less likely to develop conditions such as eczema and asthma and are less prone to some infections, such as glue ear.

Breast-feeding has advantages for you as well. Not only is breast milk free and always on "tap", at the correct temperature, breast-feeding releases hormones that encourage the uterus to shrink back to its original size more quickly. Breastfeeding for at least six months significantly reduces the risk of pre-menopausal cancer and can protect against osteoporosis and ovarian cancer.

During pregnancy the skin around your nipples will appear darker and raised sebaceous glands will appear as little bumps in the areola, the dark area surrounding the nipple. As your pregnancy progresses the nipples will grow softer. You can make them more supple by gently massaging them. Take extra care washing and drying your breasts towards the end of pregnancy, when they may leak a little, and avoid using soaps that have a drying effect on the skin. You may

find that you need to use breast pads to prevent your clothes from becoming stained.

Breast milk is free, so the only additional cost involved at first is for nursing bras and breast pads. Choose cotton, front-opening nursing bras, with adjustable straps and fastenings because the size of your breasts will change. Wait until after your 30th week of pregnancy before buying a

*Breast-feeding is the best way to nourish your baby, but if you decide to bottle feed make it a relaxing and enjoyable experience for you both.*

nursing bra – one that fits you then should fit you after the baby is born. If you want to be able to express milk, you will also need a couple of bottles and teats, sterilizing equipment, and possibly a breast pump.

## BOTTLE–FEEDING

Formula milk has been specially produced for bottle-fed babies. It contains the right balance of vitamins and minerals that a baby needs to thrive. Formula milk has more protein than breast milk, which means that it takes longer to digest. There are a number of brands to choose from and most are based on cow's milk, although alternatives are available for children who need special diets for medical reasons.

It is very important to follow the instructions when making up formula milk because too much or too little can be harmful. The baby will gradually settle into a routine but until then you will need to respond to his or her hunger just as you would if you were breast-feeding.

One of the main advantages of bottle-feeding is that you and your partner can share the feeds between you, so that you can both use the time when you are feeding to get to know your baby.

Hygiene is very important when you bottle-feed because your baby is not getting protection from the antibodies that he or she would have from breast milk. You will need to take particular care over washing and sterilizing bottles and teats until your baby is at least six months old.

As well as formula milk you will need at least six bottles and teats, with caps, a sterilizing unit or container, a bottle brush, and you may also find a bottle warmer is useful for the night feeds.

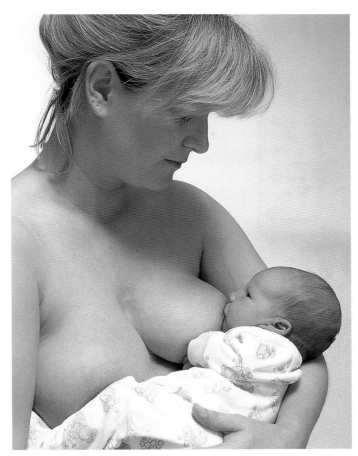

*Breast-feeding can help you bond with your baby, and the milk will give her everything she needs, including protection against infection.*

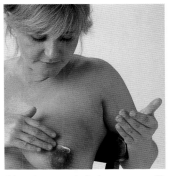

*Massaging your nipples in pregnancy will make them more supple for breast-feeding.*

### Your growing baby

Fetal brain cells continue to develop and become more sophisticated and the bone centres are beginning to harden. The baby actively practises breathing, inhaling and exhaling amniotic fluid, as more air sacs develop in the lungs. When too much amniotic fluid is swallowed, you may feel a hiccup. The baby is about 34cm/13½in long and weighs around 0.6kg/1¼lb.

# WEEK 26:
# PARENTCRAFT
# CLASSES

You should now be about to start parentcraft classes. You may choose one or more of these. Parentcraft classes show you practical techniques such as relaxation, breathing, and postures for labour and birth. The teacher can answer any questions you may have during the last few months of your pregnancy and will be able to give you information on the birth. Your partner will be welcome at some classes and you will find that they are a good way of meeting other pregnant women and sharing mutual anxieties.

The hospital and locally run classes are free, but classes such as National Childbirth Trust and Active Birth charge a fee.

### HOSPITAL CLASSES
These are run by the hospital where you plan to give birth and usually take place over six to eight weeks, starting around the 28th week. You need to attend the course that is nearest to your expected date of delivery. Some hospitals have a parentcraft teacher who co-ordinates ante-natal education. You will be

**You and your body**

If you are working you need to decide when you are going to stop. Remember that you should notify your employer in writing by the end of the 15th week before your baby is due. Your partner must also tell his employer if he intends to take Paternity Leave. If you haven't started taking regular exercise you should now, because this will help prepare your body for the rigours of labour.

taken on a hospital tour so that you can see the labour ward, post-natal ward, and the special care baby unit.

### LOCAL CLASSES
These are usually run by a midwife or a health visitor attached to your doctor's surgery or health centre.

**Active birth classes**

NATIONAL CHILDBIRTH TRUST (NCT)
NCT classes are privately run, usually by mothers who have been trained by the NCT. They need to be booked early because they are deliberately kept small and become fully booked very quickly. Although everything covered on the hospital and local parentcraft courses is included on the NCT course, the classes are more discussion-based and there are no rigid relaxation and breathing techniques. You are taught a variety of skills for dealing with labour and the birth, from which you can choose when the time comes.

ACTIVE BIRTH CLASSES
These privately run weekly classes concentrate on the physical preparation for labour and birth. You are taught a range of yoga-based stretching exercises as well as breathing and relaxation techniques. These classes are mainly for women, with a special session for fathers, and you can join them at any time.

BREATHING TECHNIQUES
Controlled breathing is important during labour and you need to practise the exercises you will be taught at your classes. Breathing needs to be slow and smooth with deep breaths, inhaled through your nose and exhaled through your mouth. A long slow breath at the beginning of each contraction will help oxygenate your blood and this may help relieve any pain caused by lack of oxygen to the muscles of your uterus. Oxygen is also carried in the blood flowing through the placenta into the umbilical cord, so if you do not get enough, your baby will suffer a shortage too.

During contractions you will be concentrating on each outward breath, as this will help you to relax your muscles. It will be important not to over-breathe during the second stage of labour, because this may make you feel dizzy and light-headed. If you do find yourself needing to breathe more quickly then you should concentrate on making each breath as light as you possibly can.

**Your growing baby**
Although still appearing rather scrawny, the baby is beginning to lay down fat under the skin. This fat will help regulate body temperature now and after the birth. The baby is around 35cm/13¾in long and weighs approximately 0.7kg/1½lb.

Gentle yoga-based exercises are ideal preparation for labour and help you to get ready physically and emotionally, so that you are in tune with the demands on your body. They should always be done under qualified supervision. Exercises include going down into a squatting position (far left and left) in anticipation of labour; massage, which particularly helps if you've got sciatica (below left), and stretching to ease pressure at the base of the spine (below right).

## THE THIRD TRIMESTER

# WEEK 27: CHOICES IN CHILDBIRTH

Now that you have entered the third trimester you should start planning the kind of birth that you want. If you are having a hospital birth, you will need to discover what facilities are on offer and then try to plan the birth around them. Although hospitals do try to accommodate a mother's wishes, not all are able to offer every type of birth.

For example, if you want a water birth, you will have to find out whether it is possible at your hospital. If you are having a home birth then having a water birth in a hired pool is easier to arrange. However, you need to remember that if complications occur during labour any decisions you make now may have to be changed.

### You and your body

You will be getting noticeably larger and will have put on weight around your chest as well as your breasts. Make sure that you are wearing the correct size of maternity bra. Avoid lying on your back too much because this may make you feel faint, as the enlarged uterus presses directly against blood vessels.

NATURAL BIRTH

This is when you go through labour and birth without any of the medical procedures that often alter the natural rhythm of labour. Natural childbirth involves the use of breathing and relaxation techniques and sometimes homeopathic remedies.

WATER BIRTH

You spend part of your time in a birth pool, which is filled with warm water, and give birth either outside the pool or in the water. The warm water eases the pain of contractions, and helps you to relax. Although there is no evidence to prove that there is an increased risk of complications if you actually have your baby in the water, you should still talk to your midwife or doctor before planning to do this.

ACTIVE BIRTH

This means that you are free to move about during labour. Keeping mobile allows the contractions to be more effective. Being in an upright position helps the baby's circulation and encourages the baby to rotate into the best position for delivery.

*If you opt for a water birth, you can have your baby in the water or outside the pool. Whichever you choose, the warm water will help ease the contractions.*

*In a natural birth you go through labour without painkillers, using only relaxation methods and maybe homeopathic treatments.*

Gravity aids the baby's descent, and giving birth in a squatting or kneeling position increases the size of the pelvic outlet.

### HIGH-TECH BIRTH
Labour is controlled by medical methods such as induction, where labour is started artificially using chemical substances, or the waters are broken manually.

Painkilling drugs are used and an episiotomy (a surgical incision in the perineum to allow passage of the baby's head when there is some fear that the perineum will otherwise be torn) may be done to enlarge the birth canal.

### CAESAREAN BIRTH
This is when the baby is delivered through an incision that is made through the wall of the abdomen into the uterus. It is done under a general anaesthetic, or sometimes with a spinal block or an epidural. If a spinal block or an epidural is used you will be awake during the delivery, although a screen is placed across your body so that you don't actually see what is happening. You will be given your baby to hold as soon as it is born. After the birth, the incisions are stitched and you will be kept in hospital for about five days. A Caesarean may be chosen if the reasons that make it necessary are evident before labour begins. This is known as an elective Caesarean. If it is decided on after labour has started, it is known as an emergency Caesarean. Reasons for a Caesarean include abnormal presentation of the baby (that is, not head-first towards the cervix), fetal distress where the baby suffers from lack of oxygen, and high blood pressure in the mother.

*When you hold your newborn baby in your arms all the hard work of labour will seem worthwhile.*

### Your growing baby
The baby's eyes are open and it will be able to see light through the skin of your abdomen. It will have started to practise sucking and may even be able to suck its thumb or fist. The baby is now about 36cm/14¼in long and weighs about 0.8kg/1¾lb.

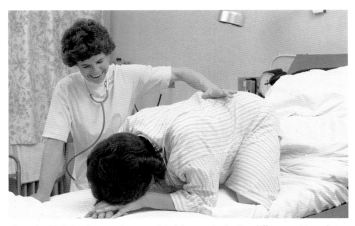

*An active birth involves moving around in labour and adopting different positions that will help your baby's descent.*

# WEEK 28: THE BIRTHPLAN

Some hospitals include a special form with your notes, on which you can make a written plan of the way you would like your labour and birth to be managed. If you haven't received one of these, talk to your midwife about drawing up your own plan.

Even if there are still some things concerning labour or the actual birth about which you are undecided, writing out a plan will help you focus on the type of birth that you want. It will also give you the opportunity to discuss the birth in detail with your partner.

When drawing up your birthplan it is important to remember that there is no right or wrong way to give birth. Your plan should reflect what you feel is right for you, while taking into account your medical history as well as the facilities available at the place where you are going to have your baby.

A birthplan is a guide to how you would like things to be, but in the event of a problem this ideal may become totally impractical so you will need to be flexible. Once you have finalized your birthplan ask for a copy to be kept with your notes so

that the doctor and midwife who attend you during labour have it to hand. Keep a copy for yourself so that your birth partner can refer to it if necessary.

BIRTH PARTNER
Although your partner will be encouraged to be with you during labour, you may prefer to have

## You and your body

Your breasts are producing colostrum, the fluid which precedes breast milk. If your breasts are leaking put breast pads or folded tissues inside your bra. If you have an ante-natal appointment you will probably have a second blood test to check for anaemia. If you are anaemic, iron supplements may be offered.

*Write a birthplan with your choices.*

## Birthplan checklist

The following questions will help you prepare your own birthplan.
- Whom do you wish to have with you during labour – your partner, your mother, a friend? You can choose more than one birth partner.
- Can your birth partner remain with you if you have to have a Caesarean or forceps delivery?
- Are there special facilities such as a birthing pool or bean bags available?
- Do you want to be free to move around during labour, or would you rather be constantly monitored while staying in bed?
- Is there any special position you want to use for the birth?
- Do you wish to wear your own clothes during labour and the birth?
- Would you like music, soft lighting, massage or other therapies to help you cope with getting through labour?

- How do you feel about pain relief? If you want to manage without any, you will need to make sure that everyone knows. If you want pain relief which sort do you want?
- Are you prepared to have an episiotomy if it is required, or would you rather tear naturally?
- Do you want your baby placed straight onto your abdomen after birth or do you want him or her cleaned up first?
- Are you going to breast-feed? If so, do you want to put your baby to the breast immediately?
- Do you want an injection to help deliver the placenta or would you prefer to wait for it to be delivered naturally after the birth?
- How soon after the birth would you like to go home, assuming that there are no complications?

*If your partner is worried about being with you during labour, talk it through with him and make your feelings known if you're counting on his support.*

another woman as your actual birth partner, especially if your partner is worried that he may not be able to cope with seeing you in pain. Whatever you decide, make sure you talk about it together so that there are no misunderstandings and you don't get upset about the final choice.

### Your growing baby

Now fully formed, the baby would be viable if it were born at 28 weeks, although the body systems are still very immature. The heart is beating at a rate of around 150 beats a minute. The baby weighs around 0.9kg/2lb.

*Once you've made your birthplan and put your feelings on your baby's birth in writing, you will feel happier.*

# WEEK 29: SPECIAL CARE

If you suffer from a medical condition or blood disorder your pregnancy will require careful managing. Your doctor will need to monitor your progress and you may have to have special ante-natal checks. If there is a possible problem, you will be offered another scan during the last trimester, which will clearly show the baby's breathing movements, how it is lying, and the position of the placenta.

**Anaemia** is caused by an abnormally low level of red corpuscles in the blood and is treated with iron supplements. You can build up your body's store of iron by eating a diet which includes red meat, whole grains, dark green leafy vegetables, nuts and pulses. Liver is not recommended during pregnancy because of the high levels of vitamin A, which could be toxic. A second blood test is done in late pregnancy to check for anaemia.

**Kidney infection** is usually caused by bacterial infection and you should contact your doctor if you think you have a kidney infection. Symptoms are pain, frequent urination accompanied by a burning sensation, and occasionally some

### You and your body

You will probably be able to feel the baby's bottom and feet as it moves around. The baby will be putting pressure on your stomach and diaphragm now and you will need to sit down and rest more often.

blood in the urine. Other symptoms that you may experience include back pain, high fever, chills, nausea, and vomiting.

**Placenta praevia** is a rare condition which usually occurs when a woman has had more than one child. The placenta is situated low in the uterus so that it blocks, or partially blocks, the cervix. The pressure of the baby on the placenta may cause painless bleeding any time after 28 weeks.

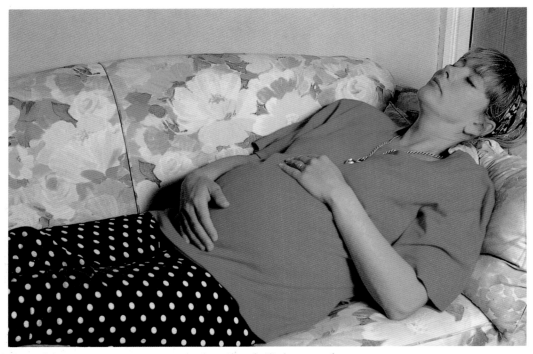

*As your baby starts to put pressure on your stomach, you'll need to lie down more often to rest.*

If this happens, you may have to stay in hospital until after your baby is born. If the obstruction is particularly severe, your baby may need to be delivered by Caesarean.

**Abruptio placentae** is when part of the placenta comes away from the wall of the uterus causing some abdominal pain and bleeding. You should call the doctor immediately. The baby could be at risk if a large part of the placenta has come away, because it will be deprived of necessary oxygen and nutrients. Sometimes a blood transfusion is necessary and in late pregnancy the baby may be delivered by Caesarean. If only a small part of the placenta has come away, you will need to have complete bedrest until the bleeding stops.

**Placental insufficiency** occurs when the placenta doesn't function efficiently and the baby grows more slowly than normal because of lack of nourishment. If this happens, you will be told to rest so that the blood flow from the placenta to the baby can improve. A urine test will also be taken to see whether the health of the baby is being affected and whether induction is going to be necessary for the birth.

*Above: If the weather is pleasant, you might well prefer to take your regular rests in the garden, but remember to support your legs. Below: Resting on your side may be more comfortable than lying on your back.*

### Your growing baby

The baby is filling almost all the space in your uterus and its head is now more or less in proportion with the rest of the body. The eyebrows and eyelashes are fully grown and the baby has quite a lot of hair which is still growing. The eyes, which can now open and close, are beginning to focus. The baby weighs around 1kg/2¼lb and is about 38cm/ 15in long.

# WEEK 30: TRAVEL/BACKACHE

There is no reason why you shouldn't travel during pregnancy, but during the later stages you should check with your doctor if you are going abroad. Airlines may not be willing to take you once you are past 28 weeks because of the risk of a premature labour occurring.

If you want to fly you will need to check with the airline before you book a ticket; the airline may insist on a medical certificate stating that it is safe for you to travel. If you wish to visit a country where immunization is required, you will have to get medical advice because some vaccines should be avoided completely in pregnancy.

You will probably want to avoid long car journeys towards the end of pregnancy because you may find them uncomfortable. When travelling by car it is important to wear your seat belt so that it fits neatly across your thighs and above your abdomen, but not across the middle. If the belt was worn across your body it could possibly cause damage to your baby if you were involved in a car accident.

### BACKACHE

This can be particularly troublesome during the last months of pregnancy. Hormones have softened your ligaments and the additional weight you are carrying inevitably puts a strain on your stomach muscles, which in turn puts strain on your back muscles. If the backache you are suffering is particularly severe, always check it out with your doctor because it can indicate the presence of a kidney infection.

### You and your body

You will feel larger and clumsier now and your movements will be slower. It is important to try to maintain good posture to prevent backache. You may have problems sleeping and become a bit breathless if you walk too fast or climb stairs.

Ease upper backache by lying on a firm surface with pillows under your head and knees. Lower backache can be helped by kneeling on all fours, with your back straight and your hands and knees well apart, then dropping your head and arching your back. Repeat this exercise several times.

You can help to avoid backache by wearing low-heeled shoes and trying not to hollow your back when you are standing. When you sit down, put a cushion in the small of your back; when you get out of a chair, push yourself right to the edge before attempting to stand up.

A firm mattress will help when you are lying down; when you get up from the lying position, roll onto your side and then push yourself slowly up. If you have to bend down, always bend your body from the knees and then squat down to pick up anything from the floor.

### Your growing baby

The baby is beginning to move about less vigorously now because it has less space to move around in the uterus. To get comfortable it is likely to adopt a curled-up position with arms and legs crossed. The baby is now about 39cm/15½in long and weighs around 1.1kg/2½lb.

*Don't fasten your seat belt over your bump as your baby could be damaged in a accident.*

*Fasten your seat belt under your bump and across your thighs to protect your baby.*

## Bending in pregnancy

**1** *In later pregnancy particularly, bend your knees, not from the waist, and pick up the object when you are squatting.*

**2** *As you get up from the squatting position, keep your back straight and lift up the object at arm's length.*

**3** *As you gradually become upright, straighten your bent knees without making any jerky movements.*

## How to relieve backache

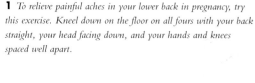

**1** *To relieve painful aches in your lower back in pregnancy, try this exercise. Kneel down on the floor on all fours with your back straight, your head facing down, and your hands and knees spaced well apart.*

**2** *Drop your head right down and arch your back to stretch out the painful muscles, hold for several seconds, then release, raising your head up again. Repeat the exercise several times for the best relief.*

# WEEK 31: DEALING WITH DISCOMFORT

**You and your body**

Breathlessness may be more of a problem now, especially if you overdo things. Try to get as much rest as possible and slow down any exercise regime to a pace that suits you. If your breasts feel uncomfortable when you go to bed, wear a maternity or specially designed sleep bra at night.

The baby is getting quite big and will be putting pressure on your diaphragm, which may mean that you are now finding it more difficult to breathe. This breathlessness should pass once the baby's head drops into the pelvis and becomes engaged in a few weeks' time. Try sitting and standing as straight as possible, and put some extra pillows behind your shoulders when you are in bed.

You are likely to need a larger size of bra towards the end of pregnancy and the one that you buy now should fit you after the baby is born. If you are intending to breast-feed, buy a front-opening nursing bra that will be suitable now and after the birth.

Choose a bra with wide adjustable straps and fastenings and which has a broad supportive band under the cups. Make sure that the cups fit comfortably and do not gape under the arms. Buy one made from cotton or a cotton mixture that will be more comfortable to wear, and allow your skin to breathe properly, particularly in hot weather.

BRAXTON HICKS CONTRACTIONS
During pregnancy you will experience contractions which may be uncomfortable but are not usually painful. These are known as Braxton Hicks contractions, which tighten the muscles of the uterus about every 20 minutes throughout pregnancy, although you have proba-bly not been aware of them during the early months. In the last weeks of pregnancy these contractions become more noticeable as they

begin to prepare the uterus for labour by drawing up the cervix and making it thinner. When you have these contractions, practise your breathing techniques for labour.

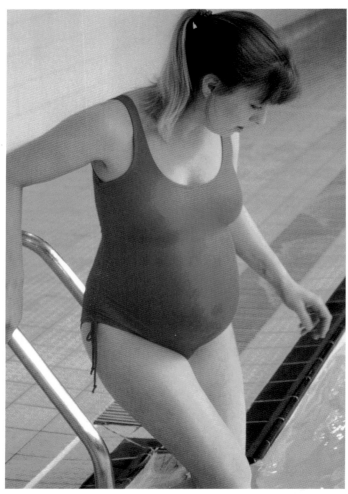

*Exercise like swimming, where you are supported in the water, will keep you fit in late pregnancy. It may also relieve backache as the motion will stretch the back muscles.*

*Above: Keep a kick count of your baby's movements on a chart.*

*Below: Try sitting in a yoga position with your back straight to alleviate the pressure your baby is putting on your diaphragm.*

## KICK COUNTS

You can check on your baby's well-being by keeping a count of the fetal movements. If there is any concern about the baby's development you may be asked to keep a kick chart recording the first 10 movements each day. For your own peace of mind you should be aware of these movements so that if for any reason they become less frequent, or even stop altogether, you will notice at once. If you are ever concerned about lack of movement, seek some medical advice from your doctor immediately because it could indicate some trouble with the baby.

As your pregnancy progresses and the baby gets bigger it has less room to manoeuvre, so movements will be more noticeable, but less frequent. By the end of your pregnancy the baby will probably move between 10 and 12 times in a 12-hour period.

### Your growing baby

The organs are almost completely developed, apart from the lungs which are still not fully mature. The brain is still growing and the nerve cells and connections are now working. A protective sheath is developing around the nerve fibres so that messages travel faster, enabling the baby to learn more. It can feel pain, will move if prodded and you can feel it jump at loud noises. The baby is around 40cm/15¾in long and weighs about 1.4kg/3lb.

# WEEK 32: POSITIONS FOR LABOUR

It is a good idea to practise some of the positions that will help you through the different stages of labour. During the first stage you should try to stay upright and keep active. Being upright will make your contractions stronger and more efficient. It will also allow gravity to keep the baby's head pressed down, which will help your cervix to dilate faster so that labour is speeded up. Remaining active will give you more control over labour so that you should feel less pain. If you are lying down, your uterus presses on the large blood vessels running down your back and this can reduce the blood flow through the placenta to and from the baby. If you feel you want to lie down during labour, try to position yourself on your side rather than on your back.

COPING WITH CONTRACTIONS

You should aim to give the baby as much room as possible in your pelvis and the best way to achieve this is by keeping your knees well apart and leaning forward so that the uterus tilts away from your spine. During the first-stage contractions it may help to lean against your partner, or if you prefer you can kneel down resting your arms and head on a cushion on the seat of a chair. If you find being upright tiring, try kneeling on all fours. This allows you to keep the weight of the baby off your lower back.

By the time your contractions are coming every few minutes you may want to adopt a squatting position, or you could try kneeling forward onto a pile of cushions or a bean bag with your legs wide apart. It may

**You and your body**

If you work, you may have left by now or will have a date when you are going to leave. Enjoy the last weeks of your pregnancy and spend time singing and talking to your baby. You may find your baby's movements uncomfortable now that it is so much bigger. Occasionally, you may feel its feet getting stuck under your ribs.

help if your partner massages your back while you are in this position.

When you reach the second stage you'll want to find a comfortable position for the birth. If you lie on your back you will literally have to push the baby uphill. If you remain upright your abdominal muscles will work more efficiently as you bear down, and gravity will help the baby out. Try squatting, supported on both sides, or with your partner supporting you from behind, so that your pelvis is at its widest and you have control over the pelvic floor

## Labour positions

**1** *Relax on all fours by flopping forward onto a pile of cushions or a bean bag to give the baby as much room as possible in the pelvis. Your partner can help by massaging your back.*

**2** *Take the weight of the baby off your spine by kneeling on the floor on all fours with your arms and legs wide apart. Keep the small of your back flat and not hollowed.*

### Your growing baby

The baby is now very energetic and it will have periods of extreme activity, and you will feel it twisting and turning. As it continues to grow it will have less and less room to move in, so it will soon settle, probably in the head-down position, ready for birth. The baby is about 40.5cm/16in long and weighs about 1.6kg/3½lb.

which you will need to relax. Kneeling with your legs wide apart and supported on both sides is another good position for pushing.

Once you have tried these positions, experiment with others which you feel may be right for you during labour. Try them on the floor, on the bed, leaning on or against furniture, or using your partner for support. This way, when you are in labour, you will already know how to get into positions that are comfortable for you and that will help you cope with contractions.

### Partner support

**1** *Practise using your partner for support during labour by leaning back against him, allowing him to take your weight.*

**2** *Stand with feet well apart and lean on your partner, putting your head on your arms to ease pressure on your uterus.*

**3** *Kneel on all fours with your forearms on the floor and your knees spread wide so that your abdomen is hanging between them. It can help to rock backwards and forwards in this position.*

**4** *In this squatting position, your pelvis is wide open and the baby's head is pressed down. You may find that it helps to place your hands on the floor to give yourself some support.*

# WEEK 33: EMOTIONS IN LATE PREGNANCY

It is not just your body that is going through great changes while you are pregnant. Your whole way of life is changing and this can lead to conflicting emotions, especially during the last few months. You may wonder how you are going to cope with all the new responsibilities and be concerned about your baby – whether it will be born perfect in every way. Vivid dreams are common at this time and can be worrying, especially if they are about the birth or babies. You may even feel occasionally that the whole thing has been a ghastly mistake and that you want to go back to the way things were before you became pregnant. Don't worry, all these feelings are quite normal.

It helps to talk about your fears and concerns, either to your partner or to a close friend who has had similar feelings. Parentcraft classes are also a good place to discuss these worries, especially as you will be with other women who are experiencing the same emotions. If you find that talking about it doesn't help and that anxiety is taking over your life, discuss how you feel with your midwife or doctor.

### YOUR PARTNER

It is easy to forget that an expectant father is also going through some emotional changes as he comes to terms with impending parenthood. He doesn't have any outward sign of the change that is about to occur in his life, but that doesn't mean he isn't feeling the same concerns as you. He also has additional worries about you and how you will cope during labour; he may even secretly fear for your safety during the birth. If he is now solely responsible for providing financially for you and the baby he

**You and your body**
Your weight gain should have slowed down. If it hasn't and you are still gaining more than 1kg/2¼lb a week, you should check with your doctor that everything is all right.

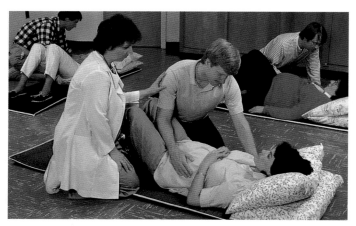

*At ante-natal classes you learn what to expect in labour and the different positions you can adopt. Your partner is usually welcome to come with you and find out how he can help.*

may be feeling considerable stress. Make time to talk to each other about your feelings and try to ensure that these last weeks before the birth are special for you both. Share the preparation for the birth so that each of you is involved in what is going to happen. Plan some treats where you can be alone together, such as dinner at a favourite restaurant, a trip to the theatre, or a weekend away at a hotel. By making time for yourselves you are less likely to have misunderstandings which could lead to hurt and disappointment.

### Your growing baby

The fingernails are fully formed although the toenails are not quite so advanced. The vernix covering the skin has become thicker. The lungs are almost fully developed and the baby will be practising breathing in preparation for the birth. It measures around 41.5cm/16½in and weighs about 1.8kg/4lb.

OTHER CHILDREN

If you have other children you may have told them about the new baby early on in your pregnancy. Very young children will need to have it explained to them over and over again, because the concept of a new baby is hard for them to grasp. Older children will probably be very excited and will enjoy being involved in any preparations you are making for their brother or sister.

How children react once the baby has arrived depends a lot on their age and personality, as well as their relationship with you. A pre-school child may react by being naughty for a period in an attempt to get your attention. A toddler who has recently been potty- trained, may start wetting or dirtying him- or herself again. Both age groups may start waking at night. Use common sense and tact to minimize any problems. Talk to your children about the new baby, encourage their help and involvement when he or she is born, but always make sure that they have special time with you on their own.

*Right: Let an older child feel your bump, and talk to him or her about their new brother or sister, so they can get used to the idea of a new family member.*
*Below: When you are spending time with your other children, talk to them about the new baby.*

# WEEK 34: OLDER FIRST-TIME MOTHERS

If you are 35 or over, you will have been offered an amniocentesis because of the higher risk of fetal abnormality. The amniotic fluid will have been screened for a number of chromosomal disorders, which include Down's syndrome and spina bifida. Of course, you don't have to have this test, but many mothers find it reassuring.

It is important that you attend all your ante-natal clinics so that a close check can be kept on you and the unborn baby all through pregnancy. Many older expectant mothers prefer to have the ante-natal care at a hospital where expert medical help is on hand. The risk to the baby during labour and birth increases with rising maternal age, but many factors affect labour, including the general health of the mother during pregnancy.

Although nearly 70 per cent of women over 30 have normal deliveries, there is a slightly greater risk of complications during labour for women who are over 35. This is usually because the baby is in distress through lack of oxygen because of placental deterioration. As a result of these complications older women are more likely to have medical intervention such as forceps.

**You and your body**

Your blood pressure may be slightly raised and you will probably be told to take things easy. Swelling of the hands and feet could also be a problem so try to get as much rest as possible, preferably with your feet up.

BIRTH AND THE OLDER MOTHER

Most older women go full term, and if you are between 30 and 34 there is no reason why you shouldn't have a natural birth. If you are 35 or over, or if there is a suggestion that your baby may be small, you may be offered continuous monitoring. This may also be necessary if there is a some sign of staining. This means

*Seeing your baby on an ultrasound scan can be very reassuring.*

that you will be unable to move around freely. But this is a small price to pay for a healthy baby.

Babies born to older mothers are more likely to be born preterm, often because of the failure of the placenta, so that the baby is no longer getting sufficient nourishment and oxygen. If this happens you will have a forceps or ventouse delivery, or you may be offered a Caesarean.

*Below: The doctor will talk about your baby and give you a printout of your scan.*

**Your growing baby**
The weight gain continues to increase. The eyes respond to bright lights and the baby will practise blinking; eyebrows and eyelashes are fully developed. A boy's testicles will have descended into the groin. The baby is 43cm/17in long and weighs about 2kg/4½lb.

*Right: Regular ante-natal checks are particularly important for older mothers.*

# WEEK 35: FINAL PREPARATIONS

Even though your baby is not due for some weeks, you should be ready in case he or she decides to put in an early appearance. Check the nursery and make sure all the baby's sheets and blankets have been washed and aired. Sort out all the baby clothes and put the ones you will want immediately after the birth in your hospital case. It's a good idea to stock up on non-perishable goods and to fill the freezer. This will save you from having to do a lot of shopping over the next few weeks and will allow you more time with the baby when you first come home.

Make sure you know where your partner is going to be over the next few weeks; if he is out and about it may be a good idea for you both to have mobile phones. Keep your car filled with petrol and make sure that you both know the quickest route to the hospital. Have a list of emergency numbers, including a local taxi firm, beside the telephone.

**You and your body**

Discuss any worries you may have about labour and birth with your doctor or midwife. You will be feeling tired and even a little fed up, so try to get as much rest as you can. Pay special attention to your diet: you will be needing another 200 calories a day during these last weeks. Some practical planning now can save time and forestall anxiety at the time of labour and delivery.

THE HOSPITAL

Pack what you want to take to hospital several weeks before the delivery date; keep the bag where you can easily get it when the time comes. Remember that there are three separate aspects to consider: labour, your hospital stay, and going-home clothes for you and the baby.

You should bring any personal items that will make life more comfortable for you during labour. Include anything from a personal stereo and your favourite music to a face cloth and massage oils. You may even want to take along a bean bag if you are planning an active labour and your hospital doesn't provide these. Leave some room for last-minute items such as an ice pack for backache and even a snack and drink for your partner. Don't forget to put your birthplan and maternity record right at the top so that you can give these to the midwife when you arrive at the hospital. It is sensible

*It is sensible to pack a small bag for your brief stay in hospital well in advance in case you have to leave in a rush. Don't forget some clothes for your new baby.*

*You might need to get to the hospital quickly, so have your bag packed and keep a local taxi number close to hand.*

*It is a good idea to buy vegetables and other food that can be cooked and frozen in preparation for when you return from the hospital.*

to pack things for labour separately, since you will want to be able to get to them quickly.

How much you pack for the hospital depends on your planned length of stay after the birth. The hospital may issue a list of the items that you will need to bring with you. But if it doesn't, ask your midwife whether you need to take in baby clothes and nappies, or contact the maternity unit direct.

If you are staying in for a few days and aren't too tired, you might want to write cards to your friends and relatives announcing your baby's arrival, so remember to include birth announcement cards, your address book, and stamps. You should also bring a supply of small change in case you need to use hospital pay phones.

You will need clothes for you and the baby when it's time for you to return home. It is sensible to pack a small bag now with all the items you think you'll want for your return journey; you can either bring it with you or your partner can bring it later. Remember that although you will feel considerably slimmer than you were before the birth, it takes a while before you get your figure back, so your going-home outfit will still need to be loose.

### Your growing baby

The baby is putting on weight each day and now fills most of the uterus, so you may find it uncomfortable when it moves around. The baby now does body rolls rather than the more energetic movements it made when it was smaller. It is now about 445cm/17½in long and weighs around 2.3kg/5lb.

# WEEK 36: DISCOMFORTS IN LATE PREGNANCY

**You and your body**

You will be able to feel the top of your uterus just below your breastbone. This can make breathing uncomfortable and you may suffer from pain in your ribcage. Your ante-natal checks will be weekly from now on.

As you find getting around more difficult and everything generally more of an effort, you may become irritable over the smallest things. You will be impatient for your baby to arrive, and concern about the impending birth and worries about how you will cope with being a parent can make you short-tempered, especially with your partner. Tell him how you are feeling so that he understands why you are being so irritable and perhaps not paying him as much attention as usual.

Aches or pains around your pubic area, in your groin, or down the inside of your legs can be caused by your baby's head pressing on the nerves, or by your pelvic joints beginning to soften in preparation for labour. Pain under your ribs is caused by the expanding uterus pushing the ribs up. These aches and pains are not serious, but they can be quite uncomfortable. Sitting or standing as straight as you can, or stretching upwards, will help ease most of these discomforts, although

you may find lying down better for relief of pelvic pain. If you get severe pain in your abdomen, or if you suffer any abdominal pain that is also accompanied by vaginal bleeding, you must get in touch with your doctor at once.

It is quite common to suffer from heartburn and nausea towards the end of pregnancy. This is caused by the enlarged uterus pressing on your stomach. It often helps to eat

*Soaking in a warm bath can help to relieve any aches and pains you are suffering.*

small meals at more frequent
intervals, rather than two or three
big meals a day.

ANTE-NATAL CHECK
If there is any concern about the size
of your pelvis in relation to your
baby's size, or there is some other
reason for the baby's delivery not
being straightforward, you will be
offered a scan and a Caesarean may
be discussed. If this is thought to be
necessary, the doctor at the hospital
will explain the medical procedures
that will be used.

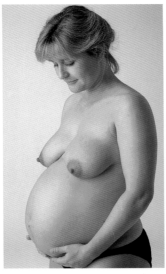

*As your baby increases in size, you may
begin to find breathing uncomfortable and
get some pain in your ribcage.*

### Your growing baby

The nervous system is maturing and
the baby is getting ready for birth
by starting to practise breathing
movements, sucking, and swallowing.
It is now about 46cm/18¼in long and
weighs around 2.5kg/5½lb.

*In this late stage of pregnancy you will probably be able to feel the top of your uterus
which is now positioned just below your breastbone.*

# WEEK 37: AS BIRTH APPROACHES

**Your growing baby**
The lanugo, the fine hair that covers the baby's body, is beginning to wear off. The baby has started to produce a hormone called cortisone, which will help the lungs to become fully matured so that they are ready to cope with breathing once the baby is born. The baby will be practising breathing although there is no air in its lungs. The baby is now about 47cm/18½ in long and weighs around 2.7kg/6lb.

Between weeks 36 and 38 the baby's head may "engage". This is when it settles downwards, deep in your pelvis ready for the birth. You should feel some relief from the pressure in your abdomen when this happens which is why it is sometimes referred to as "lightening". You will start to feel less breathless now because the baby is no longer putting any pressure on your diaphragm and your lungs. If this is not your first baby, the head may not engage until you actually go into labour.

### PREMATURE AND TWIN BIRTHS

If the baby is born before 37 weeks it will be described as being preterm or premature. Most premature babies are nursed in a special care baby unit (SCBU) or, if very sick or small, an intensive care baby unit (ICBU). Babies are given expert care and attention in these facilities, so even those who are born as young as 24 weeks have a chance of survival.

*This is probably the last time for a while that you will have time to yourself, so make the most of it and rest often.*

*With modern technology even babies as young as 24 weeks normally survive in the special baby units.*

If you are giving birth to twins, the labour doesn't usually take any longer than if you are giving birth to a single baby (singleton). Because twins tend to be smaller babies, the labour and birth can often be easier and less painful. Once the birth canal has been stretched to allow one baby to be born, the second baby will usually be born quite quickly. If twins share the placenta, they will both be born before it is delivered. Even if they are fraternal twins and each have their own placenta, they will usually be born first, although occasionally one baby is born, followed by its placenta, before the second baby arrives.

### You and your body

Your baby could arrive at any time from now until the end of week 42, so check that you have everything organized. You will probably be given the chance to visit the hospital and see where you are going to give birth. Don't be afraid to ask questions if there is anything you don't understand about hospital procedures.

Sometime between now and the birth, you may experience a sudden burst of energy, known as the nesting instinct. Don't overdo things and decide to spring-clean your whole house. Remember that you will shortly need all your energy reserves for the exhausting demands of labour.

*As the birth approaches, it is a good time for you and your partner to start making a list of names that you both like.*

# WEEK 38: INDUCTION/PAIN RELIEF IN LABOUR

**You and your body**

You will notice that the baby is moving about less now that it is head down in the uterus. You may be feeling tired and rather depressed about the waiting so try to keep busy.

Sometimes labour has to be induced because of a problem such as pre-eclampsia, bleeding, diabetes, or being well past your due date. Induction techniques include:

**Pessaries** Prostaglandins are naturally occurring hormones which help dilate the cervix. A synthetic form of prostaglandin, either in a pessary or gel, is applied internally to the cervix to soften and thin it. It may require two or three treatments before labour starts.

**Artificial rupture of the membranes (ARM)** This involves the puncturing of the membranes of the amniotic sac. Once ruptured, prostaglandins from the amniotic fluid are released and labour follows.

**Syntocinon drip** This is a concentrated synthetic form of oxytocin, a natural hormone that makes the uterus contract. Given through an intravenous drip, it acts quickly and produces contractions that may be stronger than those of natural labour. Some hospitals offer an epidural with this form of induction.

## PAIN RELIEF

If you decide to have a completely natural birth make sure that this is marked clearly on your birthplan and inform the medical staff who will be attending you during labour. Remember that you can always change your mind if you find coping with the pain too difficult. If you

have decided to opt for some form of pain relief, there are a number of options you can choose from:

**Gas and air (Entonox)** A mixture of oxygen and nitrous oxide which is breathed in through a mask or mouthpiece and takes the edge off pain. This is the most controllable form of pain relief because you hold the mask or mouthpiece and regulate the gas and air intake. The gas is processed in your lungs so it doesn't affect the baby.

**Injections** Drugs like pethidine and meptid can be given during the first stage of labour. They will help you relax and relieve pain but they can make your baby sleepy.

**Epidural** A local anaesthetic is injected into the space between your spinal column and the spinal cord, numbing the nerves that serve the uterus. An epidural or spinal block may be used if a Caesarean delivery is performed because it allows the mother to stay awake while her baby is being delivered.

An anaesthetist is needed to give an epidural injection, which takes around 15 minutes to set up, and then usually requires topping up every hour and a half.

**Transcutaneous electrical nerve stimulation (TENS)** This is a technique which involves a weak electric current being used to block pain sensations in the brain and to stimulate the release of endorphins, the body's natural painkilling

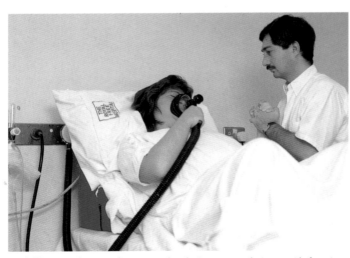

*By holding a mask to your face, you can breathe in oxygen and nitrous oxide for pain relief during contractions.*

hormones. TENS is not available at all hospitals so you may need to hire a machine before you go into labour. Your midwife should be able to give you all the necessary details.

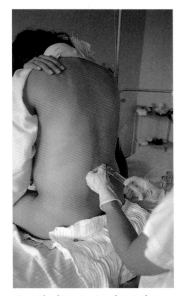

*An epidural injection into the spinal area helps deaden the nerves around the uterus.*

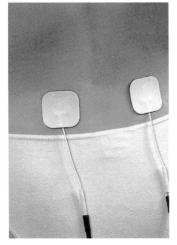

*Pads from a TENS machine can be fitted to your back to ease pain in labour.*

*At the most painful times in your labour, lean on your partner for support and encouragement. He can also massage your back if it is really painful.*

**Alternative pain relief** Both acupuncture and hypnosis can be used effectively to relieve pain during childbirth, but if you are having a hospital birth you will need to ask for permission to have a private practitioner with you during labour.

If used correctly, massage, aromatherapy, and reflexology can all help to ease labour. You should get some expert advice before the birth if you intend to use any of these techniques.

### Your growing baby

The baby has put on fat so that it now appears rounded and its skin has a pinkish look. The hair may be as long as 5cm/2in and the nails already need cutting. The vernix, which has been protecting the skin of the growing baby from the amniotic fluid, is beginning to dissolve. At this stage of your pregnancy, the baby now measures about 48cm/19in and weighs around 2.9kg/6½lb.

# WEEK 39: COMPLICATIONS DURING BIRTH

The ideal position for your baby to be born is with its head lying down with its back against your abdomen. This way it has less distance to rotate in the birth canal. Sometimes a baby is in an abnormal position which can make birth more complicated, but this does not necessarily mean that it can't be born in the normal way.

An occipito posterior position means that the baby is lying with its back towards your back and, if it fails to turn, will be delivered normally, but will be born face up. This way of lying often leads to a long, back-aching labour.

In a deep transverse arrest, the baby's head partially rotates in the birth canal and then becomes stuck with its face towards one side. The baby will need to be helped out. This can sometimes also happen if you push too hard by mistake in the second stage of labour.

Disproportion means that the baby's head is too big for your pelvis. A scan will be done to decide whether there is enough room for a normal delivery to take place. If there isn't, your baby will probably be born by Caesarean.

### Breech birth

A small number of babies don't turn in the last weeks of pregnancy. This means that their feet or bottom would come out first so the birth canal will not have been stretched enough when the head, the largest part of the baby's body, is ready to be born. Doctors have different opinions about the best way of delivering a breech baby; some insist that a Caesarean is the safest method, others believe that birth should take place under an epidural, and some think that if the mother remains mobile throughout the first stage of labour the baby will get itself into a good position for birth. It may then be helped out with forceps or by vacuum extraction.

### Birth positions

A normal birth

A breech birth

### You and your body

The waiting is nearly over and you will probably be feeling both excited and apprehensive. You may be having quite strong Braxton Hicks contractions as the cervix softens in readiness for the birth. Although you may be feeling heavy and weary, don't simply sit around waiting for something to happen. Keep up your social life and talk to other friends from your parent-craft classes who are at the same stage as you.

### Forceps delivery

In a forceps delivery, your legs will be put up in stirrups and then the forceps, which are like a pair of large, shallow metal spoons, will be inserted into the vagina and cupped around the baby's head. The doctor helps the baby out while you push.

### Vacuum extraction

Vacuum extraction (ventouse) is now used more often than the forceps method. With this technique the doctor places a suction cup on the baby's head and the baby is sucked out as you push down with each contraction.

If the birth canal is not going to be big enough for the baby's head and there is a risk that the perineum may tear, a small cut is made in this area under local anaesthetic.

### Your growing baby

The baby is now able to function on its own, although it is still getting nourishment from the placenta. The baby is in position for birth and is about 49cm/19¼in long and weighs around 3.1kg/7lb.

This type of incision is called an episiotomy and is stitched after the birth, again under local anaesthetic.

FETAL MONITORING

This keeps a check on the unborn baby's heartbeat during labour and the birth. Monitoring can be done the low-tech way by simply placing a stethoscope against the abdomen to listen to the baby's heart, or through electronic fetal monitoring (EFM). There are two types of EFM and both give a continuous readout of the baby's heart and uterine contractions; if the EFM method is used then you are having a high-tech birth.

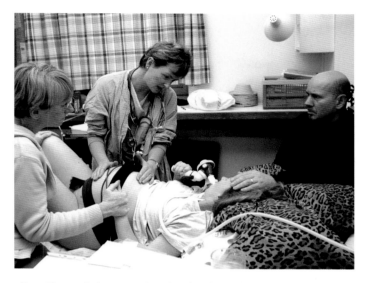

*Below: If you need a forceps delivery, your legs will be put up in stirrups.*

*Above: Electronic fetal monitoring (EFM) involves placing a belt around your bump which is attached to a monitor. This gives a continuous readout of the baby's heart.*

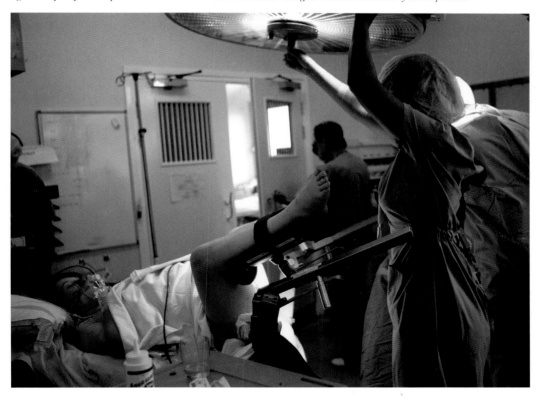

# WEEK 40: LABOUR AND BIRTH

It is unlikely that you won't recognize the beginnings of labour as the signs, when they come, are generally unmistakable. There are three main indications that labour is about to start, or has started, and they can occur in any order. Once one or more of these has occurred you should let the hospital or midwife know immediately:

**A show** The protective plug, which sealed the cervix at the neck of the uterus, comes away and passes down the vagina. It usually appears as a small amount of bloodstained mucus. A show occurs before labour starts or during the first stage.

**Waters breaking** The membranes of the amniotic sac in which your baby has been floating break, causing either a trickle or a sudden gush of clear fluid from the vagina. If the fluid is yellow, greenish, or brown in colour you will need to go to the hospital straight away because the baby may be in distress. Your waters can break hours before labour starts or when it is well underway.

**Contractions** The regular tightening of the muscles of the uterus occurs throughout labour. During the first stage, the contractions thin out and dilate the cervix from closed to 10cm/4in open; in the second stage they help to push the baby down the vagina and after the birth they then deliver the placenta (afterbirth). For most women they feel rather like bad period pains. The contractions may also be accompanied by uncomfortable backache, sickness, and diarrhoea.

## Your growing baby

Your baby is curled up, head down, in the fetal position with legs drawn up underneath and waiting to be born. He or she measures about 50cm/19¾in and weighs around 3.4kg/7½lb.

## You and your body

You will probably be impatient for labour to start as you approach your EDD. If nothing has happened by your due date try not to be too disappointed; only around five per cent of babies actually arrive on the date they were expected. Keep yourself busy and make plans for each day so that you are not just sitting and waiting for something to happen. Once you are close to your EDD you may feel more confident wearing a sanitary towel just in case your waters break.

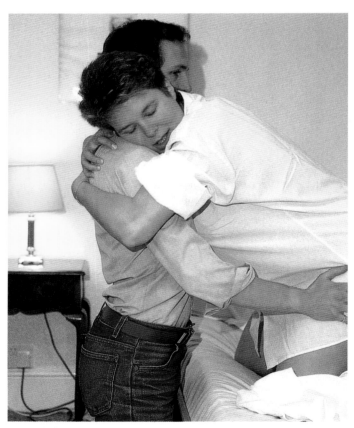

*During the first stage of labour, you can involve your partner by leaning and holding onto him for comfort and also physical support.*

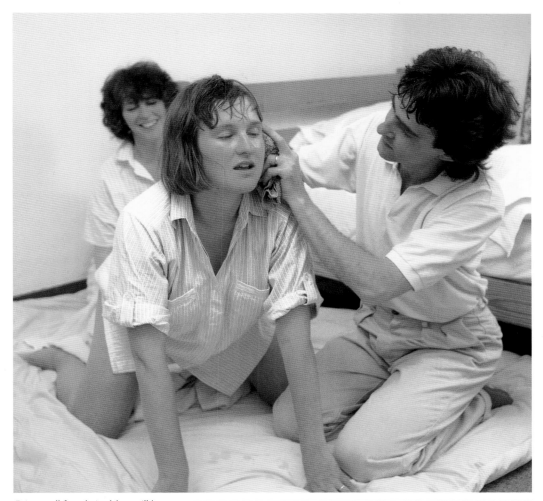

*Being on all fours during labour will keep the weight of the baby off your back as your partner helps to ease your discomfort.*

## STAGES OF LABOUR

**The first stage** There are three stages of labour and the first is usually the longest, lasting generally for up to 12 hours for a first baby. Contractions, which may have started off as mild and infrequent will, by the end of the first stage, be very strong and coming close together. Once they are coming

### Tips for labour

- Keep active for as long as you can during the first stage of labour.
- Don't be on your own: get your partner, mother or a friend to stay with you once labour has started.
- If your waters break check that the fluid is clear: yellow, greenish, or brown fluid could mean that your baby is in distress and you should go to the hospital immediately.
- Ask for pain relief if you need it.

- Try different positions to help you cope with the pain of contractions.
- Get your birth partner to make sure your wishes are known to whoever is delivering your baby. You may be too busy coping with contractions to explain clearly what you want.
- Put your baby to the breast soon after the birth. This will stimulate your milk supply and help to speed up the delivery of the placenta.

regularly every 10 minutes, or are each lasting for around 45 seconds, you should start getting ready to go to the hospital, or call the midwife if you are having your baby at home. When you get to the hospital, or the midwife attending you at home

arrives, you will be examined to see how far your cervix has dilated and your blood pressure will be checked.

Although you will be able to carry on fairly normally for quite a lot of the first stage you should have someone with you. You will need to

eat plenty of light snacks during this stage as your body is having to work very hard and will need plenty of energy in order to cope.

Towards the end of the first stage you will go into what is known as the transitional stage which can last for anything up to an hour. During this transitional period your baby moves down the birth canal and you will feel pressure on your back passage which may make you want to start pushing, even though the cervix is not fully dilated. By using the breathing techniques you have been taught you will be able to control this urge.

**The second stage** Once the cervix is fully dilated and you start pushing the baby out you have entered the second stage. It can last for as little as half an hour or for as long as two hours or more. Once the baby's head is visible to the midwife she will tell you to start pushing. When the head reaches the vaginal opening you will be told to pant in short breaths so that the head can be delivered as slowly as possible. This allows the skin and muscle of the perineum to stretch so that the head can be born. If it seems likely that you will tear badly an episiotomy, a small cut in the perineum, the area between the vagina and anus, may be given. Once the head is born your baby's body will follow quite quickly. As soon as your baby is delivered it will be lifted onto your stomach for you to see it. The umbilical cord will be clamped and cut and the midwife will check the baby to make sure that it is all right and breathing properly. You may want to put your baby straight to the breast. You'll certainly wish to admire it with your partner and welcome your child into the world.

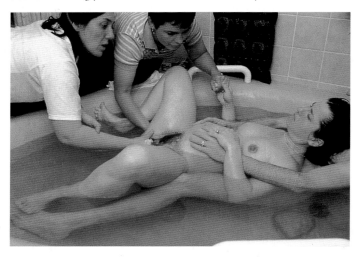

*With a water birth, contractions can be eased by the warm water. Your baby can be delivered in the water or outside.*

*If you have your baby in the water, he will be given to you immediately after the birth for you and your partner to cuddle.*

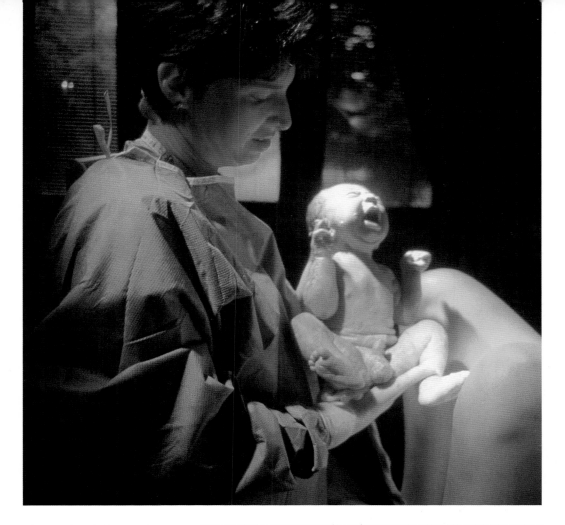

*Above: A doctor holding a newborn baby boy, with the umbilical cord still attached, at a home delivery.*
*Right: A Caesarean is performed when there are risks from natural childbirth. The baby is delivered through an incision.*

**The third stage** The final stage is the birth of the placenta, which usually takes less than half an hour. You may be offered an injection as your baby is being born to speed up the placenta's delivery. The midwife will check to see that the placenta is whole and that nothing has been left inside you. If you had an episiotomy it will be stitched up.

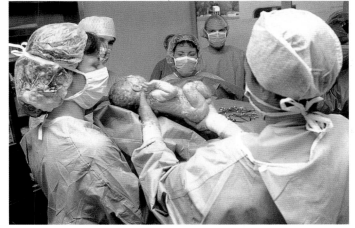

## PART TWO

# BABYCARE

A NEW BABY can seem rather overwhelming, especially if this is
your first experience of motherhood. Suddenly you are responsible
for the care and welfare of a very demanding little person who
needs looking after almost 24 hours a day. If you have never fed,
bathed or changed a baby you need to learn how to carry out these
daily routines. This section looks at basic babycare and explains, in
simple terms, everything that you are likely to need to know about
caring for your baby during the first year of life.

It is important to take care of yourself too, especially in the days
after the birth, so your post-natal care is described at the beginning
of this section.

Feeding your baby should be a special time for you both,
regardless of whether you are breast- or bottle-feeding in the early
months. But when things go wrong, or your baby doesn't feed in
the way you expect, it can be difficult to know what to do.
Breast- and bottle-feeding are discussed here, along with the latest
information on when and how to introduce first foods.

When your child is unwell it is quite natural to be concerned.
Knowing what to do and when you need to call the doctor comes
with experience. In the meantime the section on common
childhood ailments such as coughs, colds, teething and sickness tells
you how to relieve discomfort and when you should seek medical
help. There is also a comprehensive first aid section which explains
exactly what you should do if your child has an accident.

Caring for your baby will take up a great deal of your time
during the first year, so use the daily routines of bathing, feeding
and changing as a time to get to know and enjoy each other.

# POST-NATAL CARE

Although your new baby will probably give you great emotional satisfaction, you may be physically uncomfortable. Your body has gone through many changes during pregnancy and it will take a while for it to return to its pre-pregnancy state.

Six weeks after the birth your doctor will examine you to make sure that everything is returning to normal; this also gives you a chance to discuss any worries you may have. The doctor will take your blood pressure and check a sample of your urine. Your breasts and abdomen will be examined and the doctor will make sure that any stitches have healed properly. You will probably have an internal examination to check the size and position of your uterus and you may have a cervical smear test if one is due.

If your baby was born in hospital, a midwife or doctor will probably talk to you about contraception before you go home. Alternatively, you can discuss this at your six-week check. Don't take any risks; to avoid getting pregnant again you should

use contraception as soon as you resume intercourse. It is an old wives' tale that breast-feeding prevents conception.

If you were not immune to rubella (German measles) during your pregnancy, you will probably be offered the immunization before you leave hospital or at your six-week check-up. Ask your doctor if you are at all unsure about your immunity.

## YOUR BODY

Immediately after the birth your breasts will produce colostrum, a high-protein liquid full of antibodies. Then, after the pregnancy hormones decline, your main milk supply should come in around the third or fourth day. At this time the breasts swell, feel hard, and can sometimes be painful. Bathing them with warm water is soothing, and letting the baby have frequent feeds will also help.

This initial swelling subsides after a few days as both you and your baby get used to feeding. However, if you have decided to bottle-feed,

your breasts will remain full for a few days until they gradually stop producing milk. Your breasts will probably never be quite as firm as they were before pregnancy, but a well-fitting support bra will help greatly.

After delivery your abdomen will probably be quite flabby and wrinkled because of slack muscles and stretched skin. Gentle post-natal exercises will help tighten up your abdominal and vaginal muscles, so make time to do them every day. If you feel you're not disciplined enough to exercise on your own, join a local post-natal class.

Following the birth you will have a vaginal discharge which is known as lochia. This will be like a very heavy period for a few days, with the flow gradually getting lighter until it disappears within a few weeks. Use maternity pads or large sanitary towels to absorb the discharge because there is a risk of infection if you use tampons in the early weeks after the birth.

*Your newborn will find your physical presence very reassuring during the first days after the birth. She will also find your smell comfortingly familiar.*

---

## Post-natal exercises

*Pelvic floor: Lie flat on the floor with your legs drawn up and slightly apart. Close the back passage by drawing it in, hold for the count of four, then relax. Do as often as possible.*

*Tummy toner: Sit up with knees bent and feet flat on the floor. Fold arms in front. Lean back until you feel the abdominal muscles tighten, hold, then sit up and relax. Repeat several times.*

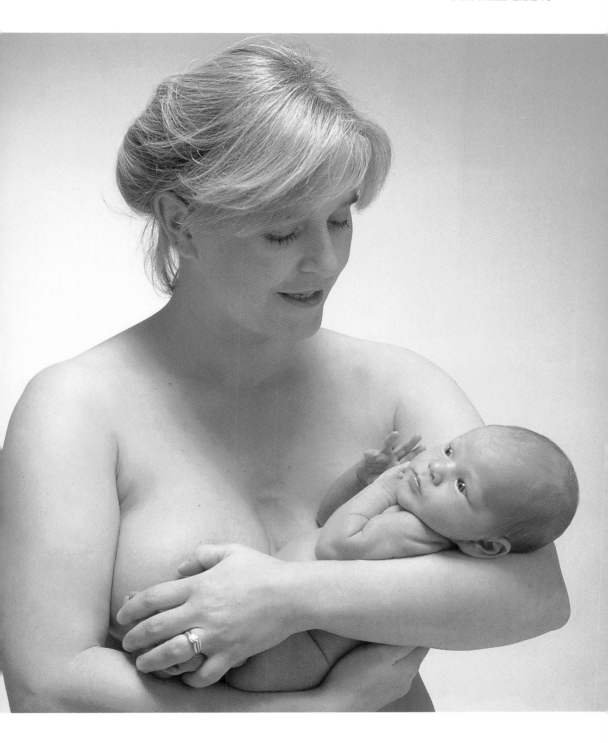

**1** *Curl-ups: This exercise will help strengthen your vertical abdominal muscles. Lie on your back with a pillow under your head, your knees bent and your feet flat on the floor.*

**2** *Pull in your abdominal muscles and, raising your head, stretch your arms towards your knees. Hold for the count of five and then relax slowly. Repeat several times.*

*Leg slide: Lie with your head on a pillow with the small of your back pressed against the floor and your knees bent. Gently slide one leg away from your body until it is fully extended, keeping the small of your back pressed against the floor for as long as you can. Slowly draw the leg back towards your body and then repeat with the other leg. Do this several times.*

Your uterus will take about six weeks to return to its original size. If you are breast-feeding you may feel it contract as you feed the baby.

If your perineum (the skin between the vagina and anus) was bruised during labour, or if you had stitches, you will find that anything that puts pressure on the area painful. Take paracetamol to relieve the pain and ease the soreness with a gel pack held against the perineum or by sitting in warm water. Try drying the area with a hand-held hair dryer, set on cool, rather than

with a bath towel. Do not put the dryer too close to your skin, or use it in the bathroom.

GETTING BACK INTO SHAPE
Despite losing the combined weight of the baby, the placenta, and the amniotic fluid, you will still be heavier than you were before you became pregnant. You may even find that you have to continue to wear maternity clothes for a short while. As your uterus shrinks during the six weeks following the birth you will lose more weight, but you will need

to watch your diet to regain your pre-pregnancy shape. Eat regularly and healthily and don't be tempted, because you're short of time, to snack on foods containing empty calories such as sweets and fizzy drinks. If the weight isn't disappearing as fast as you'd like, ask your health visitor for advice. Do not attempt any diet now or while you are breast-feeding – this would increase stress as your body is struggling to regain its equilibrium. Doing exercises will help you get your figure back, get you moving again, and make you feel fitter.

**1** *Waist trimmer: Lie on the floor with your arms away from your side, with your knees bent and feet flat. Pull in your abdominals and, with knees together, roll over to the right. Take your knees back to the middle and pause.*

**2** *Rest briefly, then pull in your abdominals again and roll your knees to the left, then back to the middle and pause. Keep your shoulders flat on the floor as you roll from side to side. Repeat six times and work up to 20.*

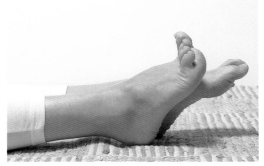

**1** *Foot exercises: These will help improve your circulation and are especially important if you are confined to bed. Lie with your legs straight and knees together and bend and stretch your feet.*

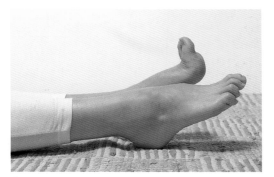

**2** *Flex one foot, pulling the toes up towards you while pointing the other foot away from you. Repeat, alternating the feet. Do this exercise quite briskly for about 30 seconds.*

## Post-natal depression

Two or three days after the birth you may suddenly feel very tearful and depressed. This is commonly called the "third day blues", or the milk blues, because it usually coincides with the milk coming into your breasts. These feelings are caused by all the hormonal changes that are going on in your body and should disappear after a few days. If they don't go away, however, you need to talk to your health visitor or doctor. You may be suffering from post-natal depression (PND) which, if left untreated, can go on for several months. Symptoms of PND include feeling unhappy and wretched as well as irritable and exhausted, yet unable to sleep. You may also lose all interest in food, or find yourself eating too much and then feeling guilty afterwards. PND is one of the most common illnesses following childbirth and it is likely that it is related to the huge hormonal changes that take place at the time of the birth, but it is still unclear as to why it affects some women so badly but not others. If you think you are suffering from PND, don't feel ashamed and don't ignore it. You need help and the sooner you ask for it the sooner you will begin to feel better and able to cope with life again. Post-natal depression is a common condition. Many women are affected by it, and it needs to be treated early on, not ignored in the hope that it will just go away on its own.

Those for strengthening the pelvic floor are among the most important post-natal exercises. The pelvic floor muscles support the bladder, uterus, and rectum, so it is vital that their tone is restored after being stretched during childbirth.

## TIREDNESS AND RELAXATION

Tiredness goes hand in hand with being a new mother, but you need rest to help your body recover from childbirth. It is tempting to use the baby's sleep times to catch up on chores, but do try to have a nap or proper rest at least once during the day. You and your child are more important than housework, so find ways to cut down the work. Accept offers of help and, if no one volunteers, don't be afraid to ask people.

Another way to cope with tiredness or stress is relaxation, so try using the ante-natal relaxation exercises to help you now. Also a long, lazy bath with a few drops of relaxing oil in the water will work wonders. For a real treat, ask your partner to give you a massage using a specially formulated oil before you go to sleep.

## HAIR AND NAILS

The condition of your hair is likely to change during this time. It may become more greasy, or the opposite may happen and it will become noticeably drier than before. You may also suffer an increase in hair loss or your hair may seem a lot thicker than it did before you became pregnant. Whichever condition applies to you, wash your hair using a mild shampoo and avoid rubbing or brushing oily hair too much as this will only stimulate the sebaceous glands to produce more oil. Dry hair should be conditioned after every wash and, if possible, allowed to dry naturally.

Your nails are made of the same tissue as your hair, so if you are having problems with one you are likely to have problems with the other. These are due to fluctuating hormone levels and as soon as these settle your hair and nails will return to normal. Meanwhile, include enough protein and B vitamins in your diet because these will help improve the condition of both your hair and nails.

*Left: A long, lazy bath with a few drops of oil, such as lavender, in the water will help you to relax.*

*Below: A stimulating rub with a loofah brush or mitt will help remove dead cells on the skin's surface, and will stimulate the circulation.*

*Below right: Try using some unscented soap or a soapless cleansing bar if your skin is very itchy.*

*Above: Eating regularly and healthily will help you to regain your pre-pregnancy shape.*

# CARING FOR YOUR NEWBORN

You may find the first weeks at home with your new baby quite difficult, especially if you are still feeling weak and emotionally down. Don't get upset if the house is a mess; it is much more important for you to spend time with your baby than to do housework. If you are still in your dressing gown at lunchtime don't worry; your baby will not care and it is how he or she feels that matters most at the moment.

Your newborn will seem fragile at first, but is actually quite tough. It is natural to be worried about how to pick your new baby up and hold him without hurting him in any way. Before you pick up your baby make sure that you have his head and neck supported with one hand, then slide the other hand underneath his back and bottom to support the lower part of his body before lifting. Hold your baby firmly against you, either cradled against your chest with one arm still supporting the head and the other holding the bottom and lower back, or cradled in your arms with your baby's head lying in the crook of one arm while your other arm supports his back and legs. Always keep any movements gentle so that you don't hurt or frighten your baby.

### THE NEWBORN AT DELIVERY

As soon as the baby is born it will be assessed on the five points of the Apgar Score: heart rate, respiratory rate, colour, activity, and response to stimulation. The baby will be given a maximum of two points for each category, so if he is pink, active, and responsive the score is 10. The Apgar Score is usually done twice – one minute after birth and five minutes after birth – and it may be done again later if there are any problems.

Your baby will also be weighed and measured by the doctor and will probably receive the first of three doses of vitamin K, by mouth, to prevent a rare bleeding illness which occasionally affects newborn babies. A second dose is given at 10 days and a third at six weeks. Vitamin K is given by injection to very premature babies or those who have had a traumatic birth.

After the birth, the umbilical cord will be cut and a plastic clamp placed about 1–2cm/½–1in from the infant's body. Over the next few days

*A newborn baby boy's genitals may appear rather big in proportion to the rest of him. This will right itself after a few days.*

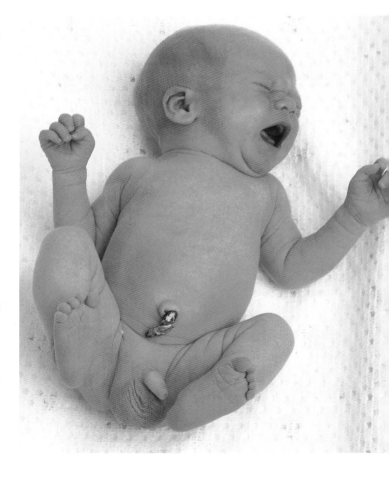

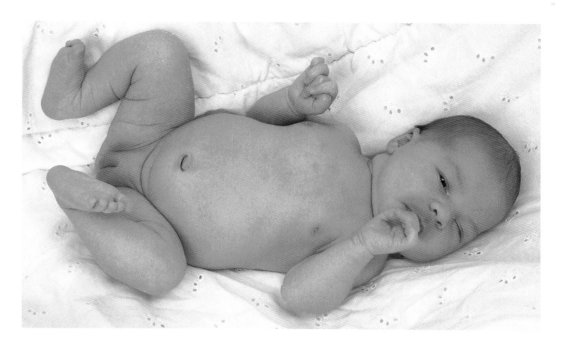

*A newborn baby loses the stump of her umbilical cord usually within the first few days after the birth.*

the cord will shrivel up and after about a week it will drop off completely. During this time the area around the cord should be kept dry and clean to avoid the risk of infection. Try to let the air get to the healing navel as much as possible so that moisture from wet nappies doesn't affect it.

Your baby has soft spots known as fontanelles on the top of the head. These are the spaces between the skull bones, where they have not yet joined. There is usually a large one on top of the skull and a smaller one further back. They will gradually fuse over the next two years. The fontanelles are covered with a tough membrane to protect the brain and you should never press them hard. If you notice a bulge or the skin seems

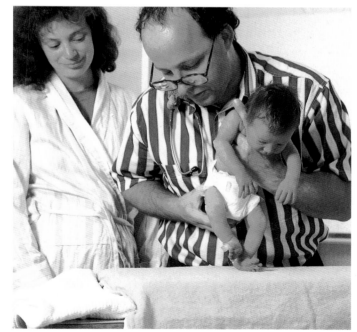

*Before you leave the hospital your newborn baby will be given a complete physical examination to check that all the organs and limbs are functioning correctly.*

very tight over the fontanelles you should get in touch with your doctor immediately.

Some babies are born with a lot of hair, others arrive almost bald. Any first hair that a baby has will rub off within a couple of months, but this will be replaced with new hair growth. The new hair may be a different colour.

Most white babies are born with eyes that appear to be blue-grey in colour. This is because melanin, the body's natural pigment, is not present in the eyes until some weeks after birth. Babies with brown or black skins may have brown eyes at birth. If your baby's eyes are going to change colour this will gradually happen over a period of weeks or even months.

Although a new baby may cry quite a bit during these early weeks there probably won't be any tears.

*Babies often scratch themselves accidentally with their nails when they are very young. Scratch mitts will stop your newborn from catching her face with her fingernails.*

## How to hold your new baby

**1** *Pick up your newborn baby by sliding one hand under his neck and head and then placing the other hand under his back and bottom to support his body.*

**2** *Lift your baby so that he is cradled against your chest with one arm supporting the head and the other holding the lower back. Holding him close to your body will make him feel secure.*

*Right: Touch is very important to a newborn and a gentle massage with a special baby oil can be soothing.*

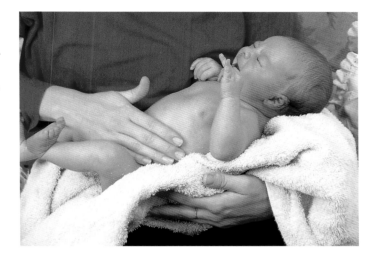

Some babies don't produce tears until they are six months old – this is not a cause for concern.

Slightly swollen or bloodshot eyes are common in newborn babies. This is caused by pressure from the birth and will disappear within a week or two. The muscles that control a new baby's eye movements are still very weak so he may look slightly cross-eyed at first. After a month or so the muscles will have developed sufficiently for the eyes to work together. However, even when looking cross-eyed, a baby can focus on things up to 20-25cm/8-10in away, so hold your face close when you are feeding or talking.

Enlarged genitals and breasts are common in both boys and girls when they are first born. In some cases the breasts may even ooze a little milk and baby girls can have a slight vaginal discharge. This is caused by your hormones, which are still in your baby's bloodstream. In a few days these effects will disappear.

### GENERAL HYGIENE

Young babies often object noisily to being undressed and immersed in a bath full of water, so don't feel you have to bathe your baby every day if the infant is unhappy about it. A top and tail wash every other day is quite sufficient until you both feel more comfortable. Always start by washing the baby's face with cooled boiled water using several pieces of cotton wool. Never use any kind of soap on the baby's face or near his eyes. If you wipe the eyes, use separate pieces of cotton wool for each one and start from the inner corner wiping

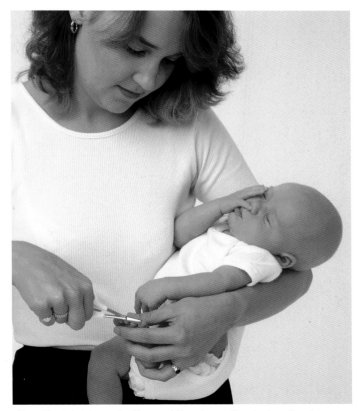

*Above: Your baby's fingernails will grow quickly and you will need to keep them short to stop him scratching himself. You may find it easier to cut the nails while your baby is asleep.*

outwards. A baby's ears and nose are self-cleaning so never try cleaning inside them with cotton wool or buds. Just gently remove any visible mucus or wax. Once you have washed his face you will need to lift up his head and clean the folds of his neck, making sure that you dry

the area carefully afterwards. Using another piece of cotton wool, wash between your baby's fingers and then dry his hands carefully.

When you have finished the top half you need to remove his nappy, wiping away any solid matter before gently cleaning his bottom. You can

use lotion to do this, or some warm water. Once the area is dry, you can apply a barrier cream to help prevent nappy rash.

Cradle cap is very common in the early months and can sometimes continue for a while. Dry white or yellow scales form a crusty cap on

**Topping and tailing**

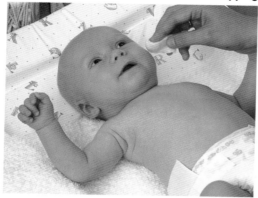

**1** *Undress your baby down to his nappy. Using cooled boiled water, and several pieces of cotton wool, gently wash his face. Never use any kind of soap on your baby's face or near his eyes.*

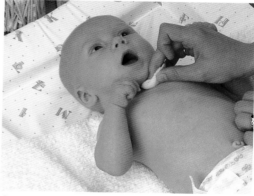

**2** *Take a piece of cotton wool and gently lift his chin so that you can wash in the folds of his neck. When you have finished, use another piece of cotton wool and carefully dry between the folds.*

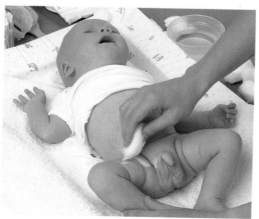

**5** *Gently wipe his bottom area with lotion or damp cotton wool making sure that you clean in all the folds and creases of his legs.*

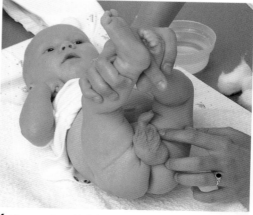

**6** *Once you have dried the nappy area, apply a small amount of barrier cream to help prevent nappy rash.*

the scalp. Rub olive oil, baby oil, or a specially formulated treatment into the scalp and then comb out the loosened flakes. Wash the baby's head afterwards with baby shampoo and dry thoroughly. You may need to repeat this treatment several times to remove all the flakes. As soon as the condition is under control you will only need to do this once a week. Cradle cap usually disappears by the time a baby reaches about eight or nine months.

A young baby's nails will grow very quickly and if not cut can cause scratches, especially on his face. You should keep his fingernails and toenails short by cutting them straight across with a pair of blunt-ended scissors. If your baby objects to this, or you find it difficult to cut his nails while he is wriggling about, try doing it while he is asleep or get someone else to hold him steady.

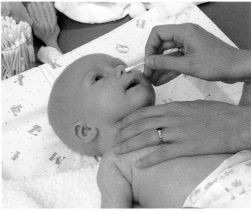

**3** *Your baby's ears and nose are self-cleaning, so don't be tempted to clean inside them with cotton buds. Take a dampened cotton bud and carefully remove any visible mucus from his nose.*

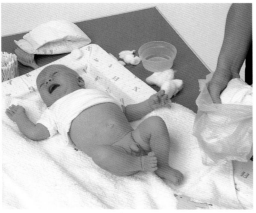

**4** *Put your baby in a clean vest and then remove his nappy, wiping away any solid matter with a clean corner before placing the dirty nappy in a bag.*

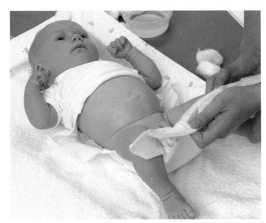

**7** *Now that your baby is clean and dry he is ready to have his nappy put on. Place the nappy under his bottom and draw it up carefully between his legs.*

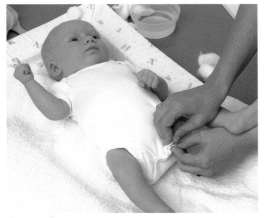

**8** *Fasten the nappy securely and once it is firmly in place pull down your baby's vest over the top of it. He is now clean and ready to be dressed again.*

# BREAST-FEEDING

Breast-feeding is the ideal way to feed a baby because breast milk is a baby's natural food containing all the required nutrients in the right proportions for the first months of life. But like any new skill, breast-feeding has to be learned and you may find it more difficult than you expected. Don't give up though, because breast-feeding really is best for your baby and for you and, once it is established, it can be a pleasure. If you are having problems, talk to your midwife or health visitor.

Ideally, you should put your baby to your breast as soon after birth as possible. The sucking will start a reaction that leads to the release of the hormones that cause both the milk to be manufactured in the breast and the let-down reflex, which allows the milk to pass through the breast to the nipple.

Immediately after the birth and for the first few days, the breasts

## Getting your baby latched on

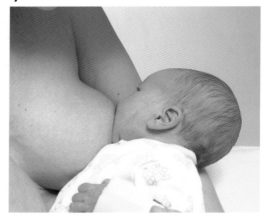

*Make sure that your baby's body is in a straight line with your breast so that she doesn't have to turn her head to feed.*

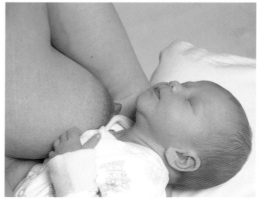

*Hold your baby in a comfortable position. Offer her the breast making sure that her mouth is open wide enough.*

*Allow your baby to feed from one breast for as long as she wants. She will let you know when she has had enough.*

produce colostrum, a high-protein liquid full of antibodies. This is followed by the actual milk coming in, which often makes the breasts feel heavy and uncomfortable. This discomfort will soon wear off once breast-feeding has become established.

At the first stage of a feed your baby gets foremilk from the breast; this has a high water content to satisfy thirst. Foremilk is followed by calorie-rich hindmilk which satisfies your baby's hunger and helps her to grow. To make sure that your baby always gets the hindmilk, you should allow her to feed for as long as she wants from one breast before you offer her the other one. If your baby has had enough when she has finished feeding from one breast, remember to start with the other breast at the next feed.

Your breasts produce milk in response to your baby's feeding, so the more your baby feeds the more milk you will produce. By letting your infant feed for as long as she wants you should be able to produce the amount of milk that is needed.

FINDING THE BEST POSITION
Finding the position which best suits both you and your baby is one of the most important factors for successful breast-feeding, so don't be afraid to experiment. Immediately after the birth, when you are still sore, you may find that sitting on a low chair with plenty of soft cushions is more comfortable than sitting in bed. You can raise your knees slightly by resting your feet on a low stool, or put a pillow on your lap to raise your baby and cushion your abdominal muscles.

Hold your baby so that her body is in a straight line with your breast so that she does not have to turn her head to feed. Sit up straight and lean

## Breast-feeding techniques

*Aim the nipple towards your baby's nose and allow her to take it into her mouth herself. When supporting your breast try not to apply pressure which can block the milk ducts.*

*Your baby may try to hold your breast or simply clench and unclench her fists while feeding. Her ears will move as she swallows.*

*When you want to remove your baby from the breast, insert a finger into her mouth to release the suction.*

## Advantages of breast-feeding

- Breast milk is designed especially for babies and it contains all the nutrients your baby needs. It is always available, at the right temperature, and it is free.
- Breast milk is easy for your baby to digest, so she is less likely to suffer stomach upsets and constipation.

- Breast milk contains antibodies which will help protect your baby against some infections.
- Breast-fed babies are less likely to develop allergies.
- Breast-feeding will help you get your figure back more quickly.

*To bring up any wind, either during the feed or once she has finished feeding, lay your baby across your knees and stroke her back gently.*

*You may prefer to wind your baby by sitting her upright on your knee, supporting her head, and gently patting her back.*

slightly forward so that the nipple drops into your baby's mouth. Make sure that she is then properly latched onto the breast. This means that your baby takes as much as possible of the areola (the dark area around the nipple) into her mouth, along with the nipple. The milk ducts lie just under the areola and your baby's sucking action on these effectively draws the milk from the breast. You may well be told to check that your baby's nose is not pushed against your breast so making it hard for her to breathe. However, if your baby is positioned properly, she will be able to breathe easily.

There is no set pattern for feeding. Some babies want to be fed every couple of hours, others can happily go for four to six hours before requiring a feed. Your baby will let you know when she is hungry and your milk supply will be regulated by supply and demand.

### EXPRESSING MILK

Expressing milk allows someone else to feed your baby with your breast milk. You can express milk with your hands or you may find it easier to use a breast pump. The best time to express is when you have the most milk, which is either in the morning or, once your baby has dropped her night feed, it may be in the evening. Milk can be expressed from your breast and kept in a sterile container in the refrigerator for up to 48 hours, or it can be frozen and kept for up to six months. Any feeding equipment or containers you use must be sterilized.

### BREAST-FEEDING PROBLEMS

If you are concerned that you are not producing enough milk, breast-feeding more often will automatically increase your supply, so don't be afraid to let your baby suck for as long as it is comfortable.

You may have a sleepy baby who needs to be woken for a feed. If your baby needs encouragement, gently brush her mouth with your nipple but don't force it into her mouth. Your baby may fall asleep at the breast after a feed but this only means that she is contented, well fed and doing all right.

Breast-feeding may hurt during the first few weeks because your milk supply has to become established and your nipples are not yet used to your baby's sucking. If the discomfort persists, however, then the positioning of your baby on the breast may not be right and you should experiment. Also check that your baby is latched on properly.

If not, your baby may just be sucking the nipple which means she won't be getting enough milk and the more she sucks the more painful it will actually become.

You may experience engorged breasts. This is when your breasts become over-full and painful. Feeding your baby frequently will help and you can ease the swelling by bathing your breasts with warm water or having a hot bath. Smooth out some milk with your fingers, stroking the breast downwards towards the nipple.

If you experience a shooting pain when your baby sucks, you may have a cracked nipple. If your baby is in the correct position even if your nipples are sore, they shouldn't hurt when you are feeding, so check your positioning. Keep sore nipples clean and dry and let the air get to them as much as possible. A nipple shield which fits over your nipple may help, but don't wear it for more than a day or two. Occasionally sore nipples can be caused by thrush in a baby's mouth. If you think this may be the case, discuss the problem with your doctor.

Finally, some nursing mothers can develop a condition called mastitis. This is an infection of the milk ducts and your breast will be inflamed, hot, and flushed in places. Bathing your breast in warm water, or holding a cold flannel against it, will help to ease any discomfort. You may also need a course of antibiotics to clear up the infection, so consult your doctor.

Sore, cracked nipples and mastitis are usually caused by your baby sucking just the nipple. Make sure your baby takes the nipple and surrounding area well into her mouth when she is feeding.

## Breast-feeding equipment

Although no equipment is essential, there are some items that will make life easier, such as feeding bras. There are other things that you may require if you decide to express milk so that you can occasionally bottle-feed. You may need:

- At least two well-fitting cotton nursing bras that allow access to a large area of the breast when your baby is feeding.
- Breast pads for use inside the bra to absorb any leaks of milk.
- Nipple shields to protect your sore nipples.
- Breast shells to fit over the nipple and collect excess milk.
- Breast pump, bottles, and teats if you intend to express breast milk.
- Sterilizing equipment.

*Breast milk can be expressed by hand, or using a manual breast pump like this. Electric pumps are also available.*

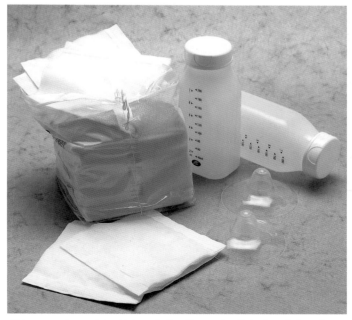

*Various accessories may help with breast-feeding. Breast pads will absorb any leakage, freezer bottles can be used to freeze breast milk, and nipple shields may help protect sore nipples.*

# BOTTLE-FEEDING

If you decide to bottle-feed you should be content with your decision. Do not feel guilty, or think that you are giving your baby second best. Such feelings will only take away the pleasure you should get from feeding your baby. Make the most of each feed by settling comfortably and giving your baby all your attention.

FORMULA MILKS

Formula milk has been specially produced to provide all the vitamins and minerals your baby needs. Most formula milk is made from cow's milk, which has been specially treated to make it easily digestible, and its nutritional quality as near to that of breast milk as possible. There are several brands to choose from and the midwife will be able to advise you. If your baby is known to have a lactose intolerance, or there is a strong family history of allergies that are connected to cows' milk, you may be advised to use an alternative to regular formula milk. Often this is a soya-based milk, but others are available. It is important that these alternatives are only introduced if recommended by your doctor.

Formula milks are available in powder forms, which are made up with cooled boiled water. It is important to follow the instructions on the tin or pack because the amounts have been calculated to make sure that a baby gets the correct balance of nutrients. Never be tempted to add more powder than is recommended because feeds that are too strong can be harmful to your baby. Ready-prepared formula milks are also available in cartons and bottles. These are more expensive than powdered formula but can be useful when you are away from home with your baby.

HOW TO BOTTLE-FEED

Prepare the formula milk according to the instructions, making up enough for 24 hours. Store the bottles in the refrigerator until

## Feeding equipment

All feeding equipment needs to be kept scrupulously clean. Bottles and teats should be washed out immediately after use and then sterilized before you make up the next batch of feeds.

You will need to have:
• Enough bottles, teats, and caps to make up feeds for a 24-hour period.
• Bottle brush for cleaning inside all the bottles.

• Sterilizer – there are four main ways of sterilizing feeding equipment: the chemical method, using a container filled with sterilizing solution; an electric steam sterilizer; a microwave steam sterilizer; boiling on the stove.
• Sterilizing solution or tablets for chemical method.
• Bottle warmer – this is optional, but can be very useful, especially when doing night feeds.

*A bottle warmer is useful at night.*

*Sterilizing equipment for bottles.*

*A microwave steam sterilizer.*

*Bringing up wind is something a father can do whether you breast- or bottle-feed.*

*Feeding should always be a special time for a baby as it helps him bond with the people closest to him. Here a father takes his turn at bottle-feeding.*

*An older baby may prefer to hold the bottle himself, but he will still need to be cuddled and you should check that the teat is always full of milk.*

needed and make sure that any unused formula is thrown away after this time. Never reuse leftover milk because it is a potential breeding ground for bacteria. Some babies are quite happy to take their bottles at room temperature but if yours prefers warm milk, heat the bottle either in a normal bottle warmer, or by standing it in a jug of hot water. Always test the temperature on the inside of your wrist to make sure that it isn't too hot before giving the bottle to your baby to drink.

Check that the milk is coming through the teat at the right speed. If your baby is having to work hard to get the milk, the flow is too slow and you need a teat with a bigger hole. If, on the other hand, your baby seems to be gulping a lot and the milk is leaking out of the corner of his mouth, the flow is too fast and the teat should have a smaller hole. If the teat flattens while you are feeding, pull it gently out of the baby's mouth to release the vacuum, then insert it again.

*All your baby's feeding equipment must be thoroughly washed before sterilization.*

## Chemical sterilizing

**1** *After washing the equipment fill the sterilizing unit with cold water.*

**2** *Add sterilizing tablets to the water and place the bottles, teats and caps in the unit.*

**3** *Check bottles are filled with water, then place tray in unit. Leave for time specified.*

## Electric steam sterilizer

**1** *Wash and rinse the feeding equipment and then place it in the sterilizing unit.*

**2** *Add water, taking care to follow the manufacturer's recommendations.*

**3** *Place lid on unit and switch on. The steam destroys any bacteria present.*

**Making up a formula feed**

**1** *Fill the bottle with the correct amount of cooled boiled water. Never use water that has been boiled more than once.*

**2** *Using the scoop provided, measure the required amount of milk, levelling off each scoopful with the back of a knife.*

**3** *Add powdered formula to the bottle. Never add extra formula as this can make the mixture too concentrated and could be harmful.*

**4** *Secure teat and place lid on bottle. Shake until the powder has dissolved. Check the milk temperature before giving it to your baby.*

You may want to encourage feeding by stroking the teat across your baby's mouth. Once his mouth has opened, place the teat between his lips and your baby should start sucking. Keep the bottle tilted so that formula fills the teat completely and your baby doesn't suck in air, which can cause wind. Never leave your baby to feed from a bottle on his own because he could vomit and choke. Don't add solids such as rusk, cereal, or baby rice to bottle feeds – this could cause choking.

The amount of milk your baby needs at feeds will change as he gains weight. At first he may take only a couple of ounces but this will increase. Your health visitor will give you a growth chart to check on progress.

Wind can sometimes be a problem, so try stopping halfway through a feed and wind your baby by holding him against your shoulder, or propping him up on your lap while you rub his back. You may want to do this after the feed has finished as well. The baby may bring back a small amount of milk during or after a feed; this is called possetting and is quite normal. If the vomiting becomes frequent or violent, you need to consult your doctor.

# INTRODUCING SOLIDS

Once milk alone no longer satisfies your baby you will need to start introducing solids into her diet. The recommended age for this is six months, but if your baby seems ready for solids before this you should talk to your health visitor or doctor. Your baby will let you know she is still hungry by wanting more after the feed is finished, or she may start chewing her fists. A baby may also begin to demand feeds more often and if she normally sleeps through the night, she may start waking up early wanting to be fed.

Breast and formula milk give babies all they require for the first six months so you don't have to worry if your baby seems satisfied with milk alone until this age. By six months of age, your baby needs the additional nourishment provided by solids, and she also needs to learn how to eat.

### HOW TO START

First solids are really just tasters to get a baby used to different textures and flavours; the main nourishment will still come from breast or formula milk. The first food should be bland and smooth, like baby rice mixed with either cooled boiled water, or formula or breast milk. To begin with offer a small amount on the tip of a clean spoon, midway through a feed, once a day. Once your baby has accepted this, you can introduce a small amount of fruit or vegetable purée, for example, banana, potato, or carrot (with no added salt or sugar), mixed with formula or breast milk.

As soon as your baby has got used to taking solids off a spoon, you can begin to introduce new foods and other solids at a second meal. If your baby obviously doesn't like the taste of something don't force matters. Try another food and reintroduce the rejected food at a later stage. At first the baby will simply try to suck anything off the spoon. But it won't take long to master getting the food off the spoon and into the back of her mouth. Once your baby can do this she will be able to cope with lumpier textures, so you can begin to mash rather than purée food. Your baby will also be able to enjoy a wider variety of tastes and textures.

### ADVANCED FEEDING

At around eight months, you can introduce food combinations such as baby cereal and fruit, or egg yolk and tomato – remember to remove the seeds from the tomato and to cook the egg thoroughly. Food can be lumpier and more solid so that it encourages your baby to start chewing. Try mincing or mashing the food with a fork.

At nine months and over, your baby is likely to be on three meals a day as well as milk, unsweetened diluted fruit juice, or water. Giving your child food at grown-up

## Making your own purée

**1** *Steam the fruit or vegetable until it is thoroughly cooked and soft, then place it in the food mill or blender.*

**2** *Without adding any sugar or seasoning, blend to a smooth consistency then remove a portion for your baby.*

**3** *Pour the remaining purée into an ice-cube tray to freeze in baby-size portions. Label and use within one month.*

meal-times will encourage her to learn social skills by watching others. As her appetite grows you can gradually increase the amount given at each meal. Offer finger foods such as slices of peeled apple, and banana; this will encourage her to feed herself. Always stay with your child while she is eating in case of choking.

As with younger babies, don't force unwanted foods; your child may simply not be ready for that particular taste. Don't ever fight over it. Take the food away, but don't offer alternatives or provide snacks between meals or let the child fill up on drinks, especially non-nourishing drinks, such as squash.

THE VEGETARIAN BABY

The principles of weaning are the same as for a non-vegetarian baby with the first solids being cereal, puréed fruit, and vegetables. However, vegetarian diets tend to be high in fibre and too much fibre is not suitable for young babies. And it can also interfere with the absorption of minerals such as calcium and iron. So your child will require a combination of cereals, milk, and vegetables which contain the right balance of energy and other nutrients for healthy growth. The diet will also need to include iron-rich foods such as dried fruit, fortified breakfast cereals, bread, lentils, eggs and green leafy vegetables. Vitamin C helps the absorption of iron from vegetables so you should give fresh orange juice, fresh fruit, or raw vegetables with every meal.

A vegan diet excludes milk and all dairy products, as well as meat and fish, and it may be unsuitable for babies. If you are considering a vegan diet it is essential that you talk

## Equipment

First foods should be mashed with a fork to a smooth purée. Alternatively, press the food with a spoon through a sieve, or process it in a blender or liquidizer. As your baby gets older she will be able to cope with lumpier foods. Your baby should have his or her own feeding utensils, which you will need to keep very clean.

To prepare and feed your own puréed foods you will need:
• Blender or liquidizer.
• Unbreakable bowl, spoon, and feeding cup.
• Bib (preferably two or three) and several face cloths.
• Ice-cube tray or similar for freezing small portions of purée.

*Use an unbreakable bowl, plastic teaspoon and feeding cup when weaning your baby.*

*A blender or sieve will purée first foods. Freeze baby-size portions in an ice-cube tray.*

*Left: By eight months a baby will be enjoying finger foods. At first he will examine the food, squashing it between his fingers as he explores its texture. Right: Once he's examined the food he will probably concentrate on trying to get it into his mouth.*

*Below right: Using both his hands to help, he eventually manages to get the food into his mouth. These are the very early stages of how a child learns to feed himself.*

to your health visitor or community dietician before beginning to wean your baby onto solid food.

### BABY FOODS

You can make your own first foods by puréeing ripe fruit or vegetables. Remove the skin and any seeds or stones, then boil, steam, or microwave until thoroughly cooked. Allow the cooked fruit or vegetable to cool, then purée. Fruits with

seeds such as strawberries will need to be sieved. Make a batch of purée, and freeze in small portions for convenience. Reheat thoroughly before use and allow it to cool before giving it to your baby.

When your baby is older and has progressed to lumpier, mixed foods she can eat the same foods as you, but remove a small portion for your baby before you add any seasoning or sugar.

Warming food for babies in a microwave is not recommended because it can result in uneven heating which could scald the child's mouth. If you have to use a microwave, stir the food well after cooking to ensure the even distribution of heat and allow it to stand for at least one minute. Check the temperature again before offering the food to the child.

### Choking

If your baby chokes while eating try to hook out the obstruction with your finger (being careful not to push it further in) while gently slapping her on the back. If this doesn't work, lay your baby face downwards with her chest and abdomen lying along your forearm and your hand supporting her head. Then slap the infant gently on the back to dislodge the obstruction.

The alternative to home-made baby food is to choose from the prepared baby foods that are widely available. One of the advantages of prepared baby foods is that they are quick and convenient. They have been formulated to make sure that, in conjunction with breast or formula milks, a baby receives a nutritionally balanced diet. Available in jars, packs and tins, there are commercially prepared baby foods available for each stage of weaning. Check the labelling for the age range for which it is suitable and, if you wish, whether it is acceptable for a vegetarian diet.

Introduce new combinations of prepared baby food with the same care as you would home-made food. Different food combinations contain several ingredients, some of which may be new to your baby. Always place the amount you require in a dish rather than feeding straight from the tin or jar. The digestive substances in your baby's saliva can find their way from the feeding spoon into the container, which can make any remaining food unsuitable for another meal. Opened tins and jars should be covered, and can be stored in the fridge for up to 48 hours.

*Always feed your baby her food using a plastic spoon. Keep the dish away from her until she learns not to put her hands in it.*

## FOODS TO WATCH

You must think carefully about the foods you introduce to your baby's diet. Some must be avoided altogether; others simply need special care in their preparation.

**High-fibre foods** Babies and young children shouldn't be given high-fibre foods such as bran because their digestive systems are too immature to cope with them.

**Salt** Never add salt to your baby's food. An infant's system can't cope with more salt than is found naturally in food. Some products, such as crisps, are usually quite salty, so you need to be aware of any salt intake from these foods.

**Sugar** Sugars occur naturally in fruit and vegetables so you should never add sugar to your baby's food or drinks as this can lead to tooth decay later and the possibility of obesity. Some manufacturers' prepared foods may contain sugars, so read food labels: sugars may be listed as glucose, sucrose, dextrose, fructose, maltose, syrup, honey, or raw/ brown sugar.

**Additional fats** Babies shouldn't have much additional fat added to their food – although the occasional knob of butter added to mashed potato will do no harm.

**Nuts** Whole nuts should never be given to a child under five years of age because of the risk of choking. Finely ground nuts may be given to children over six months unless there is a history of nut allergy in your family.

**Spices** Strong spices such as chillies, ginger and cloves are not suitable to be given to babies.

**Eggs** Since eggs can cause allergic reactions, start by offering a small amount of well-cooked yolk. Egg white is not recommended for babies under 12 months.

## FOOD ALLERGY

If either you or the baby's father have a family history of food allergies, eczema, asthma, or hayfever, your baby may have an intolerant reaction to the following foods: wheat, oats, and barley cereal; citrus fruits, eggs, nuts, and fish; dairy products, including cow's, goat's and sheep's milk. Intolerance to cow's milk is usually the result of an allergy to one of the proteins in milk or an intolerance of lactose (milk sugar). When you buy manufactured food, check the ingredients for foods that may cause an allergic reaction.

*Drinks, other than breast or formula milk, should be given in a feeder cup from the age of six months.*

*At around one year a baby will be able to manage finger food and a feeder cup without help. Never leave your baby alone when he is eating in case he chokes. Give drinks at the end of a meal or they will fill your baby up before eating.*

**Vitamin drops**
It is recommended that vitamin supplements are given to children from six months if you are breast-feeding. Bottle-fed babies do not usually require supplements until they switch to cow's milk at a year old. These vitamin supplements should be given to children up to the age of five. They are available from your health visitor at the baby clinic or you can get them from the pharmacist.

Symptoms of food intolerance or allergy include diarrhoea, vomiting after eating, or occasionally blood in stools. In extreme cases the reaction can be a generalized blotchy skin rash that occurs within an hour or so of eating the food. Your child's lips may also become swollen, the eyes puffy, and breathing a little wheezy. If breathing becomes restricted you will need to get medical help immediately. The blotchiness and swelling will disappear quickly but it should always be reported to your health visitor or doctor. These extreme reactions are rare, but if they do occur you should make sure that you avoid that particular food in future.

If your child shows an intolerance to any food, it may be that you need to change your child's diet, but this should always be done with the advice of a health professional.

MILK AND OTHER DRINKS
As the amount of food that your baby eats increases, her intake of milk will decrease. However, the recommendation is at least 600ml/1pt of breast, formula, or follow-on milk (after six months) a day, until the baby is one year old.

Follow-on milks help to meet the nutritional needs of growing babies from six months to two years. They contain more iron than other milks, plus a healthy balance of other nutrients.

In the past cow's milk was introduced into the diet at around six months, but it is now thought that it is unsuitable until the baby is at least one year old. This is because cow's milk is low in vitamins like C and D, and is particularly low in iron, all of which your baby needs for healthy growth. After a year full-fat milk should be give to the

under-fives as it provides energy, protein, and calcium, even though it has more saturated fat than breast or baby milks. Reduced-fat milks are not suitable as they are low in calories and vitamins. Skimmed milk should not be given to a child until she is at least five years of age. But if your child has a good appetite and varied diet, you may offer semi-skimmed milk at two. Always check with your health visitor first.

If your baby seems thirsty and you are still breast-feeding, your milk should provide all the liquid needed. If your baby remains thirsty you may want to offer cooled, boiled water between feeds. Try giving your baby these additional drinks from a teaspoon; this will make the idea of a spoon familiar before you start weaning on to solids. From the age of six months, any drinks other than breast or formula milk should be offered from a feeder cup.

Any water you give your baby needs to be boiled and cooled until the child is at the age when you no longer sterilize feeding equipment. Only use boiled water or bottled water sold specifically for babies – never make up a feed with, or offer your baby, bottled mineral water.

# NAPPIES

Nappies are produced in a variety of types, styles, and sizes, but the basic choice is still between disposable and towelling nappies. Ideally, you should decide which type of nappy you are going to use before your baby arrives. You will need to take into account a number of factors: your lifestyle, the amount of time and money you have available, and the type of washing and drying facilities you will be using. Whichever nappy you choose, the techniques required for changing and cleaning a baby's bottom are the same.

## CHANGING

You should change your baby whenever he is wet or dirty. The number of changes may vary from day to day, but generally you will have to change your baby first thing in the morning, after each feed, after a bath, and before bed at night. Get everything you need together before you start so that there is no reason to leave your baby unattended while you are changing the nappy. Make sure that the room where you are changing your new baby is warm and free from draughts. Lie your baby on a folded towel or changing mat, placed on the floor, a table, or on the bed, making sure that a

---

## Folding towelling nappies/Triple absorbent fold

This is particularly good for newborn babies because it makes a small, neat shape while giving extra absorbency between the legs.

**1** *Fold the nappy into four sections with the two folded edges nearest you and to your left.*

**2** *Pick up the top layer by the right-hand corner and pull it out to make a triangle.*

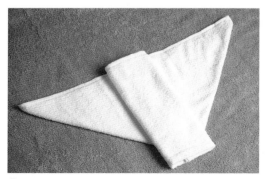

**5** *Fold these layers over again to make a thick central panel.*

**6** *Place a nappy liner over the top of the central panel.*

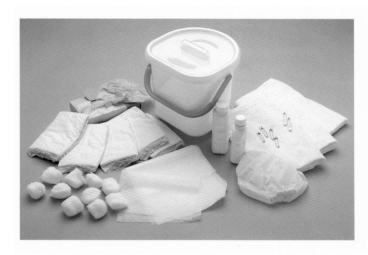

**Changing equipment:**
• Changing mat or towel.
• Clean towelling nappy, nappy liner, pins, plastic pants. Or a disposable nappy.
• Baby lotion or wipes, cotton wool.
• Bowl of warm water.
• Barrier cream.
• Bucket for dirty nappy or a plastic bag for a disposable nappy.

**3** *Turn the nappy over.*

**4** *Fold the vertical edge into the middle by a third.*

**7** *Bring the middle fold between the legs, then fold one corner across your baby's stomach and hold while you bring the second corner across. Pull taut and then pin all three layers together.*

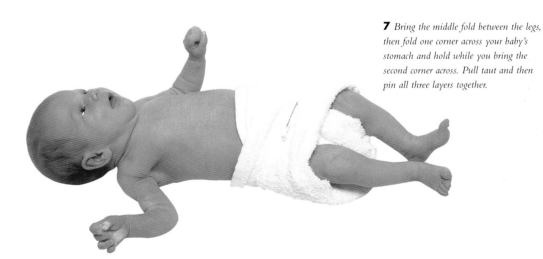

**Kite fold**

This is suitable from about three months onwards. You can adapt the size of the nappy by varying the depth when you fold the point up, before positioning the liner.

**1** *Lay the nappy out flat in front of you so that it is in a diamond shape with one of the corners nearest you.*

**2** *Fold the sides into the centre so that you form a kite shape with the nappy.*

**5** *Bring the nappy up between the baby's legs and carefully fold one side and then the other into the middle. Secure the nappy with one pin in the centre for a small baby and two pins, one on either side, for a bigger baby.*

wriggling infant cannot roll off if you are changing the nappy on a raised surface.

Remove the soiled nappy. Then clean your baby's bottom thoroughly, wiping away any solid matter with a clean corner of the used nappy, or with a damp tissue or cotton wool soaked in warm water. A baby wipe, or some baby lotion, can be used to finish cleaning the area. Once you have dried your baby's bottom, apply a small amount of a specially formulated barrier cream to protect the skin. Then put on a clean nappy.

WHAT'S IN A NAPPY
You may find the nappy of your new baby is stained dark pink or even

**3** *Fold the point at the top down towards the centre so that there is a straight edge along the top.*

**4** *Fold the bottom edge up towards the centre, adjusting the fold so that the nappy is the correct size for your baby.*

red. This is because the urine of newborns contains substances called urates. Your newborn's immature bladder cannot hold urine for very long so he may urinate as frequently as 20 times in every 24 hours. This will gradually lessen.

Your baby's first stools will be a blackish-green colour because the meconium from your amniotic fluid is working its way out of his system. Once feeding begins, the stools will change to greenish-brown and then to a yellowish-brown colour. The number of stools passed varies from baby to baby, but generally breast-fed babies pass fewer stools than bottle-fed babies.

### DISPOSABLE NAPPIES

There is no doubt that disposables are more convenient than towelling nappies. They are quick and easy to put on and remove and they don't require washing, which is a strong consideration when you think about the extra washing your baby is likely to produce without even including nappies. Their main disadvantages are that they are more expensive than their towelling counterparts and, despite their name, are cumbersome to dispose of. Most end up being wrapped and put in the dustbin; there are special plastic bags that will neutralize strong odours, and these are widely available.

Alternatively, there are a number of portable units available which will wrap and seal the dirty nappy in strong film, so that they can be stored for a number of days and then be disposed of in bulk.

Disposables work by allowing moisture to soak through a top sheet into an absorbent filling, which is protected on the outside by a waterproof backing. They come in a wide range of shapes and sizes. Most disposables have elasticated legs to ensure a snug fit, and reusable tapes so that you can check whether the nappy needs changing and adjust the leg size. Disposables need to be checked frequently because many of them are so good at keeping your baby dry that you may forget to change them.

### TOWELLING NAPPIES

These are a once-only buy which makes them more economical than disposables. Towelling nappies come in a variety of absorbencies and qualities. As a general guide the more absorbent the nappy the more expensive it is, so buy the best you can afford. The nappy can be folded in a number of different ways to fit your baby. It is held together with special pins and covered with reusable plastic pants to prevent leakage. One-way liners can be placed inside the nappy to help keep your baby dry; this method also has the added advantage of allowing you to flush any motions down the lavatory with the minimum of bother.

## Putting on a towelling nappy

Towelling nappies can be folded in a variety of ways to suit the age and sex of your child.

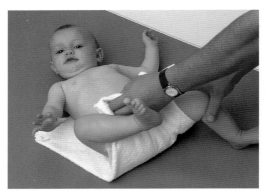

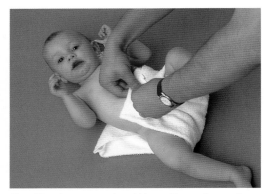

**1** *Fold nappy and place a liner in the centre. Lay your baby on the nappy with top edge at waist. Now bring nappy up between her legs.*

**2** *Holding the nappy in place, fold one side over the central panel and secure with a nappy pin.*

**3** *Fold the other side into the middle and secure. Always keep your finger between the nappy and your baby's skin when inserting the pin so that there is no risk of pricking your baby.*

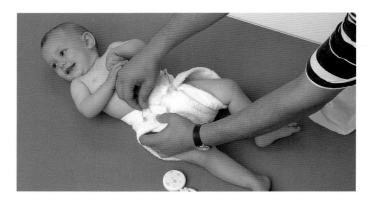

**4** *Once the nappy is securely in place you may want to put on a pair of protective plastic pants. Try not to get cross if your baby wets her clean nappy immediately and you have to start all over again.*

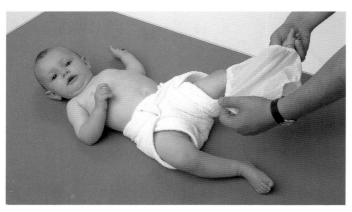

When working out the price of towelling nappies you need to take into account the cost of washing powder, the electricity used for washing and drying them, sterilizing solution, plastic wraps, nappy liners and clips. Towelling nappies are harder work than disposables because they need washing, so a washing machine and tumble dryer will make life easier for you. The nappies also need to be sterilized, rinsed, washed and dried. Then they should be aired before being reused.

SHAPED WASHABLE NAPPIES

These wash like towelling nappies but are shaped like disposables, with re-sealable fastenings and elasticated legs. They come in various sizes, and require a separate waterproof wrap. All-in-one cloth nappies are similar, but are simpler to use as they come complete with waterproof wraps.

THE ENVIRONMENTAL ISSUE

There is no arguing that disposable nappies are a great convenience for busy parents, but there are costs to the environment. Disposables, despite their name, are not 100 per cent disposable and millions of them are deposited in landfill sites every day where they will take years to break down.

Although, towelling nappies would seem environmentally friendlier, you need to assess the cost of the energy resources required to wash them and the impact on the environment of the sterilizers and detergents needed to clean the used nappy.

Whichever type of nappy you choose, you can arrange for services to handle them. You can have disposables delivered regularly for a nominal charge, at a price reduced for bulk ordering. Or, with towelling nappies, you can use a nappy laundry service and pay to have the used ones picked up and replaced with clean, sterile ones.

NAPPY RASH

Whichever nappy you choose, it is unlikely that your baby will get through the nappy years without experiencing nappy rash at some time. The key to avoiding the problem is cleanliness and frequent nappy changes, so that urine and faeces don't remain in contact with

## Putting on a disposable nappy

Disposable nappies are available in a variety of shapes, sizes and absorbencies. Always select the size which is recommended for your baby's weight.

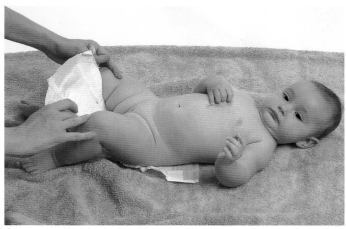

**1** *Open out the nappy with the re-sealable tabs at the top. Lay your baby on the nappy so that the top aligns with her waist. Bring the front of the nappy up between her legs.*

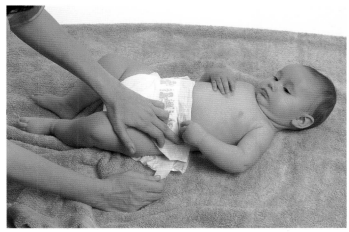

**2** *Smooth the front of the nappy so that it fits snugly round your baby's waist. Pull the adhesive tabs firmly towards the front of the nappy and fasten them to secure.*

the skin too long. Allow your baby to spend some time naked each day; this will help keep the skin clear. Nappy rash is sometimes caused by the fungus thrush, and if so an antifungal cream will be needed, so consult your doctor if the rash persists.

# DRESSING YOUR BABY

There are clothes to fit every size of newborn, from the tiny premature baby to the bouncing 10-pounder. Most baby clothes are sized by the approximate age and height of the child. Your baby probably won't require a great number of first-size clothes and may well grow into the next size within a matter of weeks – some babies are even big enough when born to go straight into second-size clothes.

Dressing and undressing your newborn can be difficult enough without having to worry about doing up complicated fastenings, so keep first clothes simple and save buttons and bows until later. Choose well-designed baby clothes that allow you to dress and undress your baby with the minimum of fuss. Look for garments that have wide, envelope necks that will stretch, so that you can slip them over baby's head easily. Stretchsuits which have fastenings up the inside leg will allow you to change a nappy without having to remove all your baby's clothes. All-in-one bodysuits, which fasten between the legs, will prevent your baby from getting cold around the middle and are ideal if you dress your baby in separates.

If you have a girl you may well be tempted to put her in dresses from the beginning, but dresses are not practical everyday wear for a young baby. They ride up and can be uncomfortable to lie on, they will allow draughts in around her middle, and they get in the way when she is starting to crawl. It is better to save them for special occasions or for when she's older.

Lacy jackets and shawls are best avoided too, as little fingers can get caught in the holes.

As your baby grows, colourful rompers and dungarees can take the place of stretchsuits. They are versatile and are suitable for both boys and girls. Rompers, which are really stretchsuits without feet, are easy to wear as they allow your baby freedom of movement. When you buy dungarees make sure that they have generous turn-ups and adjustable shoulder straps so that you get the maximum wear out of them.

When the weather is warm, babies need to be dressed in clothes that will keep them comfortably cool, and you should always cover their heads with a sun hat if you are out and about. Outerwear for cold days should be roomy enough to fit easily over everyday clothes.

## EASY-CARE FABRICS

Your baby is quite likely to get through as many as three or four changes a day so it makes sense to buy clothes made in easy-care fabrics that will wash and wear well. Check the labels before buying and avoid any garments that are going to need special treatment. Choose natural fabrics as these are best for warmth and absorbency. Pure cotton is ideal for your baby's underwear and also her stretchsuits.

Whether you are machine- or hand-washing garments, always follow the instructions on the labels so that your baby's clothes retain their shape, colour, and texture. Avoid using "biological" washing powders as these may irritate your baby's skin. It is important that all clothes are well aired and completely dry before being put away.

## FOOTWEAR

It is important that a baby's toes are never restricted by tight footwear. Check regularly that all-in-one-suits, leggings, and tights have enough room in them for the baby to wiggle her toes. Socks, bootees, and tights that have shrunk or been outgrown should be discarded. (The same care should be taken with tight collars, cuffs, mittens and also gloves.)

Your baby will not need proper shoes until she is walking and her feet need protection from the hard ground. If you do put your child in soft shoes before this, these should be made from a lightweight breathable material such as cloth or very soft leather and they must be flexible enough for you to feel her toes through them.

When you come to buy your baby's first shoes always have them fitted at a shop that offers a special fitting service for children. Both your baby's feet should be measured for length and width. If you can afford them, shoes with leather uppers are best. It is essential to check regularly that the shoes still fit and have not become too tight.

### For a first layette you will need:

- 3 baby gowns.
- pair of scratch mittens.
- shawl.
- 7 stretchsuits.
- 2 pairs of bootees or socks.
- 4 vests or bodysuits.
- warm outer wear for chilly days.
- sun hat.

## How to dress your newborn

Dressing and undressing a newborn can seem difficult at first. Always dress a newborn baby on a flat surface so that you have both hands free.

**1** *Put the all-in-one vest over your baby's head, raising her head slightly. Then widen one of the arm holes with your hand.*

**2** *Using your other hand, gently guide the arm through the sleeve. Repeat with the other arm.*

**3** *Place your hand under your baby's bottom and pull down the back of the vest.*

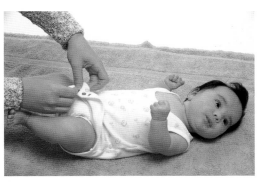

**4** *Do up the poppers between the legs and make sure that the vest isn't too tight anywhere when fastened.*

**5** *Concertina up the leg of the sock and then hold it wide as you ease it over your baby's foot.*

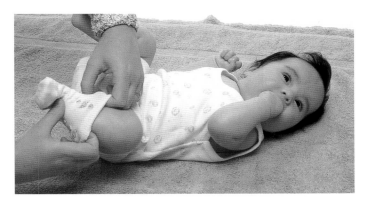

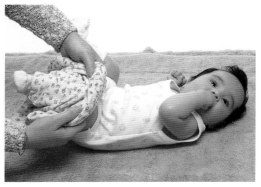

**6** *Gently place one foot in the trouser leg and then the other and pull the trousers up.*

**7** *Place your hand under your baby's bottom and lift so that you can pull the trousers up over the nappy.*

**8** *Adjust the trousers and make sure that the vest is smooth and that there are no puckers that could be uncomfortable to lie on.*

**9** *Hold the neck of the T-shirt wide as you slip it over your baby's face and then pull it down over the back of her head.*

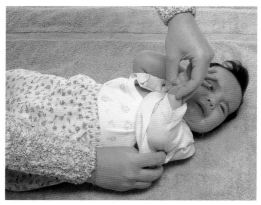

**10** *Gently ease your baby's arm through the T-shirt's sleeve and then pull the sleeve down.*

**11** *Put her other arm into the sleeve, then pull down top and tuck into her trousers. Your baby is now ready to face the day!*

*An all-in-one suit with leg fasteners is ideal for a new baby. The leg opening allows you to change the nappy easily without having to remove any of her clothes.*

*Rompers and a top are ideal for an older baby and are practical for both boys and girls. The romper straps hold the rompers in place even when your baby is being very active and will help prevent gaps occurring around the middle.*

*A more mobile baby will be happiest in trousers that will protect her legs as she learns to walk. Make sure the trouser legs clear the floor so that she doesn't trip.*

## Choose clothes carefully

You will be surprised at how quickly your baby grows during the first 12 months. Select clothes that will mix and match and allow some room for growth. Once she begins to crawl, your baby will need sensible easy-care clothes that will withstand endless washing. Make sure that neck openings are large enough and that garments are easy to unfasten for quick nappy changes. Not all clothes have to be practical; it is nice to buy a couple of special outfits that can be used for parties and days out too.

*Dresses look pretty, but are not really practical everyday wear for very young babies or once your baby becomes mobile. Keep dresses for those special occasions.*

*Rompersuits with short sleeves made in natural fibres are ideal for the summer. Synthetic fibres don't allow the skin to breathe properly and may make your baby feel hot and uncomfortable.*

*Babies don't need proper shoes until they have started to walk. Soft shoes like these are perfect for little feet in the meantime.*

# BATHING

When you bath your baby you need to get all you require together before you start. It helps if you can keep all the nappies, pins, pants, and toiletries either in a changing bag or box. A nappy bucket is essential because you'll need somewhere to put the dirty nappy and used cotton wool. A second bucket is also useful for dropping the dirty clothes into as you undress the baby. Any clean clothes and towels should be well aired before you begin and the room where you undress your baby should be warm (a minimum of 21°C/70°F) and draught-free.

When babies are tiny it is easier to bath them in a baby bath on a stand, or one that fits into the big bath, so they will be at a comfortable height for you to hold them. Before undressing your baby, fill the bath with warm water, putting the cold in first then the hot, and mix well. Add any bath preparation at this stage. Test that the water is at the right temperature. A bath thermometer will give you an accurate reading or you can use your elbow.

### For bathing you will need:

- Bowl of cooled boiled water, cotton wool and cotton buds (optional) to clean your baby's face before bathing (see topping and tailing).
- Changing mat.
- Bath towel.
- Baby bath preparation.
- Baby shampoo.
- Baby powder.
- Nappy changing equipment and a clean nappy.
- Clean clothes.

**1** *Wrap your baby firmly in a towel. Test the temperature of the bath water again then, having tucked his legs firmly under your arm, hold your baby's head over the bath, supporting his neck and back with your hand.*

**2** *Wet his head and apply a mild baby shampoo. Wash the hair with gentle circular movements, keeping the water and shampoo well away from his eyes. Once washed, rinse off the shampoo and lift your baby back onto your knee and towel his hair dry.*

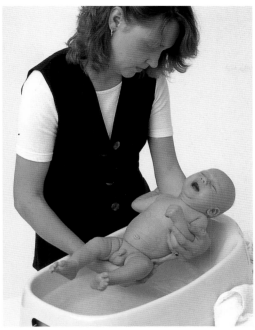

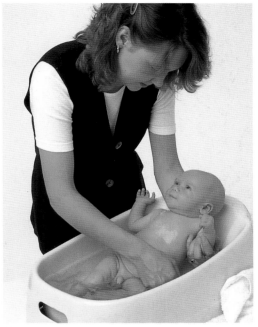

**3** *Lift your baby gently into the bath, supporting his head and back on your arm, while holding the arm that is the furthest away from you.*

**4** *This leaves your other hand free to wash under his arms and in all the folds and creases. When you have finished, lift your baby out of the bath and into a warm towel.*

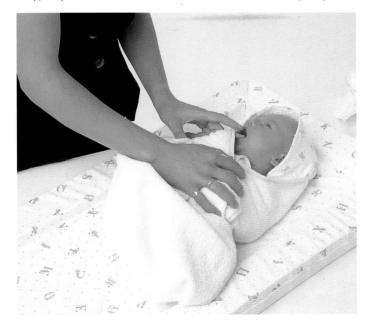

**5** *Once you have dried your baby, you may want to apply some baby powder. Put a little powder on your hands and then rub it on to the baby's body, making sure you close the lid tightly after use. Don't sprinkle it on straight from the container in case it gets into your baby's mouth or eyes. It can be dangerous for young infants to inhale powder into their lungs.*

You may find it easier to bath a very young baby in a baby bath. Some of these have their own stand; others, like the one above, fit over a big bath.

A sponge inlay which fits snugly into the bottom of the bath will prevent your baby from slipping, and will make it easier for you to hold him.

Once your baby is old enough to be bathed in the big bath you should cover the taps with a folded towel before putting him in the bath. This will prevent him from accidentally burning himself on the hot tap.

An older baby will be happy to spend time in the bath if he has bath toys to play with. Containers that can be filled and emptied and toys that float and bob about will give hours of fun and entertainment.

### Safety notes

Never leave your baby or toddler alone in the bath. It only takes a few seconds for a child to drown in as little as 5cm/2in of water.

• When drying or dressing your baby never leave him unattended on a raised surface. He could easily roll off and hurt himself.

• Always check the temperature of the bath water before putting your baby in the bath.

• If you bath your child in a conventional large bath, place a cover over the taps so that he can't burn himself. A folded towel will do.

• Use a non-slip bath mat in the bath.

• Always put the cold water in first when running the bath.

• If you are using a bath and stand, make sure that it is sturdy and secure before lifting your baby into it.

*Above: Your child may enjoy sharing his bath with others, or he may prefer to have a bath alone. If you are intending to bath two or three children together it is often easier to put the smallest into the bath first and then let the others join him one at a time.*

*Right: Not all children enjoy spending time in the bath. If one child is unhappy about bathtime don't force him to stay in longer than he wants. Always stay in the bathroom with your children so that you can be sure that they are safe.*

# SLEEPING

Your new baby has no understanding of day and night so during the first weeks of her life she will sleep and wake at random. You may find that she sleeps for 20 hours out of every 24 or for only 12 hours out of 24. Whatever pattern your baby adopts, she will be getting as much sleep as she needs.

### Average sleep pattern

| Birth | 17 hours in every 24 | |
| --- | --- | --- |
| | **Day** | **Night** |
| 3 months | 5 hours | 10 hours |
| 6 months | 4 hours | 10 hours |
| 9 months | 3 hours | 11 hours |
| 12 months | 2 hours | 11 hours |

Your baby's biological clock will dictate when she is ready for sleep in the evenings and this is a good starting point for establishing a regular bedtime. From the very

*Try not to let your baby fall asleep before putting him in his cot as he may wake feeling distressed if you are not there.*

beginning you should make the hour before bed quiet and relaxing. You may choose this time to give your baby a bath, and you will certainly want to feed and change your baby before putting her down in the cot. You may need to rock or sing to the child until sleep comes, especially if she is very young. During the first few weeks your baby may sleep better if swaddled in a blanket or sheet – this will prevent tiny limbs from jerking and twitching. These sudden involuntary movements often wake a very young baby. As your child gets older she will begin to settle on her own and you can help by providing things for amusement, such as a mobile and cot toys. Follow the same routine every night so that

*Your baby will enjoy being outside from an early age. Keep her out of direct sun in the shade and have the hood up to protect her from draughts.*

the baby begins to associate the cot with night-time and sleep.

A baby's room needs to be warm – around 18°C/65°F – so that the child doesn't wake up cold in the

### Cot death

All parents are worried about the possibility of cot death, technically known as Sudden Infant Death Syndrome (SIDS). Although the chance of this happening to your baby is remote, it is sensible to take a few simple precautions that are known to reduce the risk.
• Let your baby sleep in her own cot in your room for the first six months.
• Make sure that your baby sleeps on her back in the 'feet to foot' position, that is with her feet at the foot of the cot so that there is no danger of her wriggling down under the blankets and becoming overheated.
• Keep your baby warm, but do not let her overheat. Check your baby's temperature regularly by feeling the back of her neck or tummy. It is best to

use several lightweight blankets so that you can add or take them away to adjust the temperature. Remember that cot blankets that are folded count as two blankets.
• Use a firm mattress and don't use a duvet, baby nest, cot bumper or pillow.
• Do not smoke near your baby and keep her out of a smoky atmosphere.
• If your baby seems unwell, take her to the doctor immediately.
• Make sure your baby's room is well ventilated. Leave the door ajar or a window open (but ensure that the baby is not in a draught). The temperature in your baby's room should be around 18°C/65°F.
• Don't take your baby into your bed if you have drunk alcohol or taken any form of drugs.

### Bedtime tips

• Encourage your baby to sleep while there are background noises going on. This way she won't expect silence at bedtime.

• Put a selection of toys in the cot to provide amusement for an older baby.

• Make night feeds as quick and quiet as possible, keeping the lights low and changing the baby first. Don't do anything stimulating.

• Put the baby down to sleep in the cot at night so that she comes to associate it with sleep.

• Wrap up a newborn baby firmly so that she feels secure.

*Put your baby in the "feet to foot" position.*

during the day. Stimulate your baby by talking and playing with her in the daytime when she is awake. Keep feeding and changing down to a minimum amount of time during the night so that your baby learns that this is not a time for being sociable.

*Above: Older babies often prefer to sleep on their sides. Place the lower arm in a forward position to stop her rolling onto her stomach.*

*Below: Check your baby's body warmth regularly at night, and remove some blankets if she feels too warm.*

night. Put your baby down to sleep in a vest, nappy, and stretchsuit and cover her with a sheet and several layers of blankets. You can check for body warmth during the night by feeling the tummy or the back of the neck, then you can add or take away blankets accordingly. If your baby seems worried by the dark, leave a nightlight on near the cot.

You can help your infant to develop a better sleeping pattern by encouraging her to be more awake

# CRYING

Your response to your child's crying and the way that you comfort him can influence the bond that grows between you. There is no risk of spoiling your child by responding to his cries. It is impossible to give a young baby too much love. By going to your baby when he cries you will be showing him that you care and this in turn will help to form a deep, loving relationship between you.

## WHY BABIES CRY

Babies cry for a lot of different reasons and you need to understand what makes your baby cry so that you can provide comfort. Your newborn may cry a lot because this is the main means of communicating with you. The infant needs to be able to let you know that the world he is now in is a strange and sometimes frightening place. Once he has adapted to the new environment and you have developed a routine that

takes account of his likes and dislikes, the amount of crying will gradually start to decrease.

Hunger is the most common cause of crying and you will soon learn to recognize when your baby is hungry. The first action is to feed on demand – a young baby may need feeding every two or three hours.

Being too hot or too cold can also make a baby cry. A young baby can't regulate his own temperature and he can easily become too hot or too cold, so it is important to keep a check on an infant's temperature. You should make sure that your baby's room is kept at a constant 18°C/65°F. Wet or dirty nappies do not cause crying except when the wet nappy gets cold.

Your new baby will probably hate being undressed, even in a warm room. This is because the feel of clothing on the skin creates a secure feeling, so when it is removed the infant cries. Keep undressing to a

minimum in the first few weeks. Top and tail rather than bath your baby so that you only need to remove a bit of clothing at a time. When you do undress him completely, wrap him in a towel to give him a feeling of security.

Pain is a definite cause of crying, but it may be hard for you to locate the cause of the actual pain. If you

### Crying cures
• Movement soothes a baby so try rocking him or walking around holding him on your shoulder.
• Put your baby in a bouncing seat that will move very gently.
• Push him backwards and forwards in the pram.
• Put the baby in his car seat and go for a drive.
• Talk, sing, or croon soothingly.
• Put on the radio or TV or turn on the vacuum cleaner.
• Distract the baby with a noisy toy.
• Play a tape of calm music.
• Carry a young baby next to your body in a sling.

*Not being allowed to do what he wants, when he wants, can lead to a child's tears of frustration.*

*Waiting for a bottle to cool down can be tiresome and can lead to angry tears from a hungry baby.*

can, remove the source of the pain –
for example an open nappy pin. If
you can't find a reason for the pain,
don't just leave your baby to cry;
pick him up and comfort him.
Stay with your baby until he is
completely calm. If your baby seems
feverish or just generally unwell,
always seek medical advice.

Any baby will normally start
crying when he is tired. If you think
that this is the cause, put your child
down to sleep in a dimly lit, warm
room. If necessary, rock or sing a
soothing song to him until he has
completely calmed down and starts
to become sleepy.

*Tiredness is a common reason for tears
before bedtime.*

*The discomfort of wind after a feed can
cause a baby's tears.*

*Sometimes it all gets too much for a young child and the only way to show his feelings is to scream.*

# COLIC

Young babies sometimes have prolonged periods of crying during the day which are often attributed to colic. These crying spells often take place around the time of the evening feed, although they can happen at any time of day. Colic, if it is going to occur, usually starts within the first three weeks after birth and normally lasts until around three months, although it can go on for longer. It generally stops as abruptly as it starts, having caused your baby no harm.

Although no one knows exactly what colic is, or what causes it, many doctors believe that it is a type of stomachache that occurs in spasms, and makes the baby draw up her legs in pain. The pattern of crying would indicate cramp-like pains; the baby is miserable and distressed, then calms down for a few minutes before starting to scream again. This may continue for several hours at a time, which can become very wearing and upsetting for both of you.

### POSSIBLE CAUSES

Colic has been blamed on many things and it is worth investigating all the possibilities if your baby suffers from it. Since colic affects both bottle- and breast-fed babies the method of feeding is not thought to be the cause. However, if you are breast-feeding it could be something that you are eating that is causing the problem. Try cutting out of your diet anything you have eaten during the previous 24 hours that you think might have affected your baby. It has been suggested that the amount of feeds offered – both too little and

too much – could be to blame, or that the milk, if bottle-feeding, could be too hot or too cold, or the feeds too weak or too rich. Remember, when you make up bottle feeds it is essential to follow the manufacturer's instructions.

Other possible causes are constipation, diarrhoea, indigestion or intestinal cramps. Vigorously crying babies are almost always healthy, but if your baby looks pale or ill, seek medical advice.

There may also be a link between tension and colic, which can lead to a chain reaction. The end of the day is usually a busy time in a household and you may be tired and tense as you try to prepare the baby for bed, tidy up, and get a meal ready. Your baby is sensitive to your moods and may respond to tension by crying which, of course, increases your

anxiety, with the result that the crying becomes prolonged and ends when you are both exhausted.

### WHAT TO DO

There is no reliable treatment for colic and, although there are some over-the-counter medicines available, you should always consult your doctor before giving them to your baby. On a practical level you can rearrange your day by preparing the evening meal earlier, so that you have time to spend comforting your baby during this crying period. Although there is little you can do to ease your baby's discomfort completely, holding her against you, so that there is gentle pressure and warmth on her stomach, and rubbing her back soothingly may be of some help. Try to share the comforting with your partner to spread the strain, and remember that colic doesn't last for more than a few months so, although it is awful at the time, it will not last for ever.

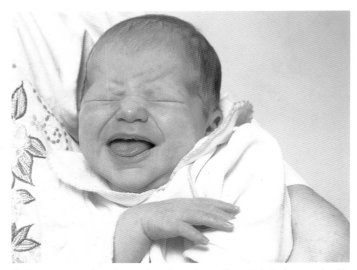

*Colic can start as early as three weeks and may last until your baby is three months old. Be patient; it will pass and it won't do your baby any harm.*

# TEETH

At around six months your baby's milk teeth will start to emerge and by the age of two-and-a-half all 20 first teeth will usually have appeared. Every tooth has two parts: the crown, which can be seen in the mouth; and the root, which anchors

*Your baby's first teeth will start to emerge at around six months old, and you should start to clean them as soon as they appear in the gums.*

the tooth to the jaw. The outside of the tooth is made of enamel, which protects the crown and provides a strong surface for chewing. Because the enamel is not fully formed when the teeth first come through, calcium and other minerals are required over the next 6–12 months to strengthen it. These minerals are found in the saliva and plaque in your child's mouth and, under normal conditions, will steadily accumulate in the teeth. But calcium and phosphates in the enamel frequently come under attack from acids that are formed by the bacteria living in plaque. These bacteria use carbohydrates, such as sugar, to generate the acid.

Your baby needs carbohydrates, but food and drink containing a lot of simple sugars such as sucrose, fructose, and glucose will speed up the production of the acids which can damage

*When he is teething your child will chew anything, even his fingers. Try offering her finger foods, such as a stick of raw carrot, as something different to chew on.*

teeth. It is not just the amount of sugar he eats that affects your child's teeth, it is also the frequency of his consumption of sugary food and drink. Drinks taken slowly, or sugary foods eaten over a long period of time, keep the sugar content of the

*Chewing and biting on things is often one of the first signs of teething in a baby, and this may occur some weeks before any teeth appear.*

*Before you start trying to brush your baby's teeth, it is a good idea to let him play with his toothbrush so that he becomes familiar with it and does not cause a fuss when you put it in his mouth.*

*Your child will find it good fun attempting to brush his own teeth from a very early age.*

*You will need to clean your child's teeth until he is old enough to do it himself. A fluoride toothpaste will help protect his teeth and gums.*

mouth high, which means that calcium and phosphates are being removed for longer and less time is available to replace them. Generally, the lower the sugar content of food and drink the better they are for the teeth because it is the total sugar levels, not just added sugar, that counts. This is why you should never add sugar to your baby's food or drinks and you should always dilute concentrated drinks and give them in a trainer cup rather than a feeding bottle.

CLEANING TEETH
As soon as your baby's first teeth appear, you should clean them every morning and night. Cleaning them before bed is especially important because the flow of protective saliva decreases when your baby is asleep, which means that any sugar in the mouth allows the plaque to stay

acidic for a prolonged period. In the morning, brush your baby's teeth to remove any build-up of plaque that has occurred during the night.

The main point of cleaning teeth is to remove as much plaque as possible, and toothpaste does this with the aid of abrasives; there are toothpastes specially formulated to be suitable for young children. A pea-sized amount of toothpaste on the brush is all that is required to clean a mouth full of teeth. You'll probably find it easiest at first to use your finger wrapped in a soft cloth and then, when your baby has got used to the idea of having his teeth cleaned, you can start to clean his teeth with a soft baby toothbrush.

Since the introduction of fluoride toothpastes, children's teeth have been healthier. Fluoride, which is present in most toothpastes, works by making the enamel stronger

*As your child starts to get teeth she will experiment with the chewing action on her favourite toys.*

against attack from plaque. The amount of fluoride children should use varies according to their age and the fluoride levels already present in the water.

THE DENTIST
Take your baby with you when you go for your own dental check-ups so that he will become familiar with the dentist and the surgery. By getting your child used to having his teeth inspected before he needs treatment, he will then experience no alarm at the thought of going to the dentist. A child usually won't need to have an actual dental check-up until he is about three years of age, when your dentist will check to see that the teeth are developing properly. The dentist will also be able to advise you about any special protective treatments available for your child.

*Cleaning your young baby's new teeth at bedtime is essential to prevent the build-up of plaque as he sleeps.*

# IMMUNIZATION

Diseases such as measles, mumps, whooping cough, rubella (German measles), diphtheria, tetanus, polio, and Haemophilus influenzae type b (HiB) – a cause of meningitis – can be very serious and, in very young children, even fatal. Immunization offers long-lasting protection against these diseases. If you are concerned about the immunizations, or are worried about allergic reactions, or if there is a family history of convulsions, don't just decide not to have your child immunized, talk to your doctor.

The five-in-one vaccination, which immunizes against diphtheria, whooping cough (Pertussis – the medical name for whooping cough), tetanus, polio and Hib is usually given as one injection at two months, three months, and four months of age. In addition, a new pneumococcal vaccine, which protects against pneumococcal infections has been introduced at two, four and 13 months. The menC vaccine that protects against meningiitis C is given at three and four months, and then as a combined injection with HiB at 12 months. With all of these it is important to complete the course to ensure the maximum immunity. MMR immunizes against measles, mumps, and rubella and is given in one injection at 13 months.

Your newborn baby may also be offered immunization against tuberculosis (TB) with a BCG vaccine if you are in or from a high-risk area, or if you come from a family that has a history of TB.

## SIDE-EFFECTS

After any immunization it is quite normal for the skin around the site of the injection to become red and sore or slightly swollen. Your child may feel a bit off-colour for a while and may run a slight temperature. If you are at all worried about your child you should ask your doctor or health visitor for advice.

Any side-effects from the five-in-one vaccine are usually mild. Your baby may become slightly feverish and appear unhappy for up to 24 hours after the injection. Very occasionally a convulsion occurs as a result of the fever, but this is over very quickly and has no lasting effect.

The MMR immunization has no immediate side-effects, although some children develop a mild fever and rash seven to 10 days after the injection, while others sometimes get a very mild form of mumps. If either of these reactions occur they are not infectious.

If your baby is feverish or acutely unwell, or has had a severe reaction to an earlier immunization, you should not have her immunized again without talking first to your doctor. Always tell the doctor who is doing the immunization if your baby is taking medication or if she has a severe allergic reaction to eggs. If the baby is vomiting or has diarrhoea it may be better to put off having the vaccination until she is better.

## OTHER COMPLICATIONS

Many parents worry about the possibility of more serious effects from these vaccines, especially from the MMR and whooping cough vaccines.

The whooping cough part of the five-in-one vaccination is the one that has in the past been linked to brain damage, but research has shown that there is no link between this and the vaccine.

Parents may be concerned about the suggested link between the MMR vaccine and autism, or the vaccine's possible link to the increase in Crohn's disease, but recent research has shown that there is no evidence to support these fears.

## THE DISEASES

Immunizations have developed over the years and many diseases that were formerly feared are no longer threats. This is the result of a sound immunization programme which has been applied to virtually all children.

Often parents are vague about the actual disease themselves, so it is worth familiarizing yourself with the conditions and their symptoms.

## Immunization timetable

| **At 2 months:** | | **At 3 months:** | |
|---|---|---|---|
| Diphtheria | | Diphtheria | |
| Whooping cough | | Whooping cough | |
| Tetanus | } 5 in 1 injection | Tetanus | } 5 in 1 injection |
| HiB | | HiB | |
| Polio | | Polio | |
| Pneumococcal | | Meningitis C | |

**Diphtheria** starts with a sore throat and then quickly develops into a serious illness which blocks the nose and throat, making it difficult and sometimes nearly impossible for a child to breathe. It can last for weeks and can often be fatal.

**Tetanus** is caused by germs from dirt or soil getting into an open wound or burn. It attacks the nervous system, causing painful muscle spasms. Immunization has made it rare, but there is still a real chance of getting it and it can be fatal.

**Whooping cough** is a highly infectious disease that causes long bouts of coughing and choking. These bouts can occur up to 50 times in one day and the cough can last two to three months. Whooping cough can cause convulsions, ear infections, pneumonia, bronchitis, and even brain damage. It can prove fatal, especially in children who are under one year of age.

**Bacterial meningitis** develops rapidly and can cause serious illness within a few hours. If left untreated seizures can occur, followed by loss of consciousness leading to coma, and in some cases it can be fatal. Even when children recover there is a risk of long-term problems such as deafness and epilepsy.

**Pneumococcal infection** can lead to meningitis, septicaemia (blood poisoning) and pneumonia if it enters the blood stream it.

**Polio** attacks the nervous system and causes muscle paralysis. If it affects the breathing the sufferer will need help to breathe and could even die. Thankfully, polio is rare in most Western countries because of immunization, but there is still a risk of contact with the disease through foreign travel, which is why immunization is still important. Adults should check to see if they need a polio booster when they take their baby for immunization.

**Tuberculosis (TB)** usually affects the lungs; symptoms include a cough, fever, or night sweats. Children are vulnerable and develop TB meningitis more often than adults.

**Measles** can be much more serious than people think because it is the disease most likely to cause encephalitis (inflammation of the brain). It begins like a bad cold with a fever and then a rash appears, which is often accompanied by a bad cough. Measles can cause ear infections, convulsions, bronchitis, and pneumonia. It can sometimes be fatal.

**Mumps** is usually a mild illness, but it can have serious complications that affect both boys and girls, and it can cause permanent deafness.

**Rubella** (German measles) is a mild disease, but one which can harm an unborn baby if a woman catches it when she is pregnant. The risk is particularly high during the first four months of pregnancy. Babies whose mothers get rubella during pregnancy can be born deaf, blind, and with heart and brain damage.

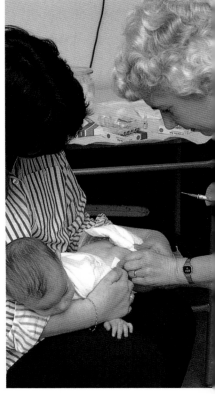

*At two months your child will be given his first immunizations. Although they will probably cause some momentary discomfort it will all soon be forgotten with a cuddle.*

---

**At 4 months:**
Diphtheria
Whooping cough
Tetanus        } 5 in 1 injection
HiB
Polio
Meningitis C and Pneumococcal

**At 12 months:**
HiB            } combined
Meningitis C

**At 13 months:**
Measles
Mumps          } MMR one injection
Rubella
Pneumococcal

# CHILDHOOD ILLNESSES

Knowing what to do when your child is ill and when you should call the doctor is something that comes with experience. Common symptoms that indicate that your child is unwell include sickness, diarrhoea, or a high temperature. These may be accompanied by unusual behaviour such as listlessness, refusing to eat, and crying for no apparent reason. However, it is not always easy to tell when a very young baby is unwell so you should trust your instincts – you know your baby better than anyone. Signs indicating that a baby is ill and you should call the doctor include refusing feeds, a fit or convulsion, extreme drowsiness, difficulty in breathing, severe diarrhoea, vomiting, high fever and the appearance of unusual rashes.

### DEALING WITH ILLNESS

Fever occurs when the body temperature rises above normal and is usually caused by an infection. If your child is feverish he will need a lot of cold fluids to drink and a dose of paracetamol syrup to bring his temperature down (aspirin should not be given to children under the age of 12, unless specifically prescribed by your doctor).

If your child is very feverish, keep him in bed and cool him down. This can be done by sponging him all over with tepid water, then covering him with a light sheet and making sure that he drinks plenty of liquids. Alternatively, put a cool fan next to the bed – but safely out of reach.

The easiest way of detecting feverish illness is by taking your child's temperature. This can be done by using a digital thermometer which is placed under your baby's arm (remember this is about 0.6°C/1°F lower than internal body temperature). Older children can hold it under their tongue. You can also use an ear thermometer or hold a fever strip on your child's forehead. Whichever method you use, make sure that you start with a low reading. A normal temperature is 37°C/98.6°F, but a child's can vary between 36°C/96.8°F and 37.5°C/99.5°F. You must phone your doctor if the temperature goes over 39°C/102°F, or if it remains above normal for more than two days.

Medicines for young children usually come in liquid form and can be given to them by dropper, or by using a specially designed spoon; older children can manage with an ordinary spoon. It is important that you know what the medicine is, what it does, and the correct dosage before you give it to your child. If you are in any doubt, check the details with your pharmacist.

*You are the best person to judge whether your child is unwell as you know him better than anyone else. As you become more experienced as a parent you will know whether you need to call the doctor. If you are unsure, it is always better to seek medical advice.*

*It may be easier to take a young baby's temperature using a fever strip. Place the strip on your child's forehead and hold it there for 15–20 seconds to get the necessary reading.*

*A more accurate way of taking a temperature is with an ear thermometer, or with a digital thermometer placed in the armpit and held in position for two or three minutes.*

## SPECIFIC CONDITIONS:
### COUGHS AND COLDS

Colds are caused by air-borne viruses, not bacteria, so antibiotics can't be used to help relieve the symptoms. If your child is suffering from a blocked or runny nose, you may need to buy a nasal decongestant or your doctor may prescribe some nose drops, particularly if the cold is hindering your baby's feeding. Seek advice from your doctor or health visitor if a cold is affecting your child's breathing. It is better to be safe than sorry.

Irritating coughs often occur with a cold so if your child has a dry cough ask your pharmacist to recommend a soothing linctus that is suitable for children.

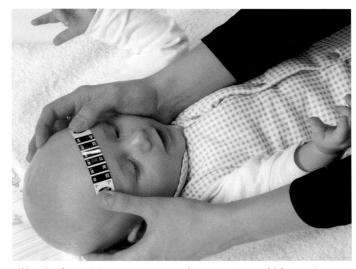

*Although a fever strip is not as accurate as a thermometer, it is useful for a quick assessment. It will show a raised temperature so that you can take the appropriate action.*

*Medicines for young children usually come in liquid form and can be given on a teaspoon. Sit your baby on your knee and hold his hands out of the way as you spoon the medicine into his mouth.*

*If your child appears hot and feverish you can help to cool him down by wiping his forehead with a face cloth that has been wrung out in cold water.*

### EAR INFECTIONS

Problems with a child's ears often accompany a cold. One of the first signs is if your baby starts pulling at one of his ears, which might appear red, but he may also just cry a lot and seem generally unwell. Paracetamol syrup will help relieve the pain, but an antibiotic may also be required to clear up any infection, so you will need to consult your doctor for advice. Do not take your child swimming with an ear infection.

### CONSTIPATION AND DIARRHOEA

If a child is having difficulty passing stools because they are hard, the problem is most likely to be constipation. A change in diet will be necessary. Including more water, fruit, vegetables, and fibre will help solve the problem. If the problem continues to persist, a mild laxative may be required. Consult your health visitor or doctor for advice.

Diarrhoea is the frequent passing of loose, watery stools. If a baby is being bottle-fed or being weaned, you should omit one or two milk feeds and solids and offer plenty of clear fluids instead, including an oral rehydration mixture if the loose stools continue. Breast-fed babies can continue their milk feeds as normal.

You should contact your doctor if the diarrhoea persists after a period of 12 hours, or if it is accompanied by vomiting because the baby could become dehydrated.

### TEETHING

The first signs of teething in a young child are often a red area on his cheek, excessive dribbling, and he starts chewing on his fingers. A teething gel, containing a local anaesthetic, will help to give some relief, but you will need to watch out for any sign of allergic reactions to the gel. These can include a noticeable reddening or swelling of the gums.

### VOMITING

If your baby starts to vomit frequently or violently, and if there is any other sign of illness, you should always contact your doctor immediately as young babies can very quickly become dehydrated if they are sick.

Older children can be sick once or twice without suffering any lasting effect. Give your child plenty of clear fluids to drink and don't bother about trying to offer him any tempting food until he feels better.

# CHILDHOOD DISEASES

There are a number of diseases that affect most children. If treated promptly, they pose no serious threat and will probably give immunity to the sufferer. The key thing for the parent is to recognize the condition as close to its onset as possible and take the appropriate action.

GERMAN MEASLES (RUBELLA)
This is usually a mild illness which causes few problems. It is rare for a child to get German measles in the first six months if the mother has had the infection or has been immunized. The incubation period is 10–21 days and the virus is spread through the coughing and sneezing of an infected person. It is infectious from the day before the rash appears and for two days after its appearance. It is very important to keep your child away from any woman who might be pregnant if you suspect German measles because it can seriously damage an unborn baby.
**Symptoms:** The first sign is usually a rash that starts on the face and then spreads to the trunk. The spots are pink, pinpoint in size, separate (not blotchy), and are not raised above the level of the skin. The rash is not

*Some babies are born with slight jaundice, a yellowing of the skin, which may need treatment with ultra-violet light. It is usually carried out in the post-natal ward.*

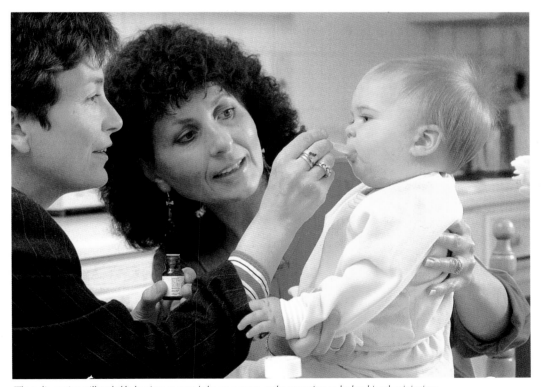

*The polio vaccine will probably be given to your baby on a spoon at the same time as he has his other injections.*

itchy and lasts for only two or three days. It may be accompanied by a slightly runny nose and a little redness around the eyes and swollen glands in the neck, the back of the head, and behind the ears. These may remain swollen for a few days.

**Treatment:** Check your child's temperature at least twice a day and give plenty of fluids if the temperature is at all raised.

**Call the doctor:** If you think your child has German measles, contact your doctor to confirm it. Do not take your child to the surgery because of possible contact with a pregnant woman.

MEASLES

It is rare for a child under six months to get measles if the mother had measles as a child, because the mother's immunity is passed on to the baby. The incubation period is 10–15 days and your child is infectious about six days before the rash appears and for five days afterwards. The virus is spread through droplets from the nose and throat of an infected person.

**Symptoms:** The first symptoms are a slightly raised temperature, runny

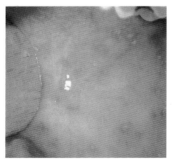

*One of the first signs of measles are Koplik's spots which appear inside a child's cheeks. The spots are small and red and have a white centre.*

nose, cough, redness of the eyes, lethargy, and loss of appetite. Two or three days later white spots about the size of a pinhead, with a surrounding red area, can be seen on the inside of the cheeks. These last for a few days then a blotchy, slightly raised, red rash appears behind the ears and on the face and then spreads to the chest during the next 24 hours. By the third and fourth day it will have spread over the arms and legs and will have reached the feet. The rash is not itchy but it will be accompanied by a high temperature. As the rash fades so the temperature falls.

**Treatment:** Bring the fever down. If your child's eyes become crusted, wipe them gently with cotton wool dipped in cooled boiled water. Your child can get out of bed as soon as she is feeling better.

**Call the doctor:** If your child is no better three days after the rash develops; if the child's temperature rises very rapidly; if earache or breathing difficulties develop.

MUMPS

This affects the glands in the neck and in front of the ears and causes swelling. Sometimes mumps causes inflammation of the testicles, but this is rare in boys before puberty. Mumps is unlikely to affect a baby under the age of six months. The incubation period is 12–21 days. Mumps is spread by droplet infection and it is infectious from two days before the swelling appears and until it disappears.

**Symptoms:** Pain and swelling in one or both of the parotid glands which are situated just in front of the ears. The swelling makes the face appear puffy and reaches its maximum in about two days. It subsides within about five days.

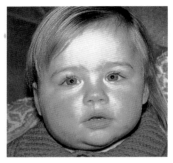

*With mumps, your child's face will become swollen and he may find it hard to swallow. Make sure he drinks plenty of liquids and give him jelly and ice cream to eat.*

**Treatment:** Give a suitable painkiller to reduce discomfort. Give your child easy-to-swallow foods such as ice cream and jelly and plenty of liquids, but avoid acidic drinks. If opening the mouth is painful, try getting her to drink through a straw. Warmth will help to soothe the swelling, so heat a soft cloth and hold it gently to her cheeks.

**Call the doctor:** If your child develops bad pains in her stomach or, if a boy, has a red testicle. Your doctor should be told if you suspect that your child has mumps.

WHOOPING COUGH

This can occur at any age and is one of the most serious common infectious diseases. The incubation period is 7–10 days and the germ is spread through droplet infection. A child is infectious from about two days before the onset of the cough until about three weeks later.

**Symptoms:** Whooping cough starts with a slight cough and sneezing and is often mistaken for an ordinary cold. It develops into severe bouts of 10-20 short, dry coughs which occur during the day and night – these are often worse during the night. In children over 18 months of age a long attack of coughing is followed by a sharp intake of breath which may produce the crowing or whooping sound. Not all children develop the whoop. During bad bouts of coughing your child may vomit, become red in the face and sweat. The cough can last for two to three months.

**Treatment:** Stay with the child during her coughing fits because they are distressing and she will need you to comfort her. Try lying her face-down across your lap while she coughs. Sleep with her at night when the cough is at its worst. Keep a bowl near her in case of vomiting and clean it afterwards with disinfectant so that the infection isn't spread. Try to keep your child entertained to distract her from coughing.

**Call the doctor:** Immediately if you suspect that your child has whooping cough. The doctor may prescribe a cough suppressant and an antibiotic. A very young baby may need to be admitted to hospital if the coughing is affecting breathing.

### CHICKENPOX

This is a highly infectious but usually mild disease in childhood (it can be serious if it occurs during adulthood). It is caused by one of the herpes group of viruses and is transmitted through direct contact with an infected person. The incubation period is 14–21 days and it is most infectious before the rash appears, which makes it difficult to isolate an infected child from others.

**Symptoms:** Chickenpox often starts with a fever, which may be accompanied by a headache and is then followed by a rash. Sometimes the only sign is the rash, which appears mainly on the trunk and

then spreads to the rest of the body and may even occur in the mouth. The rash consists of small red spots that quickly turn into itchy blisters. These gradually dry to form crusts which can remain for a few weeks. New spots appear in batches so an area may be covered in both crusty spots and new blisters. Scars only occur if the spots are scratched or if they become infected. Your child is infectious to other children until new blisters have stopped appearing,

which normally takes about one week.

**Treatment:** Treat any fever as previously described. Keep your child's nails very short to prevent her from scratching and infecting the spots. Apply calamine lotion to help reduce the itchiness. A handful of bicarbonate of soda added to a cool bath will also ease itchiness.

**Call the doctor:** If the itchiness is really causing a serious problem or if any of the spots have become infected or are very painful.

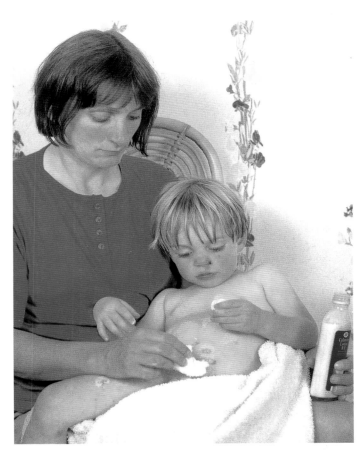

*Your child will probably feel miserable if he has chickenpox. Try to prevent him from scratching the spots as this will lead to scarring. Applying some calamine lotion to the spots will help reduce the itchiness and irritation.*

# LEARNING WITH TOYS

Playing with toys is important in a child's development because through play they learn about themselves and the world in which they live. During the first few months your child isn't capable of manipulating objects so he learns through sight, sound, and touch. A young baby likes to see things from close up and will enjoy objects that are colourful and that move or make a noise. A baby doesn't need a lot of toys because in these early months you will be his best plaything and your baby will be endlessly fascinated by your face and will study it during feeding. Sing and talk to your baby because, even though he can't understand, he will love the sound of your voice. As your baby gets older he will start imitating you and making different sounds. Encourage him by playing games such as Pat-a-cake or singing "Old MacDonald had a farm" and getting him to help with the animal noises. Your child may be able to remember simple concepts too, such as putting things in and taking them out of a container. Bath toys will give a lot of pleasure as your baby learns the fun of playing in water.

Toys will help your child learn to develop new skills, and they offer stimulation at each stage of development. For example, a very young baby will gain a lot from a simple pram toy; he can see it, touch it, suck, and smell it and by doing so will be discovering a number of new sensations. It won't take long to learn that a toy pushed out of the pram will just disappear. By performing this trick over and over again your baby will start to realize that he can make things happen which influence his world.

In the first year, toys can be used to help a child to learn hand and eye co-ordination, recognition, and then crawling and walking. As a child gets older, toys become useful props in imaginative games that teach him how to communicate with others, and help him to discover different aspects of life.

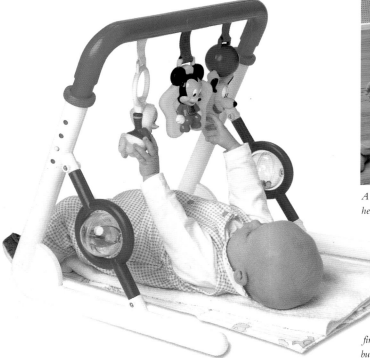

*A baby will enjoy a play mat that offers her different textures to play with. She will also be fascinated by the bright colours and bold designs featured on the mat.*

*An activity gym will keep a baby amused from a young age. At first he will just look at the hanging objects, but he will soon start to reach for the toys.*

*Left: An activity centre is always fascinating to a young baby and this one can be used as a walker too. Toys which will help your child to balance as she begins to pull herself up and then take her first steps will give her confidence.*

*Below: Although there are many attractive, well-designed toys available, don't be surprised if your baby decides that a wooden spoon and a metal pan are her favourite play things.*

There are so many toys to choose from that it's often difficult to decide which ones are right for a child at any particular stage. You should always buy the correct toys for the age of your child. Toys designed for an older child may well have loose parts on which a baby could choke. You should check all the toys a child plays with regularly to make sure that there are no loose or broken parts that could hurt him.

Your young baby will enjoy looking at a toy hung from the pram or above the cot.

## Toys for 0-6 months
- Mobile
- Rattle
- Soft toys
- Baby mirror
- Squeaker
- Baby gym
- Play mat

## Toys for 7-12 months
- Cloth or card books
- Big ball
- Soft blocks
- Beakers
- Bath toys
- Pop-up toys
- Musical toys
- Push-along toys

This rollaball can be rolled along and will help your baby's hand/eye co-ordination.

Simple toys which are colourful, tactile and chewable will interest a young baby.

As your baby learns to co-ordinate his hands, he will like to hold and feel toys that are easy to handle. This frog also has a baby-safe mirror. Your baby will be fascinated by his own reflection.

A play telephone with push buttons that make different noises will intrigue your baby and keep him amused for hours.

This colourful activity octopus has eight different-textured tentacles for your young baby to grasp and pull at. The caterpillar can be bent into different positions.

Your older baby will enjoy playing with different-sized, coloured stacking beakers.

*This stacker has different coloured rings to help an older baby recognize colours and learn how to stack the rings.*

*This shape sorter offers your child the opportunity to explore different shapes as well as colours.*

*Once your baby can sit unaided he will enjoy toys such as this train that he can push along the floor.*

*A simple shape sorter will give your older baby hours of entertainment as he discovers how to put the squares into the holes and then watch them drop inside.*

*All babies enjoy an activity centre and one that can be fixed to the side of the cot will keep your baby amused when you put him down for a rest.*

*Pull-along toys will develop and encourage your baby's mobility. They will also help him gain confidence as he learns how to push and pull the toy back and forth along the length of the floor.*

# BABY MASSAGE

Touch is an important part of your baby's physical and emotional growth, and massage is an ideal way of extending your natural inclination to caress and cuddle your baby. Massage has been used on babies in India and Africa for hundreds of years, not only to help form a bond between mother and baby, but also as a means of relieving colic, helping the digestive system, and making the developing muscles supple. It is thought that gentle stroking encourages the abdominal walls to relax, which helps to alleviate wind and ease colicky pain; massaging the young limbs will also help to strengthen them.

There are a number of specific massage techniques that can be learned, but initially your instinctive touch will be enough, just as long as you are gentle and don't try to manipulate your baby's limbs. You need to be sensitive to your baby's moods and should only massage her when she is content, perhaps between feeds or after a bath. Before you undress your baby for massage, make sure that the room is very warm and draught-free – this is important because babies lose their body heat 10 times more quickly than adults.

Remove any rings or bracelets before you begin and make sure that your fingernails are short and that there are no jagged edges that could scratch or irritate your baby. Relax your hands by stretching and shaking them, then warm them up by rubbing them together. Place a small amount of baby oil on your hands and, with your fingertips, gently massage the baby's skin using light, rhythmic movements. Start at the head and gradually work down to the feet.

Remember, a newborn needs only a feather-light, extremely gentle touch, and you must be careful when stroking the head and around the still-healing navel. The tiny infant will naturally revert to the fetal position, so you shouldn't try to straighten out her arms and legs too much. As your baby gets older you can start to apply a slightly firmer touch, using the whole of your hand in the massage. When you have finished and your baby is dressed, allow her to have a sleep if that is what she seems to want.

## Massaging tips

• Don't attempt to massage your baby if she is tired, hungry, or fretful.
• Allow yourself plenty of time so that the massage is not hurried or stressed.
• Get everything you need ready before you begin.
• Don't massage for more than 10 minutes or your baby will start to become bored.
• Talk or sing to your baby during the massage so that it is a pleasurable experience.
• If your baby isn't enjoying the massage, stop immediately and try again another time.

## How to massage your baby

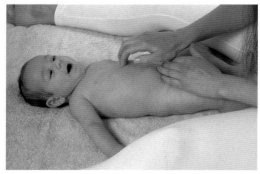

**1** *Your baby will love the feel of massage. Place him on a towel in a warm room. Take some warmed baby oil into your hand and lightly massage his chest with circular movements.*

**2** *Move on to the arms. Gently squeeze down his arms from the shoulder to the wrist. If your baby is happy repeat again up to three times.*

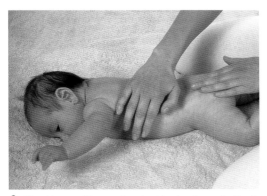

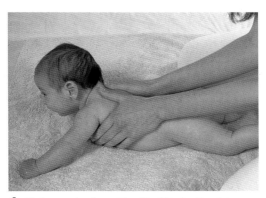

**3** *Turn him onto his stomach and, with a hand on each side of his body, massage him from his bottom up to his shoulders, crossing your hands from side to side. Work down again and repeat.*

**4** *Placing your hands on either side of his shoulders, bring your thumbs together and gently massage around your baby's neck and shoulders with a circular movement.*

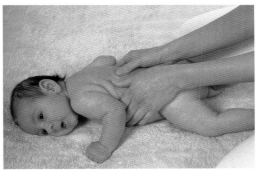

**5** *Move both your hands down to your baby's sides and softly knead his skin for a short time between your fingers. Repeat up to three times if he is happy.*

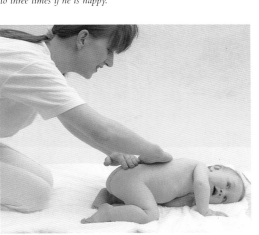

**6** *Move your hands into the centre of your baby's back and do some light kneading movements with your fingers up and down the length of his spine.*

*To finish your baby's massage, make some soft circling strokes with both hands up and down the back.*

# TRAVELLING WITH A BABY

The secret of successful travelling with children, no matter how long or short your journey, is careful planning. Young children are surprisingly adaptable, so providing that you take the essentials – food, nappies, and a favourite toy or two – your child should be quite happy to go with you.

The car is probably the easiest form of transport with a baby as you can use it as a kind of nursery on wheels, packing into it everything that you and your child are likely to require. Prepare a survival kit for the journey before you set off and keep it where it is easily accessible. The kit should include spare nappies, a change of clothes, baby wipes, changing equipment, and a mat or towel. If you are bottle-feeding or giving solids, you will also need to include some feeds plus some feeding equipment.

From birth your child should travel in the car in an approved safety restraint suitable for his age and weight. These restraints must be fixed and used properly to obtain maximum protection for your child in the event of an accident.

An older baby will need to be kept amused on the journey and the easiest way to do this is with a selection of toys. Choose toys that have been specially designed for use in the car, or ones which have suction pads that will stick on the window or the back of the front seat. These are better than loose toys, which you may find you have to retrieve each time they are dropped.

Try to make the journey as relaxed as possible by checking the route before you leave and allowing extra time to get there. This way you won't arrive late and anxious because you've had to make a number of unscheduled stops. If you are going on a long journey consider travelling at night. If you are fortunate, your child will be soothed by the motion of the car and will sleep for at least half the journey.

If the journey you are taking involves public transport, you will need to be selective about what you take with you as you'll have to transport your luggage as well as your baby. Take a similar survival kit to the one already mentioned, but make sure it is packed into an easy-to-carry holdall. If possible, take a lightweight pushchair, which you can fold with one hand, leaving the other free, or put your baby in a baby carrier, either strapped on your front if he is still very young, or on your back if he is old enough to sit up on his own.

If you are booking a seat on a train, coach or plane, always mention the fact that you are travelling with a young child when you arrange your ticket and ask for the most convenient seating accommodation available. If the rail or coach station has a lot of steps to be negotiated ask one of the staff to help you, or find out if there is a lift you can use.

Some airlines have sky cots and others will allow you to take a buggy onto the plane as hand luggage. They may even allow you to use your car seat (if it is of a suitable type) as a restraint for your child. Ask the airline or your travel agent what facilities are available for babies and older children before you set off.

Whichever method of transport you use, always shield your child from the sun, and make sure that any exposed skin is protected by a high-factor sunscreen. Keep your baby as comfortable as possible by putting him in clothes that are loose and easy to change. A number of layers of fairly thin clothing are best as this will allow you to add or take away a layer depending on how warm it is. Cars can get very hot in the summer, with the temperature creeping up considerably without you realizing it, so keep a constant check on your child while travelling.

*Once your baby can support his head, you can put him in a carrier on your back. But always make sure that it is a comfortable fit.*

*A baby sling is an ideal way for either parent to carry a young baby, both inside the house, or when they are out and about.*

# KEEPING YOUR CHILD SAFE

Although there is no such thing as a completely safe home, many accidents can be prevented by taking a few safety precautions. High-risk areas can be made safer by installing devices that have been specially designed to prevent your child getting into danger.

HALL, STAIRS AND LANDING
The most common accident in these constantly used corridor areas is a child falling down the stairs, so keep staircases blocked off at both the top and bottom.
What you can do:
• Ensure that there is no loose floor

*Stairs can be hazardous for your child and should ideally be blocked off top and bottom. Always accompany your child on the stairs and teach him to hold on as he climbs.*

covering or any trailing wire at the top of the stairs on which either you or a child could trip.
• If you have carpet on the stairs make sure that it is securely fitted and in a good state of repair.
• Make sure that the gaps between the stair spindles are no more than 10cm/4in so that a child's head cannot get stuck between them.
• Fix gates at the top and bottom of the stairs to prevent young children from having access to them.
• Check that the lighting is good, so that there is no risk of tripping on some unseen object on the stairs.
• Fit safety film or safety glass to any glass doors in these areas.
• Make sure that the front-door latch and letterbox are out of reach.

LIVING ROOMS
These rooms are more difficult to keep safe because the environment is constantly changing as people come in and out and items are moved. Frequent safety checks are needed because the danger areas change as your child becomes more mobile. Try looking at the room from your child's level. One of the biggest dangers in the living area is fire.
What you can do:
• Install a circuit-breaker.
• Install smoke alarms throughout your home.
• Fit all fires with guards.
• Use electrical plug socket covers to prevent a child poking something into the socket.
• Unplug electric fires when they are not in use.
• Make sure that all fabrics and upholstery are made from fire-resistant materials.
• Keep matches, lighters and cigarettes out of reach and regularly empty ashtrays.

*A safety gate is an essential piece of baby equipment. Fitted to the top or bottom of the stairs it will prevent your baby from climbing the stairs and falling. Placed across a doorway it will keep your child out of a room, such as the kitchen, where he could be in danger.*

*As your baby becomes more mobile he will use anything he can hold on to when pulling himself up. Once he is standing, things that were safely out of the way while he was still only sitting or crawling can now be reached.*

Ideally, don't smoke at all!
• Fit safety protectors to the corners of tables and cupboards.
• Use mats instead of tablecloths so that your child can't pull things off the table on top of her.
• Place all ornaments and breakables out of reach.
• Check the floor regularly for small objects that could be swallowed.

### KITCHEN

This is potentially the most dangerous room in the house for a young child. The most common accidents to occur in the kitchen are scalds from hot water, burns from cookers, and poisoning from cleaning products. What you can do:
• Keep the doorway blocked with a safety gate so that your child can't get in unnoticed.
• Put all sharp objects, such as knives, well out of reach of children.
• Fit safety catches to all low-level

cupboards, drawers, the fridge, and also the freezer.
• Use a shortened coiled kettle flex.
• Cook on the back rings of the hob with the pan handles facing inwards.
• Use a pan guard on the cooker.
• Never leave containers of hot liquid, such as cups or pots of tea, where your child can reach them.
• Make sure that all household chemicals and cleaning materials are kept out of reach and that their lids are always tightly screwed on.

*Kitchen cupboards have a fascination for most young children. Safeguard your child by fitting cupboards with safety catches so that he can't open them.*

### BATHROOM

Among the most common accidents to happen in the bathroom are scalds from hot water, falls in the bath or shower, poisoning from medicines, and cuts from razors, scissors and broken glass. What you can do:
• Make sure that all medicines and other dangerous objects, such as razors, are locked away in a cabinet which is placed out of easy reach of a child.
• Use a non-slip mat in the bottom

of the bath to prevent your child from slipping.
• Fit a lock to the toilet seat.
• Make sure that your child cannot reach the bathroom window by climbing on the toilet or the bath.
• Always run cold water into the bath before adding hot water and then check the temperature before putting your child into the tub.
• Make sure the water thermostat is not too high. The water should not be above 37°C/98°F.
• Hang a towel over the taps to prevent a child burning herself.
• Check that a child can't reach the door lock and lock herself in.

### NURSERY

This is the one room where a child will spend time alone, so regular

**Equipment**

• Make sure any equipment you buy conforms to the safety regulations established by the European Union (EU) and the British Standards Institute (BSI).
• Only use equipment for the age of the child it has been designed for.
• Second-hand equipment needs to be checked thoroughly for safety.
• Always use safety straps when you put your baby in a pram, pushchair, highchair, or bouncing cradle.
• Never put a bouncing cradle on a raised surface because your baby's active movements could easily make it fall off.
• When travelling in a car, always put your baby in a car seat approved for the child's weight and age.
• Use child locks on the doors.
• Don't leave your child alone in the car, even if she is firmly strapped into her seat.

safety checks need to be carried out as your child grows and becomes more adventurous.

What you can do:

• Make sure that your baby's cot and mattress conform to safety standards and that the mattress fits snugly into the cot base.

• If your child sleeps in a bed, always use a bed barrier and make sure there is a safety gate fitted at the top of the stairs.

• Use a cot light, nursery light, dimmer, or plug light to give your child reassurance at night and to allow you to look in on her without causing any disturbance.

• Install a nursery listening device so that you can monitor your child.

• Place a thermometer in the nursery to help you keep a check on the temperature. The room needs to be around 18°C/65°F.

• If you, or your partner, must smoke, protect children from coming into contact with cigarette smoke, which could put them at risk from coughs, chest infections, and even cot death. There is also some evidence linking passive smoking with the development of childhood asthma.

• Fit any windows with locks.

• Make sure you place the cot or bed away from the window.

### OUTSIDE

Many accidents happen outside the home. Even if you have your own garden you should never leave a young child outside unattended.

What you can do:

• Keep all garden tools and chemicals locked away.

• Fit locks to garden sheds and garage doors.

• Make sure that the gate to the road outside is secure.

• Always use a harness and reins, or a wrist link, when you are out on the pavement with your child.

• Make sure that the surface under any play equipment is safe for children to fall on.

• Cover up a pond or a water butt.

*A bouncing cradle can be used from around three weeks, and your baby will enjoy reclining in the soft fabric seat. He will quickly learn that by kicking his legs hard he can make the cradle bounce.*

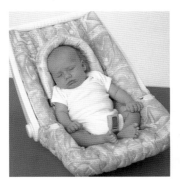

*Many infant carriers double as car safety seats for at least the first six months. They are usually light and portable so that a newborn will fit into them snugly.*

*The rear-facing infant carrier can be fitted on both the front passenger seat and the rear seat. If fitted in the front of the car the safety airbag must be disabled first.*

# FIRST AID

Many accidents can be dealt with when and where they occur. Adults with a sound knowledge of first aid can not only calm a distressed child, but they can also help to limit the effects of an accident, aid recovery, and could save a child's life. First of all you need to assess the situation and establish whether basic first aid is sufficient to treat the injury, or whether you think professional help might be required.

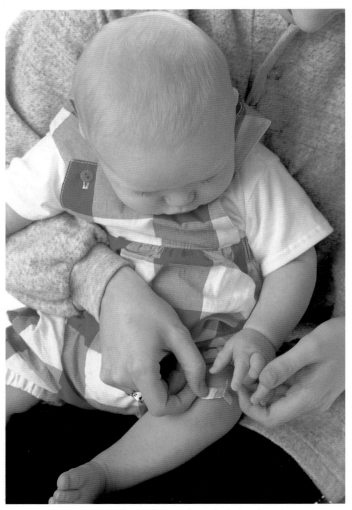

*Any minor cuts that a young baby suffers usually can be dealt with on the spot from your first aid box.*

GETTING MEDICAL HELP

If your child is unconscious or you think that he may have suffered spinal injury, after a fall, for example, always call an ambulance. If there is even a small possibility of spinal injury, do not attempt to move your child as this could cause severe damage. The best thing you can do is to keep your child warm, still, and calm until the ambulance arrives.

Time is of the essence in dealing with an emergency case that requires immediate medical attention. Should you need to get your child to the hospital urgently, and he can be moved safely, it may be quicker to take him there yourself. If possible, find someone else to drive, so that you can sit with your child in the back seat and give first aid if required. Although it is difficult, it is most important that you try to remain calm and to reassure your child. If you are unsure where the nearest hospital emergency department is, however, or have no suitable transport, then you should call an ambulance; the driver will quickly take you to the nearest suitable hospital.

If you fear that your child has injured his neck or back, call an ambulance and do not move him unless he is in immediate danger. If your child must be moved, you need extra pairs of hands to help turn him onto his back in one movement while holding his neck, shoulders and hips steady.

BREATHING

If your child has stopped breathing, start CPR at once and continue until breathing resumes. Get someone else to call an ambulance.

**Rescue breaths:**

**1** Position – lay your baby or child on his back on a firm surface.

## First aid kit checklist

It is important to have a fully stocked first aid kit in your home and you should also carry a basic kit in the car. You can buy ready-made kits, or you can make up your own by buying the items separately and storing them in an airtight container, out of the reach of children. You should check the contents regularly and replace items as they are used, so that you will always be ready for an emergency. Your home first aid kit should contain:

- assorted plasters
- cotton wool
- sterile gauze dressings
- sterile eye pad
- roll of 5cm/2in gauze bandage
- crepe bandages
- triangular bandage
- safety pins
- surgical tape
- scissors
- blunt-ended tweezers
- paracetamol syrup
- antiseptic solution or wipes
- calamine lotion
- clinical thermometer or fever strip
- doctor's telephone number
- details of your nearest hospital casualty department

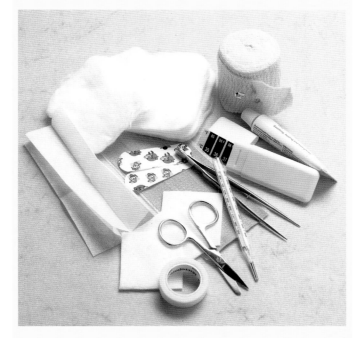

**4** Check breathing – once his airway is open he may breathe spontaneously. Place your ear near the mouth and look along the body for movement. If there is no breathing after five seconds, give two rescue breaths.

**5** With a baby, cover his nose and mouth with your lips and breathe gently into his lungs until the chest rises. With a child, tilt his head back and bring the chin forward. Pinch his nostrils, take a deep breath and seal your lips around the child's mouth. Blow steadily until his chest rises.

**6** Monitor recovery – your child's chest should rise as you blow air into the lungs, and fall when you take your mouth away. Look for this each time you raise your head to take a new breath of air. Then check for signs of circulation. These include

**2** Remove any obvious obstruction, but do not try to clear the mouth by sweeping with your fingers.

**3** Open his airway – if your child is unconscious the airway may be blocked or narrowed, making breathing difficult or impossible. With a baby, tilt his chin using one finger. With a child, place one hand on the forehead, gently pushing his head backwards while you tilt his chin with the other hand.

any movement, coughing, or normal breathing. If your child's chest fails to rise the airway may not be fully open, so readjust the position of his head and jaw and try again. Check a baby's pulse on his upper arm. With a child, check the pulse in his neck. If the heart is not beating, external chest compression is needed.

### EXTERNAL CHEST COMPRESSION

If your baby is under one year old and there are no signs of circulation start chest compressions:

**1** Place two fingers on the middle of your baby's breastbone, just below the nipples. (Use the heel of your hand on an older child.)

**2** Use your fingers to compress the chest to one-third of its total depth. Do this five times in three seconds, making the compressions smooth and rhythmic.

**3** Give one rescue breath into his lungs and then five more chest compressions.

**4** Continue with five compressions followed by one rescue breath until the heart starts beating, or emergency help arrives.

**5** Check every few minutes to see if the heart has started beating again. When it does start you must stop the chest compressions immediately.

**6** Continue with rescue breaths until your baby begins to breathe on his own.

### UNCONSCIOUSNESS AND THE RECOVERY POSITION

If a baby is unconscious but breathing, cradle him in your arms, tilting his head so that his airway is kept open, and phone for medical help. An older child should be put in the recovery position. This prevents the tongue from slipping back into his throat and obstructing his airway, and avoids choking if he vomits. Put your child into this position if unconscious, but still breathing:

**1** Lie your child on his back, face turned towards you, keeping the chin pulled down.

**2** Place the arm near you at right angles to his body, elbow bent, with the palm upwards.

**3** Fold the other arm over your child's chest with the back of his hand against his opposite cheek.

**4** Lift the furthest knee, keeping this foot flat on the ground.

**5** Keeping your child's hand pressed against his cheek, pull on the thigh furthest away from you, to roll him towards you.

**6** Tilt your child's head back with his hand supporting it. Adjust his upper leg so that it supports his body.

**7** Cover the child with a blanket and stay with him until help arrives, checking constantly for breathing and heartbeat.

### CUTS AND GRAZES

You should seek medical help if there is a serious risk of infection, even with small wounds. But treat minor wounds yourself:

**1** Clean the wound and surrounding area under running water.

**2** Use an antiseptic cream or saline solution to reduce the risk of infection.

**3** Apply a plaster or dressing once the surrounding area is dry.

*Never:*

• use a tourniquet.

Larger, more serious wounds must be treated immediately to control the bleeding and to minimize the risk of infection. Once the blood flow has been stemmed you should take your child to hospital:

**1** Control any severe bleeding by applying direct pressure to the wound. If possible use an absorbent sterile dressing.

**2** If the wound is on an arm or leg, raise and support it.

**3** Cover the wound with a sterile dressing and attach it firmly with a bandage or adhesive tape to help control the bleeding.

### BURNS AND SCALDS

Burns are caused by dry heat from flames and hot electrical equipment. Scalds are the result of wet heat, such as steam or boiling water. There is always a risk of infection with both burns and scalds because of the damage they do to the skin.

**1** Cool the damaged area under cold running water for at least 10 minutes.

**2** Try to remove anything that might constrict the area if it swells, for example, rings or tight clothing.

**3** Cover with a sterile dressing.
**4** Always seek medical advice for all minor burns and scalds.
*Never:*
• apply butter, oil or grease to the damaged area.
• burst any blisters.
• use adhesive dressings or tape.
• remove anything that is sticking to the burn.

BRUISES AND SWELLING
If your child falls and hits himself, or receives a blow, bleeding may occur under the skin that causes swelling and discoloration. This should fade over about a week. You should hold a cloth that has been wrung out in cold water, or wrapped around an ice pack, to the bruised area for about half an hour to help reduce the swelling.

STRAINS AND SPRAINS
A strain is a tear or rupture of a muscle which causes swelling and discomfort. A sprain is more serious because it involves damage to the joint itself or the ligaments that surround it. Symptoms of a sprain include swelling, acute pain, and restricted movement. Both strains and sprains require the same treatment:
**1** Avoid any activity that may overstrain the injured area until the swelling has gone down. Do not massage the injury because this may cause further damage.
**2** Cool the injury with a cold pack, a bag of ice wrapped in a towel, or a cold, wet towel. This will reduce the pain and control inflammation.
**3** Use a bandage to apply gentle compression to the injured area. This will give support and help to lessen inflammation.
**4** Raise and support the injured area as this will help reduce swelling.

APPLYING A BANDAGE
Select the width of bandage appropriate to the area to be covered.
**1** Support the injured limb while you are bandaging.
**2** Start below the injury site, and wrap the bandage around the limb, using a spiral action, overlapping by two-thirds each time.
**3** Secure with a safety pin or some adhesive tape.
**4** Check to make sure the bandage isn't restricting the circulation.
**5** Bandage injured joints by wrapping the bandage around the joint in a figure-of-eight pattern, overlapping by two-thirds each time.
*Never:*
• bandage too tightly because this can affect the circulation. If the fingers or toes of the bandaged limb are cooler or darker than the other limbs the bandage is too tight. It should be removed and reapplied, fixing it in position more loosely.
• ignore a limb injury. Always seek medical help if the leg is too painful to take your child's weight, if he is not using his arm, or if any swelling hasn't gone down after 48 hours.

BROKEN BONES
Technically, a broken or cracked bone is a fracture. All fractures should be treated with great care because any undue movement could cause further damage:
**1** Keep your child still and cover with a coat or blanket.
**2** Remove anything that might constrict any swelling around the injured area.
**3** Get medical assistance.

BITES AND STINGS
Bites from mosquitoes and midges or stings from wasps and bees can be extremely painful, causing hard, red, swollen lumps which itch intensely. A small number of people are allergic to wasp and bee stings. If your child appears to be having difficulty breathing as the result of a sting you must seek medical help immediately. In ordinary circumstances:
**1** If the sting has been left in the skin, remove it with tweezers, taking care not to squeeze the poison sack because this would force the remaining poison into the skin.
**2** Apply a cold compress to the site for quick relief from pain.
**3** Massage sting-relief cream into the area for longer-term relief.

EYE INJURIES
Eyes are delicate organs which can be damaged very easily, so immediate first aid treatment is required if an injury occurs:
• Remove any foreign object from your child's eye using a damp piece of cotton wool. If you can't do this or the pain remains after the removal, cover the eye with a clean pad and then take your child to hospital.
• If your child's eye has been injured by a blow, apply a sterile dressing, and take him to hospital for immediate treatment.
• Chemicals that are splashed into the eye should be washed out completely by flooding the eye with some clean, cold water for at least 15 minutes. Then cover the damaged eye with a clean pad and get your child to hospital.

CHOKING
This happens when a foreign object gets lodged in the throat and obstructs the airway.
*For a baby:*
**1** Lay your baby face downwards, with the chest and abdomen lying

## Choking

*If your baby is choking, you will need to take immediate action. Lay a young baby face down with her chest and abdomen lying along your forearm with your hand supporting her head. Slap her gently on the back several times.*

*With an older baby or toddler the action would be slightly different. You will need to lay her across your knees, with her head facing downward. To remove the obstruction, slap her firmly between the shoulder blades.*

along your forearm and your hand supporting his head.

**2** Slap him gently on the back.
*Note:* if your baby or child doesn't start breathing normally once the blockage is completely removed, call an ambulance and begin artificial ventilation immediately.
*For a child:*
**1** Lay your child across your knee, with his head down, and slap him sharply and firmly between the shoulder blades.
**2** If the above fails to remove the blockage, use your finger to try to hook out the object, taking care not to push it further down your child's throat.

CROUP
Croup is a noisy barking cough that may be accompanied by fever and, in severe cases, your child may breathe with a grunting noise called "stridor". Croup can be quite frightening for both you and your child, so it is very important to stay calm and to reassure him. To help remedy the situation:
• Treat simple croup with warm drinks and paracetamol syrup to bring down any fever.
• Ease severe croup by getting your baby or child to inhale steam from a kettle, or sit near a running hot tap in the bathroom or near wet towels over a radiator. Make sure that he

cannot scald himself on the source of the steam.
• If your child is very distressed or has trouble breathing or swallowing, call your doctor immediately, or take him to hospital.

DROWNING
If possible get your child out of the water straightaway, otherwise you will need to give emergency first aid in the water.
**1** Empty your child's mouth and, if his breathing has stopped, start to give him recuse breaths. Do not attempt to remove any water out of your child's stomach or from his lungs.

**2** If you carry your child, keep his head lower than the rest of his body to reduce the risk of him inhaling any water.

**3** Lay him down on a coat or blanket. Open the airway and check his breathing and pulse.

**4** Once your child is breathing normally again, remove all his wet clothes and cover him with some warm, dry ones. Give him a reviving hot drink.

**5** Always take him to hospital for a thorough check-up, even if he seems to be fine and to have recovered.

### ELECTRIC SHOCK

Most electrical accidents occur in the home, so it is vitally important to ensure that household appliances are wired correctly and kept out of the reach of young children. Severe injuries and even death can result from electric shock. But if a shock does still occur:

**1** Switch off the current and pull out the plug before touching the child. If this is not possible, use something wooden, such as a broom handle or chair that will not conduct the electricity, to move him right away from the power source.

**2** Check his breathing and heartbeat. If your child is unconscious, place him in the recovery position.

**3** Treat any burns.

**4** Cover your child to keep him warm and reassure him by talking to him calmly.

**5** Phone to get some medical assistance immediately.

*Never:*

• touch your child until the power source has been turned off.

• apply water to a burn that occurs from an electric shock while your child is still attached to the source of the electricity.

### NOSEBLEEDS

Bleeding often follows a blow to the nose, or may occur as a result of blowing the nose too hard. Sometimes there is no apparent reason for the nosebleed. The flow of blood can be quite heavy, which can be frightening, although it is not usually a serious problem:

**1** Sit your child upright with his head positioned slightly forward. Putting the head back can sometimes cause choking and cause some discomfort.

**2** Get your child to breathe through his mouth while you pinch the soft part of his nose firmly for 10 minutes until the flow of blood slows down and stops.

**3** If your child's nose is still bleeding, hold a very cold cloth or an ice pack wrapped in a cloth to his nose for a couple of minutes, then pinch his nose again.

**4** Try to ensure that your child avoids blowing his nose for several hours after a nosebleed has finally been staunched.

### POISONING

This occurs when harmful substances are inhaled or swallowed. It is important to keep all such substances locked away and out of reach of young children.

Always be on the alert and see that your child does not eat any poisonous berries or plants in the garden, or when you are out in the countryside. If you suspect poisoning, ring for an ambulance and then take immediate action:

**1** Check breathing and be ready to resuscitate if necessary.

**2** If your child is breathing, but is unconscious, place him in the recovery position and then phone for help immediately.

**3** If his lips or mouth show signs of burning, cool them by giving water or milk to sip slowly.

**4** Keep the bottle or container the poison was in, or a similar berry or fruit to take to the hospital. This will enable the medical staff to administer the correct antidote to your child as fast as possible.

*Never:*

• try to give fluids to your child if he is unconscious.

• try to make your child sick. This can be extremely dangerous as the poison could find its way into his lungs and cause severe damage to these organs as well as endangering his breathing.

### SHOCK

Severe bleeding, burns, and even fear can bring about a state of shock. You can recognize shock by an extreme loss of colour along with cold and clammy skin. The child may also be shivering and sweating at the same time. This may be accompanied by rapid breathing and dizziness, and possibly by vomiting.

Shock often occurs after a major accident, so all the casualties must be treated for shock, even if they are not showing any of the listed symptoms. In extreme cases shock can be fatal, so it requires some immediate action and should always be taken seriously:

**1** Lay your child down on his side and make sure that his breathing isn't restricted.

**2** Loosen any restricting clothing at his neck, chest, and waist. Then cover your child with a blanket or a coat, but take care not to allow him to overheat.

**3** Try to get your child to remain still and to be calm while you seek medical help.

## PART THREE

# THE FIRST YEAR

YOUR NEWBORN arrives in the world a helpless, totally dependent baby, yet, with your help, within a year she will have learned all the basic skills that she needs to build on for her future growth and development. This section takes you, month by month, through the first year of a child's development. It is, however, important to realize that your child is unique, so there is little point in comparing her with others in anything other than a general way at this stage.

You will want to help and encourage your child as she masters each new skill. Understanding how she learns to talk, crawl, walk and play will enable to you to assist her at each stage. The five senses – hearing, vision, taste, smell and touch – are all extremely important from the time your child is born. As each sense develops, your child will be discovering something new about the world in which she's living.

Being able to participate in this fascinating time in your child's life is a very special privilege. You will be part of the most exciting process in the world: the development of your child from a helpless baby to a confident, independent toddler.

# NEWBORN

Your newborn baby will probably look wrinkled and slightly blotchy at first. When he is born his skin may have a bluish tinge and the legs may even be a different colour to the rest of his body. This will only last for a short time, until oxygen from the lungs has had time to reach the bloodstream. You may also find patches of dry skin. Eyes may be reddish and slightly swollen and your baby may still be covered with vernix, the greasy white substance which has been protecting the skin from becoming waterlogged by the amniotic fluid. There may also be a covering of lanugo, fine hair which covers the shoulders, upper arms, and legs.

Your baby's head may look too big for his body. It is usually about one-quarter of the total body length and it may be a slightly odd shape because of the pressure that was put on it during the birth. His features may also appear slightly flattened from being squeezed through the pelvis. Your baby's head may be covered with very thin hair or have a thick thatch that stands up on end.

### Milestones

Your child is immediately able to:
• Hear and respond to noises.
• Focus on objects that are within 20–30cm/8–12in.
• Grip your finger tightly.
• Suck vigorously.
• Make walking movements when held on a hard surface.
• Turn towards you when you stroke his cheek.

An increase in female hormones from the placenta just before birth affects both boys and girls and your baby's genitals may be enlarged and breasts may appear slightly swollen.

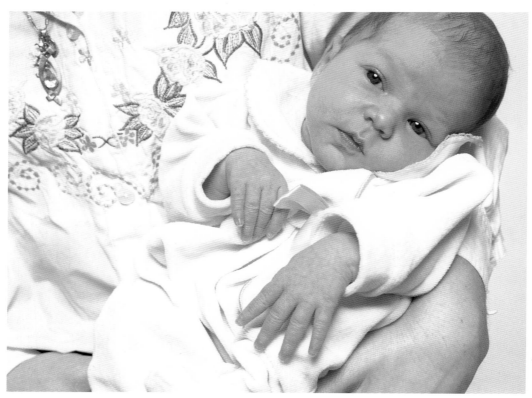

*When a baby is born he can be between 45–55cm/18–22in long and weigh anything between 2.5–4.5kg/5½–10lb.*

It is quite usual for the breasts of both boys and girls to have a milky discharge; girls may have a slight vaginal discharge as well. All these features will disappear over the next few weeks.

## SIZE

Although the average weight of a baby at birth is 3.4kg/7½lb, wide variations occur so, assuming that your baby was born around the estimated date of delivery (EDD), it could weigh anything between 2.5–4.5kg/5½–10lb. Your baby's weight is determined by a lot of factors, including your size and the size of your partner, how much weight you put on in pregnancy, and your general health.

Your baby is quite likely to lose weight during the first week. This is because it takes a little while for regular feeding to become properly established. Once an infant is feeding well his weight should remain stable for a couple of days and then, within seven to 10 days, he will regain his birth weight. A baby's weight gain is one of the easiest ways of telling whether he is thriving.

The average length of a newborn is between 48–51cm/19–20in, but as with weight, this can vary, although most babies are somewhere between 45–55cm/18–22in.

## REFLEXES

A baby is born with a number of reflexes. The rooting reflex means that your child's mouth automatically searches for your nipple; grasping is seen when your baby demonstrates a surprisingly strong grip. When on his back, your baby may adopt the tonic neck reflex – the head is turned to one side and the arm and leg on that side are extended while the opposite ones are flexed. A loud noise or the sensation of falling causes the startle or Moro reflex: the newborn extends legs, arms, and fingers, arches the back and throws the head back and then draws back the arms, fists clenched, into the chest. All these initial reflexes will gradually diminish over the next weeks and months as voluntary movements take their place.

In addition to these reflexes, every baby is born with the ability to suck, swallow, and gag so that they can feed as soon as they are born. The gagging reflex prevents a baby from choking on too much liquid and allows the child to get rid of any mucus that may be blocking up his airways.

Your newborn will probably hiccup and snuffle a lot at first. Hiccups occur because the baby's breathing rhythm is still rather jerky.

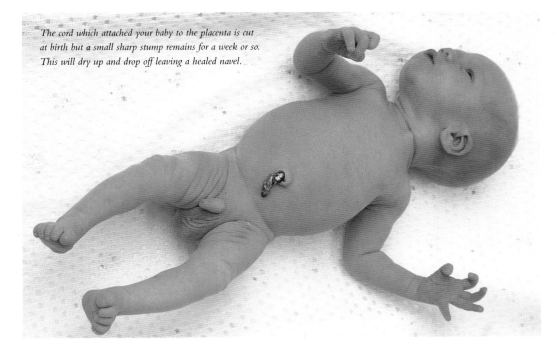

*The cord which attached your baby to the placenta is cut at birth but a small sharp stump remains for a week or so. This will dry up and drop off leaving a healed navel.*

They don't hurt, or even particularly bother the baby in fact, so you need not worry about them at all. Your baby will also make some snuffling noises. This is from learning to breathe through his nose and because the nasal passages are still very small. As the nose gets bigger the snuffling will stop.

All babies are sensitive to bright lights and this may make them sneeze when they first open their eyes. This is because the light stimulates the nerves in their nose as well as their eyes. Sneezing is also a way of clearing the nasal passages and it will prevent any dust from getting into the baby's lungs.

## CRYING

Your baby may make his first cry as soon as his chest has been delivered, others wait until they have been born or until they start to breathe normally. These first cries are often not much more than a whimper and the full-bodied cry follows later. A baby may look red and angry while crying, but this is quite normal. Crying is a baby's way of communicating as well as a means of exercising his lungs.

Hunger is the main reason for a newborn to cry, but being lonely, wet, or tired will also make a baby cry. Some babies cry because they don't like being undressed, others

when they are immersed in water. Some babies are more fretful than others so they cry more. You will quickly learn to recognize why your baby is crying and the best way to soothe him.

## NEWBORN TESTS

The first test your baby will be given is the Apgar test. The scores are recorded at one minute after birth and then again at five minutes and they reflect your newborn's general condition. Babies who score between 7 and 10 are in good to excellent condition, those who score between 4 and 6 are in fair condition, but may need some resuscitative

*A newborn baby might initially have a stepping reflex, but this will soon be replaced by voluntary movements.*

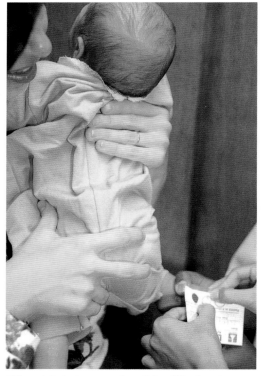

*When a baby is six or seven days old he will be given the Guthrie test to test for a range of rare diseases.*

**Apgar table**

| Score | 0 | 1 | 2 |
|---|---|---|---|
| Appearance (colour) | pale or white | body pink, extremities blue | pink |
| Heart rate | not detectable | below 100 | over 100 |
| Grimace (reflex irritability) | no response to stimulation | grimace | cough, sneeze |
| Muscle tone | flaccid (no or weak activity) | some movement of extremities | moving |
| Respiration (breathing) | none | weak, gasping, irregular | crying, regular |

measures. Babies who score under 4 will need some immediate emergency treatment.

Sometime, soon after the birth, your baby will be thoroughly checked over. A doctor will check your baby's head circumference, the fontanelles, and the roof of the mouth to see if there are any abnormalities. The doctor will listen to the heart and lungs and feel your baby's abdomen to check that the internal organs such as kidney, liver, and spleen, are the right shape and size. The genitals are also checked for abnormalities and, if your baby is a boy, the doctor will look to see that both testicles have descended. Hips will be checked for possible dislocation and all the limbs will be inspected to see they are the right length and are moving correctly. The doctor will run his thumb down the baby's spine to make sure that the vertebrae are in place. The baby's reflexes will also be checked.

The Guthrie test is usually done in the first 10 days after birth. A blood sample will be taken from the baby's heel. The blood is then tested for phenylketonuria (PKU), a rare disease which causes severe mental handicap, and for thyroid deficiency.

## SPECIAL CARE

If your baby is born several weeks early, the birth weight is low, or your child needs extra care for any other reason, he may be put in the Special Care Baby Unit (SCBU). Here the infant will be monitored so that he gets all the special treatment required. It can be distressing to see your baby in a special care unit, especially if he is surrounded by an array of strange equipment. Ask the staff to explain what the equipment is for and why your baby needs it. Try to spend as much time as you can with your baby in special care because, even if you can't pick him up and hold him, your baby will be able to hear your voice and it will soothe him. You will probably be able to touch your baby through the side of the incubator.

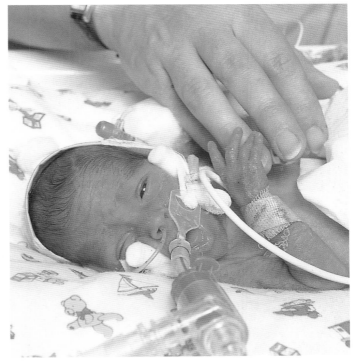

*If your baby is born early, he may have to go into the Special Care Baby Unit. Don't be afraid to ask about all the equipment he is attached to, and let him know you are there by touching and talking to him.*

# ONE MONTH

Your baby's movements are still dominated by the primary reflexes so when placed on her back your infant will adopt the tonic neck reflex posture, with her head to one side and the limbs on that side extended while the ones on the other side are flexed. If you place your baby on her front her head will turn to one side, then she will pull her knees under the abdomen and hold her arms close to her body, with her hands curled into fists. The fingers and toes will fan out when she straightens her arms or legs. If you hold your baby to stand on a hard surface she will press down and make a forward walking movement.

Although your baby was born with vision and can see colours and shapes at close range, her sight is still immature. Images which offer a high contrast and simple patterns, for example black lines on a white background, are easier for a baby to understand than paler, more complicated designs. Hold your baby upright or in a half reclining position

**Milestones**

Your child may be able to:
- Lift her head briefly while lying on her stomach.
- Focus on your face while feeding.
- Respond to a small bell being rung by moving her eyes and head towards the source of the sound.
- Follow with her eyes an object which is moved in an arc 15–25.5cm/ 6–10in away from her face.
- Turn her head towards you when you speak to her.

*Even at this early age your baby will be interested in things around him.*

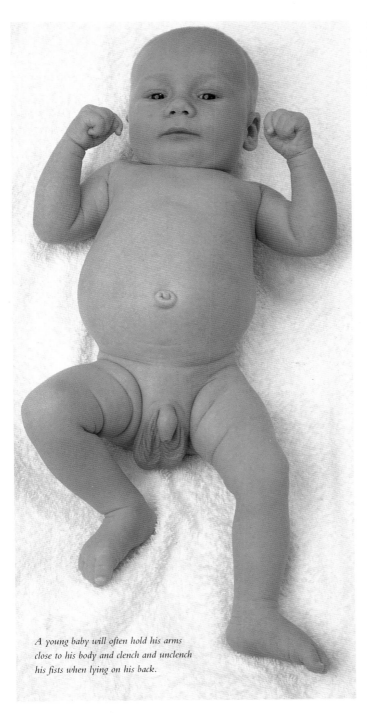

*A young baby will often hold his arms close to his body and clench and unclench his fists when lying on his back.*

if you are showing her something; this will help to keep the child's interest and will stop her dropping off to sleep. Cot books, with bold patterns and shapes which attract very young eyes, placed where a baby can see them, will help develop visual powers.

Babies can recognize their mother's smell from the earliest days and your baby will be able to distinguish between the smell of your breast milk and that of any other mother. She can also tell the difference between the smell of formula or cow's milk and your milk.

MINOR BLEMISHES

Occasionally babies may be born with some minor skin blemishes. These are usually harmless and require no treatment; they disappear on their own as the skin matures. *Milia* are tiny white spots on the face, caused by blocked oil glands. They should fade after a few days. *Stork marks or bites* are red marks which occur around the back of the neck, on the eyelids, or across the bridge of the nose. They usually disappear in the first few months. *Strawberry marks* are raised red marks that sometimes appear in the days after the birth and they may grow rapidly during the first few weeks. These usually disappear after about six months, although they can last until the child is much older. Treatment may be required if the mark has not disappeared by the time your child is in her teens. *Port wine stains* are red or purple marks that are usually found on the face and neck. These are permanent and will require treatment once your child is older. *Urticaria, or nettle rash* has a raised white centre surrounded by an

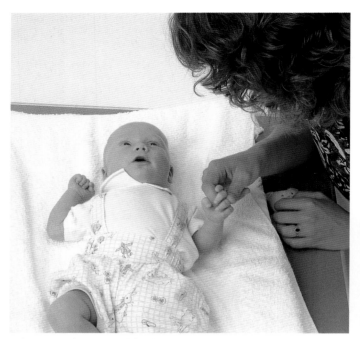

*When you are changing your baby, always make time to play and talk to him. This will make him feel secure and at ease.*

### FRESH AIR

A baby needs fresh air, so if you have a garden or secure outside area and the weather is warm enough you can let your infant sleep outside in the pram from the first week or so providing that she is well covered up and away from draughts. When it is hot, use a canopy rather than the pram hood so that the air can circulate, and make sure that the pram is in the shade. When outside, protect your baby from cats and

inflamed red area and quite commonly occurs during the first weeks. This rash doesn't require any treatment and will usually clear up after the first month.

### INFECTION

*Thrush* is a fungal infection that produces white patches on the baby's tongue, the roof of her mouth, and in her cheeks. It can be caught from unsterilized feeding teats and dummies or from the mother if she was suffering from vaginal thrush at the time of the birth. Thrush can also appear on the baby's bottom as a red rash which spreads from the anus over the buttocks. Oral thrush is treated with anti-fungal drops and thrush on a baby's bottom needs to be treated with antibiotic cream. Both can be obtained from your doctor.

*Above: White patches on the tongue are one indication that your baby has thrush. This is easily treated.*

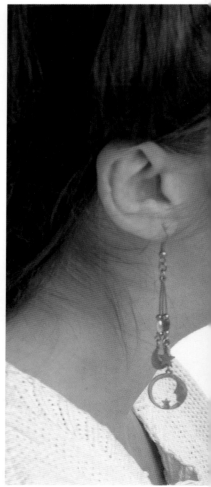

insects with a fine mesh pram net. If you have no place to leave the baby outside, put her in the cot or crib and open the window to let fresh air into the room. Don't leave a baby in her cot or pram for too long when she is awake because she will get bored. Babies need other activities to stimulate them as well as exercise.

Taking your baby on outings in a baby sling or carrier is another way of giving your baby fresh air and a convenient way for you to carry her if you don't want to push a pram. Your baby will enjoy being close to you and will be able to see the world from a different viewpoint.

### NOISE

There is no need to tiptoe around or to get people to whisper while your baby is asleep. If you do, it could mean that your baby won't be able to go to sleep if there is any noise and will wake at the least little sound, which can cause sleep problems when your child is older. A very young baby will quickly learn to sleep through the everyday noises that go on in a home, such as the television and vacuum cleaner. Sudden loud noises may wake your baby, but reassurance and a cuddle should soon settle her down again.

*When newly born your baby's vision is not well developed, so hold her up to talk to her and let her focus on your face.*

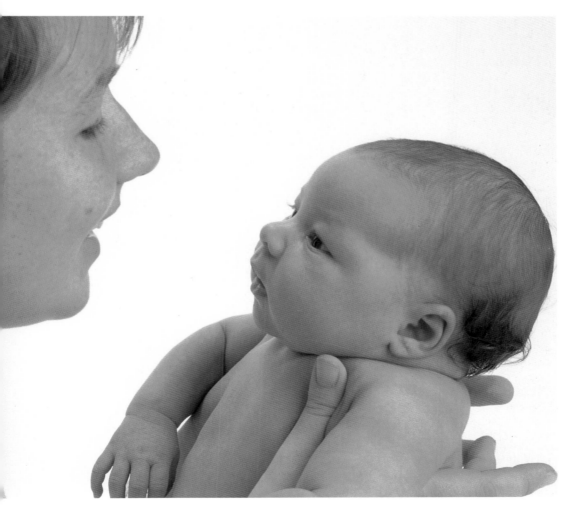

# TWO MONTHS

Your child may be able to:
• Smile.
• Begin to make cooing noises.
• Lift his head 45° when lying on his stomach.
• Grasp a rattle for a few seconds if one is put in his hand.
• Follow an object which is moved in a 180° arc above his face.

Your baby is developing quickly and, although you may not realize it, he is already trying to talk to you by making a number of vowel sounds and throaty gurgles. At first it may not seem as though these noises are actually directed at you because your baby will enjoy practising these vocal exercises as much for his own benefit as for yours. Each new noise is helping your baby discover which combinations of throat, tongue, and mouth actions make which sounds. As your baby masters each new sound you will begin to notice that he uses them to communicate vocally with you.

CRYING

Your baby now stays awake for longer periods between feeds and is usually more awake in the evenings. It is quite likely that your baby will use some of this extra waking time to cry. Of course not all babies are the same and yours may cry very little, but on average babies usually cry for two to three hours a day and much of this takes place in the evening. Often this is blamed on colic, thought to be a type of stomach or abdominal ache occurring in spasms, which makes a baby draw up

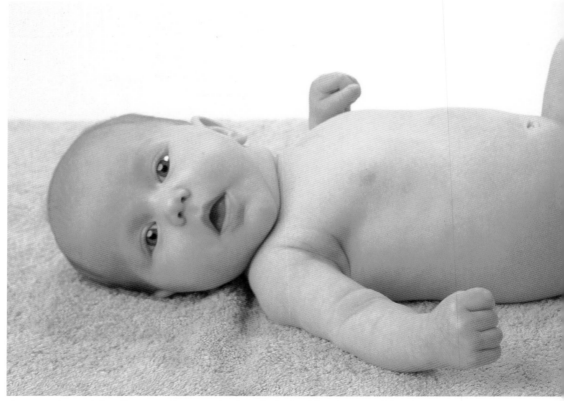

*At two months, your baby will start to smile at you and will turn her head to follow objects moved above her head.*

his legs in pain as he screams. No one knows exactly what colic is, but if it is going to occur it usually starts within the first three weeks of birth and lasts until around three months, although it can go on longer. There is no reliable treatment for colic and, although there are some over-the-counter medicines available, you should consult your doctor before giving them to your baby.

Colic isn't always the cause of excessive crying; some babies cry for no obvious reason for some time each day. If your baby does this you may be able to offer comfort by rocking, letting him suck, or by distracting him with a toy. Don't

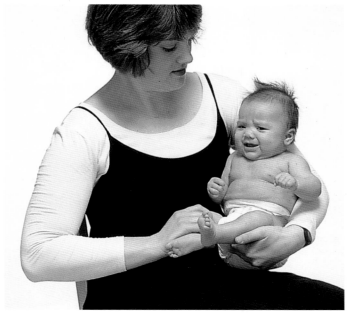

*When you support your baby in a sitting position, she can hold her head up for a minute.*

*Holding and cuddling your young baby is an important part of her getting to know you.*

leave him to cry for more than a few minutes; at this age crying is the only way to let you know that he is miserable and needs comforting.

LEARNING CONTROL

Your baby is gradually gaining control of his body. When you place the child on his stomach he will be able to lift his head, keeping the nose and mouth free to breathe. If held in a sitting position, your baby will be able to hold his head up for about a minute, and if you touch his hand with a rattle your baby will jerk his hand towards it. This is the first stage of learning when he reaches out to hold something.

SIX TO EIGHT WEEK DEVELOPMENT CHECK

The ages at which developmental screening takes place vary within each health authority and with the individual needs of the child. But in general, you can expect your child to have an initial developmental check sometime between six and eight weeks. This will be carried out

## Immunization

Your baby will be offered the first round of immunizations at two months. He'll be given two injections, usually into the upper thigh. After the immunization your child may feel a bit off-colour for up to 24 hours and may even run a temperature. Rarely, a convulsion may occur as a result of the fever, but this is over quickly and has no lasting effect. It is also quite normal for the skin around the site of the injection to become red and sore or slightly swollen. If you are at all worried about your child's reaction, contact your doctor immediately.

## Learning head movements

**1** *At this stage of development, your baby is gaining control of her body. When lying on her stomach, with her arms supporting her, she can start to lift her head.*

**2** *As she manoeuvres herself into position, she pushes hard with her legs and starts to put her weight on her arms.*

**3** *As she raises her head, pushing up with her arms, she will find she can hold it up, keeping her nose and mouth free to breathe.*

*Make sure you allow enough time to play and have fun with your baby, so that you can really get to know her.*

at the child health clinic by a doctor or health visitor, or at your doctor's surgery. These checks are part of the child health surveillance programme and their aim is to detect any problems early, to prevent illnesses, and to promote good health. If the checks detect any early signs of delayed development, or health or behaviour problems, treatment can be begun at once. A number of routine checks take place between now and when your child reaches school age. They are all important because the checks are designed to reveal hidden disabilities as well as more obvious ones.

This early check will include measuring your baby's weight, length and head circumference and noting the changes since birth. You will probably be asked questions about how your baby is feeding and sleeping. General progress will be assessed and the doctor may also carry out a series of tests to evaluate your baby's head control, use of hands, vision, hearing, and social interaction. You may be given guidance about what to expect during the next month in relation to feeding, sleeping, and development. You may also be asked questions about how you, the baby, and the rest of the family are managing with your new baby at home. This is the time to voice concerns or problems that have been worrying you.

*At six to eight weeks your baby will be given a developmental check-up at the health clinic or your doctor's surgery. This will detect any early problems.*

# THREE MONTHS

*Below: As you pull your baby up at this age, he will now be in more control of his head movements.*

Your baby will probably have begun to control her head movements, so that when held in a sitting position she can keep her head up for several seconds before it drops forward. As her neck strengthens your baby will be able to look around and turn her head to watch something moving within 15-20cm/6-8in.

### EARLY LEARNING

As babies begin to understand their own body, they will spend hours studying and moving their fingers. Their hands have opened out now and they can clasp and unclasp them, pressing the palms together. Babies enjoy playing with them and may even be able to hold a small toy for a few seconds. When your baby is lying down you will probably notice that her arms and legs make a lot of

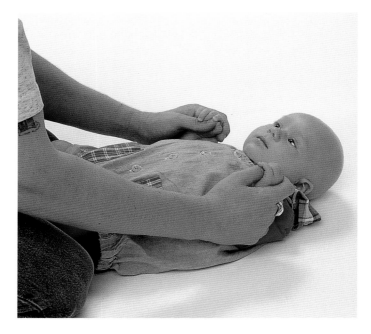

*Below: When your baby lies on the floor, he will often raise her head for several seconds before it drops forward.*

*Below: As your baby sits up, he can hold his head steady more easily because his neck has strengthened.*

*Bottom: Your baby will be fascinated by any toys in bright, primary colours that are hung over her cot.*

### Milestones

Your child may be able to:

- Smile and coo when she sees you.
- Control her head.
- Show anticipation when she is about to be fed by licking her lips.
- Enjoy looking at brightly coloured objects such as a mobile hanging over the cot.
- Play with her hands.
- Hold a small toy for a few seconds.

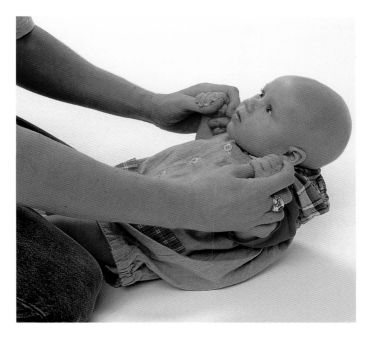

movement. She will kick vigorously, usually with alternate legs, but occasionally with both legs together.

The first smiles are reflexive, but they very quickly become social and the baby will smile at you in response to your smile or voice. The smiles will come in clusters, four or five at a time, followed by a pause of maybe half a minute before the next cluster. The baby will also respond vocally when you speak to her.

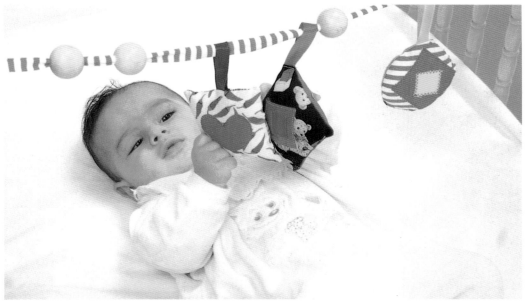

Talk to your baby and she will answer you back in her own way, using her lips and tongue as she coos and tries to imitate you. She uses her whole body to express the way she feels, making excited movements when pleased, expressing happiness and delight with gurgles and squeals. When she is angry, uncomfortable, or lonely she will tell you by crying loudly and angrily. To encourage your baby, you should respond to her behaviour with exaggerated gestures and praise, using a slow singsong voice and lots of repetition.

A baby will react to familiar situations and will show excitement when she recognizes preparation for things that she enjoys. She responds with obvious pleasure to friendly handling, especially when it is accompanied by play and a friendly voice. Bathtime and other caring routines, where she has your undivided attention for quite a while, are likely to become her favourite times of the day.

*Left: Plastic stacking toys in bright colours will soon attract the attention of your inquisitive baby who will try to grasp hold of them.*

*Below: Lying on his back, your young baby will enjoy kicking vigorously with alternate legs and sometimes with both legs together.*

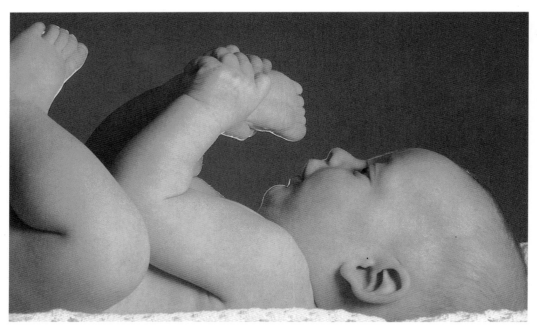

If you haven't already done so, introduce a regular bedtime routine now so that your child starts to realize that a bath, a story, and a cuddle are a prelude to being put into the cot to sleep. By about three months many babies begin to sleep for long periods at night. If your baby has started to sleep through the night you will probably find that she needs less sleep during the day and that her daytime sleep is not as deep as it was. You may find that your baby is more easily disturbed by household noises now. Encourage her to stay awake during the day by stimulating her with different toys and by playing and talking with her.

### Immunization

At three months your baby will have the next round of injections on the immunization programme. If there was any adverse reaction after the first injections tell your doctor.

*Your baby is now using her whole body to show her feelings, and will start to recognize her favourite toys.*

# FOUR MONTHS

Your baby is developing rapidly. He is awake for much longer and during these waking periods will want to be sociable and will respond with delight to conversations with you and enjoy playing simple games.

You can encourage your baby's development by spending time responding to these early attempts at sociability. Make a point of showing your baby different objects and talk about them. Your baby will also enjoy seeing and talking to himself in a mirror. Place the mirror about 15-20cm/6-8in away so that he can keep his image in focus.

Motor development and learning progress at the same rate between four and five months. Hand and eye co-ordination is being learned and your baby may be able to reach out and grasp an object. He will try hard to learn how to sit because he will have discovered that sitting up gives him a different view of the world. At first he will need you to help him balance, but as his confidence grows he will learn to adjust his legs and to use his hands to keep himself upright.

GETTING READY FOR SOLIDS
Babies get all the nourishment they require from breast or formula milk during their first six months, although you may notice that your baby begins to show the physical signs that he's getting ready for solids before this.

A baby needs to be able to have control over his head before he can move on to solid food. Even strained or puréed first foods should not be given until he can hold his head

*At four months your baby will try to sit up with your help.*

## Milestones
Your child may be able to:
• Lift his head up 90° when he is on his stomach.
• Raise himself up a little way, supported by the arms, when lying on his stomach.
• Laugh out loud.
• Hold his head steady when he is held upright.
• Roll over in one direction.
• Reach out for an object.

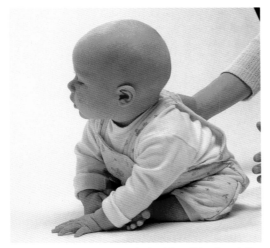

As your baby gains control over his head he will be able to hold it at different angles.

As he gets more active your baby will probably start to learn how to roll over in one direction. First, he will grab his foot with his hand and lift that leg up.

When your baby is lying flat on his stomach, he will now be able to raise his head up 90° and support himself more sturdily on his arms.

He'll then push down this leg, and helped by his bottom arm, roll his body over in one direction.

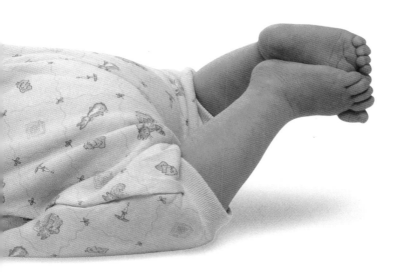

Your baby will now start to reach out for interesting toys and often try to put them in his mouth.

*A young baby is fascinated by mirrors, but at distances she can only make out vague shapes.*

*If you place your baby 15–20 cm/6–8 in away from a mirror, she will be able to focus on her image and chat to herself.*

upright when he is sitting propped up. A baby needs to be able to sit up unaided before chunkier foods that require chewing are given to him. This doesn't usually happen until about seven months.

First solids, given at around six months, are little more than tasters that get a baby used to the idea of sucking from a spoon rather than from the breast or bottle. To be able to do this the tongue thrust reflex, which the baby was born with, must have disappeared. This is the reflex that causes the tongue to push any foreign matter out of the mouth and prevents very young babies from choking. To be able to eat from a spoon your baby also needs to be able to draw in his lower lip.

Another fairly obvious sign to look out for which shows that your baby is ready for solids is if he shows any interest in the food that you are eating. If your baby watches intently while you eat and shows excitement or tries to grab your food, then he is probably telling you that he is now ready for more grown-up food himself.

Although it is recommended that babies are not given solids before six months, if you feel your child is ready before this ask your health visitor or doctor for advice.

THUMB SUCKING

Your baby will suck anything he can get into his mouth and now that he has some control over his hands, his fingers and thumbs will be preferred and he will suck them for pleasure and also for comfort. He may suck his whole hand, or one or two fingers, or he may prefer his thumb. This is quite normal and is not a sign of emotional distress, nor will it, at this age, damage the alignment of

permanent teeth. If your baby is breast-fed you need to make sure that he isn't sucking his thumb to compensate for suckling he is no longer getting at the breast, otherwise there is no harm in letting your child suck his thumb. Most children grow out of this habit over the next year or two, although a child who uses sucking his thumb as reassurance to get to sleep may take a little longer to break the habit. This is nothing to worry about.

### Immunization

At four months your baby will have the third round of immunizations. After this he will not have any further immunisations until he is one year old.

*You can now give some solids to your baby if she can hold her head upright and if food isn't rejected by her tongue.*

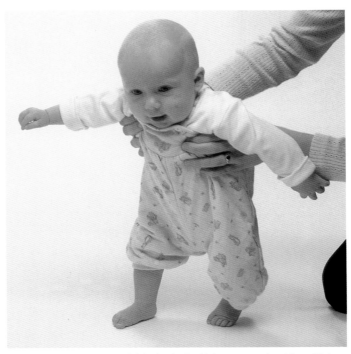

*Your baby will try to stand with help, but he shouldn't put too much weight on his legs.*

# FIVE MONTHS

Your baby's grasp of basic concepts is growing and she is thinking much faster. It is thought that a baby when she is first born will take between five and 10 minutes to get used to something new; by three months a baby may take between 30 seconds and two minutes and by six months she will take only 30 seconds. Your baby will begin to learn about cause and effect by carrying out simple experiments, such as throwing a toy out of her pram. Initially she will believe that it has vanished and won't

### Milestones

Your child may be able to:
- Hold her head steady when upright.
- Keep her head level with her body when pulled into the sitting position.
- Pay attention to a small object.
- Squeal with delight.
- Be able to say vowel-consonant combinations such as "ah-coo".

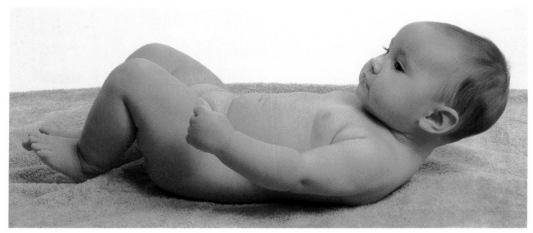

*At five months, your baby will be able to lift her head up from a lying position and hold it steady.*

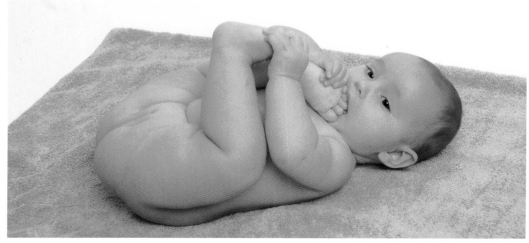

*She will love to suck things, and will often put her hands or feet in her mouth.*

*Your baby's head movements are now getting much steadier as she gains more control.*

understand where it has gone. If you pick up the toy and return it she will be both puzzled and delighted. She will do the trick again and again until she begins to realize that, by dropping the toy and getting it back, she is beginning to take control of her world by making things happen.

You can encourage your baby with her experiments by playing games such as peek-a-boo, or hiding an object that was in front of her and then making it reappear again. At this age your baby won't attempt to recover what you have hidden because she thinks that the object no longer exists because she can't see it.

It will be several months before she learns that this really isn't the case and starts looking for the hidden object herself.

TEETHING
There is no fixed time for your baby to start teething, but on average a baby's first tooth appears sometime

between now and seven months. Babies teethe differently, with some experiencing a lot of discomfort and others hardly seeming to notice their first teeth coming through. It is thought that tooth eruption follows hereditary patterns, so if you or your partner teethed especially early or late your baby may do the same.

Teething symptoms often precede the tooth itself by several weeks or even months, and vary from child to child. Drooling is often the first sign that teeth are on their way and this can start as early as 10 weeks. Excessive drooling can cause a dry skin rash or chapping on the chin and around the mouth, which should be treated with a mild skin cream. Biting is another indication of teething. Your baby may start chewing on anything she can get into her mouth as the counterpressure from chewing on a hard object helps relieve the pressure under the gums. Rubbing her gums with your finger may bring relief or you can give her something to chew on such as a chilled teething ring or a slice of carrot.

*Delight your growing baby with different types of toys to keep her interested and fully stimulated.*

Inflammation of the tender gum tissue often occurs when a tooth is coming through so your baby is likely to have red, sore gums before a tooth erupts. Ear pulling and cheek rubbing may also be a sign of teething as pain can travel along the nerve pathways to these areas. This is particularly common when the molars are coming through. If your child seems to be in pain you can give her the recommended dose of paracetamol. However, never attribute illnesses such as diarrhoea, fever, or earache to teething: if you are concerned seek medical advice.

*Your baby will often prefer a simple toy like this rattle as it is easier for her to manage and play with.*

# SIX MONTHS

Your child is beginning to show a greater interest in what is going on around him. He will turn his head quickly to familiar voices and will examine things that interest him for longer periods. If your baby hasn't started on solids yet, now is the time to introduce them.

THE BABY TAKES CONTROL
Your baby is rapidly becoming more mobile and will probably be able to pull himself into the sitting position if both hands are held. When lying on his stomach, he may find that kicking will push him along, usually backwards at first. If he becomes frustrated because he can't get to where he wants to go, don't be too eager to help him: encourage him by placing a toy just out of reach, or by placing your hands against his feet so that when he kicks he has something to push against. If you pick him up and place him where he wants to go he will not learn how to achieve this for himself.

Your baby's ability to reach and grasp is becoming more accurate and you can help him improve these skills by passing objects in such a way that he has to reach up or down or to the side for them. Toys strung across his cot or playpen will allow him to practise using these skills. Your baby will hold objects in the palm of his hands, and will be able to pass them from one hand to the other. You can encourage him by giving him two toys simultaneously, one in each hand, so that he has to reach out with both hands. If you offer him a rattle, shake it to make a noise as you hand it to him; he will reach for it immediately and then shake it deliberately to make the same noise.

Visually your baby is keenly aware of everything that is going on around him and will move his head and eyes eagerly in every direction to which his attention is attracted. He will follow what you are doing, even if you are busy on the other

## Milestones

Your child may be able to:
• Laugh, chuckle, and squeal aloud and scream with annoyance.
• Use whole hand to grasp objects and can pass them from one hand to the other.
• Move his eyes in unison and turn his head and eyes towards something that attracts him.
• Play with his feet as well as his hands.
• Can manipulate small objects.
• Start to be wary of strangers.

*Right and opposite: If you have a very active baby it is best not to put her in her high chair at meal times until her food is ready to eat or has cooled, as she will only get restless and may have a temper tantrum because she can't easily move around. A quieter baby will probably be quite happy to sit in her chair and play for a while with a stimulating toy that you have given her. If she is content to sit quietly and amuse herself until you can feed her, it will also give you peace of mind that she is safe and not getting into any other mischief as you prepare her food and drink.*

side of the room. His eyes should now move in unison. If your child appears to have a squint (with an eye turned inwards or outwards all the time) you should discuss this with your doctor who may suggest that he sees an eye specialist.

Your child is now very chatty and will vocalize tunefully both to himself and others in a singsong manner using vowel sounds and single and double syllables such as a-a, adah and er-leh. He laughs, chuckles, and squeals with delight when playing and will express anger or annoyance with loud screams.

### INTELLIGENCE

Assessing a child's IQ (intelligence quotient) when he is very young is difficult, and the motor development tests that can be used to evaluate IQ in the first year do not usually correlate well with a child's IQ later on. It is recognized that intelligence can be influenced by many factors, including stimulation, health and diet, and social aspects such as poverty. Even trauma can play a part. At this stage in your child's development you can encourage his physical, social, and intellectual growth by raising him in a stimulating environment and spending as much time as you can playing, reading, and talking to him.

*It is hard to predict how fast your baby will develop but she will be stimulated by you talking and playing with her.*

*Always buy toys that suit the age of your baby. This one has bend projections that he can easily grasp.*

*Once you have helped your baby to sit up, she will often sit quite happily and watch you as your move around the room.*

# SEVEN MONTHS

Learning to move from one place to another is a huge achievement for your baby and one which will give her a whole new perspective on the world. How this locomotion is achieved will vary from baby to baby. Some crawl on all fours, others creep by wriggling on their fronts, others roll their way from one place to another. Some push themselves backwards, which can be very frustrating for them. It is thought that the children who walk the earliest are those who have crawled first or those who have gone straight from sitting to standing. Bottom shufflers and creepers tend to walk a bit later. However, there is little to suggest that a crawler who becomes an early walker is any brighter than a creeper who walks a little later.

Your baby will be able to take some weight on her legs now and she may even be able to stand while you hold her in an upright position. Over the next couple of months she will probably learn to pull herself up from sitting, and then she will practise standing alone.

*At seven months your baby will be able to sit up and turn at the waist. She will also like to suck her thumb.*

*Your baby is developing a mind of her own and will often try to wriggle free when picked up or held.*

DEXTERITY

Your baby may start to show a preference for using her right or left hand at this age. Offer her a toy held straight in front of her and see which hand she uses to reach for it. If your baby regularly uses the same hand she is beginning to show a preference, but this is by no means a final choice. Very often the hand she uses at seven months is not the same as the one she prefers at nine months

**Milestones**

Your child may be able to:

• Put weight on legs when upright.

• Sit with minimal support.

• Look for a dropped object.

• Babble combining vowels and consonants such as "ga-ga", "ma-ma" and "da-da".

• Feed herself with finger foods.

• Begin to crawl.

*Your baby is now very much on the move and will be beginning to crawl everywhere quite quickly.*

*Your baby will hold toys in both hands with much more dexterity now. She will also still enjoy sucking them.*

*Try and talk to your baby as much as you can as he will reply with babble that mixes both vowels and consonants.*

or a year. Once your baby is able to use two hands in a coordinated way, give her something which needs one hand to hold it and another to make it work – a pot with a lid that comes off is ideal – and see which hand she uses for which action. This will give you a better idea of whether your baby is likely to be left- or right-handed, although her final choice may not be made until she reaches two years of age.

You may notice that your baby no longer grasps things in the centre of her palm to hold them. She now uses her fingers and thumb so that her grip has become very much more refined. Now that she can operate her fingers and thumb independently, rather than using them as a rake, she can pick up an object as small as a raisin to examine it.

You can encourage the baby by allowing her to feed herself. Give her a bowl and spoon and let her get on with it. At first it is a good idea for you to have a spoon too, so that you can give her the occasional mouthful while she is still working out how to get the food from the

bowl, onto the spoon and into her mouth. Finger foods will help your baby learn how to get food into her mouth using her fingers.

At around the time your baby starts to show hand preference her language also starts to become more fully developed and she will babble a lot more using both vowel sounds and consonants. Her cries also change to include both low- and high-pitched sounds and she will start to make different movements with her tongue and mouth.

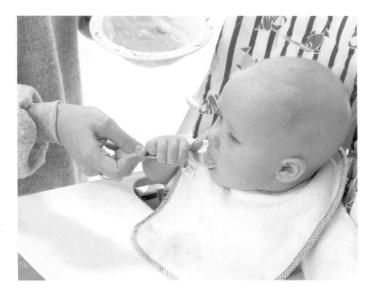

*As his hand movements improve, your baby will start to grasp toys, such as soft bricks, with his fingers and thumb.*

*You can encourage your baby to eat solids by allowing him to hold the spoon and feed himself.*

# EIGHT MONTHS

By eight months your baby will probably have started to be selective about the people with whom he is sociable. The outgoing friendliness of the earlier months may have been replaced by a certain wariness, especially of strangers. If you leave your baby with someone he doesn't know he may now burst into tears, whereas before he would have been perfectly happy, as long as he was being entertained and was warm and comfortable. This wariness of strangers often occurs at about the same time that your baby is making a surge in his development. About a month after this, your baby may start to show distress, sometimes known as separation anxiety, when you leave the room. This distress at being separated from you or your partner will probably peak at around 15 months and then gradually subside.

If your baby does suffer from separation anxiety it can be misery for both of you. The best way of easing his distress is to leave him in a familiar environment with, if possible, a familiar person or relative.

Favourite and familiar toys can also be a source of comfort.

When you are leaving your baby to go out, try to leave quickly without making a fuss and keep your goodbyes down to a minimum.

*As the bond grows stronger between you and your child, he will appreciate as much attention as you can give him.*

## Milestones

Your child may be able to:

• Stand up while holding on to something firmly.

• Get himself into a sitting position from his stomach.

• Pick up a small object. such as a raisin with, his hand .

• Turn round in the direction of a familiar voice.

• Move himself towards an out-of-reach toy.

### DISCOVERING GENITALS

It is normal for your baby to start to show an interest in his genitals at around this age. This interest is an inevitable and healthy part of your baby's development in the same way that his fascination with his fingers and toes was earlier. There is no physical or psychological harm in your baby handling his genitals and you should never make your child feel bad or think about punishing him because he is doing so.

A boy is capable of having an erection from before birth; this is simply the normal response to the touch of a sensitive organ. A baby girl has clitoral erections from a very young age too, although these are much less obvious.

### INTRODUCING BOOKS

From eight months onwards, your baby's behaviour will become more flexible and he will begin to use his own initiative in a relationship. He will give you toys as well as taking them and may start playing simple games with you. For the first time he will want to share his interest in an object with another person. This is a good time to introduce him to books, which you can sit and read together. At first he will only be interested in the rhythm and sound of the words and the colour and pattern of the pictures in the book. By speaking slowly in a singsong manner, with exaggerated emphasis in the right places, and encouraging your child to join in with simple sounds such as "moo" when he sees the picture of a cow, you will make reading a shared, enjoyable experience.

### DEVELOPMENTAL CHECK

At between six and nine months your baby will be given another developmental check by your doctor

*Your baby will happily respond to your games and will often try playful actions like grabbing your hair.*

*Left: As the grasping action is much more developed, your child will enjoy handling and playing with stacking toys. He may need guidance from you as to the order the shapes go in, and which colour should go next.*

*Opposite: A car or any toy with wheels is likely to be a particular source of interest for your baby. He may just want to sit and play with it, and only go after it if you join in and spend time pushing it back and forth to him.*

or health visitor. She will be looking to see how your baby is developing and also checking that nothing has been missed in any previous health checks. Your baby's pelvis and legs will be examined to make sure there is no congenital dislocation of the hips. If your baby is a boy, his testicles will be checked to make sure they are well down in the scrotum. A distraction test for hearing will be carried out. This involves making a noise for two seconds with something like a bell or rattle out of your baby's sight to see whether he turns towards the sound. His eyes will be checked to see that there is no sign of a potential squint. You will probably be asked if your baby has ever had any breathing problems such as wheezing, and his heart and lungs may be checked with a stethoscope. He may be weighed and his height measured and the circumference of his head checked.

If you are worried about any part of your child's development you should talk about your concerns now with your doctor. The health visitor or doctor will be able to help with any questions you may have and can also offer advice if you are experiencing problems with feeding your child or with his sleeping.

# NINE MONTHS

A nine-month-old baby is capable of showing a wide range of emotions from happiness to fear, anger, and sadness and she will use these as a means of expressing feelings at any given moment. Your child needs you to be in tune with her feelings and to understand what she is trying to express, otherwise she will become frustrated. She may begin to show signs of early independence, but she will still want the reassurance of knowing that you are nearby and ready to help out if required.

*Your baby is now constantly on the move and will use her hands to help push her forward as she crawls along.*

### MOVEMENT

Your baby can now sit alone for 10–15 minutes at a time and lean forward to pick up a toy without falling over. She can also turn her body and will stretch out for something at her side. She will spend time manipulating a toy with her hands and is able to pass the toy from one hand to the other, turning it as she does so. She uses a pincer grasp, using her finger and thumb, to pick up small items. She will poke at things with a forefinger and may even start to point. You will notice that she still cannot put down a toy she is holding. She will still drop it or press it against a hard surface to release it. If she drops a toy she will look where it has fallen, even if it has completely disappeared from view.

Your child is now very active and she will begin to move herself across the floor either by

*As she moves along she will be distracted if you call out her name, and might even topple over as her balance is still unsteady.*

*As she pushes forward with her arms, her legs will move back and forth to propel her along.*

### Milestones

Your child may be able to:

- Look for an object that she dropped out of view.
- Pull herself into a standing position.
- Pick up small objects using her finger and thumb.
- Enjoy games such as pat-a-cake.
- Wave goodbye.
- Cruise around the furniture.

crawling, or by shuffling or rolling if she can't yet crawl. She will try to pull herself to standing while holding on to something and may manage to hold herself upright for a few moments before sitting down with a bump. She won't be able to lower herself in a controlled way into a sitting position. If you hold her in a standing position she will probably make purposeful stepping movements with alternate feet as though spractising walking.

### ACTIVITY

You will notice that your child is becoming a lot more vocal now. She will shout for your attention, stop, listen for your response, and, if she doesn't get it, she will shout again. She will hold long conversations with you, babbling in a loud, tuneful way using strings of syllables such as "dad-da", "ma-ma", "aga-aga", over and over again. She not only uses this babble as a means of interpersonal communication to show friendliness or annoyance, but also as a way of amusing herself.

*After crawling for a while, your baby may try to push herself up, but will not be able to balance properly yet.*

She likes to practise imitating adult sounds, not just talking but also smacking her lips, coughing and making "brrr"-type noises.

By now your baby will be able to bite and chew her food well and she will be able to feed herself with some finger foods. She will probably try to grasp hold of the spoon as she is being fed. Let her have her own play spoon so that she can continue to practise feeding herself between the mouthfuls of food you are giving to her.

Your baby will probably enjoy games such as "peek-a-boo" and looking for something that you've half hidden while she watched. She will be delighted when she discovers the item and will show it to you with great glee. You may even be able to get her to look for something that you've completely hidden, but she won't necessarily be able to find it and this may cause her some distress and even annoyance.

If your baby seems at all worried by these first simple games you will need to encourage her to take part in them by responding to all her efforts with obvious surprise or delight. She will be happy

*All toys will be held firmly now by your baby, who will use a pincer grasp with her finger and thumb.*

*Your baby's fascination with her toes will continue and she will often be found playing with them.*

*Right: As bonding with her father continues, your baby will enjoy being lifted up in the air and other games with him.*

when you show her how much you enjoy her cleverness because she will enjoy your approval.

As your baby starts to become more confident, the games to play will become more adventurous. She will let you know when she is ready to progress to the next stage.

*Below: Your baby will not play with an older brother at this stage, but she will be interested in toys he is showing her.*

*Standing up will be a problem unless there is a support nearby. If he lets go he will sit down with a bump.*

# TEN MONTHS

You will probably have discovered by now that your child has a sense of humour. At 10 months, your baby will not only enjoy playing games with you but will also rock with laughter at some of his own antics. For example, he will enjoy splashing in the bath and this will become even more fun if he gets you wet too. The more you protest the more he will enjoy splashing you. You may also find some of the things you do make your baby laugh uproariously. Appearing around a door saying "boo" can make him squeal with laughter and he will enjoy this game over and over again. Your baby may also enjoy teasing you in return by offering you a toy and snatching it back before you can take it.

Traditional nursery rhymes and games can give your child endless fun. Try saying: "Round and round the garden, like a teddy bear, one step, two step, tickly under there!" as you run your fingers around his palm, then up his arm and end with a tickle. Another favourite is Humpty Dumpty. Build up to a climax at the point Humpty is going to fall off the wall and pretend to let

*Your child is now developing rapidly and will be trying to stand. He won't be able to do it on his own and will need your support.*

*He might try a few faltering steps, but can't easily manage these and will need to hold onto one of your hands as he moves forwards.*

### Milestones

Your child may be able to:

• Move around the furniture.

• Understand the word "no", but not necessarily obey it.

• Stand alone for a few seconds.

• Use the word "dada" to get his father's attention.

• Hold a feeder cup to drink from it.

• Roll a ball back to you.

*Supports, such as a chair, will be used by your child to pull himself up as he learns to stand.*

your baby fall too. The baby has probably reached what is sometimes known as the joint-attention stage. This is when a child is able to concentrate on more than one thing at a time. You can encourage this by pointing out things while also giving your baby some information. For example, you can show your child a cat, then tell him that when a cat speaks it says "miaow". Later, when he sees a cat again, you can ask him what the cat says. This is a great way of sharing knowledge and making learning fun.

### ESTABLISHING ROLES

Along with this sense of humour, new mobility, and the desire to share with you, comes a real talent for getting into trouble. Your baby's curiosity will lead him into all sorts of dangers and you will need to be constantly on your guard so that he isn't allowed to hurt himself. Your baby, on the other hand, may see thwarting your efforts at keeping

him out of mischief as a great way of getting a response from you. For the first time since your child was born you may begin to think about using some form of discipline.

Discipline doesn't mean rules and punishment, it means teaching the concept of right and wrong. It will be a long time before your child fully grasps the idea of what is involved, but by teaching him now, through your example and guidance, you will be helping him towards eventual self-control and showing him that he needs to have respect for other people.

It is important to remember that a baby cannot be bad because babies and toddlers do not know right from wrong. They learn about their world through experimentation, and by observing and testing adults. Introducing the concept of things being right or wrong at this early age is the first step to helping your child develop from a naturally self-centred baby to a more sensitive and caring

child. The most effective discipline is neither uncompromisingly rigid nor too permissive. Either of these extremes can leave a child feeling that he is unloved.

You need to set limits and standards that are fair and enforce them firmly, but lovingly. Never threaten to withdraw love from your child as this will badly effect his self-esteem and it is important that he knows he is loved even when you don't approve of his behaviour.

Don't smack your child. Smacking has been shown not to be an effective way to discipline a naughty child. It has many negative aspects, including teaching the child violence and that using force is the best way of ending a dispute or getting what you want.

---

*Opposite: A container with various slots for different shapes will keep a child amused as he tries to work out which one should go in the right hole.*

*A young baby 'cruises' around furniture using it for support as he moves around.*

*If a stool is at the right level, your baby may use it as a means of pulling himself up, and as a table to leave some of his toys there in easy reach.*

# ELEVEN MONTHS

Many babies speak their first word at around 11 months, although some speak as early as nine months and others don't say a word until well after a year. This is a remarkable achievement when you consider that not very long ago your child didn't even know how to smile. These first words take the longest to learn and you will need to be patient while you wait for your child to produce another new one. Sometimes these first words are learned as infrequently as one a month from now on, until your child has a vocabulary of around 10 words. After this the rate usually increases quickly, but this stage isn't reached until around 15 months of age.

### DEVELOPING SPEECH

You can help your child to build up her vocabulary by saying the names of things in which she expresses an interest. By now she can probably point at items that she wants because she will have already discovered that pointing is an effective means of communicating with you. When you pick up the item and hand it to the child you probably tell her what it is.

### Milestones

Your child may be able to:

• Say the word "mama" to attract your attention.

• Stand on her own.

• Take her first steps.

• Respond to a simple command which isn't accompanied by gestures.

• Say her first word other than "mama" and "dada".

*At 11 months your child will be much more responsive and will start reacting to simple questions and commands.*

For example, your child points at an apple, you pick up the apple and hand it to her saying something like: "You want this apple?" By doing this you are teaching your child new words; although she may not remember them straightaway, in time each word will become part of her vocabulary.

Don't worry if you are the only person who can understand your baby's first words. It is not unusual for others outside the family to be baffled by the way a baby speaks. It may well be two or three years before your child can be easily understood outside the immediate family. It is important not to keep correcting your child's pronunciation.

This will knock her confidence and she may become worried about trying to use new words. However, don't revert to using her wrongly pronounced words simply because they sound really cute. If you imitate her errors, the child will carry on using the incorrect words for much longer than she would otherwise have done.

## MOBILITY

Your baby may have started to pull herself up onto her feet; she may even be walking by holding onto the furniture. This is known as "cruising' and is a natural prelude to learning to walk. Don't be tempted to rush out and buy shoes at the first

sign of walking because the child doesn't need shoes yet, in fact they would not be good for her feet at this stage. A child needs to wear shoes when she is walking confidently and her feet will need protection when she goes outside.

Learning to walk is a matter of trial and error. You can't really do anything to help your child apart from making sure that the area she is learning to walk in is as safe as possible. But even when you have removed all the obvious hazards in your child's path you need to stay close at hand to make sure that she doesn't hurt herself.

A child is bound to experience falls while as she learns to walk and

*Your developing baby will now start to share things and will happily hand you toys, such as a ball.*

*Even though she now has some teeth, your baby will still like the sensation of putting different objects in her mouth.*

*Right: Your baby will be particularly responsive playing games now. If you keep hiding a toy and then making it re-appear it will keep her happily amused for quite a while.*

*Below left and right: Your child will enjoy standing upright with some help from you. Provided she can hang onto something with one hand, she will eagerly pick up toys from the floor to show you, wave around or suck.*

your reaction to these mishaps can colour your child's response to them as well. If you rush over in a panic every time she stumbles and demand to know if she is all right she may well shed more tears than she would if she'd really hurt herself. This over-reaction on your part may also make her lose her sense of adventure and make her afraid of attempting other normal physical development hurdles. By remaining calm and reacting with an "up you get, you're all right" sort of attitude, your child is likely to deal with minor tumbles in a matter-of-fact way.

*Left: By pushing a baby walker, your baby can walk happily around the room. Keep an eye on her so that you can help if she gets stuck in a corner. It takes time for a child to learn how to walk backwards. Below: A child will place her favourite toys on a low-level table and play with them there. When she is bored she may just leave them and go off to do something else more interesting.*

# TWELVE MONTHS

You are the parent of a year-old child. One by one all the skills that will make your baby a self-dependent and integrated member of society are being perfected. You are both teacher and observer. And now the changes come very quickly indeed.

GROWING SKILLS

If your baby isn't actually walking he should be well on his way to doing so by the end of the first year. He will probably be able to pull himself to his feet and navigate by holding onto the furniture. He will certainly be crawling, bottom shuffling, or rolling, and he will be able to get around at quite some speed. He will be able to sit for long periods and can now get into the sitting position from lying flat.

Your baby's grasp is now more refined and he will be able to pick up small objects using the thumb and the tip of the index finger. He will drop and throw toys deliberately and enjoy watching them as they fall. If a toy rolls out of sight he may look for it. He uses both hands to hold toys, but he may start to show a preference for using one hand rather than the other. When your child wants to show you something he will point using his index finger. He's curious and will want to explore everything, so make sure that your home is a safe place. This doesn't mean restricting your baby to such an extent that he becomes frustrated. Try to compromise by leaving some safe cupboards for him to get into and locking the others.

When the baby is outside he will watch people, animals, or cars with prolonged, intent regard. He will be able to recognize familiar people or animals from around 6m/20ft and will probably greet them vocally with great enthusiasm. The child responds to his own name and can understand other words such as the

## Milestones

Your child may be able to:
• Indicate what he wants in other ways instead of crying.
• Stand on his own.
• Walk a little way unaided.
• Wave goodbye to you, close relatives and friends.
• Say "mama" and "dada" with discrimination.
• Roll a ball back to you.

*At 12 months your child will be able to let you know what he wants by pointing or reaching towards an object.*

*All children vary when they first start walking, but your child may well be taking his first few steps now, so you should give him every encouragement.*

names of family members. He may be able to understand instructions such as "give it to Mummy", and he may even do as you ask.

You may find that your baby holds out his arm or leg when you ask him to while you are bathing or dressing him. You will see through his actions that he can understand much of what you say even though he can't yet express himself verbally. He babbles to himself and to you, making a lot of speech-type sounds and if he hasn't already said his first word then he soon will.

### EATING HABITS

Your baby will be joining in family meals and will probably be eating a mashed-up version of whatever everyone else eats. He is still too young to eat spicy or seasoned food, so remove his portion before adding salt and pepper and other seasoning. He enjoys finger foods but will want to imitate others at mealtimes by using a spoon. It will be difficult for him to get food onto the spoon and then the spoon into his mouth, so he may well revert to using his fingers after a few attempts.

Your child will be able to drink from a feeder cup by himself and will probably be able to drink from an ordinary cup with your help, but he's still too young to manage this on his own. If you are weaning, or are about to wean your baby off his bottle or the breast, you may want to start giving him cow's milk as his main drink. This should only be introduced into your baby's diet after the age of one year and you should always give him whole, pasteurized milk. Skimmed milk has too much protein and sodium content for babies and should not be introduced into your child's diet before the age

of five. Semi-skimmed milk can be given from two years, but only if the child is eating a very varied and adequate diet.

Your baby may be reluctant to give up the bottle because it may be a source of emotional comfort, but it is recommended that a child stops drinking from a bottle at around a year because of the adverse effect it can have on his teeth. If you don't feel that he is ready to give up his bottle completely, try to limit the number of times he has a bottle each day. Encourage him to drink from a trainer cup at meal-times and offer

him a bottle between meals and at bedtime. When you give a bottle during the day, fill it with water rather than juice or milk, because this will help reduce your child's interest in it. Insist that he drinks from it while sitting in an adult's lap and when he wants to get down take the bottle from him. Don't allow him to take his bottle to bed or to walk about with it. By restricting the use of a bottle like this you will limit the amount of potential harm it can do to his teeth.

Your baby may have as many as four or five teeth and you should

*Toys such as a cuddly, soft panda will soon become a firm favourite with your child as he will enjoy its furry texture.*

*When your child has a favourite cuddly animal he will love to carry it around, hug and squeeze it, and may want to take it with him wherever he goes.*

have been cleaning them from the time they appeared. These first teeth can be cleaned with a soft baby toothbrush and a pea-sized amount of children's toothpaste. If your baby is cutting teeth and is fretful, offer him a cold teething ring or a piece of raw carrot to chew on.

YOUR CHILD AND OTHERS
Even though he is confident and outgoing with you, your baby may still be wary of strangers. He may also suffer from shyness. This is an inherited trait which he will have got from either you or your partner, even though neither of you may appear to display the trait yourselves. Shyness can be modified, but it is rarely possible to eradicate it altogether. If you build up your child's confidence with praise and encouragement this

will help him to feel more comfortable with others and this may eventually help to diminish any shyness.

It is possible that what you consider to be shyness is actually just a normal lack of sociability. At this age your child is not ready to make friends, and he probably won't be until he is at least three years old. Until then the social limit will probably be parallel play, which is when he plays side by side with another child. Don't try to force him to play with others – pushing him may make him withdraw from social situations completely.

Don't expect a child to share his toys at this age.

Right now the only things that matter are his own needs and desires. Other children are seen as objects not people. If he displays aggressive behaviour towards other children, like biting or hitting, you need to respond immediately by removing him from the scene of the incident. Explain calmly why he shouldn't have behaved like that, then give him something to play with or point out a new object to distract him and change the subject. Of course he won't really understand what you are saying but, if you use this approach every time it happens, he will eventually understand that hitting and biting other people are just not acceptable behaviour.

*Opposite: Although your child will be perfectly happy when being held by you, he may be shy and withdrawn with other people he doesn't know.*
*Below: Your baby will interact quite happily with his father and will keep experimenting with touch.*

# SIGHT AND VISION

Although your baby practised the blinking reflex by opening and closing her eyes while in the womb, the first time she actually uses her eyes for seeing is at the moment of birth. As soon as she is born she is capable of distinguishing objects and most colours, but is only able to focus on items that are 20–30cm/8–12in away. These things will look fuzzy.

A newborn is very sensitive to bright lights and will blink and screw up her eyes if a light is shone in her face. Movement will attract a baby from birth and you may notice that yours actively seeks out moving objects. She will probably show a preference for an object which has a highly contrasting pattern rather than one which is just a solid block

of colour. As your baby begins to control her eye movements she will start tracking moving objects, which is an indication that her vision is developing well.

### YOUR BABY'S WORLD

At first your face will be of more interest to your child than anything else. It is thought that a baby is born with a simple mental template of the human face and will actively search out and stare at any human face during the first couple of months. When she is first born, whether she is able to recognize you by your individual features is open to debate, but she will certainly know the general shape of your head and hairline and by two months will have started to recognize your features.

Your baby will soon become interested in other things and by six to eight weeks will be concentrating on details, scanning faces and objects so that she can take in as much information as possible. At this age she may find it hard to disengage her attention when she is watching something and she may need you to distract her before she can

*A newborn baby's vision will be fairly limited and initially he will only be able to see a fuzzy image of you.*

remove her gaze. But by three to four months the pathways in the brain for voluntary action begin to take over and your baby starts to disengage her attention on her own.

By three months a baby can perceive colours fully, with all their different shades, and will be able to focus at different distances and to see things in 3D. From seven to eight months, as she begins to interpret what she sees, your baby starts to realize that things don't necessarily cease to exist just because she can't see them anymore. A toy dropped over the edge of

*Your young baby will become fascinated by different objects and will become difficult to distract from whatever is capturing her attention.*

*Left: If your baby spots a colourful object ahead of her when she is crawling, she will go and investigate it.*

*As your baby's eyesight improves, he will intently watch everything that is going on around him (top and above).*

*Your baby's eyes will follow a moving object which is held within his range of vision.*

the high chair will be looked for; she will also enjoy playing "peek-a-boo" because she knows now that you will definitely reappear.

Learning the size and shape of things and understanding that something that looks small at a distance is in fact bigger close up takes some time for a baby to understand. She will also have to learn that a toy stays the same shape even when it appears different when looked at from the side, top, or bottom.

It will take your baby around two years to have good vision and to be

## How you can help
• Give your baby plenty of stimulating things to look at.
• Hold an item within her range of vision and move it slowly in an arc so that she can follow it with her eyes.
• Play games like "peek-a-boo" and "hide-and-seek" with a toy or by hiding under a large cloth or blanket.
• Check that your child doesn't have a squint. If you are concerned, talk to your doctor.

able to see almost as clearly as an adult does. Her vision will continue to develop until she is four to five years of age.

A SQUINT
Many babies are born with what may appear to be a slight squint and this often remains until they have learned to control the muscles around the eyes. It is quite difficult for a baby to hold both eyes in line with each other to focus on an object, and you may notice that when your baby stares at you one of her eyes wanders out of focus. A wandering eye usually rights itself by the time a baby reaches three to four months of age, but you should always point it out to your doctor or health visitor as it may be necessary for your child's eyes to be checked thoroughly by an orthoptist.

A real squint is when the eyes never focus together on an object and, rather than moving together and then one wandering off, they are often out of alignment with each other. A squint needs to be treated from an early age so you must talk to your doctor as soon as you notice it in your child.

*A brightly coloured mobile, moving in the breeze and suspended or held from above, will delight your child and keep him amused for a long time.*

# HEARING

During the last three months in the uterus a baby will have been hearing a variety of different noises. By the time a baby is born, he will already be familiar with his mother's voice, the beating of her heart, and the sound of the amniotic fluid in which he has been floating. His ability to hear at birth is almost as good as an adult's. His hearing threshold, however, is lower, so your baby will be startled by loud, unfamiliar noises, although he will probably sleep happily through a constant loud sound such as a blaring television or loud music.

A very young baby will prefer to hear rhythmic noises that may not seem soothing to you: the noise of a washing machine or tumble dryer, the hum of the vacuum cleaner or hair dryer. These will probably reassure him and may even lull him to sleep, perhaps because he heard such sounds before birth and he

finds them both comforting and familiar. Your own child will quickly associate you and your voice with comfort – it is thought that an infant of only a few days old can actually recognize his mother's voice.

Your baby will respond to all the human voices he hears and will turn towards the sound of people talking and appear to listen intently. If he is spoken to in the exaggerated, high-pitched tone and rhythmic singsong manner, known as "motherese" that adults often instinctively adopt for babies, you will notice that your baby pays particular attention. He may even lose interest if the speaker reverts to a normal tone.

It is through hearing others speak that your baby will eventually learn to form the words which will make up early vocabulary. He will start to understand what is being said long before he can actually make the noises himself; if he has a hearing

## How you can help

• When the baby is very young, try not to let him become startled by sudden noises which make him cry.
• Talk to your child, using "motherese", the high-pitched, singsong voice that babies find appealing.
• Introduce him to many different sounds from an early age.
• Let him sleep where he is happiest rather than insisting that he should be in a quiet room on his own.

defect this knowledge and the eventual ability to speak will be affected. As your baby gets older he will start looking for the source of the different sounds that he hears and will respond with pleasure to familiar voices, words, and tunes.

### HEARING TESTS
Your baby will be offered a newborn hearing test either before you leave the maternity unit where he was born, or in the weeks after the birth at your doctor's surgery or baby clinic.

*From an early age your baby will respond to your voice and be interested in toys you are showing him.*

*He will turn towards any new or interesting noise that you make with a toy even if it is coming from behind him.*

In some areas the test may be carried out at home. You should mention if there is a close family history of hearing problems. If there is any concern, your baby can be referred to a hearing clinic.

At seven or eight months, your baby will have his next developmental check and this will include a screening test of his hearing carried out by your health visitor. By now the response to sounds should be obvious, turning his head when you speak to him and responding to different noises of varying pitch and intensity. Both ears will be tested to identify anything previously missed. If your child is deaf or partially deaf, his speech may not progress past the babbling stage and you may notice that he becomes quieter as he gets older. Any concerns about your child's hearing should be discussed with your doctor as soon as they occur.

*Your baby will study your expression and listen intently to your voice before trying to imitate you.*

# SMELL, TASTE, TOUCH

### SMELL

Newborn babies are very sensitive to smell and can remember certain smells almost from the moment they are born. They recognize their parents' natural smell and a breast-fed baby can distinguish the smell of her mother's milk from that of any other woman's just a few hours after birth. In fact, your baby will start sucking in her sleep if she smells your milk.

A bottle-fed baby will quickly learn to identify her own mother's smell and the smell of any other family members who also feed her. The smell of people who are familiar to her will help your baby distinguish between family members and people strange to her.

As your baby grows, certain smells will become associated with specific things. For example, food smells will suggest meal-times and perhaps happy social occasions, while the smell of bath preparation and baby powder will become associated with bathtime and bed. Smells that your baby finds unpleasant will make her turn her head away even when she is only a few days old.

Your baby will use her sense of smell with her other senses to learn about the world around her.

*From a young age, a baby has a highly developed sense of smell and she will delight in a sweet-smelling flower.*

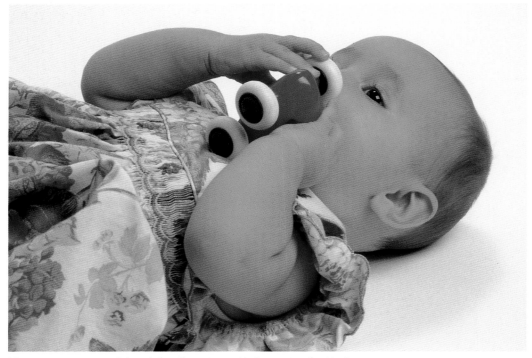

*Taste is very important to a baby and she will experiment with the sensation of sucking her toys.*

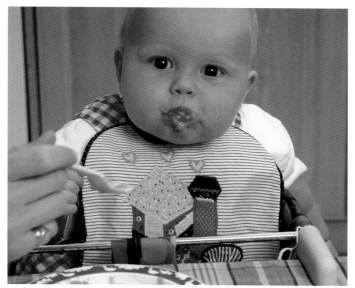

*From the moment he is born, your baby will be able to react to bitter tastes and show a preference for sweet foods.*

## How you can help

• Spend time cuddling and talking to your baby so that she really gets to know you.

• Offer your child a wide variety of tastes once she is old enough to take solids, but avoid foods that are seasoned or spicy.

• Don't encourage your child to have a sweet tooth.

• Remember that a young baby cannot control her temperature as well as an older child, so you need to keep a constant check on her to make sure she isn't too cold or if she is becoming overheated.

• Your baby's skin is very sensitive so check that her clothes aren't tight or rubbing her skin.

## TASTE

Smell and taste are intrinsically linked so it is no surprise that a baby is born with the ability to differentiate between tastes. From birth your baby's taste buds can detect sweet, sour, bitter, and salty. When offered any of these tastes she will give a definite and consistent reaction to each one. Her taste buds will become more refined with age, but even as a newborn baby she will show appreciation for sweet flavours and grimace when experiencing salty or bitter tastes.

All babies seem to be born with a preference for a sweeter taste, probably because breast milk is slightly sweet and it is important that she likes its flavour. This natural preference for sweet things won't harm your baby's teeth providing that you don't indulge her by giving her sweetened juice to drink, or adding sugar to her food when you start to wean her. When you start to introduce solids into your baby's diet it is better to encourage her to eat bland foods at first and then savoury foods and to keep sweet things to a minimum. Your baby will quickly develop her own tastes and you can help by giving her a varied diet once she is old enough to take solids. By the time she is around a year old she will use her experience of different foods she has tried to help her distinguish between the more subtle flavours. For example, one brand of baked beans will taste different to another and at a year old your child will be able to taste the difference.

## TOUCH

Your baby uses touch immediately after birth. This provides her with a means of finding out about her new environment through the textures that her skin comes into contact with, like her clothes, your clothes, and skin. Your baby can also feel through her skin whether her environment is warm or cold, wet or dry. She feels pain and discomfort and, because a young baby has more sensitive skin than an adult, you need to treat her gently.

As she matures, your baby will use touch in different ways to help her learn. Touch-sensitive nerve endings are concentrated at the end of the fingertips and around the lips, and a young baby will use her hands and mouth for exploring new objects. Gradually, after a few weeks touch will also become associated with feelings and your baby will start to connect the feeling of your nipple in her mouth or your arms around her and associate them with warmth and security. One of the most important sensory experiences for your baby is through her tongue and mouth so that sucking is not only a means of obtaining nourishment, but is also a great source of comfort for her.

*Your young baby will reach out and touch different objects, such as this furry panda, to get used to the different sensations.*

When you undress your baby you may notice that she becomes increasingly tense as you remove each layer of clothes and she may actually cry when you remove the garment nearest to her skin, usually her vest. This is not because you are clumsy, but because she physically misses the feel of her clothes against her skin. She should stop crying as soon as you dress her again. Between two and three months your child begins to use touch as a means of exploring and she will use her hands to hit out at things that are near her. By around five months she will have mastered hand and eye co-ordination and will learn by feeling and putting things in her mouth.

## BONDING
Touch plays an important part in the main bonding process. This is the formation of a close emotional relationship between you and your baby which will provide her with the love, comfort, and security that she wants.

Although your baby is born with a deep-rooted psychological need to have a close interaction with you this doesn't always happen immediately. A child's bonding with her mother is often a gradual process which may not be fully completed until the baby is a few months old.

*At a few months old a young baby will react to bright toys such as this octopus which has two different materials on the undersides of its legs. He will enjoy the feel of soft textures.*

# TALKING

Your child is born with the potential to learn to speak and a receptiveness to the influences that will help him communicate. A baby starts to learn about language while he is still in the womb, which is when he first begins to identify the voice of his mother. As a newborn he will prefer his mother's voice to any other because it will already be familiar and he will quickly associate it with warmth, comfort, and feeding.

A newborn baby's brain is tuned to pick out the texture, pattern, and rhythm of language and he will pay more attention to voices talking than any other sounds he hears. From the moment he is born your baby understands speech sounds in a way that allows him to segment the speech he hears into sound units.

Before he can speak fluently a baby has to go through distinct stages of development. In the beginning your baby's vocal skills will consist of cries and burps. The inability to speak in the early months does not actually hinder a baby's ability to become a talker. He uses this time to learn how to control his mouth and his tongue. You may notice that from a very early age your baby will move his mouth a lot, pushing his lips forwards and backwards in a kind of rhythm.

## CONVERSATIONS

One of the skills your baby has to acquire before speech is the ability to interact with people. He will begin to learn about this process very early on and by three months he will already be using communicative gestures. Try raising your eyebrows to him and then watch as he imitates you. This is the first stage of learning about holding a conversation. These gestures will be accompanied by different noises as your baby begins to develop control over dozens of separate muscles that are involved in making speech sounds. When your baby coos and gurgles at you he is learning to coordinate tongue movements while taking air in. When you respond to these early noises you will instinctively use a high-pitched, rhythmic singsong tone, repeating words in such a way that you capture your baby's attention.

*Even a very young baby will be receptive to the sound of his mother's voice because he will have heard it in the womb.*

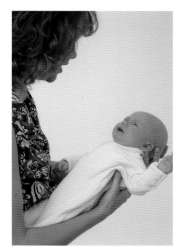

*Chat to your baby when you hold him as he will find the sound of your voice soothing and comforting.*

By around five or six months, your child will be concentrating on one-syllable words such as "ba" or "ma" which he will repeat over and over again, often when he is on his own. This use of early sounds is known as babbling, and is not yet being used as a form of communication. This is your baby's way of learning how to make new sounds. Soon after he has learned to babble you will notice that your baby starts to use his eyes to communicate with you and to direct your attention towards something that he wants.

This communication is soon followed by what is called declarative pointing: pointing as a form of interacting, rather than just as a basic means of asking you to pass him

*If you speak to your new baby in a high-pitched, singsong voice you will immediately get his attention.*

*Even at the young age of eight weeks your baby will respond to your voice and attempt to smile at you.*

something he can't reach for himself. After a month or two your baby's babbling will start to flow like speech, rising and falling as if he were holding a conversation. Although he is still not able to form words, he will understand simple words that are made clear, for example, "bottle" when you point to his feeding bottle. Understanding more than he is able to say will continue throughout baby- and toddlerhood until he can speak fluently.

FIRST WORDS

By the end of his first year your baby will probably produce his first word.

It may not seem recognizable as a word to you, but it will be a sound that he uses for one specific object, for example, "ine" for when he wants an orange. It is certainly no accident that "mama" and "dada" are often among the first recognizable words that a new baby says, because first words are simple and are associated with things that are special to a child.

Once speech has begun with your baby, he will continue to produce a handful of new words each month with the majority of this early communication being simple nouns or proper names.

**How you can help**

• Always respond to your baby's attempts at communicating with you.

• Don't be embarrassed to use high-pitched speech; it is the language your child likes best.

• Talk to your baby as you go about your daily routine and remember to speak clearly using simple words.

• Be consistent, using the same words for the same thing every time.

• Look at simple picture books with your baby. By telling him what is in each picture you will be increasing his understanding of words.

*A mother can help her child learn to talk properly by repeating words and by pointing out objects and saying the word.*

*As your baby investigates colourful items, such as a yellow flower, you can talk to him about it, telling him which are the petals, leaves and stem.*

# SOCIAL BEHAVIOUR

A newborn baby doesn't appear very sociable to the outside world because she doesn't smile or respond verbally until some weeks after birth. But her parents' reactions to the baby's ordinary behaviour lead to the development of social mannerisms. For example, wind may cause your baby to appear to smile at an early age and you respond by smiling back. Your baby will eventually realize that this movement of her mouth makes you react in this way and so will use it deliberately in the future. It is this early, simple form of communication that is the basis for your child's social development.

All babies' early social learning comes from imitating the people with whom they have the most contact, generally their mother and father. A newborn of only a few hours can imitate some adult gestures such as poking her tongue out or yawning. This ability to imitate is one of the most important tools your baby has to help her learn about life.

Through imitation your baby will eventually start communicating. You will speak to her and she will respond with "coos" and will wriggle her body in delight. This first stage of conversation will eventually develop into the ability to talk and listen. These early conversations often start during feeding, because the rhythm of feeding initiates your baby into the basics of dialogue. A baby sucks in her mother's milk in bursts with pauses in between. It is during these pauses that her mother usually fills in the gap by talking happily to her.

IMITATION BECOMES CHOICE
Social interaction between you and your baby becomes increasingly intentional on her part during the first two months of life, with much of your baby's behaviour geared towards making you react. These early conversations and the ability to imitate are just two ways of getting you to respond; the other very effective way is crying. Initially, your baby's cries are a reflex to pain, hunger, or discomfort. But crying assures a baby of adult response, especially her mother's. Her cries will increase her mother's heart rate and, if breast-feeding, her mother will automatically start producing milk. Within a few weeks a baby will have learned to expect certain reactions to her crying, such as being fed or picked up.

At around six weeks your baby will learn to smile properly, another social skill which she will be able to use to her advantage. Although her

*When young babies are placed together, they don't play with each other as they haven't yet learned how to interact. Instead they will just play on their own.*

*If you put two or three babies together in a playpen they will not play together as they haven't learned how to socialize.*

first smiles are simply facial grimaces, your response will be such that she soon discovers that by using her facial muscles in this way she is guaranteed to get you to smile back. A baby will quickly learn to repeat an action if she gets a positive reaction. However, if she regards the response she receives as negative she is less likely to repeat the action.

By three months your baby will be able to show her enjoyment of people and surroundings. She will respond to friendly adults and generally not mind who is with her as long as they are paying attention to her. She will enjoy activities such as having a bath and often show pleasure when she realizes that bathtime has arrived. Feeding will be a great source of emotional pleasure and your baby will study your face unblinkingly while she feeds.

At around four months your baby will cry more deliberately. She will

probably pause after crying to see if anyone is coming in response, before crying again. She has learned that crying brings attention and this new ability to manipulate is the start of some exciting discoveries.

CHANGING BEHAVIOUR PATTERNS
Somewhere after six months your child may change from a social, happy baby, who will go to anyone and reward complete strangers with smiles, to one who overnight has become wary of people she doesn't know. Your baby has reached the stage when she needs time and space to handle each new sight and sound, and a stranger may present her with too many new, unfamiliar things to be taken in at one time. This new wariness leads to what is known as "stranger anxiety". It often manifests itself as loud protestations when your baby is about to be separated from you. She is at the stage of

*As your baby will feel safe with you, try to show her different toys and items to interest her and attract her attention.*

development when she is becoming more sensitive to change and appears to be suddenly more dependent. She may try to avoid upsetting or stressful events by crying, clinging to you, or turning away from what is upsetting her. Towards the end of her first year she may start to use objects such as a favourite blanket, bottle, or thumb as a comforter.

Over the next six months your baby will probably show an increasing reticence with strangers but will be very responsive to people with whom she is familiar. She may become very clinging so that any separation from you is accompanied by real distress. This attachment may cause you problems, but it is in fact an important stage of development. She now recognizes individuals as people and is beginning to develop selective, permanent relationships. She will use these relationships as a safe base from which to explore the world. Now that she is getting older, your baby will use her developing

*A baby will sit with her brother because he is familiar. She will be interested in his toys but won't play with him.*

vocal skills to create noise – this guarantees the attention that gives her the reassurance she needs. She may use mimicry to make you laugh and the more you show your appreciation the more she will repeat the antic which is amusing you. This is her first real control over her social environment.

By the time she is a year old, your child will probably have grasped the idea that she exists as an entity. She may even begin to use a word or

*Your baby will sit quite happily on your knee, but may be wary of moving to his grandmother who is less familiar to him.*

*A baby will soon learn to recognize his older sister and will happily let her help him to stand up.*

sound to describe herself as a means of expressing this. Her social skills, however, are still very limited and she will show little interest in anyone outside her immediate circle of well-known people. Other children hold very little appeal for your child at this age and are more likely to be treated as inanimate objects rather than playmates.

It will be another year or two before your child has enough social understanding to develop friendships with other toddlers.

### How you can help

- Encourage your baby to imitate you by exaggerating your responses to her actions.
- Smile at your baby to let her know how pleased you are when she smiles at you.
- If she becomes wary of strangers don't force her to be sociable.
- When you have to leave your baby, say goodbye quickly; don't prolong the parting.

# MOBILITY

All babies go through the same stages of mobility, but how fast they move from one to another varies considerably. Your baby may walk independently before he is a year old, or he may be content to shuffle along on his bottom or hands and knees until well after this. Your baby's mobility takes place in a set order, starting at his head and working down to his toes. He won't be able to sit upright or crawl until he can hold up his head, and he won't be able to walk until he can move his body along, either by crawling or doing a bottom shuffle.

Finally, your baby will learn to control his arms and legs before gaining control of his hands and feet. At each stage it will take time for the movements he has learned to progress from being awkward, rather clumsy and uncoordinated to the smooth, controlled movements he will ultimately achieve.

### MAKING PROGRESS

A newborn baby has no control over his head, which will flop around if left unsupported. By about eight weeks, control of the head and neck begins and you may notice your baby practising lifting his head and holding it for a few seconds before letting it flop down again. At around three months most babies are able to hold their heads up steadily so that they can look around and examine the world about them.

The next stage in mobility comes when your baby starts to roll around, first from side to back and then, a few weeks later, from back to side. The way a baby rolls is highly individual and your baby will roll when he's ready and in his own way. Rolling is another way of practising control over his body and your baby will do it over and over again until he's mastered what to him is a new movement. The result of this

### How you can help
• Hold your baby upright so he can bounce his legs up and down on your lap to help strengthen his muscles.
• Sitting a little way away from your baby, persuade him to come to you. Do this to encourage both crawling and walking.
• Once he can sit upright, you can help your baby learn to balance by placing toys slightly out of reach so he has to stretch out for them.
• To get your baby to twist around, place a toy behind him and then support him as he turns.
• Push-along toys will encourage your baby to crawl and walk.

movement will change your baby's view of the world and once he has discovered this, rolling becomes a new function: a means of getting closer to something that he wants. Your baby will have been using his legs to push with since he was born, although the first stepping movements he made as a newborn were a reflex

*All babies' first movements will be uncoordinated, but they soon learn a basic crawl and to sit upright unaided.*

*When your baby is placed on his stomach at a few months old he will attempt to crawl.*

*He will lift up his arms and legs in the swimming motion that is the prelude to crawling.*

*Before she's a year old, your baby will start to stand and balance holding onto a chair if you hold it steady for her.*

*She will grasp firmly onto the bottom part of the chair and start to pull herself up. Try to encourage her as much as possible.*

*As she straightens into an upright position, she will need support from the chair you are holding.*

*Now she is standing confidently, she will start to look around her to see what else is going on in the room.*

*As your baby starts to crawl, he will move towards interesting toys.*          *When he is nearer the toys, he will probably reach out for them.*

action. At around four months if you put your baby down on his abdomen, he will be able to lift his shoulders, arms, and legs off the floor and move them in a swimming-type motion, and by around five-and-a-half months your baby should be able to sit with some support, his back straight and shoulders braced. By around six months he will probably be able to support himself in a crawling position, although he won't be able to go anywhere just yet. By seven months he will be able to sit upright using his arms for support. Once he has done this he will quickly learn to sit unaided, and he will also enjoy standing and bouncing vigorously while you hold him.

By eight or nine months he will have learned to control his movements and he will be able to move his arms and legs in order to propel himself either backwards or forwards. Once he has mastered this he will be off and it will only be a matter of time before he starts trying to stand up on his own. By about nine months he will be able to sit and reach in front, upwards, to the side and behind him without falling over.

As soon as he has learned to crawl at around nine months he will be ready to start pulling himself up into a standing position using you, or the furniture, for support. At this stage he will not have mastered sitting down so when he wants to sit he will simply let go and land down on the floor with a resounding bump. He probably won't be able to control his sitting movement until he is 11 to 12 months old.

Before he's a year old your baby will start to cruise around the furniture, taking little sideways steps. Once he can move around like this with some confidence he will let go with one hand. As soon as he is able to let go with his remaining hand, perhaps to cross a gap in the furniture, he will begin to get the confidence to walk about unaided.

Your baby's first steps on his own will be very wobbly and ungainly, with his feet placed wide apart to help him balance. But once he becomes more mobile his legs will straighten and he'll become steadier on his feet.

*By eight or nine months your baby will be able to crawl around on the floor.*

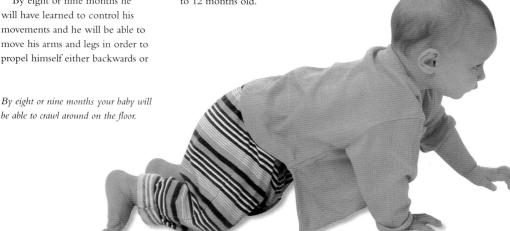

*Your baby will try to stand with your help.*

*Lift him up supporting his arms.*

*Once up, he will need your hand to balance.*

*A baby walker can help a child to take her first steps and practise walking.*

*Once crawling your baby will go all over.*

*Other types of baby walker can be sat in and propelled along by your child's feet.*

*A young baby will enjoy a baby bouncer, but make sure it is firmly attached.*

*Your child's first steps are often wobbly and his movements may seem awkward.*

# PLAY

*Introduce your baby to games by teaching him nursery rhymes like "This little piggy went to market".*

A baby is born with the potential to learn and play. She can see, hear, and feel. She is aware of her environment and will respond from birth to brightly coloured, moving objects and to sounds. She learns all the time and play is one of the ways in which she develops new skills, while toys are the play tools that she uses to stimulate herself at each stage of development. Toys don't have to be elaborate; your child will invent her own games and use everyday objects as toys when she is young. Watching you and trying to imitate your voice and facial expressions will provide hours of entertainment in the early months. Ultimately, the toy that a child enjoys and plays with most will give her the greatest learning experience, and in the first weeks of life this "toy" will be you.

Your child will change rapidly during the first year so that a toy that entertains her at two months will not appeal to her when she is a year old. As she develops, your child will need different stimuli and the choice of toys for each stage of development should reflect these different needs. It is also very important that the toys you give a child are appropriate to this age. A toy designed for a younger child will be boring, while a toy for an older child may be too complicated and may even be dangerous if it contains small pieces on which a young baby could choke.

## BIRTH TO THREE MONTHS

During the first few months, your baby is developing her basic senses – touch, sight, and sound. She needs toys which will stimulate these senses

*Your child will be fascinated by nursery rhymes that involve actions that use his hands.*

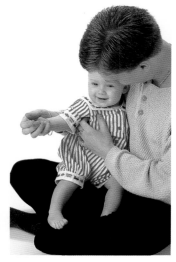

*Because the end of "round and round the garden" includes tickling your baby, he will associate it with fun and ask for more.*

*As your child develops she will start to enjoy playing games with you such as "peek-a-boo".*

*As you teach her the game, she will enjoy "hiding" behind the chair and peeking out at you from behind the legs.*

### Games to play

• Gently bounce your baby up and down on your knee in rhythm to a nursery rhyme.

• Hold her palm open and play "round and round the garden" ending up with a tickle under her arm.

• Use her toes to play "this little piggy went to market".

• Take your baby as your partner and dance around the room with her in your arms.

*You can buy your baby many expensive toys, but she'll still enjoy playing with simple kitchen utensils. Always make sure they have no sharp edges.*

and give experience of colours, textures, materials and shapes. A good first toy is a mobile, hung where your baby can study it at leisure. It doesn't have to be expensive – one made from pictures cut from a magazine and suspended from a coat hanger will be just as effective as one you buy. Once your baby begins to wave her hands around and tries to swipe at things, she will enjoy toys that make a noise or that react to her actions, a rattle for example. This will give your child a sense of control as well as encouraging the development of manual skills and hand and eye co-ordination.

A newborn baby's hands are usually held closed in fists, but she will gradually relax them so that if you place an object in her open palm she will close her hand around it for a few seconds. The strong grasp reflex she was born with will have disappeared so that she will probably drop the object within a few seconds. By the age of two or three months

*An activity centre is ideal for babies around nine months as they will love to push the buttons and manipulate all the different shapes and knobs.*

she will try reaching out to touch things. These first grasping movements are important steps learning hand-eye co-ordination.

Once your baby is old enough to sit in a bouncing cradle she will be able to see more of the world around

her and her hands will be free to explore. A toy fastened across the front of the cradle will encourage her to bring her hands forward to try and hit it to make it move. Once she has done this, she will want to do it again and again; gradually she sees that she is responsible for making this happen and her movements become more deliberate.

A newborn is acutely aware of sounds and will already have become familiar with your voice while in the womb. Talking and singing to your baby from the time she is born will encourage her to listen and help her develop her own speech later. As she gets older, hold her on your lap and try having a conversation with her. Say something, then wait until your baby makes a noise in response. Her response will be slow at first so allow her plenty of time. These conversations will help her learn about taking turns, listening, and copying – all essential parts of communication. Once your baby has got used to life outside the womb,

*As she starts to move around, your baby will get pleasure from pushing a baby walker. She will also enjoy trying to put plastic shapes in the right holes on the walker.*

she will find touch and the freedom to move her limbs exciting. Different textures will give her new sensations of touch, so offer her various things to feel that will give her experience of rough, soft, silky, or smooth textures. Bathing and changing times will provide an opportunity for your baby to explore touch and sensation. She will like the feeling of not being hampered by nappies and clothing and should enjoy the sensation of warm water next to her skin. Try tickling her gently, blowing raspberries on her abdomen, and kissing her toes when she is undressed.

### THREE TO SIX MONTHS

As your baby grows and her movements become more controlled, she will reach out for things and take them in her hands. Her grip becomes stronger and she will be able to hold a wider variety of items. This means that she will start to experience the difference between things that are light and heavy, soft and hard. Her curiosity will be endless and every object will be a plaything. She may prefer to use her mouth rather than her hands to explore things at this age, so it is important to make sure that she can't get hold of anything which could do her any harm.

Your baby will probably play happily for short periods on her own, but she needs you to encourage her. When you play with your baby get her to do things for herself; allow her to use her hands and eyes to work out what she wants to do with the toy she is holding. It is better to give your child only a few selected items to play with at this age because she won't be able to concentrate on more than one thing at a time.

A stimulating, inviting environment is important for all creative play. Toys that are piled up in a jumble are not as inviting to a child as toys which are laid out for her in an attractive, inviting way.

### SIX TO TWELVE MONTHS

Once your baby can support herself sitting up and has started to make her first attempts at moving around, she will want toys that she can manipulate. This is the ideal time to give your child an activity centre with lots of different knobs and handles for her to twist and turn. By around seven or eight months she will want to find out what things can do and will bang objects on the ground or table to find out if they make a noise or wave them in the air to see what happens.

As her manipulative skills develop she will learn that she can use her hands and arms simultaneously and will start to bang things together. She will be able to reach out to you with both arms when she wants to be picked up. It takes a while longer for her to learn how to let go of items she is playing with, but you can encourage her by giving her an object, then holding out your hand and asking for it back.

*A young baby will enjoy being read to from a simple board book and will be interested in touching the pages. She will soon learn how to recognize the book's pictures.*

*Your child will often put different things in her mouth to investigate them.*

Once she's got the hang of this game she will love it and keep you busy for hours!

As she becomes more mobile, your baby will want to be into everything and her natural curiosity could lead her into danger, so you need to pay constant attention to safety. One of your baby's favourite pastimes will be emptying things out of containers. She will take things out of cupboards with just as much enjoyment as she will empty shapes out of a shape sorter. Once she has emptied a container she will want to examine the contents in great detail and will bang things together and may put them in her mouth before discarding them and moving on to the next object. When she has mastered this

she will soon learn that she can put things back into the container and will spend ages tipping things out and putting them back again. She will try doing this with different objects and may discover that some of them don't fit. As your child plays she will be learning about the nature of the objects, how they behave, and their relative size and shape.

Water play can be introduced now and your baby will enjoy filling and emptying plastic beakers while she is having her bath. Give her toys which have different sizes of holes in them so that she can spend time sprinkling or pouring the water from one container into another.

Once your baby has started to crawl, give her toys that roll and move when they are pushed along so that she can go after them. Later, as she starts taking her weight on her legs, you can encourage her and help her balance with sturdy push-along

*A baby walker will help your child to walk and some double as an activity centre.*

toys, such as a brick trolley. This will give her something to hold onto until she feels confident enough to let go and walk unaided.

BOOKS

It is never too early to introduce your baby to books. Start at an early age with brightly coloured rag books that your baby can chew as well as handle, or simple board books. At first she will enjoy these books as objects to be explored but, if you sit her on your knee and talk to her about the pictures in the book, she will soon learn to recognize them. Encourage her by making the noises of any animals pictured in the books and then getting her to do the same.

*By just giving your baby one toy at a time to play with, she will be able to concentrate on it more fully.*

### Games to play

• "Pat-a-cake, pat-a-cake, baker's man" is a rhyme to which your baby will enjoy clapping. When you get to "prick it and pat it and mark it with ..." use your baby's own initial and then her name when you come to "put in the oven for ...".

• Blowing bubbles using either a made-up solution and a wand or washing-up liquid and your hands.

• "Peek-a-boo": use your hands to cover your face; then later hide and seek: hide objects under a soft cloth for your baby to find.

• Hold your baby's hands securely and rock her gently backwards and forward while singing "Row, row, row the boat ...".

• Sit your baby on your knee facing towards you and hold her firmly by the hands as you bounce her in time to "Humpty Dumpty". When you get to the big fall allow your baby to drop through your knees while holding her firmly.

# PART FOUR

## COOKING FOR BABIES AND TODDLERS

A baby has specific nutritional requirements, very different from those of an adult. Many new parents are apprehensive of their ability to cater for their baby's needs – especially when children have a mind of their own, and can reject the carefully chosen and prepared food. This section sets out to explain the latest guidelines for feeding babies and young children. It explains clearly which are the highly nutritious foods, packed with the protein and vitamins that an active child needs, and warns against foods that do not provide enough calories or that may cause allergic reactions.

We all know commercially prepared food can be bad for us and it is sometimes hard to judge how much salt and sugar has been added. Home cooked food is delicious, and can be just as quick to make. This section is packed with recipes, each fully illustrated and set out clearly, step by step. Many recipes have been specially created to work for the entire family with only a little adaptation. The same basic ingredients and methods of preparation can be tailored to create three meals: for a baby, a fussy toddler and for two hungry parents. This section is also packed with tips to help make meals a calm, pleasant time, where you can relax and enjoy your family's company.

# INTRODUCTION

Part Four, Cooking for Babies and Toddlers, aims to explain all you need to know about feeding your young family. Set out in three easy-to-use sections, it is packed with over 200 recipes, all beautifully illustrated with colour pictures – from first purées to tempting toddler meals then moving on to food for all the family.

In the very early days all a baby needs is milk, but as it grows so too will its nutritional needs. By four months most babies will have doubled their birth weight and will be ready to begin mini-mouthfuls of smooth purée.

Although this marks an exciting time in your baby's development it can also cause immense worry for a new parent. We all want to provide the best for our child and what better start in life than to begin laying the foundations for a healthy diet? But what do you do if your child just refuses to eat? This section has practical tips that may provide some of the answers.

If your child has any food allergies or sensitivities, read each recipe to make sure that it doesn't contain a problem ingredient.

## FIRST FOODS

Section one covers everything you need to know about introducing those first spoonfuls of smooth puréed foods: including when to begin weaning, the signs to look out for, what foods to serve and when, basic equipment, plus sound nutritional advice, helpful

guidelines on food preparation and masses of colourful and exciting recipes to tempt your baby.

You will almost certainly find that health professionals, friends and relatives will offer you differing, perhaps contradictory, advice. Some will be useful, while some will turn out to be outdated or inappropriate: the difficulty is sorting through the confusion to find something reliable. This section draws upon current dietary information to provide helpful advice on feeding your baby.

## FOOD FOR TODDLERS

In the second section we move on to feeding an energetic toddler. By this stage your baby will probably have tripled her birth weight and will have begun to feed herself and may be developing strong likes and dislikes. Many young children go through a stage of extreme food fads, causing frustration and worry for parents. Again, we have included down-to-earth tips and practical advice on coping with a fussy eater, plus lots of easy recipes to tempt your child.

## FAMILY MEALS

In the third section the recipes have been devised to feed the whole family from one basic set of ingredients prepared at the same time. With step-by-step instructions we illustrate how to mash food for your baby, make a mini-meal for your fussy toddler and how, by adding a few extra ingredients, to simultaneously transform this simple meal into something more exciting for Mum and Dad.

about 50 per cent of energy as fat. As your child progresses to a mixed diet, the proportion of energy supplied by fat decreases and is replaced by carbohydrate. However, it is important that the energy is provided by fat up to the age of two, as too much carbohydrate may be too bulky for a young infant.

Adequate energy is necessary to sustain growth. Fat is a very useful source of energy and the main source of the fat-soluble vitamins, A, D, E and K, while also providing essential fatty acids that the body cannot make itself. It is best to obtain fat from foods that contain other essential nutrients, such as full-fat (whole) milk, cheese, yogurt, lean meat and small quantities of oily fish.

Try to include a portion of carbohydrate in every meal once your child is over nine months: for example, bread, potatoes, rice or pasta for energy. Encourage young

*Above and below: Start with simple vegetable purées. Sit your baby in a high-chair with a strap, or on your lap with a dish towel to protect your clothes.*

**FOOD AND YOUR CHILD**
Childrens' nutritional needs are very different from our own. Forget about low-fat, high-fibre diets. Young children require nutrient-dense foods to meet their rapid levels of growth. Requirements for protein and energy are high in proportion to the child's size. Tiny tummies mean children are unable to eat large quantities of food, while at the same time they are usually very active. Their appetites can vary enormously, but the range of foods that they will eat may be very limited. Consequently, it is vital that the foods which are eaten contain a variety of nutrients, in combination with calories, while still fitting in with family meals. High-fibre foods can be very filling without providing sufficient levels of protein, vitamins and minerals.

For young infants fat is the major source of dietary energy: both breast milk and infant formula contribute

*Below: Babies are easily encouraged to take pleasure in their food, however simple. Give your baby finger food as well as a spoon and bowl.*

children to eat a variety of fruit and vegetables. As with adults, try to keep salt intakes to a minimum; fried foods or very sugary foods should be discouraged and served only as a special treat. As children approach school age they should gradually be pushed towards a diet that is lower in fat and higher in fibre, in line with the guidelines for adults.

Snacks are also important as young children require high calorie levels and cannot meet this requirement in three meals a day. Try to encourage healthy snacks such as mini ham sandwiches, cubes of cheese or wedges of apple instead of chocolate biscuits.

Obviously, having a healthy, well-balanced diet is essential for any age group, but acquiring social skills is also important. Our children learn from us and so it is vital to eat together as a family, if not every day, then as often as possible. It is never too early for the youngest member of the family to start learning how to behave at the table – though to begin with it will probably be a messy experience. Your child will soon regard family meals as a sociable and enjoyable time.

We hope that this book will make meal-times fun for the entire family and help to minimize any problems you may come up against when feeding your baby and toddler.

Below: *Don't deprive the children of cakes at party-time, but include some healthy dips and savouries, too.*

Above: *Giving your child the best possible start in life is a major concern, but good food planning is easy to achieve.*

# First Foods

Introducing your baby to the delights of solid food heralds the beginning of a new and exciting stage in your baby's development. You will know she is ready when she seems unsatisfied after a milk feed, or shows an interest in what you are eating. Although it will be a few months yet before she is able to share in family meals fully, the foods that you give your baby now are important not only for their nutritional benefits but also in laying down the first foundations for a healthy diet through childhood and beyond.

Start your baby with baby rice that is barely warm and only slightly thicker than milk – then move to bland mashed vegetables and fruits. For those first spoonfuls, sit your baby on your lap in a familiar position, but once she is accustomed to the idea, put her in a baby chair on the floor, or in a portable car seat. It won't be long before she is ready for a high-chair. Remember that hygiene is still very important, and you should continue to sterilize equipment until your baby is six-and-a-half months old.

# Weaning from Milk Feeds to Solids

Most babies are ready to begin those first few mini-mouthfuls of mashed or puréed foods at around six months and will soon progress to a mixed diet of solid foods. By this age, babies need the extra energy, protein, iron and other essential nutrients that are found in solids in order to help them develop and grow. Your baby will also be progressing from sucking to biting and chewing – as many breast-feeding mothers find out!

Remember that every baby has individual needs, so don't be surprised if your baby seems ready for solids a little earlier or later than other babies of the same age. Don't feel pressurized by friends with young babies, or helpful relatives. Be guided by your own baby.

Below: *Your baby will very quickly take an interest in your hand and the spoon, and will play as she eats.*

Right: *When the signs are right, start your baby with a few mouthfuls of mashed vegetables or fruit after a milk feed, or in the middle of one, if this works better. If the food is hot, make sure you stir it and test it before giving it to your baby.*

Below right: *When your baby starts picking up food and putting it into his mouth, he is ready to try solid foods.*

## WHAT TO LOOK OUT FOR

If your baby:
- still seems hungry after you have increased the milk feed
- wants feeding more frequently
- shows a real interest in the foods that you are eating
- picks up food and puts it in his or her mouth, wanting to chew
- can sit up

If your baby is showing some or all of these signs, then he or she is probably ready to begin solids. Some babies may show these signs earlier than six months, but the majority should not be given solid foods before six months as their digestive systems can't cope. Be guided as well by any family history of allergies, eczema or asthma. Studies suggest that babies fed on breast or formula milk a bit longer are less likely to develop such complaints.

In the early days of weaning, your baby is not dependent on solid food for the supply of nutrients as this is still met by milk feeds. Don't worry if she only takes a taste of food to begin with – the actual experience of taking food off a spoon is the most important thing at this stage. However, as your baby grows older, solid foods are essential for supplying all the vital minerals and vitamins she needs.

### WHAT ABOUT MILK FEEDS?

During the early stages of weaning, solids are given in addition to normal feeds of breast or formula milk. As mixed feeding continues, your baby will naturally cut down on the number of milk feeds, but milk will remain an important part of a child's diet.

Up to six months your baby should be having four to five milk feeds a day, and by age one your baby needs at least 600ml/1 pint full-fat (whole) milk a day. Milk will still contribute 40 percent of the energy she uses up. Health professionals recommend that children should not be given cow's milk as their main drink until after 12 months, due to low levels of iron and vitamins C and D. Mothers may be advised to go on to fortified formula when breast feeding has finished. Small amounts of cow's milk may be used in cooking from six months, but it is better to use formula milk.

Above: *Every baby is different. There is no need to be worried if your baby seems ready for solids earlier or later than other babies.*

Full-fat cow's milk can be given to children between one and two, while semi-skimmed (low-fat) milk can be gradually introduced to those over two, providing the child eats well. Skimmed milk should not be given to children under five.

Only give pasteurized milk to children. UHT or long-life milk is a useful standby for holidays and travelling as it doesn't need to be refrigerated. However, once opened treat it as full-fat pasteurized milk.

Some people prefer to give goat's or sheep's milk believing it is less allergenic and offers additional nourishment, although this cannot be substantiated. Goat's milk is deficient in folic acid and must not be given to babies under six months. Boil goat's milk before use, as it may be sold unpasteurized.

### WEANING FROM BREAST OR BOTTLE

You can go on breast feeding your baby, as well as giving solid food, for as long as you wish. However, many mothers are quite relieved when their baby is happy to try a feeder

cup or bottle along with their lunch-time "solid" meal. Once solids become established the number of daytime milk feeds naturally tails off, with just the special morning and evening comfort feeds continuing until you and your baby are ready to stop.

Whether bottle or breast and bottle feeding, try to wean your baby off the bottle completely by the age of one. Otherwise your baby may find it difficult to give the bottle up, and comfort sucking on a teat can be a hard habit to break.

Once your baby can sit up, you can introduce a lidded feeding cup, initially at one meal a day, then at two and so on. But do make sure that you cuddle your baby while giving a drink, so that the baby still enjoys the closeness and security of being with her mother or father. There may be a few setbacks when your baby is teething or unwell, but be guided by your baby.

Above: *It won't all happen at once: a mixed period of feeding with breast, bottle and simple solids is perfectly natural and healthy.*

Above: *Bottles are a wonderful aid, but try to wean your baby off them by age one, or the sucking habit can be difficult to break.*

# Introducing Solid Food

Many parents find that around late morning, after their baby's morning sleep, is the best time to introduce solids. The baby is happy and nicely hungry without being frantic. Offer a small milk feed to take the edge off her immediate hunger and make her feel secure, and then go on to offer solid food. Finish with the rest of the milk feed or "second side".

## SITTING COMFORTABLY
If you are feeding a slightly younger baby, you might like to hold her securely on your lap while offering the first spoonfuls. However, most babies will be comfortable fed in a high-chair.

## FIRST SPOONFULS
Baby rice is often the most successful first food because its milky taste and soft texture seem vaguely familiar to the baby. Begin by trying a teaspoonful of bought baby rice, add a little previously boiled water, expressed breast milk or formula milk as the pack directs, and mix to make a smooth runny purée, slightly thicker than milk. Test the temperature on the edge of your lip, it should be just lukewarm – too hot and you may put the baby off solids completely. Offer tiny amounts on the end of a sterilized teaspoon. Go at your baby's pace and don't try to hurry things.

Above: *First baby rice will be barely warm, and only very slightly thicker than milk.*

Above: *At about six months your baby will be ready to sit safely in a high-chair. You should always use a strap to make sure she is safely fastened in.*

Learning to eat from a spoon is quite a skill, and your baby may start spitting out the food until she has mastered the technique of taking food off the spoon and transferring it to the back of her mouth. It is possible that she may not like the taste of the food. If you started with baby rice, then go on to potato or parsnip purée mixed into the baby rice. If your baby seems reluctant, then abandon the feed and go back to breast or bottle feeding – your baby may simply not be ready for solids yet.

You could try solids again a few days later – there's plenty of time. Never force-feed and never add solid foods to a baby's bottle, as it can lead to choking, which can be dangerous.

## BABY APPEARS TO GAG
Some babies just cannot cope with solids at first and may seem distressed and almost gag on the food.

Try thinning down the food even more, as it may be too thick. Alternatively, you may be putting too much on the spoon: try offering your baby a little less. If neither of these seems to help, stop solids and breast or bottle feed as usual, giving your baby plenty of reassuring cuddles. Try again in a few days' or weeks' time.

## INTRODUCING VEGETABLES
After rice, gradually introduce mashed or puréed potato, carrot, parsnip and swede (rutabaga), or puréed apple or pears. As always, be guided by your baby: this is a slow process so don't try to hurry your baby if she is not ready, or you will run the risk of discouraging her altogether.

## SPOON FEEDING FOR THE FIRST TIME

**1** Sit your baby on your lap in a familiar position. Always test the temperature of the food.

**2** Offer the spoon to your baby. Go slowly and if the spoon or food is rejected try again another day.

**3** When your baby has taken her first solid food, sit her quietly for a little while in an upright position.

After a week or two your baby may be ready to try two mini-meals a day. Increase the amount of food to 10ml/2 tsp, even 15ml/3 tsp if your baby seems ready. You may be able to slightly reduce the amount of formula or breast milk you use to make the purée, so that it is not quite so sloppy. If your baby likes the flavour, then offer it again for a few meals before introducing a new taste. If your baby spits it out, then go back to baby rice or try mixing the new flavour with a little baby rice so that it is milder and more palatable.

Try to follow your baby's appetite and pace; most babies will stop when they have had enough. Don't be tempted to persuade your baby to finish off those last few spoonfuls. It's a bad habit to force or encourage anyone to clear the plate if they are full. If you do it with a baby, she'll probably be sick!

Adopt a feeding schedule to suit you both. In the early days it may be easier to give the baby breakfast before older children get up, or after they're at school, when the house is quieter. Six to eight weeks into solid feeding, your baby will probably be ready for three small meals a day. Again, be guided by her needs and appetite, so don't introduce a third meal until you feel she is really ready. Aim to feed your baby at roughly equal time intervals that will eventually coincide with as many family meals as possible.

### TIPS

- Take advice from your doctor or health visitor, particularly if your baby was premature.
- Sterilize all equipment before use up to the age of about six-and-a-half months.
- Don't force your baby if she doesn't seem ready for solids – be guided by her and let it happen at its own pace.
- Maintain milk feeds and offer plain boiled water or very diluted fruit juice as well.
- Try one taste at a time and continue with this until your baby is accustomed to it. If she doesn't like it, don't offer it again for a few days.
- Allow plenty of time for feeding, particularly at first.
- Choose a time of day when you and your baby are relaxed.
- Talk to your baby quietly and encourage her to eat.
- Never leave your baby alone when feeding her.
- Remember, babies don't mind repetition – they've been living on milk for months!

*Above: You can build up the diet from baby rice to items like mashed or puréed carrot, parsnip, apple or pear, gradually leaving more texture as your baby seems ready.*

## EQUIPMENT

Choose a small plastic spoon, preferably with a shallow bowl that is gentle on your baby's gums. Look out for packs of weaning spoons in pharmacies or baby-care shops. If you don't want to buy a lot of equipment right away, you may find it useful to mix small quantities of baby rice in the sterilized cap of a bottle. Alternatively, use a small china ramekin or plastic bowl. Plastic bowls with suction feet or insulated linings are also perfectly adequate and will be useful later on when your baby gets bigger. All equipment must be scrupulously clean (and sterilized if your baby is under six-and-a-half months old).

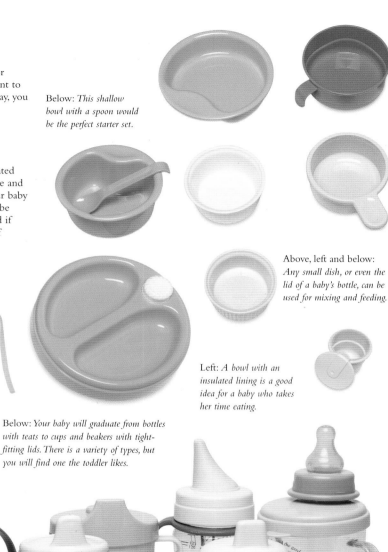

Below: *This shallow bowl with a spoon would be the perfect starter set.*

Above, left and below: *Any small dish, or even the lid of a baby's bottle, can be used for mixing and feeding.*

Below: *A bib is even more essential once your baby is taking solid foods.*

Left: *A bowl with an insulated lining is a good idea for a baby who takes her time eating.*

Below: *Your baby will graduate from bottles with teats to cups and beakers with tight-fitting lids. There is a variety of types, but you will find one the toddler likes.*

## FEEDING TWINS

Probably the easiest way to feed twins is to sit the babies side by side and offer food from one bowl. Twins can get rather frustrated if you have to keep picking up different bowls and spoons. Try to be adaptable and if you find a way that works then stick with it. Encourage finger foods slightly earlier: perhaps a mini ham sandwich, cooked broccoli floret or carrot stick.

Wait until each child has finished their main course before offering dessert, as the slow eater will be distracted and want to go on to dessert too.

Looking after twins can be exhausting so you may find serving sandwiches for lunch an easier option, and this will give you a chance to eat something too. Serve cooked food for the evening meal.

## DRINKS

Although your baby will need less milk for nourishment, she will still need something to drink, especially in hot weather. Always offer at least two drinks during the day and also a drink with every meal.

### You can give:

- breast, formula milk or, at over one year, full-fat (whole) cow's milk
- cooled boiled water
- well-diluted pure unsweetened fruit juice

*Above: Dilute juices with boiled and cooled water.*

You can stop boiling the water for the baby's drinks when you stop sterilizing her feeding equipment, but always make sure you provide water from the mains supply and allow the tap to run before using it. Never use water from the hot tap.

If you have a water softener make sure that you use a tap connected directly to the mains supply and independent of the water softener. Artificially softened water is not recommended as salts are added during the softening process. Check with your doctor or health visitor before giving a baby bottled water, as the mineral content varies and you will need to choose a low-mineral brand such as those that are labelled "spring water". As a general rule, bottled water is not really necessary unless you are on holiday (vacation) where it is unsafe to drink the water.

Some fruit drinks contain a lot of added sugar, so check the label for sucrose, glucose, dextrose, fructose, maltose, syrup, honey or concentrated fruit juice. If you do give concentrated drinks to your baby, make sure you dilute them correctly, and do not give them too often. Pure fruit juices contain no

*Above: If you have twins, put their chairs side by side at meal-times.*

*Below: Drinks fill up the baby's tummy – so offer drinks after food.*

added sugar. At first, dilute them with one part juice to three parts water. The amount of water can be reduced as the child matures. Offer drinks at the end of meal times once your baby has settled into three meals a day.

Never allow a baby to use a bottle of juice as a comforter or go to sleep with a bottle in his mouth, as this can result in serious tooth decay.

# Sterilizing and Food Preparation

For babies older than six months, it isn't necesssary for the first solids to be completely smooth and soft, and you can start introducing some texture quite quickly, depending on your baby's preferences. Fork-mashing is simple and easy, but there are several useful pieces of kitchen equipment to help you with larger quantities.

For ease and speed, an electric liquidizer is by far the best. You may be able to buy a liquidizer attachment for your mixer, or purchase a free-standing liquidizer unit. A food processor works well, but make sure the food is blended to the required smoothness before offering it to your baby, as processors can miss the odd lump, especially when processing small quantities. A hand-held electric multimixer has the bonus of reducing washing up by mixing foods in the serving bowl. If you prefer to purée food by hand, then a sieve (strainer) or hand mill are both perfectly adequate and are much cheaper alternatives.

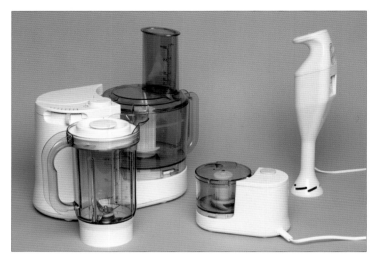

Above: *There is a huge range of brand-name food processors and blenders on the market, many of which have attachments for puréeing.*

Left: *The basics — manual mashers, or a sieve — take longer but will do the job just as well.*

Above: *A purpose-designed liquidizer will make perfect purée in seconds. This is the right tool for making large batches.*

Above: *This hand-held blender takes a little longer, but the results are just as reliable. They are easy to clean and store.*

Above: *Making purée manually the old-fashioned way — with a sieve and spoon — is time-consuming but highly satisfying.*

## FOOD HYGIENE

Young babies can easily pick up infections, so it is vitally important that all equipment is scrupulously clean before use.

● Always wash your hands before handling food or feeding equipment.

Above: *Rule one – always wash your hands with soap and warm water before feeding your baby or handling food.*

● Items such as bottles, feeding spoons and serving bowls should be sterilized until your baby is six-and-a-half months old. Sterilize equipment by boiling it in a pan of water for 25 minutes, immersing it in a container of cold water with sterilizing fluid or a tablet, or by using a steam sterilizer. Larger items such as a sieve, knife, pan, blender or masher, or plastic chopping board should be scalded with boiling water.

Above: *Scald larger objects such as chopping boards, spoons, sieves and pans with boiling water to sterilize.*

● Sterilize all baby equipment until your baby is six-and-a-half months; milk bottles, teats and so on should be sterilized until she begins to use a cup.

Above: *Boiling for 25 minutes is still the simplest way of sterilizing baby equipment.*

Right: *Always cover baby food at all times – even when stored in the refrigerator.*

Below: *Always keep the surfaces around where your baby eats scrupulously clean.*

● Never use equipment used for the family pet when preparing baby food. Keep a can opener, fork and dish specifically for your pet, and make sure other members of the family are aware of this.

● Once cooked, cover all baby food with a lid or plate and transfer to the refrigerator as soon as possible. Food should not be left for longer than 1½ hours at room temperature before either refrigerating or freezing.

## SOLUTION STERILIZER

1 Fill the sterilizer to the required height with cold water, and add sterilizing tablets or liquid.

2 Pack the items to be sterilized into the container. Bottles will fit into the spaces provided.

3 Make sure no air gets trapped in the container – or these pockets will not be properly sterile. Push everything down with the "float".

4 Place the lid on and leave for the length of time specified in the instructions. Rinse everything afterwards in boiling water.

## STEAM STERILIZER

1 Measure the specified amount of water into the base of the steamer as directed in the instructions.

2 Pack the bottles and teats into the container: steamers have less capacity for dishes, which will need to be boiled separately.

Left: *There is a wide range of sterilizing equipment to choose from. This group, all specially designed for bottles and teats, comprises two steam sterilizing units that operate electrically and a traditional container that holds the bottles efficiently in cold water sterilizing solution.*

## STERILIZING IN THE MICROWAVE

Microwave ovens are not suitable for general day-to-day sterilizing without special equipment, and many health authorities and mother-and-baby experts recommend against using the microwave for this purpose. However, microwave sterilizing units can be purchased for sterilizing bottles, and if you are using one, the manufacturer's instructions should be followed closely.

*Right: This purpose-designed sterilizing unit is specially made for microwave use. Add about 5mm/¹/4in water to the base before putting in the bottles.*

## BATCH COOKING

Cooking for a baby can be very frustrating. Those spoonfuls of lovingly and hygienically prepared food, offered with such hope and spat out so unceremoniously can leave you feeling quite indignant.

Save time by cooking several meals in advance. Freeze mini-portions in ice-cube trays, great for those early days when you need only one cube for lunch, and flexible enough for later on when your baby's appetite has grown to two or three cubes per meal.

Spoon the mixture into sterilized ice-cube trays and open freeze until solid. Press the cubes into a plastic bag, seal, label and return to the freezer. Keep single batches of food in the same bag so that the different flavours don't combine.

Recycle yogurt containers, cottage cheese containers with lids, small plastic boxes with lids, or use disposable plastic cups and cover them with clear film (plastic wrap). Sterilize the containers using sterilizing fluid or tablets. Cover all prepared foods and label them clearly so that you know what they are and on which date they went into the freezer.

Most foods should be used within three months if stored in a freezer at – 18°C/0°F. Defrost plastic boxes in the refrigerator overnight. Ice cubes can be left to defrost at room temperature in a bowl or on a plate, loosely covered with clear film.

## BATCH COOKING TIPS

1 It is just as quick (and very much cheaper in the long run) to make a larger batch of purée as a smaller quantity for a single meal.

2 Freeze in meal-size portions in sterilized ice-cube trays: these can later be put into freezer bags for storing.

3 Make sure the bags are carefully labelled and dated. Keep only for the period specified in your freezer handbook.

# Reheating, Freezing and Using a Microwave

**HOW TO REHEAT BABY FOOD**
Although reheating food sounds relatively straightforward, it is vitally important that the following rules are followed, as tepid food provides the perfect breeding ground for bacteria, especially if left uncovered in a warm kitchen and reheated several times.
• Don't reheat food more than once. It is a health risk, and can be dangerous.

• If you have a large batch of baby food, then reheat just a portion in a pan and leave the remaining mixture in a covered bowl in the refrigerator. If your baby is still hungry after the feed, then reheat a little extra again, with the remaining mixture left in the refrigerator.
• Reheat small quantities of baby food in a sterilized heat-proof container, covered with a saucer or

small plate and put into a small pan half filled with boiling water. Alternatively, spoon larger quantities straight into a pan, cover and bring to the boil.
• Make sure food is piping hot all the way through to kill any bacteria. Food should be 70°C/158°F for a minimum of 2 minutes. Take off the heat and allow to cool. Test before serving to your baby.

**REHEATING TIPS**

1 Reheat small quantities in a sterilized bowl, covered with a dish or foil.

2 Place the bowl into a pan half filled with boiling water. Make sure the food is cooked through.

3 For larger quantities, put the food straight into the pan and bring to the boil.

**FREEZING**

• When using a freezer for storing home-made baby foods, use up the foods as soon as possible, as the texture preferred by the child will change very quickly as she develops.
• Keeping a well-stocked freezer of basic provisions can be a life-saver: there is nothing worse than going shopping with small children, especially when they're tired, and freezing will save you trip after trip.
• Make sure to always label foods so you know exactly when they went into the freezer, and double check against this handy list of storage dates:

| Meat and poultry | |
|---|---|
| Beef and lamb | 4–6 months |
| Pork and veal | 4–6 months |
| Minced (ground) beef | 3–4 months |
| Sausages | 2–3 months |
| Ham and bacon joints | 3–4 months |
| Chicken and turkey | 10–12 months |
| Duck and goose | 4–6 months |
| **Fish** | |
| White fish | 6–8 months |
| Oily fish | 3–4 months |
| Fish portions | 3–4 months |
| Shellfish | 2–3 months |
| **Fruit and vegetables** | |
| Fruit with or without sugar | 8–10 months |
| Fruit juices | 4–6 months |
| Most vegetables | 10–12 months |
| Mushrooms and tomatoes | 6–8 months |

| Dairy produce | |
|---|---|
| Cream | 6–8 months |
| Butter, unsalted (sweet) | 6–8 months |
| Butter, salted | 3–4 months |
| Cheese, hard | 4–6 months |
| Cheese, soft | 3–4 months |
| Ice cream | 3–4 months |
| **Prepared foods** | |
| Ready-prepared meals, highly seasoned | 2–3 months |
| Ready-prepared meals, average seasoning | 4–6 months |
| Cakes | 4–6 months |
| Bread, all kinds | 2–3 months |
| Other yeast products and pastries | 3–4 months |

*Chart published by kind permission of the Food Safety Advisory Centre*

Above: *Many parents will find a microwave helpful and time-saving if used carefully. t can be used for heating milk and drinks (for toddlers – not newborns), for defrosting, reheating and cooking preprepared foods.*

## USING A MICROWAVE

Health advisers do not recommend using a microwave for reheating, as the food heats up unevenly, but if you decide to microwave baby food, then make sure you stir the food thoroughly after cooking. Leave the dish to stand for 2–3 minutes before stirring again so that "hot spots" are well stirred into the mixture, and always check the temperature before serving. Choose the type of dish carefully as some ceramic dishes can get very hot; plastic or pyrex dishes are the most successful in the microwave, heating food quickly but staying relatively cool themselves.

1 Cover with clear film (plastic wrap), pierce and place in the oven.

2 When cooked, remove from the microwave oven and stir.

## MICROWAVING TIPS

• Never warm milk for a newborn or young baby in the microwave.

• For older children, warm milk in a bottle without the teat or in an uncovered feeder beaker for 30–45 seconds. Stir well and always test the temperature of the milk (*not* the temperature of the container) before serving to make sure that the milk is an even and comfortable temperature. Seek advice from your doctor or health visitor.

• To defrost ice cubes of baby food, press three into a baby dish, cover with clear film (plastic wrap) and thaw in the microwave on Defrost (30%) for 1–2 minutes. Stir well then re-cover and microwave on Full Power (100%) for 1 minute. Stir well to avoid hot spots, then test the temperature.

# Choosing a High-chair

There is a surprisingly wide choice of high-chairs available in a range of finishes, colours and price levels, so make sure you shop around before you buy. Those shown here are just a selection of the many different chairs that are available.

## CONVERTIBLE CHAIRS
Designed for babies between four weeks and six months, these chairs can convert from a high-chair into a swing, and some models will also convert into a baby chair and rocker too. It is best to buy one of these when the baby is very young so that you get maximum use from it. The only disadvantage may be the space required for the frame. The ease in converting from one type of chair to another varies from model to model, so you would be well advised to practise in the shop before choosing which one to buy. Most chairs have white painted frames.

## THREE-IN-ONE CHAIRS
Various designs on the market convert into a separate chair, chair and table or high-chair. Some simply clip apart, while others require a little help with a screwdriver. There are good rigid structures available with a wide range of decorative seat patterns. They are available in wood or white finishes. The low chair is suitable for children up to four years old if used without the tray.

## ELEVATOR CHAIRS
These chairs are slightly more expensive, but will convert from a high-chair to a low chair. Some models have adjustable tray settings to fit a growing child. The frames are mostly available in white metal, with attractive seating.

**Three-in-one-type**

**Elevator type**

### TIPS
● For maximum use of a high-chair, buy a booster cushion for the early days when your baby first begins to use the chair. Adjust the tray position as well, if possible.
● Check that the high-chair is easy to clean – dried-on food in cracks can be impossible to clean off. Look out for possible dirt traps on the seat or around the tray fixing.
● Make sure that the chair is sturdy and rigid – it will need to withstand considerable wear.

Above: *A portable clip-on chair.*

● If using a clip-on high-chair make sure that the table is suitable and will be able to withstand the weight of your child. Never, in any circumstances, fix on to glass.

## FOLDING CHAIRS

These less expensive chairs, available in wood or white finishes, usually fold up in a scissor movement. Some can be folded crossways for packing into the boot (trunk) of the car. Before buying, check how easy they are to fold out and up, and make sure the frame is rigid when opened out.

**Folding type**

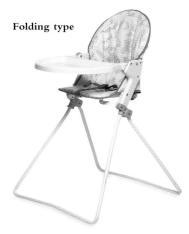

## COUNTRY-TYPE CHAIRS

These are sturdy wooden high-chairs usually with a wooden tray and attractive spindle features. The seat can be hard for the baby, so it is best to buy a fitted chair cushion.

## PORTABLE CHAIRS

There are two main types available:
• A very simple cloth tie, useful for visiting friends or eating out, as it will fold up and fit in a bag. However, it is not really suitable for everyday use as the child is literally tied on to the chair and so cannot reach the table to feed himself.
• Clip-on seats where the frames are placed under and over the edge of a dining table. Check that the table is strong enough and is not likely to overbalance before you put your baby in the chair.

**1** Undo the tray catches by pressing both sides at once, and fold the tray upwards.

**2** Undo the side catches that keep the frame rigid so the chair can scissor in two.

**3** This allows you to fold the chair over on to itself: the design is incredibly neat and compact.

**4** It is now ready for storing, putting out of the way, or placing in the boot (trunk) of the car.

### TIPS

• Always use a safety harness. Although most high-chairs have a three-point lap strap, you will probably have to buy straps that will go around your baby's body and clip on to the chair. It is amazing how quickly a baby learns to wriggle out of a high-chair when you're not looking.
• Never leave a child in a high-chair unattended.

Above: *Always strap your baby in tightly.*

# STAGE 1: FIRST TASTES – EARLY WEANING

OFFICIAL GUIDELINES NOW RECOMMEND THAT WEANING TAKES PLACE AT SIX OR SIX-AND-A-HALF MONTHS, BUT THERE ARE SOME BABIES WHO SHOW INTEREST IN EATING SOLIDS AT AN EARLIER AGE. YOU SHOULD NOT INTRODUCE SOLID FOODS BEFORE YOUR BABY IS 17 WEEKS OLD – AND BE SURE TO ASK YOUR DOCTOR OR HEALTH VISITOR FOR ADVICE BEFORE STARTING EARLY WEANING. BEGIN BY OFFERING ONLY A TEASPOONFUL OF BABY RICE OR VERY SOFT RUNNY PURÉE ONCE A DAY. MILK IS STILL PROVIDING YOUR BABY WITH ALL HER NUTRITIONAL NEEDS, BUT THESE EARLY FOODS WILL BE THE FOUNDATIONS ON WHICH LATER EATING HABITS ARE BUILT, SO IT SHOULD BE A POSITIVE EXPERIENCE.

## Suitable Foods

**FOODS TO INCLUDE**
- baby rice mixed with water, breast or formula milk.
- mild-tasting fork-mashed vegetables – beginning with potato then carrot, parsnip, or swede (rutabaga).
- mild, naturally-sweet fruit purées made with eating apples or pears.

Below: *If your baby seems ready to start taking solids at around four to five months old, start with a teaspoon and build gradually to two and finally three meals a day.*

**Baby rice**

**Apple**

**Swede (rutabaga)**

**Pear**

**Potato**

**Carrot**

**Parsnip**

## FOODS TO AVOID

- highly spiced foods
- salt as this causes the kidneys to overwork. Avoid seasoning with salt or adding stock cubes, bacon and salami to foods
- cows' milk (give breast or formula milk feeds instead)
- foods containing gluten, found in wheat, oats, rye and barley (check pack labels)
- eggs
- meat, fish, poultry
- citrus and berry fruits – can result in allergic reactions in some babies
- nuts, either whole or ground
- honey
- fatty foods

Right: *Adult favourites – but these must be avoided at this age, even as treats.*

Note: If you have a family history of allergies, your doctor or health visitor may also advise you to avoid other foods. Check with them.

Above: *A world of foodstuffs opens up over the months: but introduce them gradually, and at the right time.*

# Baby Rice

Mix 5-15ml/1-3 tsp rice with cooled boiled water, formula or breast milk as the pack directs. Cool slightly and test before serving.

Left: *Plain baby rice will be the staple for your baby for the first few weeks of solids – then gradually add flavour and variation.*

# Vegetable Purées

**Makes: 175ml/6fl oz/¾ cup**

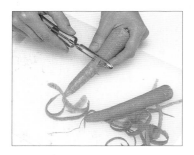

1 Peel 125g/3½oz potato, parsnip, carrot or swede (rutabaga) and chop into small dice.

2 Steam over a pan of boiling water for 10 minutes, until soft.

3 Press through a sieve (strainer), mix with 60–75ml/4–5 tbsp formula or breast milk, depending on the vegetable used. Spoon a little into a bowl, test on a spoon and cool if needed. Cover the remaining purée and transfer to the refrigerator as soon as possible. Use within 24 hours.

• **To microwave**: put the vegetable or vegetables in a microwave-proof bowl with 30ml/2 tbsp formula or breast milk. Cover with clear film (plastic wrap), pierce and cook on Full Power (100%) for 4 minutes. Leave to stand for 5 minutes, then press through a sieve (strainer) and mix with 30–45ml/2–3 tbsp formula or breast milk. Cool and serve as above.

# Fruit Purées

**Makes: 120ml/4fl oz/¹/₂ cup**

1 Peel, quarter and core 1 dessert apple or 1 ripe pear.

2 Thinly slice and put in a small pan with 15ml/1 tbsp water, formula or breast milk.Cover and simmer for 10 minutes, until soft.

• **To microwave:** place the apple or pear in a microwave-proof bowl with water, formula or breast milk. Cover with clear film (plastic wrap), pierce and cook on Full Power (100%) for 3 minutes. Leave to stand for 5 minutes, then press through a sieve (strainer). Cool and serve as above.

3 Press through a sieve (strainer). Spoon a little purée into a serving bowl, test on a spoon and cool if needed. Cover, transfer to the refrigerator, and use within 24 hours.

Top: *Pear and apple purée (top) will bring a smile to any baby's face (above).*

# STAGE 2: AROUND SIX TO SIX-AND-A-HALF MONTHS

IF YOU BEGIN WEANING AT SIX MONTHS, START WITH BABY RICE AND RUNNY VEGETABLE AND FRUIT PURÉE. IF YOU HAVE ALREADY INTRODUCED YOUR BABY TO SOLIDS, INCREASE THE VARIETY OF FOODS OFFERED AND START TO COMBINE FOOD TASTES. PURÉE CAN BE A THICKER COARSER TEXTURE, BUT MAKE SURE THERE ARE NO PIPS (SEEDS) OR BONES. ALWAYS CHOOSE THE BEST, FRESHEST INGREDIENTS AND MAKE SURE UTENSILS ARE SCRUPULOUSLY CLEAN.

## Suitable Foods

**FOODS TO INCLUDE**
● wide selection of vegetables, including fresh or frozen peas, corn, cauliflower, broccoli, cabbage, spinach, celery, mushrooms and leeks
● fruits – banana, apricots, peaches, plums, strawberries, raspberries, melon (Warning: offer tiny amounts of soft berry fruits as some children may be allergic to them.)
● chicken
● mild-tasting fresh or frozen fish – plaice, cod, haddock, trout
● small quantities of very lean red meat
● small quantities of split peas and red lentils, and very well-cooked or canned whole chickpeas and beans
● gluten-free cereals – rice, cornflour (cornstarch)

Celery

Mixed vegetables

Cabbage

Broccoli

Spinach

Corn

Fish

Chicken

Lean red meat

Plums

Apricots

Banana

Melon

Above: *Every day brings a new taste:*
*these young gourmets can't wait!*

**Chickpeas**

**Cocoa**

**Split peas**

**Cornflour
(cornstarch)**

**Lentils**

**Rice**

## FOODS TO AVOID
- gluten-based cereals, wheat flour and bread
- cow's milk and milk products
- eggs
- citrus and berry fruits
- nuts, ground or whole
- honey
- fatty foods
- salt and highly spiced foods

Below: *Even healthy adult foods such*
*as wholewheat bread and oranges should*
*be avoided.*

# Going Vegetarian

A vegetarian diet can provide all the necessary nutrients for health and vitality, but it is important to balance the baby's diet to ensure that she receives adequate supplies of protein, vitamins D and B12, calcium and iron.

The basic guidelines are the same as for weaning any other baby: introduce flavours slowly and be guided by your baby. The biggest differences are obviously in the type of foods offered. Instead of obtaining protein from meat and fish, your baby will receive it from other protein-rich food. These include eggs, beans, peas, split lentils, and grains, finely ground nuts or nut creams, sunflower seed spread, milk and dairy products, and vegetarian cheese where available.

Vegetarians need to make sure that sufficient iron is included in their baby's diet. If she is over six months, offer prune juice, puréed apricots, molasses, refined lentils and cereals, particularly fortified breakfast cereals. Green vegetables and well-mashed beans, if over eight months, are also a good source of iron. Vitamin C aids the absorption of iron from plant sources, so make sure you serve fresh green vegetables or fruit in the meal. Your doctor may also think it is beneficial for your baby to take vitamin drops.

If you plan to bring the baby up as a vegan and so omit dairy products and eggs from the diet, then it is vital to consult your doctor or dietician.

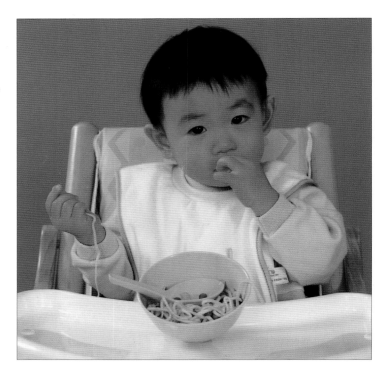

Vegetarian diets tend to be bulky and lower in calories than a diet containing meat, so make sure you include foods that are protein and calorie rich, with little or no fibre, such as eggs, milk and cheese. These can be mixed with smaller quantities of vegetables, fruit and cereals. Fibre-rich foods can also be difficult for a child to digest as many nutrients

Above: *Raising your child as a vegetarian takes special planning and care to make sure all the necessary nutrients are included.*

may pass straight through the body. To ensure your baby is getting the correct amount of vitamins, minerals and food energy her diet should include foods from the four groups on the opposite page.

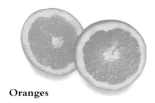

**Oranges**

**Carrots**

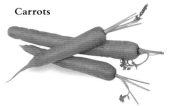

**Cucumber**

**Grapes**

**Cereals and grains:** baby rice no earlier than 17 weeks; pasta, bread, oats and breakfast cereals from 6 months.

**Fruit and vegetables:** begin with potato, carrot, apple and pear at 6 to 6½ months, progressing to stronger-flavoured foods such as broccoli, beans, oranges and plums as your baby develops.

**Dairy produce:** including milk, cheese, fromage frais and yogurt from 6 months.
*Note:* Make sure cheese is rennet-free. If you are unsure, ask the delicatessen assistant, or check the packet if pre-packed.

**Beans, peas and lentils:** split and softly cooked lentils from 6–6½ months. Gradual introduction of tofu, smooth peanut butter, hard-boiled egg from 6 months. Well-cooked, mashed dried beans and peas and finely ground nuts from nine months. Do not give whole nuts to the under-fives.

To make sure your baby is thriving and happy, irrespective of the type of diet, make sure you check your baby's weight at regular intervals at the health clinic.

**Baby dhal**

**Split peas**

**Lentils**

# Autumn Harvest

**Makes: 600ml/1 pint/2½ cups**

115g/4oz carrot

115g/4oz parsnip

115g/4oz swede (rutabaga)

115g/4oz potato

300ml/½ pint/1¼ cups formula milk

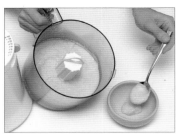

1 Trim and peel the carrot, parsnip, swede and potato, and place in a colander. Rinse under cold water, drain and chop.

2 Place the chopped vegetables in a pan with the formula milk, then bring to the boil, cover and simmer for 20 minutes, or until they are very soft.

3 Purée, mash or sieve (strain) the vegetables until they are smooth.

4 Spoon a little into a bowl. Test the temperature and cool if necessary, before giving to the baby.

5 Cover the remaining food and transfer to the refrigerator as soon as possible. Use within 24 hours.

- Suitable for freezing.

**TIP**

Thin the purée down with a little extra formula milk if your baby prefers a very soft purée.

# Mixed Vegetable Platter

**Makes: 600ml/1 pint/2½ cups**

115g/4oz carrot

175g/6oz potato

115g/4oz broccoli

50g/2oz green cabbage

300ml/½ pint/1¼ cups formula milk

1 Peel the carrot and potato. Rinse, chop and place in a pan. Wash the broccoli and cabbage and cut the broccoli into florets and the stems into thin slices. Shred the cabbage finely.

2 Add the milk to the carrot and potato, bring to the boil, then cover and simmer for 10 minutes.

3 Add the broccoli stems and florets and cabbage, and cook, covered, for 10 minutes, until all the vegetables are tender.

4 Purée, mash or sieve (strain) the vegetables until smooth.

5 Spoon a little into a bowl. Test the temperature and cool if necessary, before giving to the baby.

6 Cover the remaining food and transfer to the refrigerator as soon as possible. Use within 24 hours.

• Suitable for freezing.

# Carrot, Lentil and Coriander Purée

**Makes: 600ml/1 pint/2½ cups**

350g/12oz carrots

175g/6oz potato

50g/2oz/¼ cup red lentils

2.5ml/½ tsp ground coriander

300ml/½ pint/1¼ cups formula milk

1 Trim and peel the carrots and potatoes and then chop into small cubes and place in a pan. Rinse the lentils thoroughly, discarding any black bits.

2 Add the lentils, coriander and milk to the pan and bring to the boil, then cover and simmer for 40 minutes, until the lentils are very soft. Top up with a little extra boiling water if necessary.

**TIP**

The mixture thickens on cooling so any remaining mixture will need to be thinned slightly with a little formula milk before reheating for the next meal.

3 Purée, mash or sieve (strain) the mixture until smooth.

4 Spoon a little into a bowl. Test the temperature and cool if necessary, before giving to the baby.

5 Cover the remaining purée and transfer to the refrigerator as soon as possible. Use within 24 hours.

• Suitable for freezing.

# Red Pepper Risotto

**Makes: 600ml/1 pint/2½ cups**

50g/2oz/¼ cup long grain rice

300ml/½ pint/1¼ cups formula milk

75g/3oz red (bell) pepper

75g/3oz courgette (zucchini)

50g/2oz celery

**1** Place the rice and milk in a pan, bring to the boil and simmer, uncovered, for 5 minutes.

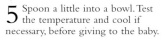

**2** Discard the core and seeds from the pepper and trim the courgette and celery. Place the vegetables in a colander and rinse under cold water, then chop them into small pieces.

**3** Add the vegetables to the rice mixture, bring to the boil, cover and simmer for about 10 minutes, or until the rice is soft.

• Suitable for freezing.

**4** Purée, mash or sieve (strain) the rice mixture until smooth.

**5** Spoon a little into a bowl. Test the temperature and cool if necessary, before giving to the baby.

**6** Cover the remaining food and transfer to the refrigerator as soon as possible. Use within 24 hours.

# Parsnip and Broccoli Mix

**Makes: 600ml/1 pint/2½ cups**

225g/8oz parsnips

115g/4oz broccoli

300ml/½ pint/1¼ cups formula milk

**1** Trim and peel the parsnips and place in a colander with the broccoli. Rinse the parsnips and broccoli under cold water. Chop the parsnips and cut the broccoli into florets, slicing the stems.

**2** Put the parsnips in a pan with the milk, bring to the boil, then cover and simmer for about 10 minutes.

**3** Add the broccoli and simmer for a further 10 minutes, until the vegetables are soft.

**4** Purée, mash or sieve (strain) the vegetable mixture to make a completely smooth purée.

**5** Spoon a little into a bowl. Test the temperature and cool if necessary, before giving to the baby.

**6** Cover the remaining purée and transfer to the refrigerator as soon as possible. Use within 24 hours.

• Suitable for freezing.

# Turkey Stew with Carrots and Corn

**Makes: 600ml/1 pint/2½ cups**

175g/6oz potato

175g/6oz carrot

115g/4oz turkey breast, skinned and boned

50g/2oz/⅓ cup frozen corn

300ml/½ pint/1¼ cups formula milk

1 Trim and peel the potato and carrots, rinse under cold water and then chop into small cubes.

2 Rinse the turkey and cut into thin strips. Place in a small pan with the potato and carrot.

**TIP**
Bring the mixture to the boil in a flameproof casserole and transfer to a preheated oven 180°C/350°F/ Gas 4 and cook for 1¼ hours if preferred.

3 Add the corn and milk. Cover and simmer for 20 minutes, until the turkey is cooked. Purée, mash or sieve (strain) the mixture until smooth.

4 Spoon a little into a bowl. Test the temperature and cool if necessary, before giving to the baby.

5 Cover the remaining food and refrigerate. Use within 24 hours.

• Suitable for freezing.

# Chicken and Parsnip Purée

**Makes: 600ml/1 pint/2½ cups**

350g/12oz parsnips

115g/4oz chicken breast, skinned and boned

300ml/½ pint/1¼ cups formula milk

1 Peel the parsnips, and trim the woody tops and bottoms. Rinse and chop roughly.

2 Rinse the chicken under cold water and cut into small pieces.

3 Place the parsnips, chicken and milk in a pan. Cover and simmer for 20 minutes, or until the parsnips are tender.

4 Purée, mash or sieve (strain) the mixture until smooth.

5 Spoon into a bowl. Test the temperature and cool if necessary, before giving to the baby.

6 Cover the remaining purée and transfer to the refrigerator as soon as possible. Use within 24 hours.

- Suitable for freezing.

**TIP**
For a very smooth purée, drain all the liquid into a liquidizer and add half the solids, blend until smooth, then add the remaining ingredients. If using a food processor, add all the solids and a little liquid, process until smooth, then add the remaining liquid.

# Cock-a-Leekie Casserole

**Makes: 600ml/1 pint/2½ cups**

50g/2oz leek

275g/10oz potatoes

115g/4oz chicken breast, skinned
  and boned

300ml/½ pint/1¼ cups formula milk

1 Halve the leek lengthways and
rinse under running water to
remove any dirt or grit.

2 Peel potatoes and cut into small
dice. Rinse the chicken and cut
into pieces and thinly slice the leek.

3 Place the vegetables and chicken
in a pan with the milk.

4 Bring the mixture to the boil,
cover with a lid and simmer
gently for 20 minutes, until the
potatoes are just tender. Purée, mash
or sieve (strain) the mixture until it is
completely smooth.

5 Spoon a little into a bowl. Test
the temperature and cool if
necessary, before giving to the baby.
Use within 24 hours.

• Suitable for freezing.

**TIP**
You can vary the texture of this
recipe depending on how you
purée the mixture. A fine sieve
(strainer) produces the finest
consistency, then a food processor,
while a food mill gives the coarsest
texture. Starchy vegetables thicken
the purée and bind it together. Any
root vegetable can be used for this
recipe, but make sure it is
thoroughly cooked before blending.

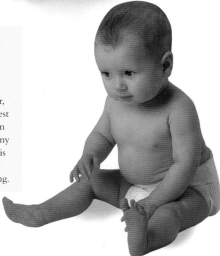

# Trout and Courgette Savoury

**Makes: 600ml/1 pint/2½ cups**

275g/10oz potatoes

175g/6oz courgettes (zucchini)

115g/4oz pink trout fillet

250ml/8fl oz/1 cup formula milk

1 Peel the potatoes, trim the courgettes and rinse under cold water. Dice the potatoes and cut the courgettes into slices.

2 Place the vegetables in a pan. Rinse the trout and arrange on top, then pour over the milk. Bring to the boil, cover and simmer for 15 minutes, until the potatoes and fish are cooked.

3 Lift the trout out of the pan and peel off the skin. Break it into pieces with a knife and fork, checking carefully for any bones.

4 Purée, mash or sieve (strain) the fish, the vegetables and the liquid until quite smooth.

5 Spoon a little into a bowl. Test the temperature and cool if necessary, before giving to the baby.

6 Cover any remaining food and transfer to the refrigerator as soon as possible. Use within 24 hours.

- Suitable for freezing.

# Fisherman's Pie

**Makes: 600ml/1 pint/2½ cups**

350g/12oz potatoes

90g/3½oz brick frozen skinless cod

25g/1oz/¼ cup frozen peas

25g/1oz/2 tbsp frozen corn

300ml/½ pint/1¼ cups formula milk

1 Peel and rinse the potatoes and cut into even pieces. Place in a pan with the fish, peas, corn and milk.

2 Bring to the boil, cover and simmer for 15 minutes, until the potatoes are very tender.

3 Lift the fish out of the pan and break into pieces with a knife and fork, checking carefully and removing any small bones.

4 Purée, mash or sieve (strain) the fish, vegetables and cooking liquid until completely smooth.

5 Spoon a little into a bowl. Test the temperature and cool if necessary, before giving to the baby.

6 Cover the remaining purée and place in the refrigerator as soon as possible. Use within 24 hours.

• Suitable for freezing.

# Apple Ambrosia

**Makes: 300ml/½ pint/1¼ cups**

1 eating apple

25g/1oz flaked rice

300ml/½ pint/1¼ cups formula milk

1 Quarter, core and peel the apple. Slice thinly and place in a pan with the rice and milk.

2 Bring to the boil then simmer over a gentle heat for 10–12 minutes, until the rice is soft, stirring occasionally with a wooden spoon.

4 Spoon into a bowl. Test the temperature and cool if necessary, before giving to the baby. Cover the remaining purée and transfer to the refrigerator as soon as possible. Use within 24 hours.

**VARIATION**
**Chocolate Pudding**
Cook the rice as above but without the apple. Stir 25g/1oz milk chocolate dots and 15ml/1 tbsp caster (superfine) sugar into the hot rice and then purée or mash until smooth. Spoon into small dishes and cool as necessary.

3 Purée or mash the apple and rice mixture until completely smooth.

# Fruit Salad Purée

**Makes: 350ml/12fl oz/1½ cups**

1 nectarine or peach

1 dessert apple

1 ripe pear

25g/1oz fresh or frozen raspberries
  or strawberries

1 Halve the nectarine or peach,
discard the stone (pit), then peel
and chop. Peel, quarter and core the
apple and pear and slice thinly.

2 Put the prepared fruits, the hulled
raspberries or strawberries and
15ml/1 tbsp water in a pan. Cover
and simmer for 10 minutes, until the
fruit is soft.

3 Press the mixture through a
sieve (strainer) or process and then
sieve (strain) to remove the berry pips
(seeds). Discard the pips.

4 Spoon a little into a baby bowl.
Test the temperature and cool if
necessary, before giving to the baby.

5 Cover the remaining purée and
transfer to the refrigerator as soon
as possible. Use within 24 hours.

• Suitable for freezing.

**TIP**
Babies tend to eat smaller
quantities of dessert, so it is best
to open freeze purée in a sterilized
ice cube tray. Transfer the cubes
to a plastic bag once frozen.

**VARIATION**
**Peach and Melon Blush**
To make 175ml/6fl oz/¾ cup, take
1 ripe peach and ¼ ripe Charentais
melon. Peel and halve the peach,
discard the stone (pit) and cut up
the fruit. Scoop the seeds out of the
melon and cut away the skin.
Roughly chop the melon into pieces.
  Purée or sieve (strain) the fruit until
completely smooth. Spoon a little
into a bowl and serve.

# Stage 3: Seven to Nine Months

From seven to nine months is a rapid development period for your baby. By eight months, babies are usually quite good at holding things, so let your baby hold a second spoon while you are feeding her, to help develop co-ordination. This is the first step towards self-feeding. All the recipes from the previous section can still be made for your growing baby; just adjust the texture so that foods are slightly coarser.

## Suitable Foods

### FOODS TO INCLUDE
- wheat-based foods, pasta, bread – first fingers (thin slices) of toast or bread sticks
- breakfast cereals such as those made up with cows' milk
- cow's milk and dairy foods, e.g. yogurt, cottage cheese, mild Cheddar and Edam cheese
- red meat, but make sure you trim off fat and gristle
- hard-boiled egg yolk
- citrus fruits
- fingers of cooked carrot, broccoli
- smooth peanut butter

Breakfast cereal

Breakfast cereal

Mild cheeses

Yogurt

Lean red meat

Cottage cheese

Pasta

Bread

Cooked egg yolk

Citrus fruit

Peanut butter

Fish

Broccoli and carrot

Above: *From seven to nine months your baby will develop rapidly.*

**FOODS TO AVOID**
- egg white
- whole or chopped nuts
- canned fish in brine
- organ meats – liver, kidney
- chillies and other very spicy foods
- salty foods
- sugary foods

Right: *There is still a wide range of fatty, salty and spicy foods that must be avoided.*

# Shepherd's Pie

**Makes: 600ml/1 pint/2½ cups**

| |
|---|
| 2 tomatoes |
| ¼ onion |
| 225g/8oz potato |
| 50g/2oz button (white) mushrooms |
| 115g/4oz lean minced (ground) beef |
| 250ml/8fl oz/1 cup water |
| 15ml/1 tbsp tomato ketchup |
| pinch of dried mixed herbs |

4 Add the tomatoes, potato, mushrooms and onion and cook for a further 3 minutes. Stir well to blend all the flavours together.

5 Add the water, ketchup and herbs. Bring to the boil, then reduce the heat, cover and simmer for 40 minutes, until the meat and vegetables are tender.

6 Process or mash the meat and vegetables just enough to give the desired consistency.

7 Spoon a little into a bowl. Test the temperature and cool if necessary, before giving to the baby.

8 Cover the remainder and refrigerate. Use within 24 hours.

1 Make a cross cut in each tomato, put in a small bowl and cover with boiling water. Leave to stand for 1 minute and then drain and peel off the skins. Cut into quarters and scoop out the seeds.

2 Finely chop the onion, chop the potato and slice the mushrooms.

3 Dry-fry the beef in a pan for 5 minutes, stirring until browned all over.

• Suitable for freezing.

# Braised Beef and Carrots

**Makes: 600ml/1 pint/2½ cups**

175g/6oz potato

225g/8oz carrots

¼ onion

175g/6oz stewing beef

300ml/½ pint/1¼ cups water

pinch of dried mixed herbs

1 Preheat the oven to 180°C/ 350°F/Gas 4. Peel and chop the potato, carrots and onion, and place in a flameproof casserole.

2 Rinse the beef, cut away any fat and gristle and cut into small cubes using a sharp knife.

3 Add the meat, water and herbs to the casserole, bring to the boil and then cover and cook in the oven for 1½ hours, or until the meat is tender and the vegetables are soft.

4 Process or mash the ingredients to the desired consistency and spoon a little into a bowl. Test the temperature and cool if necessary, before giving to the baby.

5 Cover any unused food and transfer to the refrigerator as soon as possible. Use within 24 hours.

• Suitable for freezing.

**TIP**
Replace the carrots with any other root vegetable, such as parsnip or swede (rutabaga), if wished.

# Lamb Hotpot

**Makes: 600ml/1 pint/2½ cups**

115g/4oz potato

115g/4oz carrot

115g/4oz swede (rutabaga)

50g/2oz leek

115g/4oz lamb fillet

300ml/½ pint/1¼ cup water

pinch of dried rosemary

1 Peel the potato, carrot and swede, then rinse and chop into small cubes. Halve the leek lengthways, rinse well and slice. Place all the vegetables in a pan.

2 Rinse the lamb under cold water and chop into small pieces, discarding any fat.

3 Add the meat to the pan with the water and rosemary. Bring to the boil, cover and simmer for 30 minutes or until the lamb is thoroughly cooked.

4 Process or mash the ingredients to the desired consistency.

5 Spoon a little into a bowl, test the temperature and cool if necessary, before giving to the baby.

6 Cover the remaining food and transfer to the refrigerator as soon as possible. Use within 24 hours.

• Suitable for freezing.

# Lamb and Lentil Savoury

**Makes: 600ml/1 pint/2½ cups**

115g/4oz lamb fillet

115g/4oz swede (rutabaga)

1 celery stick

25g/1oz/2 tbsp red lentils

15ml/1 tbsp tomato ketchup

350ml/12fl oz/1½ cups water

**1** Rinse the lamb under cold water, trim off any fat and chop into small pieces. Peel the swede, place in a colander with the celery and rinse with cold water. Chop into cubes and place in a pan.

**2** Put the lentils in a sieve (strainer) and rinse under cold water, picking out any black bits. Add to the pan with the lamb and ketchup.

**3** Add the water and bring to the boil, then cover and simmer for 40 minutes, or until the lentils are soft. Top up with extra water during cooking if necessary, then process or mash just enough to give the desired consistency.

**4** Spoon a little into a bowl, test the temperature and cool if necessary, before giving to the baby.

**5** Cover the remaining food and transfer to the refrigerator as soon as possible. Use within 24 hours.

● Suitable for freezing.

**VARIATION**

Substitute green lentils or split peas for the red lentils and a small courgette (zucchini) for the celery stick.

# Country Pork and Runner Beans

**Makes: 450ml/³⁄₄ pint/1⁷⁄₈ cups**

115g/4oz lean pork

115g/4oz potato

115g/4oz carrot

75g/3oz runner (green) beans

pinch of dried sage

350ml/12fl oz/1½ cups water

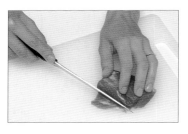

1 Rinse the pork under cold water, trim away any fat and gristle and chop into small cubes.

2 Peel the potato and carrot, trim the beans, rinse and chop.

**TIPS**

If runner beans are unavailable use French (green) beans, sugar snap peas or broccoli. Look out for ready-prepared diced pork in the supermarket. Cut into smaller pieces and be sure to remove any gristle before cooking.

3 Put the pork, potato and carrot in a pan with the sage and water. Bring to the boil, cover and simmer for 30 minutes.

4 Add the beans and cook, covered, for a further 10 minutes, until all the vegetables are tender.

5 Process or mash to the desired consistency, then spoon a little into a bowl. Test the temperature before giving to the baby.

6 Cover and transfer the remaining food to the refrigerator. Use within 24 hours.

• Suitable for freezing.

**VARIATION**

Instead of the pork, use any lean meat in this recipe, such as chicken or turkey. Add broad (fava) beans, with the outer skin removed, in place of the runner beans.

# Pork and Apple Savoury

**Makes: 600ml/1 pint/2½ cups**

| |
|---|
| 175g/6oz lean pork |
| 175g/6oz potato |
| 175g/6oz swede (rutabaga) or parsnip |
| ¼ onion |
| ½ eating apple |
| 300ml/½ pint/1¼ cups water |
| pinch of dried sage |

1 Preheat the oven to 180°C/ 350°F/Gas 4. Rinse the pork under cold water, trim away any fat and gristle, then chop. Peel and chop the vegetables. Peel, core and chop the apple.

2 Put the meat, vegetables, apple, water and sage in a flameproof casserole, cover and bring to the boil, stirring once or twice.

3 Cover and cook in the oven for 1¼ hours, until the meat is tender, then process or mash to the desired consistency.

4 Spoon a little into a bowl, test the temperature and cool if necessary, before giving to the baby.

5 Cover the remaining food and transfer to the refrigerator as soon as possible. Use within 24 hours.

• Suitable for freezing.

**TIP**
The mixture can be cooked in a pan on the stove for 40 minutes, if preferred.

# Nursery Kedgeree

**Makes: 600ml/1 pint/2½ cups**

50g/2oz/¼ cup long grain rice

25g/1oz/2 tbsp frozen peas

350ml/12fl oz/1½ cups formula milk

90g/3¼oz brick frozen skinless cod

2 hard-boiled egg yolks

**1** Place the rice, peas, milk and fish in a pan, bring to the boil, cover and simmer for 15 minutes, until the fish is cooked and the rice is soft.

**2** Lift the fish out of the pan and break into pieces with a knife and fork, checking for bones.

**3** Stir the fish into the rice mixture and add the egg yolks.

**4** Mash with a fork to the desired consistency. Alternatively blend in a food processor or liquidizer, or press through a sieve (strainer).

**5** Spoon a little into a bowl, test the temperature and cool if necessary, before giving to the baby.

**6** Cover the remaining kedgeree and transfer to the refrigerator as soon as possible. Use within 24 hours.

- Suitable for freezing.

**TIP**

Peas can be quite difficult to mash down. Check before giving to the baby as whole peas are difficult for her to chew.

# Mediterranean Vegetables

**Makes: 600ml/1 pint/2½ cups**

3 tomatoes

175g/6oz courgettes (zucchini)

75g/3oz button (white) mushrooms

115g/4oz red (bell) pepper

20ml/4 tsp tomato ketchup

250ml/8fl oz/1 cup water

pinch of dried mixed herbs

40g/1½oz dried pasta shapes

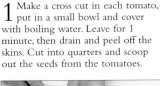

**1** Make a cross cut in each tomato, put in a small bowl and cover with boiling water. Leave for 1 minute, then drain and peel off the skins. Cut into quarters and scoop out the seeds from the tomatoes.

**2** Trim the courgette and mushrooms and cut away the core and seeds from the pepper.

**TIP**
For adventurous eaters add ½ clove crushed garlic at Step 3.

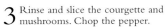

**3** Rinse and slice the courgette and mushrooms. Chop the pepper.

**4** Put the vegetables in a pan with the ketchup, water and herbs. Cover and simmer for 10 minutes, or until tender.

**5** Meanwhile cook the pasta in boiling water for 8–10 minutes, until tender. Drain.

**6** Mix the vegetables and pasta together and process or mash.

**7** Spoon a little into a bowl, test the temperature and cool if necessary, before giving to the baby.

**8** Cover remaining mixture and refrigerate. Use within 24 hours.

- Suitable for freezing.

# Pasta with Sauce

**Makes: 600ml/1 pint/2½ cups**

115g/4oz carrot

50g/2oz Brussels sprouts

25g/1oz green beans

25g/1oz/2 tbsp frozen corn

50g/2oz dried pasta shapes

350ml/12fl oz/1½ cups formula milk

50g/2oz Cheddar or mild cheese

1 Peel the carrot, discard any discoloured outer leaves from the sprouts and trim the beans. Rinse and then chop into pieces.

2 Place the prepared vegetables, corn, pasta and milk in a pan, bring to the boil and then simmer, uncovered, for 12-15 minutes, until the pasta is cooked.

**TIP**

Vary the vegetables depending on what you have in the refrigerator.

3 Grate the cheese and add to the vegetables, stirring until the cheese has completely melted.

4 Process or mash just enough to give the desired consistency, then spoon a little into a bowl. Test the temperature and cool if necessary, before giving to the baby.

5 Cover the remaining food and transfer to the refrigerator as soon as possible. Use within 24 hours.

• Suitable for freezing.

# Apple and Orange Fool

**Makes: 250ml/8fl oz/1 cup**

2 eating apples

5ml/1 tsp grated orange rind and
  15ml/1 tbsp orange juice

15ml/1 tbsp custard powder

5ml/1 tsp caster (superfine) sugar

150ml/¼ pint/⅔ cup formula milk

1 Quarter, core and peel the apples. Slice and place the apples in a pan with the orange rind and juice.

2 Cover and cook gently for 10 minutes, stirring occasionally until the apples are soft.

3 Blend the custard powder and sugar with a little of the milk to make a smooth paste. Bring the remaining milk to the boil and stir into the custard mixture.

4 Return the custard to the pan and slowly bring to the boil, stirring until thickened and smooth.

5 Process or mash the apple to the desired consistency. Add the custard and stir to mix.

6 Spoon a little into a bowl, test the temperature and cool if necessary, before giving to the baby.

7 Cover the remaining fool and transfer to the refrigerator as soon as possible. Use within 24 hours.

• Suitable for freezing.

# Orchard Fruit Dessert

**Makes: 450ml/³⁄₄ pint/1⁷⁄₈ cups**

1 ripe pear

225g/8oz ripe plums

15ml/1 tbsp caster (superfine) sugar

15ml/1 tbsp custard powder

150ml/¹⁄₄ pint/²⁄₃ cup formula milk

1 Quarter, core, peel and slice the pear. Wash the plums, then cut in half, stone (pit) and slice.

2 Put the fruit in a pan with 15ml/1 tbsp water and 10ml/2 tsp of the sugar. Cover and cook gently for 10 minutes, until soft.

3 Blend the custard powder, remaining sugar and a little of the milk to make a smooth paste.

4 Bring the remaining milk to the boil and gradually stir into the custard mixture. Pour the custard back into the pan and bring to the boil, stirring, until it is both thickened and smooth.

5 Process or mash the fruit to the desired consistency and stir in the custard. Spoon a little into a bowl, test the temperature and cool if necessary, before giving to the baby.

6 Cover the remaining custard and transfer to the refrigerator as soon as possible. Use within 24 hours.

- Suitable for freezing.

# Peach Melba Dessert

**Makes: 175ml/6fl oz/³⁄₄ cup**

1 ripe peach

25g/1oz fresh or frozen raspberries

15ml/1 tbsp icing (confectioners') sugar

115g/4oz Greek (US strained plain) yogurt

1 Halve the peach, discard the stone (pit), then peel and slice. Place in a pan with the raspberries and 15ml/1 tbsp water.

2 Cover and cook gently for 10 minutes, until soft.

3 Purée and press through a sieve (strainer) to remove the raspberry pips (seeds).

**TIP**
The finished dessert is not suitable for freezing, but the sweetened fruit purée can be frozen in sections of an ice-cube tray. Defrost cubes of purée and mix each cube with 15ml/1 tbsp yogurt.

4 Set aside to cool, then stir in the sugar and swirl in the yogurt. Spoon a little into a baby dish.

5 Cover the remaining dessert and transfer to the refrigerator. Use within 24 hours.

**VARIATION**
**Bananarama**
To make a single portion, use ½ a small banana and 15ml/1 tbsp of Greek (US strained plain) yogurt. Mash the banana until smooth and add the yogurt. Stir to mix and serve immediately. Do not make this dessert in advance, as the banana will discolour while standing.

# STAGE 4: NINE TO TWELVE MONTHS

GRADUALLY PROGRESS FROM MINCED (GROUND) TO CHOPPED OR ROUGHLY MASHED FOOD. BY NOW YOUR BABY WILL BE ABLE TO JOIN IN WITH FAMILY MEALS AND EAT A LITTLE OF WHAT YOU ARE EATING. ENSURE THAT YOUR BABY IS EATING THREE MAIN MEALS AND TWO TO THREE SNACK MEALS PER DAY. YOUNG CHILDREN DEVELOP AT AN INCREDIBLY FAST RATE AND SO NEED TO EAT LITTLE AND OFTEN TO SUSTAIN ENERGY AND GROWTH LEVELS. AGAIN, FOODS FROM THE PREVIOUS SECTIONS CAN STILL BE SERVED TO YOUR BABY; JUST ADJUST THE TEXTURES AS NECESSARY.

## Suitable Foods

**FOODS TO INCLUDE**
- whole eggs
- finely ground nuts
- more flavourings – stock (bouillon) cubes if part of a family-size casserole
- greater selection of finger foods – slices of peeled fruit (such as dessert apple or pear), raw carrot and cucumber sticks, small squares of cooked chicken
- selection of foods from the four main food groups – carbohydrates (cereals, bread, potatoes, rice, pasta); fruit and vegetables; protein (meat, poultry, fish, eggs, beans, peas, lentils, tofu, nuts); milk and milk products (cheese, yogurt, butter).

**Apple, carrot and cucumber**

**Ground nuts**

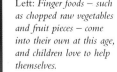

**Whole egg**

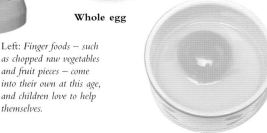

Left: *Finger foods – such as chopped raw vegetables and fruit pieces – come into their own at this age, and children love to help themselves.*

Above and below right: *Active children develop at a fast rate and need to eat little and often to sustain their energy levels.*

Below: *Though now a very small list, there are still some foods it is important to omit.*

**FOODS TO AVOID**
- keep salt to a minimum and omit if possible
- sugar: add just enough to make the food appetizing without being overly sweet
- honey

- fat: trim visible fat off raw meat, grill rather than fry
- organ meats – liver, kidney

# I can feed myself!

Encouraging your baby to feed herself can be a truly messy business. Some babies are interested from a very early age, and those little fingers seem to move like lightning grabbing the bowl or the spoon you're using to feed them with. Give your baby a second spoon to play with, leaving you more able to spoon in the lunch.

As your baby grows, offer her a few finger foods to hold and hopefully eat, while you continue to feed from a spoon. Cooked carrot sticks, broccoli and cauliflower florets are soft on a young mouth and easy to chew. As your baby grows, you can introduce bread sticks and toast fingers.

Encourage your baby to pick up foods, and as her co-ordination improves and she gets the idea, more food will actually go where it is intended. Try to cut down on the mess by rolling up your baby's sleeves and covering clothes with a large bib, preferably with sleeves.

Above: *A bib with sleeves.*

Remove any hair bands and have a wet flannel at the ready.

Although it is tempting not to allow a baby to feed herself, try not to be frustrated by the mess. Babies that are encouraged to feed themselves will probably be more adventurous later on, and you will probably find there is less mess than with a baby who is always spoon fed

## TEACHING YOUR BABY TO FEED HIMSELF

1 Cover your baby well – this can be very messy! Give him a spoon of his own to play with.

2 While you are feeding your baby, allow him to play with the food – with his hands or the spoon.

3 Let your baby use the cup and spoon by himself. Don't worry about spillage – there are bound to be lots of slips at this stage.

4 Keep tissues or a damp flannel available and clean as you go. Be patient and take things slowly.

and keeps grabbing at the bowl. In addition, she will be able to join in your family meals and also give you the chance to eat your own meal before it gets cold.

### WHAT TO DO IF YOUR CHILD CHOKES

- Don't waste time trying to remove food from your baby's mouth unless it can be done easily.
- Turn your baby, head down, supporting her head with your forearm and slap firmly between the shoulder blades.
- If this does not work, try again.
- Don't hesitate to ring your doctor or emergency services if worried.

Above: *Don't be afraid to take quick, firm action in an emergency.*

### COPING WITH THE MESS

As babies grow so too does the amount of mess! It is incredible how just a few tablespoons of lunch can be spread across so many surfaces and so many items of clothing.

- Choose a large bib. Fabric bibs with a plastic liner are the most comfortable for babies to wear when tiny, moving on to a plastic pelican-style bib to catch food as they grow older. Check the back of your baby's neck as these can rub.

Above: *A hard plastic "pelican" bib.*

- If you plan to feed your baby in the dining room, then protect the carpet with an old sheet, pieces of newspaper, or a plastic tablecloth or groundsheet. It is vital to take this with you if visiting friends.
- Give your baby a second spoon or small toy to play with so that she doesn't try to grab the laden spoon that you are holding.

Left: *It is a real delight when your baby can begin to eat independently. Not only can you start to eat with your baby, and relax a little more, but he will also enjoy setting his own pace and eating his meal in the order he chooses. At this stage, the family can usually return to eating together around the table as a group.*

Above: *A plastic tablecloth or groundsheet on the floor will prevent carpet stains.*

## FINGER FOODS

Finger foods are not only fun to eat but help your baby's co-ordination. Snacks play an important part in a young child's diet as appetites may be small, but energy and growth needs are great. Choose foods that are nutrient dense and avoid sweet sugary snacks such as chocolate biscuits (cookies).

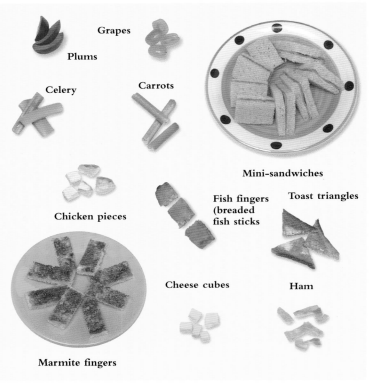

Grapes

Plums

Celery

Carrots

Mini-sandwiches

Chicken pieces

Fish fingers (breaded fish sticks

Toast triangles

Cheese cubes

Ham

Marmite fingers

Above: *Your baby can eat at his own pace until he is full.*

## TIPS

- Make sure the baby is comfortable either on your lap or strapped into a baby chair or high-chair.
- Check the temperature of the food and make sure it is not too hot.
- Change the texture of the food: some babies like quite wet mixtures, some hate lumps, some like a few lumps for interest, others prefer food they can pick up – mini ham sandwiches, thick slices of grilled fish fingers (breaded fish sticks), even picking up peas and corn.
- Encourage your baby to feed herself; don't worry about the mess – your baby is still learning – but just mop up at the end.

- Try to keep calm. If your baby keeps spitting food out, you may find it less upsetting to offer bought food rather than home-made so you don't feel you've wasted time cooking.
- Try not to let your baby see you're upset or annoyed. Even a one-year-old can sense the power she can have over you.
- If solid meals are well established, give her a drink at the end of the meal so that she is not full with milk before she begins.
- Avoid biscuits (cookies) and sweet things – your baby will soon learn that if she makes a fuss when the savoury is offered, dessert will soon follow.

- Remember no baby will starve herself. Often babies who have been good eaters become more difficult to feed. Continue offering a variety of food and don't despair.

Above: *Give drinks at the end of the meal, or they will fill your baby up before he eats.*

# Coping with a fussy eater

All children are fussy eaters at some stage. If meal-times are always calm and plates always clean, then your family must be one in a million. Even very young children learn the power they have over their parents, and meal-times give them a great opportunity to exercise it.

## THE BABY SEEMS TO HAVE A SMALL APPETITE

Babies' appetites, like adults', vary enormously. Don't force feed your baby; if she's been eating well and then turns her head away or starts spitting out the food, it's a clear indication that she's had enough, even if the amount seems very small to you. Resist the temptation to encourage your baby to clear the dish: it is never helpful to force children of any age, and can be extremely counter-productive. Towards the end of the first year, a baby's weight gain usually slows down, and babies who have been good eaters become more difficult to feed. If you're worried, talk to your health visitor or doctor and regularly check your baby's weight.

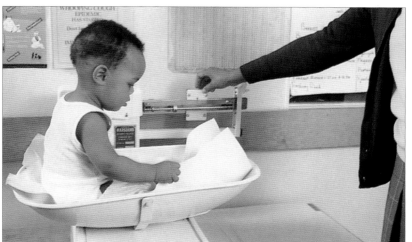

Above: *Don't worry when you encounter resistance in feeding: there never has been a baby that likes all foods, all the time.*

Left: *If you have any serious anxieties, see your doctor or health visitor and get your baby's weight checked regularly.*

# The Importance of a Varied Diet

Once your baby progresses to more varied fruit and vegetable purées you are really beginning to lay down the foundations for a healthy eating pattern and sound nutritional habits that will take your baby through childhood and into adult life.

It is vitally important to include portions of food from each of the four main food groups – carbohydrates such as cereal, pasta and bread; fruit and vegetables; protein such as meat, fish and eggs; milk and milk products – every day. Don't forget to make sure that the types of food you choose are suitable for the age of your child.

Left: *Your baby is now at the age where the diet can and should be as diverse as any adult's. Variety is crucial for health reasons, and also has the benefit of allowing you many options for encouraging and maintaining the kind of interest in all types of food that will ensure good eating habits develop for the future.*

**Group 1:** *Cereals, bread, potatoes, rice and pasta.*

**Group 2:** *Fruit and vegetables* – bland tastes to start, such as potato, swede (rutabaga) and parsnip, then stronger flavours and a wider variety.

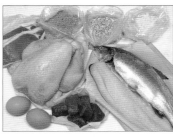

**Group 3:** *Meat and meat alternatives* – meat, poultry, fish, eggs, peas, beans, lentils, tofu, finely ground nuts.

**Group 4:** *Milk and milk products* – milk, including soya milk, cheese, yogurt (plain at first, then flavoured).

**Group 5:** *Sugars.*

**Group 6:** *Fats and oils.*

There are two more food groups that add palatability to the diet as well as contributing energy.

It is not recommended that you add sugar to baby foods or give lots of sugary drinks, particularly in the early days of weaning. Many of us have an inherent need for sweetness, but to cater to this without building in bad habits, try and include foods in the diet that are naturally sweet. Choose dessert apples instead of very sharp cooking apples, and mix bananas or ripe apricots with sharper-tasting fruits.

For those foods that are very sharp try to add 5ml/1tsp sugar per portion, so they become palatable without being overly sweet. Given the choice, your baby would prefer sweet flavours to savoury, so make sure you include a good range of tastes in the diet. Too much sugar or too many sweetened foods or drinks at this stage could lead to tooth decay

before the teeth are even through. Try to avoid offering biscuits (cookies) as a mid-morning or afternoon snack. Instead, encourage your baby to eat:

- a piece of banana
- a plain bread roll
- a few triangles of toast
- a milky drink
- a small container of yogurt

Watch the amounts of fat and oil you include in the diet. Avoid frying, especially when preparing first foods, as young babies have difficulty digesting such foods. As your baby develops, you can spread toast fingers with a little butter or margarine as easy-to-hold finger food. Maintain the milk feeds and introduce full-fat (whole) cow's milk after one year as the main drink of the day. Don't be tempted to serve skimmed (skim) milk, as the valuable fat-soluble vitamins A and D will be lost, and your baby may not get the energy needed for growth.

## HOME-MADE OR MANUFACTURED FOODS?

Most parents use a combination of the two. Bought baby foods are convenient and often easier to use if going out for the day or until your baby's meals coincide with those of the rest of the family. Dried baby foods can be useful

Above: *A piece of fruit or chopped vegetable is always preferable to a biscuit.*

in the very early days, when your baby is eating only a teaspoon of food at each meal. On the other hand, home-made foods can be batch-cooked or made with some of the ingredients from the main family meal and are often less trouble than you might expect. Added to this is the satisfaction of knowing your baby has eaten a wholesome meal and hopefully is acquiring a taste for home cooking.

Left: *Home-made foods have the advantage that you know exactly what is in them. But there are some excellent products available for purchase that can save you time and effort and add hugely to your repertoire without any loss of dietary value.*

# Lamb Couscous

**Makes: 750ml/1¼ pint/3 cups**

115g/4oz carrot

115g/4oz swede (rutabaga)

¼ onion

175g/6oz lamb fillet

5ml/1 tsp oil

10ml/2 tsp vegetable purée (paste)

30ml/2 tbsp currants or raisins

300ml/½ pint/1¼ cups water

50g/2oz couscous

1 Peel the carrot, swede and onion, rinse and chop. Rinse the lamb, trim off any fat, and chop.

2 Heat the oil in a pan, and fry the lamb until browned.

3 Add the vegetables, cook for 2 minutes, then stir in the vegetable purée, currants and water. Cover and simmer for 25 minutes.

4 Put the couscous in a sieve (strainer) and rinse under cold running water. Cover and steam the couscous over the lamb pan, for 5 minutes.

5 Chop or process the lamb mixture to the desired consistency. Fluff up the couscous with a fork and add to the lamb mixture stirring well.

6 Spoon a little into a bowl, test the temperature and cool if necessary, before giving to the baby.

7 Cover the remaining food and transfer to the refrigerator as soon as possible. Use within 24 hours.

• Suitable for freezing.

**TIP**
Look out for vegetable purée in tubes on the same shelf as the tomato purée in the supermarket.

# Paprika Pork

**Makes: 600ml/1 pint/2½ cups**

175g/6oz lean pork

75g/3oz carrot

175g/6oz potato

¼ onion

¼ red (bell) pepper

5ml/1tsp oil

2.5ml/½ tsp paprika

150g/5oz/⅔ cup baked beans

150ml/¼ pint/⅔ cup water

1 Preheat the oven to 180°C/ 350°F/Gas 4. Rinse the pork under cold water, pat dry and trim away any fat or gristle. Cut the pork into small cubes.

2 Peel the carrot, potato and onion. Cut away the core and remove any seeds from the pepper. Put into a colander, rinse under cold water, then chop into small pieces.

4 Bring back to the boil, then cover and cook in the oven for 1¼ hours, until the pork is tender.

5 Chop or process the casserole to the desired consistency, then spoon a little into a bowl. Test the temperature and cool if necessary, before giving to the baby.

6 Cover the remaining food and transfer to the refrigerator as soon as possible. Use within 24 hours.

● Suitable for freezing.

3 Heat the oil in a flameproof casserole, add the pork and fry for a few minutes, stirring until browned. Add the vegetables, cook for 2 minutes, then add the paprika, baked beans and water.

**TIP**

If using a food processor to chop the baby's dinner, drain off most of the liquid. Process, then stir in enough liquid for desired texture.

# Chicken and Celery Supper

**Makes: 600ml/1 pint/2½ cups**

| |
|---|
| 175g/6oz chicken thighs, skinned and boned |
| ¼ onion |
| 225g/8oz carrots |
| 75g/3oz celery |
| 5ml/1 tsp oil |
| 10ml/2 tsp vegetable purée (paste) |
| 250ml/8fl oz/1 cup water |

1 Rinse the chicken under cold water, pat dry, trim off any fat and cut into chunks.

2 Trim and rinse the vegetables and cut into small pieces.

3 Heat the oil in a pan, add the chicken and onion, and fry for a few minutes, stirring until browned. Add the carrots, celery, vegetable purée and water. Bring to the boil, cover and simmer for 20 minutes, until tender.

4 Chop or process the mixture to the desired consistency. If using a food processor, process the solids first and then add the liquid a little at a time.

5 Spoon a little into a bowl, test the temperature and cool if necessary, before giving to the baby.

6 Cover the remaining casserole and transfer to the refrigerator as soon as possible. Use within 24 hours.

- Suitable for freezing.

**TIP**

For extra flavour, add home-made stock instead of the water, or use commercial stock, but make sure it does not have a high sodium level.

# Cauliflower and Broccoli with Cheese

**Makes: 600ml/1 pint/2½ cups**

175g/6oz cauliflower

175g/6oz broccoli

175g/6oz potato

300ml/½ pint/1¼ cups formula milk

75g/3oz Cheddar or mild cheese

5 Spoon a little into a bowl, test the temperature, and cool if necessary, before serving to the baby.

6 Cover the remaining food and transfer to the refrigerator as soon as possible. Use within 24 hours.

- Suitable for freezing.

1 Rinse the vegetables, then break the cauliflower and broccoli into florets. Slice the tender stems, but cut out and discard the woody core of the cauliflower. Peel and chop the potatoes into cubes.

4 Process or mash the mixture to the desired consistency, adding a little extra milk if necessary.

2 Place the vegetables and milk in a pan, bring to the boil, cover and simmer for 12–15 minutes, until quite tender.

3 Grate the cheese and add to the vegetables, stirring until the cheese has melted.

# Tagliatelle and Cheese with Broccoli and Ham

**Makes: 600ml/1 pint/2½ cups**

115g/4oz broccoli

50g/2oz thinly sliced ham

50g/2oz Cheddar or mild cheese

300ml/½ pint/1¼ cups formula milk

50g/2oz tagliatelle

5 Chop or process the mixture to the desired consistency and then spoon a little into a bowl. Test the temperature and cool if necessary, before giving to the baby.

6 Cover the remaining food and transfer to the refrigerator as soon as possible. Use within 24 hours.

• Suitable for freezing.

4 Add the ham and cheese to the broccoli and pasta, stirring until the cheese has melted.

1 Rinse the broccoli and cut into small florets, chopping the stalks. Chop the ham and grate the Cheddar cheese.

2 Pour the formula milk into a pan, bring to the boil and add the tagliatelle. Simmer uncovered for 5 minutes.

3 Add the broccoli and cook for 10 minutes, until tender.

**TIP**

Pasta swells on standing, so you may need to thin the cooled leftover mixture with extra formula milk before reheating.

# Baby Dahl

**Makes: 600ml/1 pint/2½ cups**

50g/2oz/¼ cup red lentils

¼ onion

2.5ml/½ tsp ground coriander

1.25ml/¼ tsp turmeric

350ml/12fl oz/1½ cups water

75g/3oz potato

75g/3oz carrot

75g/3oz cauliflower

75g/3oz green cabbage

1 Rinse the lentils under cold water, discarding any black bits.

2 Chop the onion and add to a pan with the lentils, spices and water.

3 Bring to the boil, cover and simmer for 20 minutes.

4 Chop the potato, carrot and cabbage. Break the cauliflower into small florets.

5 Stir the vegetables into the pan. Cook for 12–15 minutes.

6 Chop or process the dahl to the desired consistency, adding a little extra boiled water if necessary.

7 Spoon a little dahl into a bowl, test the temperature and cool if necessary, before serving to the baby.

8 Cover the remaining dahl and transfer to the refrigerator as soon as possible. Use within 24 hours.

• Suitable for freezing.

# Fish and Cheese Pie

**Makes: 450ml/³/₄ pint/1⁷/₈ cups**

| |
|---|
| 225g/8oz potato |
| 50g/2oz leek |
| 50g/2oz button (white) mushrooms |
| 90g/3½oz brick frozen skinless cod |
| 250ml/8fl oz/1 cup formula milk |
| 50g/2oz grated Cheddar, or mild cheese |

1 Peel the potato, halve the leek and trim the mushrooms. Place all the vegetables in a colander and rinse well with cold water, drain, then chop the vegetables.

2 Place the vegetables in a pan with the frozen cod and milk. Bring to the boil, cover and simmer for 15 minutes, until the fish is cooked and the potatoes are tender when pierced with a knife.

3 Lift the fish out of the pan with a slotted spoon and break into pieces with a knife and fork, checking carefully for bones.

4 Return the fish to the pan and stir in the grated cheese. Chop or process the mixture to give the desired consistency.

5 Spoon a little into a bowl, test the temperature and cool if necessary, before serving to the baby.

6 Cover the remaining fish pie and transfer to the refrigerator as soon as possible. Use within 24 hours.

• Suitable for freezing.

# Fish Creole

**Makes: 450ml/³/₄ pint/1⁷/₈ cups**

50g/2oz celery

50g/2oz red (bell) pepper

300ml/½ pint/1¼ cups water

50g/2oz/¼ cup long grain rice

10ml/2 tsp tomato ketchup

90g/3½oz brick frozen skinless cod

1 Trim the celery and discard the core and seeds from the pepper. Rinse and chop the vegetables.

2 Bring the water to the boil in a pan and add the vegetables, rice, ketchup and cod.

3 Bring back to the boil, then reduce heat, cover and simmer for 15 minutes, until the rice is tender and the fish is cooked.

4 Lift the fish out of the pan with a slotted spoon. Use a knife and fork to check for bones.

6 Spoon a little fish mixture into a small bowl, test the temperature and cool if necessary, before giving to the baby.

7 Cover the leftover fish creole and transfer to the refrigerator as soon as possible. Use within 24 hours.

• Suitable for freezing.

5 Stir the fish back into the pan and then chop or process.

# Chocolate Pots

**Makes: 2**

5ml/1 tsp cocoa

5ml/1 tsp caster (superfine) sugar

150ml/¼ pint/⅔ cup formula or
  cow's milk

1 egg

1 Preheat the oven to 180°C/
350°F/Gas 4. Blend the cocoa
and sugar with a little of the milk in a
small bowl to make a smooth paste.
Stir in the remaining milk and then
pour the mixture into a pan.

2 Bring just to the boil. Beat the
egg in a bowl, then gradually stir
in the hot milk, mixing well until the
mixture is smooth.

3 Strain the mixture into two
ramekin dishes to remove any
egg solids.

4 Place the dishes in a roasting pan
or shallow cake tin (pan). Pour
boiling water into the pan to come
halfway up the sides of the dishes.

5 Cook in the oven for 15–20
minutes, or until the custard has
set. Leave to cool.

6 Transfer to the refrigerator as soon
as possible. Serve one dessert and
use the second within 24 hours.

# Vanilla Custards

**Makes: 2**

1 egg

5ml/1 tsp caster (superfine) sugar

few drops vanilla essence (extract)

150ml/¼ pint/⅔ cup formula or
cow's milk

**1** Preheat the oven to 180°C/
350°F/Gas 4. Using a fork, beat
the egg, sugar and vanilla essence
together in a bowl.

**2** Pour the milk into a small pan
and heat until it is just on the
point of boiling.

**3** Gradually stir the milk into the
egg mixture, whisking or
beating until smooth.

**4** Strain into two ramekin dishes
and place in a roasting pan. Add
enough boiling water to come
halfway up the sides of the dishes.

**5** Bake for 15–20 minutes, or until
the custard has set. Cool and
serve as for **Chocolate Pots.**

# Marmite Bread Sticks

**Makes: 36**

little oil, for greasing

150g/5oz packet pizza base mix

flour, for dusting

5ml/1 tsp Marmite (yeast extract spread)

1 egg yolk

1 Brush two baking sheets with a little oil. Put the pizza mix in a bowl, add the quantity of water as directed on the package and mix to make a smooth dough.

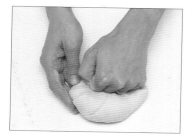

2 Knead on a lightly floured surface for 5 minutes, until smooth and elastic.

3 Roll out to a 23cm/9in square. Cut into strips 7.5cm × 1cm/3 × ½in, twisting each to give a corkscrew effect. Arrange on the baking sheets, slightly spaced apart.

4 Mix the Marmite and egg yolk together and brush over the bread sticks. Loosely cover with oiled clear film (plastic wrap) and leave in a warm place for 20–30 minutes to rise.

5 Meanwhile preheat the oven to 220°C/425°F/Gas 7. Bake the bread sticks for 8–10 minutes, until well risen. Loosen but leave to cool on the baking sheet.

6 Serve one or two sticks to the baby. Store the rest in a plastic box for up to three days.

• Suitable for freezing up to three months in a plastic bag.

# Bread Fingers with Egg

**Makes: 16**

2 slices bread

1 egg

30ml/2 tbsp formula or cow's milk

little butter and oil, for frying

1 Trim the crusts off the bread, then cut each slice in half.

2 Beat the egg and milk in a shallow dish and dip the bread, one slice at a time, into the egg until coated on both sides.

3 Heat a little butter and oil in a frying pan. Add the bread and fry until browned on both sides.

4 Cool slightly, cut into fingers and serve to the baby as finger food or as part of a meal.

# Cheese Straws

**Makes: 42**

little oil for greasing

175g/6oz/1½ cups plain (all-purpose) flour

75g/3oz/6 tbsp butter or margarine, cut into pieces

115g/4oz grated Cheddar or mild cheese

1 egg, beaten

**1** Preheat the oven to 200°C/ 400°F/Gas 6. Brush two baking sheets lightly with oil.

**2** Place the flour in a bowl, add the butter or margarine and rub in until the mixture resembles fine breadcrumbs. Stir in the grated cheese.

**3** Reserve 15ml/1 tbsp beaten egg and then stir the rest into the pastry mixture. Mix to a smooth dough, adding water if necessary.

**4** Knead lightly and roll out on a floured surface to a rectangle 30 × 20cm/12 × 8in. Brush with the remaining egg.

**5** Cut into strips 7.5 × 1cm/ 3 × ½in and place on the baking sheets, spaced slightly apart.

**6** Bake in the oven for 8–10 minutes, until golden brown. Loosen from but leave to cool on the baking sheets.

**7** Serve one or two sticks to the baby and store the rest in a plastic box for up to 1 week.

• Suitable for freezing up to three months in a plastic box, interleaved with baking parchment.

**TIP**
Begin making these with mild cheese, and as your child gets more adventurous, change to stronger flavoured cheese.

# Mini Cup Cakes

**Makes: 26**

50g/2oz/4 tbsp soft margarine

50g/2oz/¼ cup caster (superfine) sugar

50g/2oz/⅓ cup self-raising (self-rising) flour

1 egg

**1** Preheat the oven to 180°C/350°F/ Gas 4. Place 26 paper mini muffin cases on a large baking sheet.

**2** Put all the ingredients for the cake into a mixing bowl and beat together well until smooth.

**3** Divide the mixture among the cases and cook for 8–10 minutes, until well risen and golden.

**4** Transfer the cakes to a wire rack and leave to cool completely, then peel the paper off one or two cakes and serve to the baby.

**5** Store the remaining cakes in a plastic box for up to three days.

• Suitable for freezing up to three months in a plastic box.

**TIP**

Cut a cup cake in half crossways and spread one half with a little sugar-free jam. Replace top half and serve to the baby.

# Shortbread Shapes

**Makes: 60**

little oil, for greasing

150g/5oz/1 cup plain (all-purpose) flour

25g/1oz/3 tbsp cornflour (cornstarch)

50g/2oz/¼ cup caster (superfine) sugar

115g/4oz/½ cup butter

extra sugar, for sprinkling (optional)

**1** Preheat the oven to 180ºC/ 350ºF/Gas 4. Brush two baking sheets with a little oil.

**2** Put the flour, cornflour and sugar in a bowl. Cut the butter into pieces and rub into the flour until the mixture resembles fine breadcrumbs. Mould to a dough with your hands.

**3** Knead lightly and roll out on a floured surface to a 5mm/¼in thickness. Stamp out shapes with small cookie or petits fours cutters.

**4** Transfer to the baking sheets, sprinkle with extra sugar, if liked, and cook for 10–12 minutes, until pale golden. Loosen with a knife and leave to cool on the baking sheets, then transfer to a wire rack.

**5** Offer the baby one or two shapes and store the rest in a plastic box for up to one week.

**TIP**
These biscuits (cookies) will keep well in the freezer for three months. Pack in rigid plastic boxes and thaw in a single layer. If you prefer, you can freeze them before baking. Wrap well to prevent them taking up flavours from other food.

# FOOD FOR TODDLERS

Once your child has reached 12 months he or she will be enjoying a varied diet, and eating habits and their personal food preferences will be developing. It is now vitally important to lay the foundations of a good and well-balanced eating regime.

This is a time when food fads may also develop. Try to weather this period of fussy eating – all children will experience it at some time, and even good eaters will go through a picky stage. Hopefully, the fad will go as quickly as it came, but while it lasts, meal-times can become a nightmare.

# Coping With a Fussy Eater

We all have different sized appetites whatever our age, and young children are no exception. Children's appetites fluctuate greatly and often tail off just before a growth spurt. All children go through food fads; some just seem to last longer and be more difficult than others.

A toddler's appetite varies enormously, and you may find that she will eat very well one day and eat hardly anything the next. Be guided by your toddler, and try to think in terms of what the child has eaten over several days rather than just concentrating on one day.

At the time, it can be very frustrating and worrying. Try not to think of the food that you have just thrown away, but try to think more in the long term. Jot down the foods that your child has actually eaten over three or four days, or up to a week. You may actually be surprised that it isn't just yogurts and crisps after all!

Once you have a list, you may find a link between the foods your child eats and the time of day. Perhaps your child eats better when eating with the family, or when the house is quiet. If you do find a link, then build on it. You might find that your child is snacking on chocolate, doughnuts or soft drinks when out with friends, and that fussiness at home is really a full tummy. Or it may be that by cutting out a milk drink and a biscuit (cookie) mid-morning and offering a sliced apple instead, your child may not be so full at lunchtime. Perhaps you could hide the biscuit tin (cookie jar) once visitors have had one, so that tiny hands can't keep reaching for more.

If your toddler seems hungrier at breakfast, then you could offer French toast, a grilled sausage or a few banana slices with her cereal.

Above: *Don't panic about food rejection. Be patient and keep a journal listing what your child actually does eat.*

Right: *Fresh, healthy snacks of fruit, such as apples, will preserve your child's appetite for main meals.*

Although this may all sound very obvious, when rushing about caring for a toddler and perhaps an older child or new baby as well, life can become rather blurred, and it can be difficult to stand back and look at things objectively.

**REFUSING TO EAT**

A child will always eat if she is hungry, although it may not be when you want her to eat. A child can stay fit and healthy on surprisingly little. Providing your child is growing and gaining weight, then don't fuss, but if you are worried, talk to your doctor or health visitor. Take the lead from your child, never force feed a child and try not to let meal-times become a battleground.

## MAKING MEAL–TIMES FUN

Coping with a fussy eater can be incredibly frustrating. The less she eats, the crosser you get, and so the spiral goes on as your toddler learns how to control meal-times. To break this vicious circle, try diffusing things by involving your child in the preparation of the meal. You could pack up a picnic with your child's help, choosing together what to take. Then go somewhere different to eat – it could be the back garden, the swings or even the car. Alternatively, have a dollies' or teddies' tea party or make a camp under the dining table or even in the cupboard under the stairs.

Even very young children enjoy having friends round for tea. If your child is going through a fussy or non-eating stage, invite over a little friend with a good appetite. Try to take a back seat, and don't make a fuss over how much the visiting child eats compared to your own.

Above: *Changing the scene and breaking routine can help greatly.*

Below: *Making the meal a special event can distract the child from any eating worries.*

Above: *Getting your child to help you cook the food will encourage her to eat it, too.*

Above: *Children are more likely to eat with friends of their own age around them.*

## 10 TIPS TO COPE WITH A FUSSY EATER

**1** Try to find meals that the rest of the family enjoys and where there are at least one or two things the fussy child will eat, as well. It may seem easier to cook only foods that your child will eat, but it means a very limited diet for everyone else, and your child will never get the chance to have a change of mind and try something new.

**2** Serve smaller portions of food to your child.

**3** Invite round her friend with a hearty appetite. A good example sometimes works, but don't comment on how much the visiting child has eaten.

**4** Invite an adult who the child likes for supper – a granny, uncle or friend. Sometimes a child will eat for someone else without any fuss at all.

**5** Never force feed a child.

**6** If your child is just playing with the food and won't eat, quietly remove the plate without a fuss and don't offer dessert.

**7** Try to make meal-times enjoyable and talk about what the family has been doing.

**8** Try limiting snacks and drinks between meals so your child feels hungrier when it comes to family meal-times. Alternatively, offer more nutritious snacks and smaller main meals if your child eats better that way.

**9** Offer drinks after a meal so that they don't spoil the appetite.

**10** Offer new foods when you know your child is hungry and hopefully more receptive.

Above: *Remember to give drinks after the meal, not before.*

### EATING TOGETHER

Sharing meals as a family should be a happy part of the day, but can turn into a nightmare if everyone is tired or you feel as though the only things your children will eat are chips (french fries). There is nothing worse than preparing a lovely supper, laying the table and sitting down with everyone, and then one child refuses to eat, shrieks her disapproval or just pushes the food around the plate. However hard you try to ignore this behaviour, the meal is spoiled for everyone, especially if this is a regular occurrence. It's not fair on you or anyone else.

If you feel this is just a passing phase, then you could try just ignoring it and carry on regardless. Try to praise the good things, perhaps the way the child sits nicely at the table or the way she holds a knife and fork. Talk about the things that have been happening during the day, rather than concentrating on the meal itself. Try to avoid comparing your child's appetite with more hearty eaters. With luck, this particular fad will go away.

However, if it becomes a regular thing and meal-times always seem more like a battleground than a happy family gathering, perhaps it's time for a more serious approach.

### First steps

● Check to see if there is something physically wrong with your child. Has she been ill? If she has, she may not have recovered fully. If you're worried, then ask your doctor.
● Perhaps your child has enlarged adenoids or tonsils which could make swallowing difficult, or perhaps she has a food allergy, such as coeliacs disease – an intolerance to gluten, which may be undiagnosed, but which would give the child tummy pains after eating. Again, check with your doctor.
● Is your child worried or stressed? If your family circumstances have changed – the arrival of a new baby, or if you've moved recently – your child may be unhappy or confused.
● Is your child trying to get your attention?

Above: *Good seating of the right height will contribute to comfort and relaxation.*

**Secondly**

Look at the way in which you as a family eat. Do you eat at regular times? Do you sit down to eat or catch snacks on the move? Do you enjoy your food, or do you always feel rushed and harassed? Children will pick up habits from their parents – bad ones as well as good. If you don't tend to sit down to a meal, or you have the habit of getting up during meal-times to do other jobs, then it's hard to expect your child to behave differently.

**Finally**

Talk things over with the whole family. If you all feel enough is enough, then it's time to make a plan of action. Explain that from now on you are all going to eat together where possible, when and where you say so. You will choose the food, there will be three meals a day and no snacks. Since milk is filling and dulls the appetite, milky drinks will only be given after a meal; during the meal water or juice will be provided.

It is important to involve the entire family in this strategy so that there is no dipping into the biscuit tin (cookie jar) or raiding the cupboard for crisps (potato chips) after school. Make sure that the fussy eater is aware of what is going to happen and give a few days' notice so that the idea can sink in.

Once you have outlined your strategy, work out your menus and

**Happy Families**

stick to them. Include foods your child definitely likes, chicken or carrots for instance, and obviously avoid foods your child dislikes although you could introduce some new foods for variety. Set yourself a time scale, perhaps one or two weeks, and review things after this period has elapsed.

**PUTTING THE PLAN INTO ACTION**

Begin your new plan of action when the entire family is there to help, such as a weekend, and stick to it. Make a fuss of the plans so it seems more like a game than a prison sentence. Add a few flowers to the table or a pretty cloth to make it more special.

Begin the day with a normal breakfast, but give the fussy eater the smallest possible portion. If the child eats it up, then offer something you know your child likes, such as an apple, a few raisins or a fruit yogurt.

As the days progress, you could offer a biscuit (cookie) or milkshake as a treat.

Give plenty of encouragement and praise, but be firm if the child plays up. If she behaves badly, take her to a different room or to the bottom of the stairs and explain that the only food is what is on the table. Sit down with the rest of the family, leaving the fussy eater's food on the table, and try to ignore the child.

If the child changes her mind just as you're about to clear the table, then get the other members of the family to come back and wait until the fussy eater has finished.

Continue in this way with other meals. Don't be swayed if your child says she will eat her food watching TV or if she wants her dessert first. Explain that she must eat just like everyone else or go without.

If she begins to cry, sit her down in another room and return to the table. This is perhaps the hardest thing of all.

After a few days, there should be a glimmer of progress. Still offer tiny portions of food, followed by foods that you know your child will eat as a treat. Keeping to a plan like this is hard, but if the entire family sticks together and thinks positively, then it is possible. Keep to the time span you have decided, then suggest you all go to your local pizza or burger restaurant, and let the fussy eater choose what she likes.

**Fat Cat**

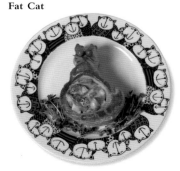

**Veggie Burger**

**Tuna Fish Cakes**

# A Balanced and Varied Diet

Give your child a selection of foods in the four main food groups daily:

**Cereal and filler foods:** include three to four helpings of the following per day – breakfast cereals, bread, pasta, potatoes, rice.

**Fruit and vegetables:** try to have three or four helpings per day. Choose from fresh, canned, frozen or dried.

**Meat and/or alternatives:** one to two portions per day – meat (all kinds, including burgers and sausages), poultry, fish (fresh, canned or frozen), eggs (well cooked), lentils, peas and beans (for example, chickpeas baked beans, red kidney beans), finely chopped nuts, smooth peanut butter, seeds, tofu, and Quorn.

**Dairy foods:** include 600ml/1 pint of milk per day or a mix of milk, cheese, and yogurt. For a child who stops drinking milk, try flavouring it or using it in custards, ice cream, rice pudding or cheese sauce. A carton of yogurt or 40g/1½oz of cheese have the same amount of calcium as 190ml/⅓ pint of milk.

## THE IMPORTANCE OF BREAKFAST

Breakfast is a vitally important start for any young child. Count back: your child may have had a meal at 5 o'clock the previous day, and if she misses breakfast at 8 o'clock she will not have eaten for 15 hours. Allow time to sit down, and don't rush your child. Offer milk and cereals, orange juice diluted with a little water, not squash (orangeade), a few slices of fruit and half a piece of toast, preferably spread with smooth peanut butter or Marmite.

Above: *Cereal and filler foods, such as bread, pasta and rice.*

Above: *Fruit and vegetables, including frozen, dried and canned goods.*

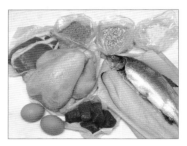

Above: *Meat and meat alternatives, such as beans, peas, lentils and nuts.*

Above: *Dairy foods such as milk, cheese and yogurt.*

**Marmite toast**

**Sliced pears**

## FATS

As adults we are all aware of the need to cut down on our fat consumption, but when eating together as a family, bear in mind that fat is a useful source of energy in a child's diet. The energy from fat is in concentrated form, so that your child can take in the calories she needs for growth and development before her stomach becomes overfull. Fat in food is also a valuable source of the fat-soluble vitamins, A, D, E and K, as well as essential fatty acids that the body cannot make by itself.

In general, fat is best provided by foods that contain not just fat but other essential nutrients as well, such as dairy products, eggs, meat and fish. Full-fat (whole) milk and its products such as cheese and yogurt, and eggs contain the fat-soluble vitamins A and D, while sunflower (sunflower-seed) oil, nuts and oily fish are a good source of various essential fatty acids.

It is wise to cut down on deep frying and to grill (broil) or oven bake foods where possible. All children love crisps (potato chips), but keep them as a treat rather than a daily snack.

### FRUIT AND VEGETABLES

Fresh fruit and vegetables play an essential part in a balanced diet. Offer fresh fruit, such as slices of apple or banana, for breakfast and the evening meal, and perhaps thin sticks of raw carrot and celery for lunch. Instead of biscuits (cookies), offer your child raisins, apricots, satsumas, carrots or apple slices if she wants a mid-morning or afternoon snack. Keep the fruit bowl within easy reach so your child may be tempted to pick up a banana as she walks through the kitchen.

Above: *A good mixture of the four basic food types will provide maximum energy and vitality for growing children.*

### SNACKS

Young children cannot eat enough food at meal-times to meet their needs for energy and growth, and snacks can play a vital part in meeting these needs. However, keep biscuits and crisps as a treat. They contain little goodness and are bad for the teeth. At meal-times keep sweets (candy) out of sight until the main course has been eaten.

Above: *Keep sweets and chocolate as treats – give fruit and vegetables as snacks.*

**Bread sticks**

**Raisins**

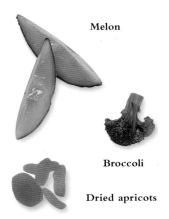

**Melon**

**Broccoli**

**Dried apricots**

# LUNCH SPECIALS

N OW THAT YOUR BABY HAS PROGRESSED FROM PURÉED TO CHOPPED FOOD, YOU CAN BEGIN TO
COOK MORE GROWNUP LUNCHES. TRY TO INTRODUCE A RANGE OF DIFFERENT FOODS TO
GIVE A BALANCED DIET AND A VARIETY OF TASTES, BUT DON'T BE DISHEARTENED IF THERE ARE A
FEW HICCUPS ALONG THE WAY.

## Sticky Chicken

**Serves 2–4**

4 chicken drumsticks

10ml/2 tsp oil

5ml/1 tsp soy sauce

15ml/1 tbsp smooth peanut butter

15ml/1 tbsp tomato ketchup

small baked potatoes, corn and
tomato wedges, to serve

1 Preheat the oven to 200°C/
400°F/Gas 6 and line a small
shallow baking tin (pan) with foil.
Rinse the drumsticks under cold
water, pat dry and peel off the skin.
Make three or four slashes in the meat
with a sharp knife and place in the tin.

**TIP**
If more convenient, use the peanut
butter and ketchup mixture over
chicken thighs or kebabs instead.

2 Blend the remaining ingredients
and spread thickly over the top
of the chicken drumsticks. Cook in
the oven for 15 minutes.

3 Turn the drumsticks over and
baste with the peanut butter
mixture and meat juices.

4 Cook for a further 20 minutes or
until the juices run clear when
the chicken is pierced with a knife.

5 Cool slightly, then wrap a small
piece of foil around the base of
each drumstick. Arrange on plates
and serve with small baked potatoes,
hot corn, and tomato wedges.

# Coriander Chicken Casserole

**Serves 2**

2 chicken thighs

¼ small onion

1 small carrot, about 50g/2oz

50g/2oz swede (rutabaga)

5ml/1 tsp oil

2.5ml/½ tsp ground coriander

pinch of turmeric

5ml/1 tsp plain (all-purpose) flour

150ml/¼ pint/⅔ cup chicken stock

salt and pepper (optional)

mashed potatoes and peas, to serve

**1** Preheat the oven to 180°C/350°F/Gas 4. Rinse the chicken under cold water, pat dry and trim away any excess skin if necessary. Chop the onion, carrot and swede.

**2** Heat the oil in a frying pan, add the chicken and brown on each side. Add the vegetables.

**TIP**
Chop the meat for very young toddlers. Serve older children the whole thigh to make them feel more grown up, then help with cutting.

**3** Stir in the coriander, turmeric and flour, then add the stock and a little salt and pepper, if liked. Bring to the boil, then transfer to a casserole.

**4** Cover and cook in the oven for 1 hour. Spoon on to serving plates or into shallow dishes, cool slightly and serve the chicken casserole with mashed potatoes and peas.

# Chicken and Cheese Parcels

**Serves 2**

1 boned and skinned chicken breast, about 150g/5oz

25g/1oz Cheddar or mild cheese

1 slice lean ham, cut into 4 strips

15ml/1 tbsp oil

new potatoes, broccoli and carrots, to serve

**1** Rinse the chicken under cold water, pat dry with kitchen paper and cut in half crossways. Place each half between two pieces of clear film (plastic wrap) and flatten with a rolling pin until each piece is about 10cm/4in square.

**2** Cut the cheese in half and place a piece on each escalope (US scallop). Wrap the chicken around the cheese to enclose it completely.

**3** Arrange two pieces of the ham crossways over each of the parcels, securing them underneath with cocktail sticks (toothpicks). Brush the chicken parcels with oil.

**TIP**
You could wrap the parcels with halved rashers (strips) of rindless streaky (fatty) bacon, if preferred.

**4** Place on a piece of foil and chill until ready to cook.

**5** Preheat the grill (broiler). Cook the chicken for 10 minutes, turning once, until browned. Remove the cocktail sticks, cool slightly, then arrange on two plates and serve with new potatoes, steamed broccoli florets and sliced carrots.

# Peppered Beef Casserole

**Serves 2**

115g/4oz lean braising steak

¼ small onion

¼ small red (bell) pepper

¼ small yellow (bell) pepper

5ml/1 tsp oil

30ml/2 tbsp canned red kidney beans, drained and rinsed

5ml/1 tsp plain (all-purpose) flour

150ml/¼ pint/⅔ cup lamb stock

15ml/1 tbsp tomato ketchup

5ml/1 tsp Worcestershire sauce

45ml/3 tbsp couscous

a few drops of oil

40g/1½oz/3 tbsp frozen peas

salt and pepper (optional)

5 Bring to the boil, stirring, then transfer to a casserole dish, cover and cook in the oven for about 1½ hours, or until the meat is tender.

6 Just before serving place the couscous in a bowl, cover with boiling water and leave to soak for 5 minutes. Drain into a sieve (strainer) and stir in a few drops of oil.

7 Bring a pan of water to the boil, add the peas, and place the sieve of couscous over the pan. Cover and cook for 5 minutes.

8 Spoon the casserole on to two plates or dishes. Fluff up the couscous with a fork, drain the peas and spoon on to the plates. Cool slightly before serving.

1 Preheat the oven to 180°C/ 350°F/Gas 4. Rinse the meat under cold water and pat dry. Trim away any fat and cut into small cubes.

2 Chop the onion, remove the seeds and core from the peppers and cut into small cubes.

3 Heat the oil in a pan, add the beef and onion and fry gently until browned, stirring frequently.

4 Add the peppers and kidney beans, then stir in the flour, stock, tomato ketchup, Worcestershire sauce and a little salt and pepper if liked.

# Lamb Stew

**Serves 2**

| |
|---|
| 115g/4oz lamb fillet |
| ¼ small onion |
| 1 small carrot, about 50g/2oz |
| ½ small parsnip, about 50g/2oz |
| 1 small potato |
| 5ml/1 tsp oil |
| 150ml/¼ pint/⅔ cup lamb stock |
| pinch of dried rosemary |
| salt and pepper (optional) |
| crusty bread, to serve |

1 Rinse the lamb under cold water and pat dry. Cut away any fat from the meat and cut into small cubes. Finely chop the onion, then dice the carrot and parsnip and cut the potato into slightly larger pieces.

2 Heat the oil in a medium-size pan, add the lamb and onion, and fry gently until browned. Add the carrot, parsnip and potato, and fry the lamb and vegetables for a further 3 minutes, stirring.

3 Add the lamb stock, dried rosemary and a little salt and pepper, if liked. Bring to the boil, cover and simmer for 35–40 minutes, or until the meat is tender and moist.

4 Spoon the stew into shallow bowls and cool slightly before serving with crusty bread.

# Mexican Beef

**Serves 3–4**

| |
|---|
| ¼ small onion |
| 1 strip red (bell) pepper |
| ½ small courgette (zucchini) |
| 115g/4oz lean minced (ground) beef |
| 1 small garlic clove, crushed |
| 45ml/3 tbsp canned baked beans |
| 45ml/3 tbsp beef stock |
| 15ml/1 tbsp tomato ketchup |
| 18 corn chips |
| 25g/1oz/¼ cup grated Cheddar or mild cheese |
| green salad, to serve |

1 Finely chop the onion and dice the pepper and courgette.

2 Dry fry the onion and meat in a medium-size pan, stirring until browned all over.

3 Stir in the remaining ingredients and bring to the boil, stirring. Cover and simmer the mixture for 15 minutes, stirring occasionally.

4 Place the corn chips on plates, spoon on the mixture and sprinkle the grated cheese over the top. Serve with a green salad.

# Lamb and Celery Casserole

**Serves 2**

| |
|---|
| 115g/4oz lamb fillet |
| ¼ onion |
| 1 small carrot, about 50g/2oz |
| 1 celery stick |
| 25g/1oz button (white) mushrooms |
| 5ml/1 tsp oil |
| bay leaf |
| 10ml/2 tsp plain (all-purpose) flour |
| 175ml/6fl oz/¾ cup lamb stock |
| salt and pepper (optional) |
| mashed potatoes and baby Brussels sprouts, to serve |

1 Preheat the oven to 180°C/350°F/Gas 4. Rinse the lamb under cold water and pat dry, then trim off any fat and cut into small cubes. Chop the onion and carrot, rinse the celery and mushrooms, pat dry and slice thinly.

2 Heat the oil in a frying pan, add the lamb, onion and bay leaf and fry gently until the lamb is browned, stirring frequently. Add the remaining vegetables and fry for a further 3 minutes, until they are softened and lightly browned.

**VARIATION**
For a more unusual flavour, substitute fennel for the celery. Its slight aniseed taste goes well with lamb.

3 Stir in the flour, then add the stock, and a little salt and pepper, if liked. Bring to the boil and then transfer to a casserole, cover and cook in the oven for 45 minutes or until the meat is tender.

4 Spoon the casserole on to plates, discarding the bay leaf. Cool slightly, then serve with mashed potatoes and tiny Brussels sprouts.

# Shepherd's Pie

**Serves 2**

½ small onion

175g/6oz lean minced (ground) beef

10ml/2 tsp plain (all-purpose) flour

30ml/2 tbsp tomato ketchup

150ml/¼ pint/⅔ cup beef stock

pinch of mixed herbs

50g/2oz swede (rutabaga)

½ small parsnip, about 50g/2oz

1 medium potato, about 115g/4oz

10ml/2 tsp milk

15g/½oz/1 tbsp butter or margarine

½ carrot

40g/1½oz/3 tbsp frozen peas

salt and pepper (optional)

1 Preheat oven to 190°C/375°F/ Gas 5. Finely chop the onion, and place in a small pan with the mince and dry fry over a low heat, stirring, until the mince is evenly browned.

2 Add the flour, stirring, then add the ketchup, stock, mixed herbs and seasoning, if liked. Bring to the boil, cover and simmer gently for 30 minutes, stirring occasionally.

3 Meanwhile, chop the swede, parsnip and potato, and cook for 20 minutes, until tender. Drain.

4 Mash with the milk and half of the butter or margarine.

5 Spoon the meat into two 250ml/8fl oz/1 cup ovenproof dishes. Place the mashed vegetables on top, fluffing them up with a fork. Dot with butter or margarine.

6 Place both the pies on a baking sheet and cook for 25–30 minutes, until browned on top and bubbly.

7 Peel and thinly slice the carrot lengthways. Stamp out shapes with petits fours cutters. Cook in a pan of boiling water with the peas for 5 minutes. Drain and serve with the shepherd's pies. Remember that baked pies are very hot when they come out of the oven. Always allow to cool slightly before serving to children.

# Tuna Fish Cakes

**Serves 2–3**

| |
|---|
| 1 large potato, about 225g/8oz |
| knob (pat) of butter or margarine |
| 10ml/2 tsp milk |
| 5ml/1 tsp lemon juice |
| 100g/3½oz can tuna fish |
| 40g/1½oz/3 tbsp frozen corn, defrosted |
| flour, for dusting |
| 1 egg |
| 60ml/4 tbsp ground almonds |
| 50g/2oz green beans |
| ½ carrot |
| 6 frozen peas |
| 15ml/1 tbsp oil |
| salt and pepper (optional) |

1 Peel and cut the potato into chunks and then cook in a pan of boiling water for about 15 minutes until tender. Drain and mash with the butter or margarine and milk.

2 Add the lemon juice and a little salt and pepper, if liked. Drain the tuna fish and stir into the potato with the defrosted corn.

3 Divide the mixture into six and pat each portion into a fish shape with floured hands.

4 Beat the egg in a dish and place the ground almonds on a plate. Dip the fish cakes into the egg and then into the almonds, making sure they are completely covered. Place on a floured plate and chill until ready to cook.

5 Trim the beans, and peel and cut the carrot into sticks a little smaller than the beans. Cook in a pan of boiling water with the peas for about 5 minutes.

6 Meanwhile heat the oil in a frying pan, and fry the fish cakes for 5 minutes, until golden brown and crisp, turning once.

7 Drain and arrange on serving plates with pea "eyes" and bean and carrot "pond weed". Cool slightly before serving.

# Fish and Cheese Pies

**Serves 2**

| |
|---|
| 1 medium potato, about 150g/5oz |
| 25g/1oz green cabbage |
| 115g/4oz cod or hoki fillets |
| 25g/1oz/2 tbsp frozen corn |
| 150ml/¼ pint/⅔ cup milk |
| 15ml/1 tbsp butter or margarine |
| 15ml/1 tbsp plain (all-purpose) flour |
| 25g/1oz/¼ cup grated Red Leicester or mild cheese |
| 5ml/1 tsp sesame seeds |
| carrots and mangetouts (snowpeas), to serve |

1 Peel and cut the potato into chunks and shred the cabbage. Cut any skin away from the fish fillets and rinse under cold water.

2 Bring a pan of water to the boil, add the potato and cook for 10 minutes. Add the cabbage and cook for a further 5 minutes until tender. Drain.

3 Meanwhile, place the fish fillets, the corn and all but 10ml/2 tsp of the milk in a second pan. Bring to the boil, then cover the pan and simmer very gently for 8–10 minutes, until the fish flakes easily when pressed with a knife.

4 Strain the fish and corn, reserving the cooking liquid. Wash the pan, then melt the butter or margarine in the pan. Stir in the flour, then gradually add the reserved cooking liquid and bring to the boil, stirring until thickened and smooth.

5 Add the fish and corn with half of the grated cheese. Spoon into two small ovenproof dishes.

6 Mash the potato and cabbage with the remaining 10ml/2 tsp milk. Stir in half of the remaining cheese and spoon the mixture over the fish. Sprinkle with the sesame seeds and the remaining cheese.

7 Cook under a preheated grill until the topping is browned. Cool slightly before serving with carrot and mangetout vegetable fishes.

# Surprise Fish Parcels

**Serves 2**

| ½ small courgette (zucchini) |
| 175g/6oz smoked haddock or cod |
| 1 small tomato |
| knob (pat) of butter or margarine |
| pinch of dried mixed herbs |
| new potatoes and broccoli, to serve |

1 Preheat the oven to 200°C/
400°F/Gas 6. Tear off two pieces
of foil, then trim and thinly slice the
courgette and divide equally
between the two pieces of foil.

2 Cut the skin away from the fish,
remove any bones, cut into two
equal pieces and rinse under cold
water. Pat the haddock dry and place
on top of the courgettes.

3 Slice the tomato and arrange
slices on top of each piece of
haddock. Add a little butter or
margarine to each and sprinkle with
mixed herbs.

4 Wrap the foil around the fish and
seal the edges of each piece to
make two parcels, then place the
parcels on a baking sheet and cook
in the oven for 15–20 minutes,
depending on the thickness of the fish.

5 To test if they are cooked, open
up one of the parcels and insert a
knife into the centre. If the fish flakes
easily, then it is ready.

6 Cool slightly, then arrange the
parcels on plates and serve with
new potatoes and broccoli.

# Cowboy Sausages and Beans

**Serves 2**

3 chipolata sausages

¼ small onion

1 small carrot, about 50g/2oz

1 strip red (bell) pepper

5ml/1 tsp oil

200g/7oz can baked beans

10ml/2 tsp Worcestershire sauce

fingers of toast, to serve

1 Press the centre of each sausage, twist and cut in half to make two small sausages.

2 Finely chop the onion, then dice the carrot and the pepper, discarding the core and seeds.

3 Heat the oil in a frying pan, add the sausages and the chopped onion and fry until browned.

**TIP**
Check the beans towards the end of cooking – you may need to add a little extra water.

4 Add the remaining ingredients and stir in 30ml/2 tbsp water. Cover and cook for 15 minutes, or until the carrot is cooked.

5 Spoon on to serving plates or into dishes, cool slightly and serve with fingers of toast.

# Mini Toad-in-the-Hole

**Serves 2**

3 chipolata sausages

5ml/1 tsp oil

60ml/4 tbsp plain (all-purpose) flour

1 egg

60ml/4 tbsp milk

salt

baked beans and green beans, to serve

1 Preheat the oven to 220°C/ 425°F/Gas 7. Press the centre of each sausage with your finger, twist and then cut in half. Brush two 10cm/4in tartlet tins (muffin pans) with oil. Add the sausages and cook for about 5 minutes.

2 Place the flour, egg and a pinch of salt in a bowl. Gradually whisk in the milk, beating until a smooth batter is formed.

3 Pour into the tins, quickly return to the oven and bake for 15 minutes, until risen and golden.

4 Loosen with a knife and turn out on to serving plates. Cool slightly and serve with baked beans and steamed green beans.

# Pork Hotpot

**Serves 2**

175g/6oz lean pork

¼ small onion

5ml/1 tsp oil

5ml/1 tsp plain (all-purpose) flour

40g/1½oz/3 tbsp frozen corn

pinch of dried sage

150ml/¼ pint/⅔ cup chicken stock

1 medium potato, about 150g/5oz

1 carrot, about 75g/3oz

knob (pat) of butter or margarine

salt and pepper (optional)

broccoli and Brussels sprouts,
  to serve

1 Preheat the oven to 180°C/
350°F/Gas 4. Rinse the pork
under cold water, pat dry, trim away
any fat and cut into small cubes. Peel
and finely chop the onion.

2 Heat the oil in a frying pan, add
the cubed pork and onion and
fry until golden brown, stirring.

3 Add in the flour and stir until
blended, then add the corn, dried
sage, stock and a little salt and pepper,
if liked. Bring to the boil and then
turn the mixture into a shallow
ovenproof dish.

4 Peel and thinly slice the potato
and carrot. Arrange slices so that
they overlap on top of the pork
mixture. Dot with butter or
margarine. Cover with foil and cook
in the oven for about 1 hour, until the
potatoes are tender.

5 Remove the foil and brown
under the grill (broiler) if liked.
Spoon on to serving plates, cool
slightly, then serve with steamed
broccoli and Brussels sprouts.

**TIP**
If you are cooking for only one
child, make the hotpot in two
dishes. Cool one, cover with clear
film (plastic wrap) and freeze for
up to three months.

# Pork and Lentil Casserole

**Serves 2**

| |
| --- |
| 175g/6oz boneless spare-rib pork chop |
| ¼ small onion |
| 1 small carrot, about 50g/2oz |
| 5ml/1 tsp oil |
| 1 small garlic clove, crushed |
| 25g/1oz red lentils |
| 90ml/6 tbsp canned chopped tomatoes |
| 90ml/6 tbsp chicken stock |
| salt and pepper (optional) |
| swede (rutabaga) and peas, to serve |

**1** Preheat the oven to 180°C/ 350°F/Gas 4. Trim off any excess fat from the pork and cut in half. Finely chop the onion and dice the carrot.

**2** Heat the oil in a frying pan, add the pork and onion and fry until the pork is browned on both sides.

**3** Add the garlic, lentils and carrots and stir gently to mix.

**4** Pour in the chopped tomatoes, stock and seasoning, if liked, and cook briefly to bring to the boil. Transfer to a casserole, cover and cook in the oven for 1¼ hours.

**5** Spoon portions on to serving plates or shallow dishes and cool slightly. Serve with diced buttered swede and peas.

**TIP**
Teaching a child to use a knife and fork can be frustrating. Spare-rib pork chops are wonderfully tender when casseroled and so very easy to cut with a child's knife.

# Sticky Ribs and Apple Slaw

**Serves 2**

225g/8oz short pork ribs

10ml/2 tsp oil

10ml/2 tsp tomato ketchup

10ml/2 tsp hoisin sauce

1 medium potato, scrubbed but not
  peeled

knob (pat) of butter or margarine

*For the Apple Slaw*

½ carrot

½ eating apple

25g/1oz white cabbage

10ml/2 tsp sultanas (golden raisins)

30ml/2 tbsp mayonnaise

carrot slices, tomato wedges and
  celery sticks, to serve

4 Meanwhile peel the carrot, and
peel, quarter and core the apple.
Coarsely grate the apple and carrot
and finely chop the cabbage.

5 Place in a bowl with the sultanas
and mayonnaise and mix well.

6 Arrange the ribs on serving
plates. Halve the baked potato,
add a little butter or margarine
to each half and serve with the pork
ribs, together with star-shaped carrot
slices, celery sticks and tomato
wedges and spoonfuls of coleslaw.

**TIP**
Check the temperature of the ribs
before serving, as they stay very
hot for a surprisingly long time.
Nothing will put a child off more
than food that is very hot. Toddlers
prefer their food to be lukewarm.

1 Preheat the oven to 200°C/
400°F/Gas 6. Rinse the pork ribs
under cold water, pat dry and put on
a roasting rack set over a small
roasting pan. Mix the oil, ketchup
and hoisin sauce, and brush over the
ribs, reserving any extra mixture.

2 Pour a little boiling water into
the base of the roasting pan. Prick
the potato all over with a fork and
then place in the oven with the spare
ribs, preferably on the same shelf.

3 Cook for 1 hour, turning the
pork ribs once during cooking
and brushing with any of the
remaining ketchup mixture.

# Mini Cheese and Ham Tarts

**Makes 12**

*For the Pastry*

115g/4oz/1 cup plain (all-purpose) flour

50g/2oz/4 tbsp margarine

*For the Filling*

50g/2oz/½ cup mild cheese

2 thin slices ham, chopped

75g/3oz/½ cup frozen corn

1 egg

120ml/4fl oz/½ cup milk

pinch of paprika

salt and pepper

carrot and cucumber sticks, to serve

1 Preheat the oven to 200°C/400°F/ Gas 6. Place the flour in a bowl, add the margarine and rub in with your fingertips until the mixture resembles fine breadcrumbs.

2 Stir in 20ml/4 tsp water and mix to a smooth dough. Lightly knead and roll out on a floured surface.

3 Stamp out twelve 7.5cm/3in circles with a fluted cookie cutter, re-rolling the pastry as necessary. Press into a tartlet tin (muffin pan).

**TIP**
Encourage children to eat more vegetables by serving them with a yogurt dip flavoured with tomato purée (paste).

4 Grate the cheese, mix with the ham and corn, and divide among the pastry cases.

5 Beat together the egg, milk, salt and pepper and pour into the tarts. Sprinkle with paprika.

6 Cook in the oven for 12–15 minutes, until well risen and browned. Serve warm with carrot and cucumber sticks.

# GOING GREEN

Getting children to eat more than a few frozen peas and the odd carrot can be an uphill battle. Encourage them to be a little more adventurous by mixing their favourite foods with some new vegetables.

## Pick-up Sticks

**Serves 2**

5cm/2in piece of leek

25g/1oz green beans

1 strip red (bell) pepper

1 celery stick

25g/1oz beansprouts

1 small carrot, about 50g/2oz

5ml/1 tsp oil

15ml/1 tbsp tomato ketchup

5ml/1 tsp soy sauce

pinch ground ginger

grilled (broiled) sausages, to serve

1 Rinse the leek, beans, pepper, celery and beansprouts. Peel the carrot. Halve any large beans and beansprouts. Cut the remaining vegetables into thin strips.

2 Heat the oil in a frying pan, add all the vegetables except the beansprouts and fry for 3 minutes, stirring all the time.

3 Add the beansprouts, ketchup, soy sauce, ginger and 10ml/2 tsp water. Cook for a further 2 minutes, stirring until the vegetables are hot.

4 Spoon on to serving plates and leave to cool slightly. Serve with grilled sausages.

**TIP**
Don't overcook the vegetables. They should be quite crisp, and firm enough for your child to pick up.

# Spinach Pancakes with Ham and Cheese

**Serves 2–3**

50g/2oz fresh spinach, leaves only

50g/2oz plain (all-purpose) flour

1 egg yolk

300ml/½ pint/1¼ cups milk

15ml/1 tbsp oil

*For the Filling*

15ml/1 tbsp margarine

15ml/1 tbsp plain (all-purpose) flour

25g/1oz/¼ cup grated Red Leicester
or mild cheese

40g/1½oz thinly sliced ham, chopped

40g/1½oz button (white) mushrooms,
thinly sliced

**1** Wash the spinach leaves well in cold water and then place in a frying pan, set over a medium heat. Cover and cook gently for 2–3 minutes, until the spinach has just wilted, stirring occasionally. Drain off any excess liquid and cool.

**2** Put the flour, egg yolk and a little salt and pepper, if liked, into a bowl. Whisk in half of the milk to make a smooth batter. Finely chop the spinach and stir into the batter.

**3** Melt the margarine in a pan, stir in the flour and then gradually stir in the remaining milk and bring to the boil, stirring continuously until smooth. Add the cheese, ham and mushrooms and stir to mix. Heat, cover and keep warm.

**4** Heat a little oil in a frying pan, pour off excess, then add 30ml/2 tbsp pancake batter, tilting the pan so that the batter covers the base. Cook for a few minutes until browned, then flip over and cook the other side until golden. Slide the pancake on to a plate and keep warm.

**5** Continue making pancakes until all the batter is used up.

**6** Fold the pancakes into quarters, then spoon a little of the ham mixture into each one. Arrange the pancakes on plates and serve with tomato wedges and new potatoes.

**TIP**

If offering spinach to your child for the first time, make sure that the filling includes foods that you know are liked. Omit or add ingredients as necessary.

# Cauliflower and Broccoli with Cheese

**Serves 2**

1 egg

75g/3oz cauliflower

75g/3oz broccoli

15g/½oz/1 tbsp margarine

15ml/1 tbsp plain (all-purpose) flour

150ml/¼ pint/⅔ cup milk

40g/1½oz/⅓ cup grated Red
  Leicester or mild cheese

½ tomato

salt and pepper (optional)

1 Put the egg in a small pan of cold water, bring to the boil and cook for about 10 minutes until the egg is hard-boiled.

2 Meanwhile, cut the cauliflower and broccoli into florets and thinly slice the broccoli stalks. Cook in a pan of boiling water for about 8 minutes, until just tender.

3 Drain the vegetables and dry the pan. Melt the margarine, stir in the flour, then gradually mix in the milk and bring to the boil, stirring until thickened and smooth.

**TIP**
Making a face or fun pattern can be just enough to tempt a fussy eater to try something new.

4 Stir two-thirds of the cheese into the sauce together with a little seasoning, if liked. Reserve two of the broccoli florets and stir the remaining vegetables into the sauce.

5 Divide the mixture between two heat-resistant shallow dishes and sprinkle with the remaining cheese.

6 Place under a hot grill (broiler) until golden brown and bubbling.

7 Make a face on each dish with broccoli florets for a nose, a halved tomato for a mouth and peeled and sliced hard-boiled egg for eyes. Cool slightly before serving.

# Potato Boats

**Serves 2**

| |
|---|
| 2 small baking potatoes |
| 5cm/2in piece leek |
| 25g/1oz button (white) mushrooms |
| 10ml/2 tsp oil |
| 25g/1oz/2 tbsp frozen corn |
| 15ml/1 tbsp milk |
| knob (pat) of butter |
| ½ small courgette (zucchini), grated |
| 1 carrot, about 50g/2oz, grated |
| 2 slices processed cheese |
| 1 slice ham |
| salt and pepper (optional) |

1 Preheat the oven to 200°C/
400°F/Gas 6. Prick the potatoes
with a fork and bake for 1 hour, until
soft. Alternatively, prick well and
then microwave on a sheet of
kitchen paper on High (full power)
for 7–8 minutes.

2 Halve the leek lengthways, wash
thoroughly to remove any grit
and then slice thinly. Rinse the
mushrooms, pat dry and thinly slice.

3 Heat 5ml/1 tsp oil in a frying
pan and gently fry the leek,
mushrooms and corn for about
3 minutes, until softened, stirring
frequently. Turn into a bowl and
keep warm.

4 When the potatoes are cooked,
cut in half and scoop the centres
into the bowl with the leek and
mushroom mixture. Add the milk,
butter and a little salt and pepper if
liked, and stir to mix. Pile the
mixture back into the potato shells.

5 Reheat the remaining 5ml/1 tsp
of oil and fry the grated
courgette and carrot for 2 minutes,
until softened. Spoon on to two
small plates and spread with a fork to
cover the bases of the plates.

6 Arrange two potato halves on
each plate. For sails, cut the
cheese and ham into triangles and
secure to potatoes with cocktail
sticks. Cool slightly before serving.

# Fat Cats

**Serves 2**

oil, for greasing

200g/7oz frozen puff pastry, defrosted

a little flour, for dusting

beaten egg, to glaze

50g/2oz broccoli

25g/1oz/2 tbsp frozen mixed vegetables

15ml/1 tbsp butter or margarine

15ml/1 tbsp plain (all-purpose) flour

100ml/3½fl oz/½ cup milk

30ml/2 tbsp grated Cheddar or mild
cheese

a little mustard and cress (fine curled
cress), to garnish

1 Preheat the oven to 220°C/
425°F/Gas 7 and lightly brush a
baking sheet with a little oil. Roll out
the pastry thinly on a surface lightly
dusted with a little flour.

2 Using a shaped cookie cutter,
stamp out four 13cm/5in cat
shapes. Place two cats on the baking
sheet and brush with egg.

3 Cut a large hole in the centres of
the two remaining cats and place
the shapes on top of the other two cats.

**VARIATION**
Ring the changes by making this
recipe using different shaped cookie
cutters for the pastry shapes. Get
your child to choose his favourite.

4 Brush the tops with egg and
cook for 10 minutes, until the
pastry is well risen and golden.

5 Meanwhile chop the broccoli
and cook in a small pan of boiling
water with the frozen vegetables for
5 minutes. Drain.

6 Dry the pan and melt the butter
or margarine. Stir in the flour
and then gradually add the milk.
Bring to the boil, stirring all the time
until thickened and smooth.

7 Reserve two peas, two pieces of
carrot, and two pieces of red bell
pepper. Stir the remaining vegetables
into the sauce with the grated cheese.

8 Enlarge the cavity in the centre
of each pastry cat by scooping
out a little of the pastry. Spoon in the
vegetable mixture and arrange on
two serving plates. Garnish with
halved peas for eyes, halved carrot
strips for whiskers and red pepper
noses. Add mustard and cress. Cool
slightly before serving.

# Potato, Carrot and Courgette Rösti

**Serves 2–4**

1 small potato, about 115g/4oz

½ carrot, about 25g/1oz

½ courgette (zucchini), about 25g/1oz

10ml/2 tsp vegetable oil

sausages and baked beans, to serve

**1** Grate the potato, carrot and courgette into a bowl and mix together thoroughly.

**2** Place several sheets of kitchen paper on a surface and put the vegetables on top. Cover with more kitchen paper and press down to soak up all the excess liquid.

**3** Heat the oil in a frying pan and spoon the vegetables into the pan to form eight rounds. Flatten slightly with a fork and fry four of the rounds for 5 minutes, turning once until the potatoes are thoroughly cooked and the rösti is golden brown on both sides.

**4** Lift out of the pan and cook the remaining mixture. Cool slightly and serve with grilled sausages and baked beans.

# Veggie Burgers

**Serves 2–4**

1 large or 2 small potatoes, about 225g/8oz

1 carrot, about 50g/2oz

25g/1oz broccoli

25g/1oz Brussels sprouts

1 egg yolk

15ml/1 tbsp plain (all-purpose) flour

15ml/1 tbsp freshly grated Parmesan cheese

15ml/1 tbsp oil

salt and pepper (optional)

canned spaghetti hoops, strips of ham, wedges of cucumber, and tomato ketchup, to serve

**2** Meanwhile, cut the broccoli into small florets, chop the stem finely and thinly slice the Brussels sprouts. Rinse under cold water then add to the potatoes and carrots for the last 5 minutes of cooking.

**1** Cut the potato and carrot into chunks and cook in boiling water for 15 minutes, until tender.

**3** Drain the vegetables thoroughly and then mash together. Add the egg yolk, and a little salt and pepper, if liked, then mix well.

**4** Divide into four and shape into burgers with floured hands. Coat in flour and Parmesan cheese.

**5** Heat the oil in a frying pan, add the burgers and fry for 5 minutes, turning once until golden brown. Cool slightly, then serve with canned spaghetti hoops, strips of ham, a few cucumber wedges and a little tomato ketchup. Add a face with peas, carrot and cucumber.

**TIP**
To make a spider, add cooked green bean legs, a red (bell) pepper mouth and yellow pepper eyes.

# Vegetable Lasagne

**Serves 2–3**

¼ small onion

50g/2oz carrot

50g/2oz courgette (zucchini)

50g/2oz aubergine (eggplant)

25g/1oz button (white) mushrooms

10ml/2 tsp oil

1 small garlic clove, crushed

225g/8oz can chopped tomatoes

pinch of mixed herbs

15ml/1 tbsp butter or margarine

15ml/1 tbsp plain (all-purpose) flour

150ml/¼ pint/⅔ cup milk

60ml/4 tbsp grated mild cheese

3 sheets pre-cooked lasagne

salt and pepper

mixed salad, to serve

1 Finely chop the onion and carrot, and finely dice the courgette and aubergine. Wipe and thinly slice the mushrooms.

2 Heat the oil and fry the vegetables for 3 minutes until softened. Add the garlic, tomatoes and herbs, then bring to the boil, cover and simmer for 5 minutes.

3 Melt the butter or margarine in a pan, stir in the flour. Add the milk and bring to the boil, stirring, until thickened. Stir in half of the grated cheese and a little salt and pepper.

4 Preheat the oven to 180°C/ 350°F/Gas 4. Spoon one-third of the vegetable mixture into the base of an ovenproof dish, then add a little sauce. Add a slice of lasagne, then cover with half of the remaining vegetable mixture and half the remaining sauce.

5 Add a second sheet of pasta and top with the remaining vegetable mixture. Add a third sheet of lasagne and top with the remaining cheese sauce. Sprinkle with the remaining cheese.

6 Cook for 50–60 minutes, checking after 30 minutes and covering loosely with foil if the topping is browning too quickly. Spoon on to serving plates and leave the lasagne to cool slightly. Serve with a little mixed salad.

# Aubergine Bolognese

**Serves 2**

50g/2oz aubergine (eggplant)

1 strip red (bell) pepper

1 strip yellow (bell) pepper

5cm/2in piece of leek

1 carrot, about 50g/2oz

10ml/2 tsp oil

1 small garlic clove, crushed

25g/1oz/2 tbsp frozen corn

25g/1oz/2 tbsp red lentils

225g/8oz can chopped tomatoes

250ml/8fl oz/1 cup vegetable stock

pinch of dried herbs

50g/2oz dried pasta shapes

knob (pat) of butter or margarine

30ml/2 tbsp grated cheese (optional)

salt and pepper

**1** Rinse the aubergine, peppers and leek, peel the carrot and then finely dice all the vegetables.

**2** Heat the oil in a medium-size pan, add the diced vegetables and gently fry for 3 minutes, stirring frequently, until slightly softened.

**3** Add the garlic, corn, lentils, tomatoes, stock, herbs and a little salt and pepper.

**4** Bring to the boil, cover and simmer for about 30 minutes, stirring occasionally and adding a little extra stock if necessary.

**5** In the last 10 minutes of cooking, bring a pan of water to the boil and add the pasta. Cook for 10 minutes, until tender.

**6** Drain, toss in a little butter or margarine. Spoon on to plates and top with the aubergine bolognese. Sprinkle with cheese.

**TIP**
Sprinkle the diced aubergine with salt, leave to drain in a colander for 30 minutes, then rinse. This removes any bitter taste.

# Quick Meals

If you've had a busy day, rustle up these quick and tasty toddlers' meals – they all cook in 10 minutes or less, and there is a wide variety of recipes to choose from. Remember the importance of fun presentation, to tempt your toddler to try new foods.

## Speedy Chicken Pie

**Serves 2**

1 celery stick

25g/1oz/2 tbsp frozen corn, defrosted

30ml/2 tbsp mayonnaise

2.5ml/½ tsp ground coriander

75g/3oz cold cooked chicken

½ small packet plain crisps (US potato chips)

15ml/1 tbsp grated Red Leicester or mild cheese

salt and pepper (optional)

peas and broccoli, to serve

2 Spoon into a shallow ovenproof dish and level the surface.

3 Roughly crush the crisps and sprinkle over the chicken. Top with the grated cheese and cook for 10 minutes, until hot and bubbly.

4 Cool slightly, then serve the pie with peas and broccoli.

1 Preheat the oven to 220°C/425°F/ Gas 7. Rinse the celery, slice thinly and place in a bowl with the corn, mayonnaise, ground coriander and a little salt and pepper, if liked. Dice the chicken, add to the bowl and mix well.

**VARIATION**
**Mexican Chicken Pie**
Replace the ground coriander with ground cumin and replace the crisps with about 30ml/2 tbsp crumbled plain tortilla chips.

# Skinny Dippers

**Serves 2**

150g/5oz boneless, skinless chicken
  breast

25g/1oz/¼ cup grated Cheddar or
  mild cheese

50g/2oz/1 cup fresh breadcrumbs

15g/½oz/1 tbsp butter or margarine

115g/4oz frozen oven chips (french
  fries)

½ small carrot, cut into thin strips

½ small courgette (zucchini), cut into
  thin strips

45ml/3 tbsp tomato ketchup

1 Rinse the chicken under cold
  water and pat dry with kitchen
paper. Cut into thin strips.

2 Mix the grated cheese and
  breadcrumbs on a plate. Melt
the butter or margarine in a small
pan or in a dish in the microwave
on High (full power) for 20 seconds,
then toss the chicken strips in the
butter or margarine and roll in the
breadcrumb mixture.

3 Arrange the chicken and chips
  on a foiled-lined baking sheet.
Preheat the grill (broiler) and bring a
pan of water to the boil.

4 Grill the chicken for 6–8 minutes
  and the chips 8–10 minutes, until
both are well browned, turning
once. When the chicken is ready,
keep warm in a shallow dish while
the chips finish cooking.

5 Cook the vegetables for
  5 minutes in the pan of boiling
water, until tender.

6 Spoon the ketchup into two
  ramekins or egg cups and place
in the centre of two serving plates.
Drain the vegetables and divide the
vegetables, chicken and chips between
the two plates. Allow to cool slightly
before dipping into ketchup.

**TIP**
Keep a supply of fresh breadcrumbs
in a sealed plastic bag in the
freezer. There is no need to
defrost, just take out as much
as you need and use from frozen.

# Sweet and Sour Chicken

**Serves 2**

50g/2oz/¼ cup long grain white rice

1 carrot, about 50g/2oz

1 courgette (zucchini), about 50g/2oz

2 skinless chicken thighs

10ml/2 tsp oil

25g/1oz/2 tbsp frozen peas

5ml/1 tsp cornflour (cornstarch)

5ml/1 tsp soy sauce

10ml/2 tsp tomato ketchup

60ml/4 tbsp orange juice

1 egg, beaten

**1** Cook the rice in boiling water for 8–10 minutes, until tender.

**2** Meanwhile, peel the carrot, trim the courgette and cut both into thin strips. Bone the chicken and cut into small chunks.

**3** Heat 5ml/1 tsp of the oil in a frying pan, add the carrot, courgette, chicken and peas, and fry for 5 minutes, stirring occasionally.

**4** Blend the cornflour with the soy sauce and then stir into the pan together with the ketchup and orange juice. Cook gently, stirring all the time, until the sauce is glossy and has thickened.

**TIP**

Make the meal into an occasion and serve the food in Chinese bowls with Chinese spoons – chopsticks may be a little too tricky to manage. All children love the idea of eating in a restaurant with a parent to wait on them.

**5** Drain the rice thoroughly. Add the remaining oil to the rice together with the beaten egg and cook over a gentle heat, stirring until the egg has scrambled.

**6** Spoon the rice and sweet and sour chicken on to serving plates and cool slightly before serving.

# Ham and Tomato Scramble

**Serves 2**

2 slices ham

1 tomato

1 small strip yellow (bell) pepper

2 eggs

15ml/1 tbsp milk

2 slices bread

a little butter

salt

**1** Finely chop the ham. Halve the tomato, scoop out and discard the seeds, then chop into small dice. Finely chop the strip of pepper.

**2** Beat the eggs and milk together and season with a little salt. Toast the bread lightly.

**3** Heat a small knob (pat) of butter in a pan, add the eggs, ham, tomato and pepper and cook gently, stirring all the time until cooked to taste. Cool slightly.

**4** Butter the toast and cut into shapes with small fancy-shaped cookie cutters. Arrange on plates with the ham and tomato scramble.

**TIP**
If you don't have any special cutters, then cut the toast into tiny triangles and squares with a knife.

# Ham Salad Clown

**Serves 2**

2 slices ham

1 cherry tomato

2 slices apple

1 slice cheese

2 currants (raisins)

2 slices hard-boiled egg

a little mustard and cress (fine curled cress)

2 long slices carrot

**TIP**
Have fun varying the ingredients for the clown. Use cheese slices, radishes, peaches, lettuce and red (bell) pepper to change the appearance and features.

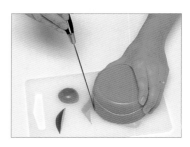

**1** Cut two large rounds from the slices of ham using a cookie cutter or the top of a glass or other container as a guide. Arrange on two plates and add a halved tomato for a nose and a slice of apple for the mouth, trimming if needed.

**2** With a knife, cut out small triangles or stars of cheese for eyes, place on the ham and add halved currants (raisins) for eye balls.

**3** Halve the egg slices and add to the face for ears. Snip the mustard and cress for hair and use snipped pieces of carrot for a ruff.

# Spanish Omelette

**Serves 2**

| |
|---|
| 2 thin slices ham |
| 1 strip red (bell) pepper |
| 15ml/1 tbsp frozen peas |
| 50g/2oz frozen oven chips (french fries) |
| 5ml/1 tsp oil |
| 1 egg |
| salt and pepper |
| tomato wedges, to serve |

1 Chop the ham and pepper. Mix the pepper and peas. Slice the oven chips.

2 Heat the oil in a non-stick frying pan, and fry the chips for 5 minutes, stirring, until lightly browned. Add the pepper and peas and cook, stirring, for a further 2 minutes. Stir in the chopped ham.

3 Beat together the egg, 10ml/2 tsp water and a little salt and pepper, and pour into the pan, tilting it so that the egg mixture covers the base evenly.

4 Cook over a medium-low heat for 2–3 minutes, until the base of the omelette is set and browned. Loosen the edges and invert the pan on to a plate to turn out the omelette. Then slide the omelette back into the pan and cook the second side for a few more minutes, until golden.

5 Cut the omelette into wedges, arrange on two plates and cool slightly. Serve with tomato wedges.

# Pasta with Ham Sauce

**Serves 2**

50g/2oz dried pasta shapes

50g/2oz/½ cup frozen mixed vegetables

30ml/2 tbsp margarine

30ml/2 tbsp plain (all-purpose) flour

150ml/¼ pint/⅔ cup milk

50g/2oz/½ cup grated Red Leicester or mild cheese

2 slices ham, chopped

salt and pepper

1 Cook the pasta in a pan of boiling water for 5 minutes. Add vegetables and cook for 5 more minutes until pasta is tender. Drain.

2 Melt the margarine in a medium-size pan and stir in the flour. Gradually add the milk and bring to the boil, stirring, until the sauce is thick and smooth.

3 Stir two-thirds of the grated cheese into the sauce and add the drained pasta and vegetables, the ham and a little salt and pepper.

4 Spoon into two shallow dishes and sprinkle with the remaining cheese. Cool slightly if necessary.

**TIP**
This recipe works equally well if you use a 100g/3½oz can tuna, drained, in place of the ham. You could serve the ham with rice, if you prefer.

# Quickie Kebabs

**Serves 2–3**

1 tomato

3 slices ham

½ small yellow (bell) pepper

6 button (white) mushrooms

6 cocktail sausages

10ml/2 tsp tomato ketchup

10ml/2 tsp oil

canned spaghetti, to serve

1 Preheat the grill (broiler). Cut the tomato into six wedges and cut each slice of ham into two strips. Roll up each strip. Cut the pepper into six chunks, discarding any seeds. Wipe the mushrooms.

2 Make six kebabs by threading a tomato wedge, a ham roll, a piece of pepper, a mushroom, and a sausage on to six cocktail sticks (toothpicks).

**TIP**
Use two rashers (strips) of rindless bacon, if preferred. Halve and roll up, and use in place of the ham.

3 Line a grill pan with foil and arrange the kebabs on top. Blend the ketchup and oil, and brush over the kebabs. Grill for 10 minutes, turning once and brushing with the juices until the vegetables are browned and the sausages are thoroughly cooked.

4 Cool slightly, then arrange on plates with canned spaghetti.

# Sausage Wrappers

**Serves 2**

4 slices ham

10ml/2 tsp tomato relish or barbecue sauce

4 sausages

baked beans and grilled potato shapes, to serve

1 Spread one side of each slice of ham with relish or sauce.

2 Cut each piece of ham into three thin strips and wrap each sausage in three strips, securing them in place with cocktail sticks (toothpicks).

3 Grill (broil) for 10 minutes, turning several times until the ham is browned and crisp.

4 Cool slightly then remove the cocktail sticks and serve the sausage wrappers with baked beans and grilled potato shapes.

**TIP**
Use four pieces of rindless streaky (fatty) bacon instead of ham, if preferred.

# Corned Beef Hash

**Serves 2**

1 potato, about 175g/6oz

10ml/2 tsp oil

50g/2oz green cabbage

115g/4oz corned beef

pinch of turmeric

15ml/1 tbsp tomato ketchup

hard-boiled egg slices, to garnish

1 Dice the potato and cook in a pan of boiling water for 3–4 minutes, until softened. Drain.

2 Heat the oil in a medium-size frying pan, add the diced potato and fry for 3 minutes, until golden.

3 Meanwhile, chop the cabbage and dice the corned beef.

4 Add the cabbage and turmeric to the pan with the potatoes and cook for 2 minutes. Stir in the corned beef and cook for 2 minutes.

5 Stir in the ketchup and spoon on to two plates. Cool slightly before serving. Garnish with the hard-boiled egg slices.

**TIP**
The hash can be garnished with tomato wedges, if liked.

# Cannibal Necklaces

**Serves 2**

45ml/3 tbsp stuffing mix

60ml/4 tbsp boiling water

115g/4oz lean minced (ground) beef

5ml/1 tsp oil

½ carrot

1 strip red (bell) pepper

1 strip green (bell) pepper

a little tomato ketchup

1 Put the stuffing mix in a bowl and pour over the boiling water. Set aside for 5 minutes to soak.

2 Stir the meat into the stuffing mix and shape into 10 small balls with floured hands.

3 Preheat the grill (broiler). Arrange the meat balls on a piece of foil on top of the grill pan and brush lightly with a little oil. Grill (broil) for 7–8 minutes, until well browned, turning once during cooking.

4 Meanwhile, thinly slice the carrot and cut the pepper into chunks, discarding the core and seeds.

5 Arrange the meat balls around the bottom edge of two serving plates. Leave spaces in between.

**TIP**

If you're feeling adventurous, liven up simple meals by piping the child's initials on to the edge of the plate, the appropriate number for their age or even a short word like "hello".

6 Place carrot and pieces of red and green pepper between each meat ball and complete with a line and bow of ketchup for necklace strings, straight from the bottle, or pipe the ketchup if preferred.

# Beef Burgers

**Serves 2**

¼ small onion

25g/1oz button (white) mushrooms

115g/4oz lean minced (ground) beef

115g/4oz frozen oven chips (french fries)

2 burger buns

10ml/2 tsp tomato ketchup

1 tomato

salt and pepper (optional)

1 Finely chop the onion, wipe and chop the mushrooms. Place the meat in a mixing bowl, add the onion and mushrooms and a little salt and pepper, if liked, and mix together thoroughly. Alternatively blend the mixture in a processor.

2 With floured hands shape two 7.5cm/3in burgers or press the mixture into a plastic burger press or upturned pastry cutter.

3 Preheat the grill (broiler). Tear off two large pieces of foil. Fold up the edges and place on a grill pan. Put the burgers on one piece and the chips on the other.

4 Cook the burgers and chips for 10 minutes, turning the food once. Remove from the grill rack and keep warm. Split the burger buns in half and toast on one side only.

5 Spread the bases of the buns with ketchup, slice the tomato and place on the buns. Top each with a burger and the second bun half. Cut in half and arrange on serving plates with the chips. Cool slightly if necessary before serving.

# Four Fast Fishes

**Serves 2**

115g/4oz hoki or cod fillet

½ egg, beaten

60ml/4 tbsp fresh breadcrumbs

10ml/2 tsp sesame seeds

10ml/2 tsp oil

15ml/1 tbsp frozen peas

4 frozen corn kernels

1 carrot

canned spaghetti rings, to serve

1 Cut away and discard any skin from the fish and rinse. Pat dry and cut into four pieces.

2 Put the egg in a saucer and place the breadcrumbs and sesame seeds on a plate. Dip pieces of fish in egg and then in breadcrumb mixture to coat the fish.

3 Heat the oil in a frying pan, add the fish and fry for 4–5 minutes, turning once, until the fish pieces are golden brown and cooked.

4 Meanwhile cook the peas and corn in a pan of boiling water for 5 minutes. Cut the carrot into long thin slices and then cut out fin and tail shapes and tiny triangles for mouths.

5 Arrange the pieces of fish on two plates with the carrot decorations, corn for eyes and peas for bubbles. Serve with warmed canned spaghetti rings.

**TIP**
You can freeze the uncooked breaded portions to provide a quick meal at a later date when you are pushed for time. Freeze them on a tray and then wrap them well to prevent the odour tainting other food in the freezer.

# Tuna Risotto

**Serves 2**

5ml/1 tsp oil

¼ onion, finely chopped

50g/2oz long grain white rice

50g/2oz frozen mixed vegetables

1 small garlic clove, crushed

10ml/2 tsp tomato ketchup

100g/3½oz can tuna fish in water

salt and pepper (optional)

1 Heat the oil in a small pan and fry the chopped onion for about 3 minutes, until softened.

2 Add the rice, mixed vegetables, garlic, tomato ketchup and 250ml/8fl oz/1 cup water and a little salt and pepper, if liked.

3 Bring to the boil and simmer uncovered for 10 minutes. Drain the tuna and add to the rice mixture, stirring to mix. Cook for 3–4 minutes, stirring occasionally, until the water has been absorbed by the rice and the rice is tender.

4 Spoon on to plates and cool slightly before serving.

**TIP**
If liked use cold leftover cooked chicken, lamb or beef in place of the tuna.

# Fish Finger Log Cabins

**Serves 2**

4 frozen fish fingers (breaded fish sticks)

25g/1oz green cabbage

8 mangetouts (snow peas)

2 frozen peas

1 strip green (bell) pepper

1 strip red (bell) pepper

1 Grill (broil) the fish fingers for 10 minutes, turning once until golden. Meanwhile, finely shred the cabbage and cook in boiling water for 3 minutes. Add the mangetouts and peas and cook for a further 2 minutes. Drain well.

2 Arrange two fish fingers side by side on each plate. Trim the mangetouts and use them to make a roof, slightly overlapping the edges of the fish fingers.

3 Cut four windows from the green pepper and two doors from the red pepper and add to the log cabins, using peas as door handles. Arrange the shredded cabbage to look like grass.

**VARIATION**
**Sausage Log Cabin**
Use four grilled (broiled) cocktail chipolata sausages for each cabin. Make the roof from green beans and use shredded spinach for the grass.

# TOAST TOPPERS

ALL CHILDREN, EVEN THE FUSSIEST OF EATERS, LOVE BREAD AND TOAST, AND THERE IS NO QUICKER CONVENIENCE FOOD. RING THE CHANGES WITH THESE SUPER-SPEEDY SNACKS THAT WILL MAKE MEAL-TIMES FUN.

## Shape Sorters

**Serves 2**

4 slices bread

butter or margarine, for spreading

30ml/2 tbsp smooth peanut butter

50g/2oz/½ cup grated Cheddar or
  mild cheese

4 cherry tomatoes

3 slices cucumber

**VARIATION**
**Pizza Shape Sorters**
Spread the shapes with tomato
ketchup. Chop a tomato finely, and
sprinkle over the shapes, then add
some grated mild cheese. Grill (broil)
until bubbly and golden.

1 Toast the bread lightly on both
sides and remove crusts. Stamp
out shapes using square, star,
triangle and round cutters.

2 Spread the shapes with butter or
margarine and then peanut
butter. Place the shapes on a baking
sheet and sprinkle with cheese.

3 Grill (broil) until the cheese is
bubbly. Cool slightly, arrange on a
plate and serve with tomato wedges
and quartered cucumber slices.

## Happy Families

**Serves 2**

3 slices bread

butter or margarine, for spreading

3 slices processed cheese

2 slices ham

a little mustard and cress (fine curled
  cress)

1 strip red (bell) pepper

½ carrot

small pieces of cucumber

1 Stamp out shapes of men and
women from the bread, using
small cutters. Spread with a little
butter or margarine.

2 Stamp out cheese dresses using
the woman cutter and trimming
off the head. Press on to three of the
bodies. Cut out cheese jumpers and
ham trousers and braces. Add to the
male shapes.

3 Snip off the leaves from mustard
and cress and use for eyes. Cut
tiny red pepper mouths and make
necklaces and bow ties from the
carrot and cucumber, using flower
cutters. Arrange on plates.

# French Toast Butterflies

**Serves 2**

| |
|---|
| 4 small broccoli florets |
| 8 peas |
| 1 small carrot |
| 1 slice Red Leicester or mild cheese |
| 2 slices ham |
| 2 slices bread |
| 1 egg |
| 10ml/2 tsp milk |
| 5ml/1 tsp vegetable oil |
| a little tomato ketchup |

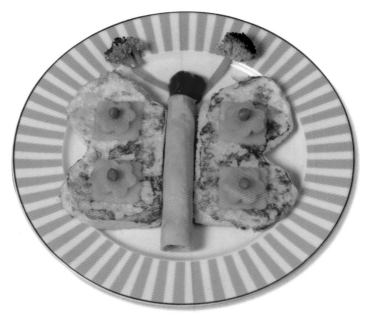

1 Cook the broccoli florets and the peas in a pan of boiling water for 5 minutes. Drain well.

2 For each butterfly, cut four thin slices of carrot and cut into flower shapes with a petits four cutter. Cut out four small squares from the cheese.

3 Cut four thin strips from the rest of the carrot for antennae. Roll up each piece of ham and arrange in the middle of two serving plates, to make the two butterfly bodies.

4 Cut butterfly wings from the bread, using a small knife.

**TIP**
Vary the ingredients for the butterfly decorations. Make a body from a grilled sausage if preferred.

5 Beat together the egg and milk and dip the bread in to coat both sides thoroughly. Heat the oil in a medium-size frying pan and fry the bread until golden on both sides.

6 Assemble the butterfly, using the French toast for the wings and decorating with the carrot, cheese, broccoli and peas. Use a blob of ketchup for the head.

# Tuna Flowers

**Serves 2–3**

6 thin slices bread

25g/1oz butter, plus extra if
  necessary

10ml/2 tsp plain (all-purpose) flour

75ml/5 tbsp milk

60ml/4 tbsp grated Red Leicester or
  mild cheese

100g/3½oz can tuna fish, drained

50g/2oz/4 tbsp frozen mixed
  vegetables, defrosted

½ carrot

6 slices cucumber, halved

a little mustard and cress (fine curled
  cress)

salt and pepper (optional)

**1** Preheat the oven to 200°C/
400°F/Gas 6. Cut out six flower
shapes from the bread, using a 9cm/
3½in scalloped cookie cutter. Flatten
each piece slightly with a rolling pin.

**4** Stir the flour into the remaining
butter (you should have about
10ml/2 tsp left). Gradually stir in the
milk and bring to the boil, stirring
until the sauce is thick and smooth.

**5** Stir in 30ml/3 tbsp of the cheese,
the tuna, the mixed vegetables
and a little salt and pepper, if liked.

**6** Heat through and then spoon
into the baked bread cups and
sprinkle with remaining cheese.

**7** Arrange the tuna cups on
serving plates. Cut the carrot
into thin strips for flower stems and
add to the plate, with halved
cucumber slices for leaves and
mustard and cress for grass.

**2** Melt the butter in a pan or
microwave. Brush a little over
one side of each piece of bread and
then press the bread, buttered side
downwards, into sections of a patty tin
(muffin pan). Brush the second side of
the bread with a little more butter.

**3** Bake in the oven for about 10–
12 minutes, until crisp and
golden around the edges.

# Noughts and Crosses

**Serves 2**

8 green beans

¼ red (bell) pepper

6 slices snack dried sausage

2 slices bread

butter or margarine, for spreading

115g/4oz Cheddar or mild cheese

**TIP**

To vary the topping, use thin strips of carrot or ham for the grid, sliced sausage, frankfurter or carrot for the noughts (zeros), carrot, green (bell) pepper or cucumber for the crosses.

1 Trim the beans, thinly slice the pepper, discarding any seeds, and thinly slice the sausage.

2 Cook the beans in boiling water for 5 minutes. Toast the bread lightly on both sides and spread with butter or margarine. Thinly slice the cheese and place on the toast.

3 Drain the beans and arrange four on each piece of toast to form a grid. Add crosses made from pepper strips and noughts from pieces of the sausage.

4 Grill (broil) the toasts until the cheese is bubbly. Arrange on plates and cool slightly before serving.

# Cheese Strips on Toast

**Serves 2**

2 slices bread

butter or margarine, for spreading

50g/2oz Cheddar or mild yellow cheese

50g/2oz red Leicester or mild red cheese

2 cherry tomatoes, to serve

1 Toast the bread lightly on both sides, then spread each slice with butter or margarine.

**TIP**

If your child likes ketchup or peanut butter, add a thin scraping underneath the cheese slices for a surprise flavour.

2 Thinly slice the cheese and then cut into strips about 2.5cm/1in wide. Arrange alternate coloured cheese strips over the toast and grill (broil) the toasts until bubbly.

3 Cool slightly, then cut into squares, arrange on plates and serve with cherry tomato wedges.

# Speedy Sausage Rolls

**Makes 18**

8 slices multigrain white bread

225g/8oz cocktail sausages

40g/1½oz/3 tbsp butter or
  margarine

carrot and cucumber sticks, to serve

**1** Preheat the oven to 190°C/
375°F/Gas 5. Trim the crusts off
the bread and cut into slices a little
smaller than the sausages.

**2** Wrap each piece of bread around
a sausage and secure with a
halved cocktail stick (toothpick). Place
the sausage rolls on a baking sheet.

**3** Melt the butter or margarine in a
small pan or in the microwave and
brush over the prepared sausage rolls.

**4** Bake in the oven for 15 minutes,
until browned. Cool slightly
and remove the cocktail sticks.
Arrange on a plate and serve with
carrot and cucumber sticks.

**TIP**
Spread a little tomato relish or
ketchup, or a little mild mustard
over the bread before wrapping it
around the sausages, to give a
sharper flavour. If the bread is
thickly cut, flatten it slightly with a
rolling pin, before wrapping around
the sausages.

# Pizza Clock

**Serves 3–4**

20cm/8in ready-made pizza base

45ml/3 tbsp tomato ketchup or pizza
  sauce

2 tomatoes

75g/3oz/¾ cup grated mild cheese

pinch of dried marjoram

1 green (bell) pepper

1 large carrot

1 thick slice ham

1 Preheat oven to 220°C/425°F/
Gas 7. Place the pizza base on a
baking sheet and spread with
ketchup or pizza sauce. Chop the
tomatoes and scatter over the pizza
with the cheese and marjoram.

2 Place directly on an oven shelf
and bake for 12 minutes, until
the cheese is bubbly. (Place a baking
tray on the shelf below the pizza to
catch any drips of cheese.)

3 Meanwhile halve the pepper, cut
away the core and seeds and
stamp out the numbers 3, 6, 9 and 12
with small number cutters. Peel and
thinly cut the carrot lengthways and
stamp out the numbers 1, 2, 4, 5, 7,
8, 10 and 11. Arrange on the pizza to
form a clock face.

4 Cut out a carrot circle. Cut two
clock hands, each about 7.5cm/
3in long from the ham. Arrange on
the pizza with the circle of carrot.

5 Place the pizza clock on to a
serving plate and arrange the
numbers around the edge. Cool the
pizza clock slightly before cutting
into wedges and serving.

**TIP**
If preferred, make a smaller version
of this using half a toasted muffin.
Top as above and grill (broil) until
the cheese melts. Add ham hands
and small pieces of carrot to mark
the numbers.

# Spotted Sandwiches

**Serves 2**

1 hard-boiled egg

30ml/2 tbsp mayonnaise

2 slices white bread

2 slices brown bread

a little mustard and cress (fine curled cress)

½ small carrot

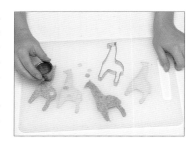

**1** Peel and finely chop the egg, place in a small bowl and blend well with the mayonnaise.

**2** Stamp out giraffe shapes from the brown and white bread, using an animal cookie cutter.

**3** Cut tiny rounds from each shape, using the end of a metal piping tube, and then replace the rounds with opposite-coloured bread circles.

**4** Spread the egg and mayonnaise over half of the shapes and top with the remaining shapes. Arrange on plates with snipped mustard and cress for grass and shaped carrot slices for flowers.

# Sandwich Snails

**Serves 2**

1 strip red (bell) pepper

small piece cucumber

15ml/1 tbsp frozen corn, defrosted

25g/1oz/¼ cup grated Cheddar or mild cheese

15ml/1 tbsp mayonnaise

1 slice bread

2 cooked sausages

a little shredded lettuce

**1** Cut away any seeds from the pepper and cut out four small squares for the snails' eyes. Cut four strips of cucumber for their antennae. Finely chop the remaining pepper and cucumber and mix with the corn, cheese and mayonnaise. Place in a bowl.

**2** Trim the crusts off the bread, cut in half and overlap two short edges together to make a long strip. Flatten slightly with a rolling pin so that the bread bonds together.

**VARIATION**
For pasta snails, use large shell pasta instead of the bread, and stuff with the cheese mixture.

**3** Spread the bread with the cheese mixture and roll up tightly. Squeeze together, then cut in half crossways to make two rounds.

**4** Arrange each slice, cut side uppermost, on two serving plates. Arrange the sausages as bodies, and use the cucumber strips for antennae and the red pepper squares for the eyes. Arrange the shredded lettuce as grass.

# EASY DESSERTS

WITH A YOUNG FAMILY TO FEED, DESSERTS NEED TO BE QUICK, LIGHT AND TASTE GOOD WITHOUT THE KIDS REALIZING THAT THEY'RE HEALTHY TOO! REMEMBER TO KEEP SUGAR TO A MINIMUM.

## Fruit Fondue

**Serves 2**

150g/5oz tub ready-to-serve low-fat custard

25g/1oz milk chocolate

1 eating apple

1 banana

1 satsuma or clementine

a few strawberries or seedless grapes

1 Pour the custard into a pan, add the chocolate and heat, stirring all the time until the chocolate has melted. Cool slightly.

2 Quarter the apple, core and cut into bitesize pieces, slice the banana and break the satsuma or clementine into segments. Hull the strawberries and wash the grapes.

3 Arrange the fruit on two small plates, pour the custard into two small dishes and place on the plates. The fruit can be dipped into the custard, using either a fork or fingers.

**TIP**
Add the chocolate to a tub of custard and microwave on Full Power (100%) for 1½ minutes, or until the chocolate has melted. Stir and spoon into dishes. Cool slightly.

# Strawberry Ice Cream

**Makes 900ml/1½ pints/3¾ cups**

300ml/½pint/1¼ cups double (heavy) cream

425g/15oz can custard

450g/1lb strawberries

teddy bear wafers, to decorate

strawberries, to decorate

1 Whip the cream until softly peaking, then fold in the custard.

2 Hull the strawberries and then rinse and pat dry. Process to make a smooth purée, then press through a sieve (strainer) into the cream and custard. Fold together.

3 Pour the mixture into a plastic tub and freeze the ice cream for 6-7 hours, until half frozen.

4 Beat the ice cream with a fork or process in a food blender until smooth, then return the tub to the freezer and freeze until solid.

5 Remove the ice cream from the freezer 10 minutes before serving so that it can soften slightly. Scoop into serving bowls and decorate each with teddy bear wafers and extra fruit, such as strawberries.

**VARIATIONS**
**Strawberry Ripple Ice Cream**
Purée and sieve (strain) an extra 250g/9oz strawberries and sweeten with 30ml/2 tbsp icing (confectioners') sugar. Swirl this into the half-frozen ice cream at Step 4 and then freeze until solid.

**Apricot and Chocolate Chip Ice Cream**
Whisk 300ml/½ pint/1¼ cups double (heavy) cream, and fold in 425g/15oz can custard. Drain and purée the contents of a 425g/15oz can apricot slices in natural juice and stir into the cream with the finely grated rind of 1 orange. Pour into a plastic tub, freeze until mushy and then beat well. Stir in 100g/3½oz packet chocolate dots and freeze again until solid. Scoop into serving dishes and decorate the ice cream with orange segments and wafers, if liked.

# Raspberry Sorbet

**Makes: 900ml/1½ pints/3¾ cups**

10ml/2 tsp powdered gelatine

600ml/1 pint/2½ cups water

225g/8oz/1¼ cups caster (superfine) sugar

675g/1½lb raspberries, hulled

grated rind and juice of ½ lemon

**1** Put 30ml/2 tbsp water in a cup, sprinkle the gelatine over and set aside for a few minutes to soak.

**2** Place the water and sugar in a pan and heat, stirring occasionally, until the sugar has completely dissolved.

**3** Bring to the boil and boil rapidly for 3 minutes. Remove from the heat, add the gelatine mixture to the syrup and stir until completely dissolved. Leave to cool.

**4** Liquidize or process the raspberries to a smooth purée, then press through a sieve (strainer) into the syrup. Stir in the lemon rind and juice.

**5** Pour into a plastic tub and freeze for 6–7 hours, or until the mixture is half frozen.

**6** Beat the sorbet with a fork or transfer to a food processor and process until smooth. Return to the freezer and freeze until solid.

**7** Remove the sorbet from the freezer 10 minutes before serving to soften slightly, then scoop into dishes with a melon baller or small teaspoon.

**VARIATION**
**Summer Fruit Sorbet**
Follow the recipe up to Step 3. Put a 500g/1¼lb pack of frozen summer fruits into a second pan. Add 60ml/4 tbsp water, cover and cook for 5 minutes until soft, then purée and sieve (strain), add to the syrup and continue as above.

# Yogurt Lollies

### Makes 6

150g/5oz tub strawberry yogurt

150ml/¼ pint/⅔ cup milk

10ml/2 tsp strawberry milkshake
  powder

1 Mix the yogurt, milk and
milkshake powder together.

2 Pour the mixture into six small
lolly (popsicle) plastic moulds. Add
the handles and freeze overnight.

3 Dip the moulds into hot water,
count to 15, then flex handles and
remove. Serve at once.

**TIP**
Store lollies (popsicles) for up to a
week in the freezer. Make sure
they are tightly covered, as they
can pick up other flavours.

# Jolly Jellies

### Serves 4

150g/5oz packet strawberry jelly
  (flavoured gelatine)

2 ripe plums

175g/6oz fromage frais or Greek
  (US strained plain) yogurt

4 dolly mixtures (round candies)

10ml/2 tsp sugar or chocolate strands

1 Cut the jelly into pieces. Place in
a bowl and pour over 150ml/
¼ pint/⅔ cup boiling water. Stir
until dissolved, then set aside to cool.

2 Halve the plums, cut away the
stones (pits) and reserve four thin
slices. Chop the remaining fruit and
divide among four small dishes.

3 Stir the fromage frais or yogurt
into the jelly and pour into the
dishes. Chill in the refrigerator
until set.

4 Decorate with sliced plums for
mouths, halved dolly mixtures
for the eyes and sugar or chocolate
sugar strands for hair.

**TIP**
If the fussy eater doesn't like
different textures, finely chop or
purée the plums before adding to
the jelly (flavoured gelatine) so the
child doesn't know it's not just jelly!

# Pancakes

**Serves 2–3**

| |
|---|
| 50g/2oz/⅓ cup plain (all-purpose) flour |
| 1 egg |
| 150ml/¼ pint/⅔ cup milk |
| 15ml/1 tbsp vegetable oil |
| *For the filling* |
| 1 banana |
| 1 orange |
| 2–3 scoops ice cream |

1 Sift the flour into a bowl, add the egg and gradually whisk in the milk to form a smooth batter. Whisk in 5ml/1 tsp of the oil.

2 To make the filling, slice the banana thinly or in chunks. Cut the peel away from the orange with a serrated knife, then cut the orange into segments.

3 Heat a little of the remaining oil in a medium-size non-stick pan, pour off any excess oil and add 30ml/2 tbsp of the batter. Tilt the pan to evenly coat it and cook for a couple of minutes, until the pancake is set and the underside is golden.

4 Loosen the edges with a knife, then toss the pancake or turn with a knife. Brown the other side and then slide out on to a plate. Fold in four and keep warm.

5 Cook the rest of the batter in the same way until you have made 6 pancakes. Place two on each plate.

6 Spoon a little fruit into each pancake and arrange on serving plates. Top with the remaining fruit and a scoop of ice cream, and pour over a little maple syrup. Serve at once.

# Traffic Light Sundaes

**Serves 6**

½ packet lime jelly (flavoured gelatine)

½ packet orange jelly

½ packet strawberry jelly

2 kiwi fruits

275g/10oz can mandarin oranges

6 scoops vanilla ice cream, to serve

12 strawberries to decorate

4 Add a little kiwi fruit and continue making layers using the orange jelly and mandarins and topping with the strawberry jelly.

5 Add half the strawberries, top with a scoop of ice cream and decorate with the remaining strawberries. Serve immediately.

1 Make up each jelly in a separate bowl with boiling water according to the instructions on the packet. Cool, then transfer to the refrigerator and allow to set.

2 Peel and slice the kiwi fruits, hull and rinse the strawberries and cut in half. Drain the mandarins.

3 Chop all of the jellies and divide the lime jelly equally among six sundae glasses.

**TIP**

This is a great recipe for a party – simple but ever popular. For smaller numbers of children, halve the recipe to make three. For tiny children, make up half-size sundaes in plastic cups.

# Cheat's Trifle

**Serves 2**

2 slices Swiss roll (jelly roll)

20ml/4 tsp orange juice

1 mandarin orange

50g/2oz strawberries

150g/5oz tub ready-to-serve custard

10ml/2 tsp Greek (US strained plain) yogurt

2 sugar flowers, to decorate

**TIP**
Use 150ml/¼ pint/⅔ cup leftover custard if you have it or make custard with custard powder and 150ml/¼ pint/⅔ cup milk.

1 Put a slice of Swiss roll in the base of two ramekin dishes and spoon the orange juice over the top. Peel the mandarin orange and divide the segments between the dishes.

2 Hull, rinse and chop the strawberries. Place in dishes.

3 Spoon the custard over the strawberries, top with yogurt and decorate with sugar flowers.

# Baked Bananas

**Serves 2**

2 medium bananas

2 small scoops ice cream

1 Preheat the oven to 180°C/ 350°F/Gas 4. Separate the unpeeled bananas and put on a baking sheet. Cook for 10 minutes, until the skins have blackened and the bananas feel quite soft.

2 Hold the banana in a dish towel, make a slit along the length of the banana and peel off the skin. Peel the second banana.

3 Slice and arrange each as a ring on a plate. Place a scoop of ice cream in the centre of each plate.

**TIP**
For an adult version, slit the banana and spoon in a teaspoon or two of coffee cream liqueur, eat out of the skin with a teaspoon.

# QUICK CAKES AND BAKES THE KIDS CAN MAKE

COOKING IS FUN, AND THE EARLIER YOU LEARN, THE MORE FUN IT IS. EVEN THE FADDIEST EATER CAN BE AN ENTHUSIASTIC COOK, AND HELPING TO DECIDE WHAT TO COOK FOR A MEAL CAN MAKE A CHILD MORE WILLING TO SIT DOWN WITH THE FAMILY AND HAND ROUND THEIR HOME-MADE GOODIES. LEARNING TO WEIGH OUT INGREDIENTS, AND TO MIX, SPREAD AND SPOON OUT, ALL HELPS WITH CO-ORDINATION AND ENCOURAGES A BASIC INTEREST IN AND LOVE OF FOOD.

**Getting ready**
• Find a large apron or cover the child's clothes with an old adult-size shirt with the sleeves cut down.
• Always wash the child's hands before you start to cook.

• Choose a sturdy chair for your child to stand on next to the work surface or table. Alternatively, put a large cloth on the floor, set scales, bowls, ingredients etc out, and prepare food sitting down.

• Make it clear to your child that only the adult opens the oven door and touches pans on the stove.
• Keep knives and scissors out of the way; provide blunt, round-ended scissors if required.

## Orange and Apple Rockies

**Makes 24**

oil, for greasing

115g/4oz/½ cup margarine

225g/8oz/2 cups self-raising (self-rising) flour

1 large eating apple

50g/2oz ready-to-eat dried apricots

50g/2oz sultanas (golden raisins)

grated rind of 1 small orange

75g/3oz/⅓ cup demerara (raw) sugar

1 egg

15ml/1 tbsp milk

apple slices, to serve

1 Preheat the oven to 190°C/375°F/ Gas 5 and brush two baking sheets with a little oil. Rub the margarine into the flour with your fingertips until the mixture resembles fine breadcrumbs.

2 Peel, core and finely chop the apple, chop the apricots and stir into the flour mixture with the sultanas and orange rind. Reserve 30ml/2 tbsp of the sugar and stir the rest into the mixture.

3 Beat the egg and milk, add to the flour mixture and mix until just beginning to bind together.

4 Drop spoonfuls, well spaced apart, on to the baking sheet. Sprinkle with the reserved sugar and bake in the oven for 12–15 minutes. Transfer to a serving plate and serve warm or cold with apple slices.

**TIP**
Freeze any left-over rockies in a plastic bag for up to three months.

# Date Crunch

**Makes 24 pieces**

225g/8oz packet digestive biscuits (graham crackers)

75g/3oz stoned (pitted) dates

75g/3oz/⅓ cup butter

30ml/2 tbsp golden (light corn) syrup

75g/3oz sultanas (golden raisins)

150g/5oz milk or dark (bittersweet) chocolate

**1** Line an 18cm/7in shallow baking tin (pan) with foil. Put the biscuits in a plastic bag and crush roughly with a rolling pin. Finely chop the dates.

**2** Gently heat the butter and syrup in a small pan until the butter has melted.

## TIP

For an alternative topping, drizzle 75g/3oz melted white and 75g/3oz melted dark (bittersweet) chocolate over the biscuit, to make random squiggly lines. Chill until set.

**3** Stir in the crushed biscuits, the dates and sultanas and mix well. Spoon into the tin, press flat with the back of a spoon and chill for 1 hour.

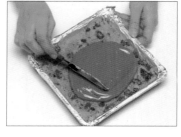

**4** Break the chocolate into a bowl, melt over hot water, and then spoon over the biscuit mixture, spreading evenly with a palette knife. Chill until set.

**5** Lift the foil out of the tin and peel away. Cut the biscuit into 24 pieces and arrange on a plate.

# Chocolate Dominoes

**Makes 16**

oil, for greasing

175g/6oz/³⁄₄ cup soft margarine

175g/6oz/⁷⁄₈ cup caster (superfine) sugar

150g/5oz/²⁄₃ cup self-raising
(self-rising) flour

25g/1oz cocoa powder (unsweetened)

3 eggs

*For the Topping*

175g/6oz/³⁄₄ cup butter, softened

25g/1oz cocoa powder (unsweetened)

300g/11oz/3 cups icing
(confectioners') sugar

a few liquorice strips and 115g/4oz
packet M & M's, for decoration

1 Preheat the oven to 180°C/350°F/
Gas 4. Brush an 18 × 28cm/7 × 11in
baking tin (pan) with a little oil and
line with baking parchment.

2 Put all the cake ingredients in a
bowl and beat until smooth.

3 Spoon into the tin and level the
surface with a palette knife.

4 Bake in the oven for 30 minutes,
or until the cake springs back
when pressed with the fingertips.

5 Cool in the tin for 5 minutes, then
loosen the edges with a knife and
turn out on to a wire rack. Peel off
the paper and allow the cake to cool.

6 Turn the cake on to a chopping
board and cut into 16 bars.

7 To make the topping, place the
butter in a bowl, sift in the cocoa
and icing sugar and beat until smooth.
Spread the topping evenly over the
cakes with a palette knife.

8 Add a strip of liquorice to each
cake, decorate with M & M's for
domino dots and arrange the cakes on
a serving plate.

**VARIATION**
**Traffic Light Cakes**
**Makes 16**
To make Traffic Light Cakes omit the
cocoa and add an extra 25g/1oz/3 tbsp
flour. Omit the cocoa from the icing
and add an extra 25g/1oz/3 tbsp icing
(confectioners') sugar and flavour with
2.5ml/½ tsp vanilla essence (extract).
Spread over the cakes and decorate
with eight halved red, yellow and
green glacé (candied) cherries to look
like traffic lights.

# Marshmallow Krispie Cakes

**Makes 45**

oil, for greasing

250g/9oz bag toffees

50g/2oz/4 tbsp butter

45ml/3 tbsp milk

115g/4oz marshmallows

175g/6oz Rice Krispies

1 Lightly brush a 20 × 33cm/8 × 13in roasting pan with a little oil. Put the toffees, butter and milk in a pan and heat gently, stirring until the toffees have melted.

2 Add the marshmallows and Rice Krispies and stir until well mixed and the marshmallows have melted.

3 Spoon into the pan, level the surface and leave to set. Cut into squares, put into paper cases and serve.

# Mini-muffins

**Makes 24**

200g/7oz/1½ cups plain (all-purpose) flour

10ml/2 tsp baking powder

50g/2oz/¼ cup soft light brown sugar

150ml/¼ pint/⅔ cup milk

1 egg, beaten

50g/2oz/4 tbsp butter or margarine, melted

50g/2oz glacé (candied) cherries

50g/2oz ready-to-eat dried apricots

2.5ml/½ tsp vanilla essence (extract)

1 Preheat the oven to 220°C/ 425°F/Gas 7 and place 24 petits fours cases in two mini patty tins (muffin pans).

2 Place the flour, baking powder and sugar in a bowl and add the milk, egg and melted butter or margarine. Stir thoroughly until the mixture is smooth.

3 Chop the cherries and apricots and stir into the muffin mixture with the vanilla essence.

4 Spoon the muffin mixture into the paper cases so they are about three-quarters full.

5 Cook for 10–12 minutes, until well risen and browned. If you have just one tin cook in two batches.

**TIP**
For older children, spoon the mixture into 12 medium-size muffin cases. Muffins are best served warm from the oven. If they aren't eaten immediately, they can be frozen for up to three months.

**VARIATIONS**
**Chocolate Chip Muffins**
Substitute 25g/1oz unsweetened cocoa powder for 25g/1oz/2 tbsp flour. Omit the cherries, apricots and vanilla and substitute 50g/2oz white and 50g/2oz plain (semisweet) chocolate dots.

**Orange and Banana Muffins**
Substitute 2 small mashed bananas for 60ml/2fl oz/¼ cup milk. Omit the cherries, apricot and vanilla, and add 15ml/1 tbsp grated orange rind.

# Cup Cake Faces

**Makes 12**

| |
|---|
| 115g/4oz/⅔ cup margarine |
| 115g/4oz/⅔ cup caster (superfine) sugar |
| 115g/4oz/1 cup self-raising (self-rising) flour |
| 2 eggs |
| *For the Topping* |
| 50g/2oz/¼ cup butter |
| 115g/4oz/1 cup icing (confectioners') sugar |
| pink food colouring |
| 115g/4oz packet M & M's |
| 2 red liquorice bootlaces |
| 12 dolly mixtures |
| 75g/3oz plain (semisweet) chocolate |

**1** Preheat the oven to 180°C/350°F/ Gas 4. Place 12 paper cake cases in the sections of a patty tin (muffin pan). Put all the cake ingredients into a bowl and beat until smooth.

**2** Divide the cake mixture among the cases and cook for 12–15 minutes, until well risen and the cakes spring back when pressed with a fingertip. Leave to cool.

**3** Meanwhile, make the topping: beat the butter in a bowl, sift in the icing sugar and beat the mixture until smooth. Stir in a little pink food colouring.

**4** Spread the icing over the cakes. Add M & M eyes, short pieces of liquorice for mouths and a dolly mixture nose.

**5** Break the chocolate into pieces, melt in a bowl over a pan of gently simmering water and then spoon into a baking parchment piping (pastry) bag. Snip off the tip and pipe hair, eye balls, glasses and moustaches on to the cakes.

**6** Carefully arrange in a single layer on a serving plate and allow the icing to set before serving.

## VARIATION
### Alphabet Cakes
Make up a half quantity of cake mixture as above and spoon into 24 mini muffin or petits fours cases. Put into sections of a patty tin (muffin pan) or petits fours tin (pan), or arrange on a baking sheet close together, and cook for 8–10 minutes, then cool. Blend 225g/8oz/2 cups sifted icing (confectioners') sugar with 30ml/2tbsp water until smooth. Add a little water if necessary, to make a thick spoonable icing. Spoon 30ml/2 tbsp into a piping (pastry) bag fitted with a small nozzle. Spoon half the remaining icing into a separate bowl and colour pink. Colour the remaining icing blue. Spoon the icing over the cakes, smooth the surface and pipe on letters of the alphabet. Leave to set.

# Gingerbread People

**Makes 24**

oil, for greasing

225g/8oz/2 cups plain (all-purpose) flour

5ml/1 tsp ground ginger

1.5ml/¼ tsp ground cinnamon

7.5ml/1½ tsp bicarbonate of soda (baking soda)

50g/2oz/4 tbsp margarine

115g/4oz/⅔ cup soft light brown sugar

45ml/3 tbsp golden (light corn) syrup

30ml/2 tbsp milk

75g/3oz dark (bittersweet) chocolate

2 packets M & M's

**1** Brush two baking sheets with a little oil. Sift the flour, spices and bicarbonate of soda into a bowl.

**2** Place the margarine, sugar and syrup in a pan and heat until the margarine has melted.

**3** Remove from heat and stir in the flour mixture and milk. Mix to a firm dough, chill for 30 minutes.

### TIP
Chocolate decorations soften biscuits (cookies), so eat on the day or decorate as many biscuits as you will eat and store the rest in an air-tight container for up to four days.

**4** Preheat the oven to 160°C/325°F/Gas 3. Knead the dough lightly and roll out on a floured surface. Cut out gingerbread men and women with 9cm/3½in cutters. Place on the baking sheets, re roll the trimmings, stamp out nine gingerbread people and continue until all the dough is used.

**5** Cook for 10 minutes, until golden, and then set aside to cool and harden a little on the baking sheets. Loosen while still warm.

**6** Break the chocolate into a bowl and melt over hot water, then spoon a little chocolate over the gingerbread men for trousers. Place on the baking sheets to set.

**7** Spoon the remaining chocolate into a piping (pastry) bag fitted with a small nozzle and pipe faces on the gingerbread people and some swirls for petticoats on the women. Pipe two dots on all the people for buttons and stick on M & M's. Leave to set before serving.

# Bread Animals

**Makes 15**

| |
|---|
| oil, for greasing |
| 2 × 280g/10oz packets white bread mix |
| a few currants (raisins) |
| ½ small red (bell) pepper |
| 1 small carrot |
| 1 egg |

1 Brush two large baking sheets with a little oil. Put the bread mixes in a large bowl and make up as directed on the packet, with warm water.

2 Knead on a lightly floured surface for 5 minutes, until the dough is smooth and elastic. Return the dough to the bowl, cover with oiled clear film (plastic wrap) and leave in a warm place for ¾–1 hour, until it has doubled in size.

3 Preheat the oven to 220°C/ 425°F/Gas 7. Knead the dough again for 5 minutes and then divide into five pieces.

4 To make snakes, take one piece of dough, cut into three and shape each into a 15cm/6in snake, making a slit in one end for the mouth. Twist the snakes on the baking sheet. Insert two currants for eyes. Cut out a thin strip of pepper, cutting a triangle at one end for the forked tongue.

5 For hedgehogs, take another piece of dough and cut into three. Shape each into an oval about 6cm/2½in long. Place on the baking sheet and add currant eyes and a red pepper nose. Snip the dough with scissors to make the prickly spines.

6 For the mice, take a third piece of dough and cut into four pieces. Shape three pieces into ovals, each about 6cm/2½in long and place on the baking sheet. Shape tiny rounds of dough for ears and wiggly tails from the fourth piece of dough. Press on to the mice bodies and use the currants for eyes.

7 Cut small strips of carrot and use for whiskers.

**TIP**

Give a portion of the prepared dough to your children, with some chopped dried fruits, and allow them to create their very own bread animals.

8 For the crocodiles, cut another piece of dough into three. Take a small piece off each and reserve. Shape the large pieces into 10cm/4in long sausages. Make slits for the mouths and wedge open with crumpled foil. Add currant eyes. Shape the spare dough into feet and press into position. Make criss-cross cuts on the backs.

9 For rabbits, take the final piece of dough and cut into three. Take a small piece off each for tails. Roll the remaining pieces of dough into thick sausages 18cm/7in long. Loop the dough and twist twice to form the body and head of rabbit. Use the rest for tails.

10 Cover the shapes with oiled clear film and leave in a warm place for 10–15 minutes. Brush with beaten egg and cook for 10–12 minutes, until golden.

11 Serve warm or cold, split and filled with ham or cheese.

# Cheese Shapes

**Makes 15**

| |
|---|
| oil, for greasing |
| 350g/12oz/3 cups self-raising (self-rising) flour |
| pinch of salt |
| 115g/4oz/½ cup margarine |
| 115g/4oz Cheddar or mild cheese |
| 2 eggs, beaten |
| 60ml/4 tbsp milk |
| 10ml/2 tsp sesame seeds |
| 10ml/2 tsp poppy seeds |

1 Preheat the oven to 220°C/425°F/Gas 7.

2 Place the flour and salt in a bowl, add the margarine and rub in with your fingertips, or use an electric mixer, until the mixture resembles fine breadcrumbs.

3 Grate the cheese, reserve 30ml/2 tbsp and stir the rest into the flour. Add three-quarters of the beaten eggs and milk to the flour and mix to a soft dough.

4 Knead the dough lightly and roll out thickly on a surface that has been dusted with flour.

5 Stamp out numbers with 7cm/3in cutters and arrange well spaced apart on two baking sheets. Re-roll trimmings and stamp out more shapes to use up the pastry.

6 Brush the tops of the numbers with the reserved egg. Sprinkle five of the numbers with sesame seeds, five with poppy seeds and the remainder with grated cheese.

7 Cook for 12–15 minutes, until well risen and browned. Cool slightly, then arrange the shapes on a plate and serve warm.

# Marmite and Cheese Whirls

**Makes 16**

oil, for greasing

250g/9oz frozen puff pastry, defrosted

flour, for dusting

2.5ml/½ tsp Marmite

1 egg, beaten

50g/2oz Red Leicester, Cheddar or mild cheese, grated

carrot and cucumber sticks, to serve

1 Preheat the oven to 220°C/425°F/Gas 7 and brush a large baking sheet with a little oil.

2 Roll out the pastry on a floured surface to a large rectangle, about 35 × 25cm/14 × 10in.

3 Spread the pastry with Marmite, leaving a 1 cm/½in border. Brush the edges of the pastry with egg and sprinkle the cheese to cover the Marmite.

**TIP**
Omit the Marmite and use peanut butter if preferred. If the shapes become a little squashed when sliced, reform into rounds by opening out the layers with the end of a knife.

4 Roll the pastry up quite tightly like a Swiss roll (jelly roll), starting from a longer edge. Brush the outside of the pastry with beaten egg.

5 Cut the roll into thick slices and place on the baking sheet.

6 Cook for 12–15 minutes until the pastry is well risen and golden. Arrange on a serving plate and serve warm or cold with carrot and cucumber sticks.

# FAMILY MEALS

Eating together as a family takes on a new dimension as your family grows and there's a baby, fussy toddler and parents to feed together. Rather than attempting to prepare three different meals or to make one very simple meal you know the children will like, opt instead to cook three meals from one basic

set of ingredients: a simple baby dinner, an eye-catching meal for even the fussiest of toddlers and a spicy dinner for the grown-ups.

The recipes are aimed at a baby aged nine months and over, a toddler or small child aged eighteen months to four years, and two adults.

# Eating Together

Family meal-times should be a
pleasure, but they can all too often
turn into a battleground. Whatever
family rules you have about table
manners, it's important that the family
knows about them and that you are
consistent. What matters to some
families may not be important to you.
If you want your children to stay at
the table until everyone has finished,
make sure everyone understands this.
Some parents may feel it's more
relaxing if the children leave the table
once they have finished, leaving the
adults to eat the rest of their meal in
relative peace. Whatever you decide,
stick to it, and don't be browbeaten by
well-meaning grandparents or
friends. Try to eat together as a family
at least once a day, even if you don't all

Left: *Part of the fun of
eating together is sharing
the preparation, too.
Children love helping in
the kitchen, and this
involves them in the meal
from the very start.*

Below: *A relaxed but
polite atmosphere will
enhance enjoyment and
consequently encourage
good eating habits.*

Similarly, beware of tiny hands reaching out from the high-chair to grab a mug of hot coffee or snatch a sharp knife.

Offer a variety of foods at each meal, some foods you know your toddler and baby will like and foods that you like too, so that everyone is happy. Offer very tiny portions of foods that are new or ones that your child is not very keen on, and encourage your child to have at least one mouthful.

Encourage the baby to feed herself with easy-to-pick-up finger foods. This gives the adults a chance to eat their food, too. Don't worry about the mess until you get to the end of the meal.

For added protection when your toddler is eating at the table, use a wipe-clean place mat and cover the seat of the dining chair with a towel or dish towel. Better still, buy a thin padded seat cover that is removable and machine-washable but will tie on to the seat securely.

Children cannot bear to eat foods that are too hot, not just because they may burn their mouth, but because of the frustration. Not being able to eat when the food is there and

eat the same food, so that your toddler can learn how to behave by watching the rest of the family. Explain to other members of the family that you are all setting an example for the baby – a great way to make everyone pull their socks up, whatever their age.

It is never too early to encourage children to help: laying (setting) the table can become quite a game, especially if dolly or teddy has a place set too. Passing plates, bread and salt and pepper can be perilous to begin with but with a little practice becomes second nature.

Transform a dull Monday meal-time into a special occasion with a few flowers or candles (well out of reach of very tiny children) and pretty table mats and paper napkins for added decoration.

Try to avoid using a tablecloth with very young children, as they can pull the cloth and everything with it on to the floor and themselves, with appalling consequences if there's a hot teapot or hot casserole dish.

*Above: Laying the table is another task that children delight in, and another way to make them feel part of the family meal-time.*

*Below: Even if the child is too young to have exactly the same food, sharing the table is important.*

they are hungry can lead to great outbursts of temper. Many children actually prefer their food to be just lukewarm. Cool broccoli quickly by rinsing with a little cold water. Spoon hot casseroles on to a large plate so they cool quickly, and always test the temperature of foods before serving to a child.

## TABLE MANNERS

Toddlers can be incredibly messy, but try not to be too fussy and just wipe sticky hands and faces at the end of the meal. Enjoyment is the key. If your child is eating her meal with enthusiasm rather than style, then that is the most important part at the beginning – table manners will come as your child becomes more experienced and adept with a knife and fork.

Be understanding and flexible, as small children have a lot to learn when they begin to join in at family meals. An active toddler has to learn how to sit still – quite an art in itself – how to hold a knife and fork and how to drink from a cup,

*Below and below right: Never forget that food and eating are meant to be fun – don't discipline the child just for the sake of it, and don't impose adult rules too quickly.*

and somehow watch what everyone else is doing and join in too.

The baby has to adapt to sitting up at the table in his high-chair and waiting for an adult to offer him a spoonful of food. Not surprisingly, there can be a few tantrums and accidents, not to mention a mess. Try not to worry. Offer a few finger foods after a bowl of minced food so that the baby can feed himself, giving you a chance to finish your own meal and tidy up.

Above: *Good manners and sharing provide the perfect atmosphere for good eating.*

Left: *Unusual and varied environments, and the different types of food that go with them, provide huge additional pleasure, and will also help to familiarize your child with situations he will encounter later.*

## TIPS

- Offer cubes of cheese at the end of a meal to help counteract the potentially harmful effects of any sugary foods eaten.
- Try to encourage children to eat more fruit. Cutting it into small pieces and arranging it on a plate can prove very inviting.
- Encourage children of all ages to drink full-fat (whole) milk, either cold, warm or flavoured, as it is a valuable source of the fat-soluble vitamins A and D and the important mineral calcium, vital for healthy bones and teeth.
- If you reheat baby food in the microwave, make sure you stir it thoroughly and leave it to stand for a couple of minutes so any hot spots can even out. Always check the temperature before serving.

- Always make sure a baby is well strapped into a high-chair and never leave children unattended while eating, in case of accidents.
- Children love the novelty of eating somewhere different. If it's a nice day, why not have a picnic in the local park. If eating outside, make food up separately.
- Snacks can play a vitally important part in a young child's diet, as their growth rate is so high it can be difficult to provide sufficient calories and protein at meal-times alone.
- Make sure you coordinate main meals and snacks so that you serve different foods and so that the snacks won't take the edge off the child's appetite for the main meal of the day.

- Try to limit sweets (candies) or cakes and fatty crisps (potato chips).
- Offer slices of fresh fruit, a few raisins or dried apricots, squares of cheese, a fruit yogurt or milky drink, Marmite or smooth peanut butter on toast.
- Make food fun and allow your child to choose where she eats her snack, e.g. in the camp in the garden or at the swings.

# MEATY MAIN MEALS

TRYING TO PLEASE THE WHOLE FAMILY ALL OF THE TIME CAN BE A BIT OF A TALL ORDER, ESPECIALLY WHEN TRYING TO COOK TASTY MEALS ON A BUDGET. TRY THESE DELICIOUS NEW WAYS WITH QUICK-TO-COOK MINCE AND CHOPS, PLUS A SPEEDY STIR-FRY, OR SLOW-COOK BEEF BOURGUIGNON WITH CREAMED POTATOES, OSSO BUCCO PORK WITH RICE OR LAMB HOTPOT.

## Mediterranean Lamb

3 lamb chump chops

350g/12oz courgettes (zucchini)

½ yellow (bell) pepper

½ red (bell) pepper

3 tomatoes

1 garlic clove, crushed

15ml/1 tbsp clear honey

few sprigs of fresh rosemary, plus extra to garnish

15ml/1 tbsp olive oil

200g/7oz can baked beans

salt and freshly ground black pepper

crusty bread, to serve

1 Rinse the chops under cold water, pat dry, trim off fat and place in the base of a grill (broiler) pan. Trim and slice the courgettes, cut away the core and seeds from the peppers and then rinse and cut into chunky pieces. Rinse and cut the tomatoes into quarters and arrange the vegetables around the lamb.

2 Season two of the chops for the adults with garlic, honey, rosemary and salt and pepper, and drizzle oil over the vegetables.

3 Cook under a hot grill for 12–14 minutes, turning once, until the lamb is well browned and cooked through and the vegetables are browned.

4 Warm the baked beans in a small pan. Drain and transfer the unseasoned chop to a chopping board and cut away the bone and fat. Thinly slice half the meat for the toddler and arrange on a plate with a few of the vegetables and 30–45ml/ 2–3 tbsp of the baked beans.

5 Chop or process the remaining lamb with four slices of courgette, two small pieces of pepper, two peeled tomato quarters and 15–30ml/1–2 tbsp of baked beans, adding a little boiled water if too dry. Spoon into a dish for the baby and test the temperature of the children's food before serving.

6 For the adult's portions, discard the cooked rosemary. Spoon the pan juices over the chops and garnish with fresh rosemary. Serve with crusty bread.

### TIP

Lamb varies in price throughout the year. Depending on the season and price you may prefer to use lamb cutlets or loin chops. Allow two chops per adult and reduce the cooking time slightly, as these chops are smaller. Do not give honey to young children.

# Lamb Hotpot

350g/12oz lamb fillet

1 onion

1 carrot

175g/6oz swede (rutabaga)

15ml/1 tbsp sunflower oil

30ml/2 tbsp plain (all-purpose) flour

450ml/¾ pint/1⅞ cups lamb stock

15ml/1 tbsp fresh sage or 1.5ml/
¼ tsp dried

½ dessert apple

275g/10oz potatoes

15g/½oz/1 tbsp butter

225g/8oz Brussels sprouts

salt and freshly ground black pepper

**1** Preheat the oven to 180°C/
350°F/Gas 4. Rinse the lamb
under cold water, pat dry, trim away
any fat and then slice thinly. Peel and
chop the onion, carrot and swede.

**2** Heat the oil in a large frying pan
and fry the lamb, turning until
browned on both sides. Lift the lamb
out of the pan, draining off any
excess oil, and transfer one-third to a
small 600ml/1 pint/2½ cup casserole
dish for the children and the rest to a
1.2 litre/2 pint/5 cup casserole dish
for the adults.

**3** Add the vegetables to the pan
and fry for 5 minutes, stirring
until lightly browned.

**4** Stir in the flour, then add the
stock and sage. Bring to the
boil, stirring, then divide between
the two casserole dishes.

**5** Core, peel and chop the apple and
add both to the larger casserole
dish with a little seasoning.

**6** Thinly slice the potatoes and
arrange overlapping slices over
both casserole dishes. Dot with
butter and season the larger dish.

**7** Cover and cook in the oven for
1¼ hours. For a brown topping,
remove the lid and grill (broil) for a
few minutes at the end of cooking,
until browned. Cook the Brussels
sprouts in boiling water for 8–10
minutes, until tender, and drain.

**8** Chop or process half the hotpot
from the small casserole, with a
few sprouts for the baby, adding
extra gravy if needed, until the
desired consistency is reached.
Spoon into a baby dish.

**9** Spoon the remaining child's
hotpot on to a plate, add a few
sprouts and cut up any large pieces.
Test the temperature of the
children's food before serving.

**10** Spoon the hotpot for the
adults on to serving plates
and serve with Brussels sprouts.

**TIP**
Traditionally neck (cross rib) or
scrag end of lamb would have
been used for making a hotpot.
This cut does require very long
slow cooking and can be fatty with
lots of bones so not ideal for
children. Fillet of lamb is very lean,
with very little waste and makes a
tasty and healthier alternative.

# Beef Korma

350g/12oz lean minced (ground) beef

1 onion, chopped

1 carrot, chopped

1 garlic clove, crushed

400g/14oz can tomatoes

pinch of dried mixed herbs

25g/1oz pasta shapes

50g/2oz creamed coconut or
120ml/4fl oz/½ cup coconut milk

50g/2oz button (white) mushrooms

50g/2oz fresh spinach leaves

15ml/1 tbsp hot curry paste

salt and freshly ground black pepper

boiled rice, warm naan bread and a
little grated Cheddar cheese, to serve

1 Dry fry the meat and onion in a
medium-size pan, stirring until the
beef has browned.

2 Add the carrot, garlic, tomatoes
and herbs, bring to the boil,
stirring, and then cover and simmer
for about 30 minutes, stirring
occasionally.

3 Cook the pasta in a small pan of
boiling water for 10 minutes, until
tender. Drain.

4 Meanwhile place the coconut or
coconut milk in a small bowl, add
120ml/4fl oz/½ cup of boiling water
and stir until dissolved. Wipe and slice
mushrooms, and wash and drain
spinach, discarding any large stalks.

5 Transfer one-third of the meat
mixture to another pan. Stir the
coconut mixture, curry paste and
salt and pepper into the remaining
meat mixture and cook for about
5 minutes, stirring.

6 Mash or process one-third of the
pasta and reserved meat mixture to
the desired consistency for the baby
and spoon into a small dish.

7 Spoon the remaining pasta and
reserved meat mixture into a small
bowl for the older child.

8 Stir the mushrooms and spinach
into the curried beef and cook for
3–4 minutes, until the spinach has just
wilted. Spoon on to warmed
serving plates for the adults and
serve with boiled rice and warmed
naan bread. Sprinkle the toddler's
portion with a little grated cheese. Test
the temperature of the children's food
before serving.

## TIPS

Weigh spinach after it has been
picked over and the stalks have
been removed or, buy ready-
prepared spinach. If you can't get
creamed coconut, use 120ml/4fl
oz/½ cup coconut milk instead, or
soak 25g/1oz/1 cup desiccated
(dry unsweetened shredded)
coconut in 150ml/¼ pint/⅔ cup
boiling water for 30 minutes, then
strain and use the liquid.

# Bobotie with Baked Potatoes and Broccoli

3 medium baking potatoes

1 onion, chopped

350g/12oz lean minced (ground) beef

1 garlic clove, crushed

10ml/2 tsp mild curry paste

10ml/2 tsp wine vinegar

90ml/6 tbsp fresh breadcrumbs

15ml/1 tbsp tomato purée (paste)

25g/1oz sultanas (golden raisins)

15ml/1 tbsp mango chutney

1 medium banana, sliced

2 eggs

20ml/4 tsp turmeric

120ml/4fl oz/½ cup skimmed milk

4 small bay leaves

225g/8oz broccoli, cut into florets

30ml/2 tbsp fromage frais or Greek
(US strained plain) yogurt

200g/7oz can baked beans

salt and freshly ground black pepper

**1** Preheat the oven to 180°C/
350°F/Gas 4. Scrub the potatoes,
insert a skewer into each and bake
for 1½ hours, until tender.

**2** Place the chopped onion and
225g/8oz of the beef in a pan and
dry fry, until browned all over, stirring
frequently.

**3** Add the garlic and curry paste,
stir well and cook for 1 minute,
then remove from the heat and stir in
the vinegar, 60ml/4 tbsp of the
breadcrumbs, the tomato purée,
sultanas and a little salt and pepper.

**TIP**
Serve any leftover adult portions
cold with salad.

**4** Chop up any large pieces of
mango chutney and stir into the
meat mixture with the banana slices.
Spoon into a 900ml/1½ pint/3¾ cup
ovenproof dish and press into an
even layer with the back of a spoon.

**5** Place the dish on a baking sheet,
cover loosely with foil and cook
for 20 minutes.

**6** Meanwhile, mix the remaining
beef with the remaining
breadcrumbs, then beat the eggs
together and stir 15ml/1 tbsp into
the meat. Make eight small
meatballs about the size of a grape
for the baby. Form the remaining
beef into a 7.5cm/3in burger, using an
upturned cookie cutter as a mould.

**7** Blend the turmeric, milk and a
little salt and pepper with the
remaining eggs. Remove the cover
from the bobotie, and lay the bay
leaves over the meat.

**8** Pour the egg mixture over.
Return to the oven for a further
30 minutes, until well risen and set.

**9** When the adults' portion is
ready, heat the grill (broiler) and
cook the burger and meatballs until
browned, turning once. The burger
will take 8–10 minutes, while the
meatballs will take about 5 minutes.

**10** Cook the broccoli in boiling
water until tender and drain.

**11** Cut the bobotie for the adults
into wedges and serve with
baked potatoes topped with fromage
frais or Greek yogurt and broccoli.

**12** Serve the toddler's burger
with half a potato, warmed
baked beans and a few broccoli
florets. Serve the baby's meatballs
with chunky pieces of peeled potato
and broccoli. Spoon a few baked
beans into a small dish for the baby.
Test the temperature of the food
before serving to the children.

# Moussaka

1 onion, chopped

350g/12oz minced (ground) lamb

400g/14oz can tomatoes

1 bay leaf

1 medium aubergine (eggplant), sliced

2 medium potatoes

1 medium courgette (zucchini), sliced

30ml/2 tbsp olive oil

2.5ml/½ tsp grated nutmeg

2.5ml/½ tsp ground cinnamon

2 garlic cloves, crushed

salt and freshly ground black pepper

*For the Sauce*

30ml/2 tbsp margarine

30ml/2 tbsp plain (all-purpose) flour

200ml/7fl oz/1 cup milk

pinch of grated nutmeg

15ml/1 tbsp freshly grated Parmesan
 cheese

20ml/4 tsp fresh breadcrumbs

1 Dry fry the onion and lamb in a pan until browned, stirring. Add the tomatoes and bay leaf, bring to the boil, stirring, then cover and simmer for 30 minutes.

2 Place the aubergine slices in a single layer on a baking sheet, sprinkle with a little salt and set aside for 20 minutes. Preheat oven to 200°C/400°F/Gas 6.

3 Slice the potatoes thinly and cook in boiling water for 3 minutes. Add the courgette and cook for 2 minutes, until tender.

4 Remove most of the slices with a slotted spoon and place in a colander, leaving just enough for the baby portion. Cook these for 2–3 minutes more until soft, then drain. Rinse the vegetables and drain well.

5 Rinse the salt off the aubergine and pat dry. Heat the oil in a frying pan and fry the aubergines until browned on both sides. Drain.

6 Spoon 45ml/3 tbsp of the meat mixture into a bowl with the baby vegetables and chop or purée to the desired consistency.

7 Spoon 60ml/4 tbsp of the meat mixture into an ovenproof dish for the older child. Arrange four slices of potato, a slice of aubergine and three slices of courgette on top.

8 Stir the spices, garlic and seasoning into the remaining lamb mixture, and cook for 1 minute and then spoon into a 1.2 litre/ 2 pint/5 cup shallow ovenproof dish discarding the bay leaf.

9 Arrange the remaining potatoes overlapping on top of the lamb, and then add the aubergine slices, tucking the courgette slices in between the aubergines in a random pattern.

10 To make the sauce, melt the margarine in a small pan, stir in the flour, then gradually add the milk and bring to the boil, stirring until thickened and smooth. Add a pinch of nutmeg and a little salt and pepper.

11 Pour a little of the sauce over the toddler's portion, then pour the rest over the adults' portion. Sprinkle the larger dish with Parmesan cheese and 15ml/3 tsp breadcrumbs, sprinkling the remaining breadcrumbs over the toddler's portion.

12 Cook the moussakas in the oven. The larger dish will take 45 minutes, while the toddler's portion will take about 25 minutes.

13 Reheat the baby portion, and test the temperature of the children's food before serving.

# Chilli con Carne

3 medium baking potatoes

1 onion, chopped

450g/1lb lean minced (ground) beef

1 carrot, chopped

½ red (bell) pepper, cored, seeded and diced

400g/14oz can tomatoes

10ml/2 tsp tomato purée (paste)

150ml/¼ pint/⅔ cup beef stock

3 small bay leaves

30ml/2 tbsp olive oil

115g/4oz button (white) mushrooms, sliced

2 garlic cloves, crushed

10ml/2 tsp mild chilli powder

2.5ml/½ tsp ground cumin

5ml/1 tsp ground coriander

200g/7oz can red kidney beans, drained

40g/1½oz frozen mixed vegetables

15ml/1 tbsp milk

knob (pat) of butter or margarine

60ml/4 tbsp fromage frais or Greek (US strained plain) yogurt

15ml/1 tbsp chopped fresh coriander (cilantro) leaves

salt and freshly ground black pepper

green salad, to serve

1 Preheat the oven to 180°C/ 350°F/Gas 4. Scrub and prick the potatoes and cook in the oven for 1½ hours. Dry fry the onion and beef in a pan until browned. Add the carrot and red pepper and cook for 2 minutes.

2 Add the tomatoes, tomato purée and stock and bring to the boil. Transfer one quarter of the mixture to a 600ml/1 pint/2½ cup casserole dish, add 1 of the bay leaves, cover with a lid and set aside.

3 Spoon the remaining meat mixture into a 1.2 litre/2 pint/ 5 cup casserole. Heat 15ml/1 tbsp of the oil in the same pan and fry the mushrooms and garlic for 3 minutes.

4 Stir in the spices and seasoning, cook for 1 minute, then add the drained red kidney beans and the remaining bay leaves and stir into the meat mixture. Cover and cook both dishes in the oven for 1 hour.

5 When the potatoes are cooked, cut into halves or quarters and scoop out the potato, leaving a thin layer of potato on the skin.

6 Brush the potato skins with the remaining oil and grill (broil) for 10 minutes, until browned.

7 Boil the frozen mixed vegetables for 5 minutes and mash the potato centres with milk and a knob of butter or margarine.

8 Spoon the meat from the smaller casserole into an ovenproof ramekin dish for the toddler and the rest into a bowl for the baby. Top both with some of the mashed potato.

9 Drain the vegetables, arrange two pea eyes, carrot pieces for the mouth and mixed vegetables for hair on the toddler's dish.

10 Spoon the remaining vegetables into a baby bowl and chop or process to the desired consistency. Test the temperature of the children's food before serving.

11 Spoon the adults' chilli on to warmed serving plates, add the potato skins and top with fromage frais or Greek yogurt and chopped coriander. Serve with a green salad.

# Beef Bourguignon with Creamed Potatoes

450g/1lb stewing beef

15ml/1 tbsp vegetable oil

1 onion, chopped

30ml/2 tbsp plain (all-purpose) flour

300ml/½ pint/1¼ cups beef stock

15ml/1 tbsp tomato purée (paste)

small bunch of fresh herbs or 1.5ml/
    ¼ tsp dried

2 garlic cloves, crushed

90ml/6 tbsp red wine

75g/3oz shallots

75g/3oz button (white) mushrooms

25g/1oz/2 tbsp butter

450g/1lb potatoes

175g/6oz green cabbage

30–60ml/2–4 tbsp milk

salt and freshly ground black pepper

a few fresh herbs, to garnish

**1** Preheat the oven to 160°C/
325°F/Gas 3. Trim away any fat
from the beef and cut into cubes.

**2** Heat the oil in a frying pan, add
half of the beef and fry until
browned. Transfer to a plate and fry
the remaining beef and the chopped
onion until browned.

**3** Return the first batch of beef to
the pan with any meat juices, stir
in the flour and then add the stock
and tomato purée. Bring to the boil,
stirring, until thickened.

**4** Spoon one-third of the beef
mixture into a small 600ml/
½ pint/1¼ cup casserole dish for
the children, making sure that the
meat is well covered with stock.
Add a few fresh herbs or half a dried
bay leaf. Set the casserole aside.

**5** Add the remaining herbs, garlic,
wine and seasoning to the beef
in the frying pan and bring to the
boil. Transfer the beef to a 1.2 litre/
2 pint/5 cup casserole dish. Cover
both dishes and cook in the oven
for about 2 hours, or until the meat is
very tender.

**6** Meanwhile, halve the shallots if
they are large, wipe and slice
the mushrooms, cover and put to
one side.

**7** Half an hour before the end of
cooking, fry the shallots in a
little butter until browned, then add
the mushrooms and fry for 2–3
minutes. Stir into the larger casserole
and cook for the remaining time.

**8** Cut the potatoes into chunky
pieces and cook in a pan of
boiling, salted water for 20 minutes.
Shred the cabbage, discarding the
hard core, rinse and steam above the
potatoes for the last 5 minutes.

**9** Drain the potatoes and mash
with 30ml/2 tbsp of the milk and
the remaining butter.

**10** Chop or process one-third of
the child's casserole with a
spoonful of cabbage, adding extra
milk if necessary. Spoon into a dish
for the baby, with a little potato.

**11** Spoon the remaining child's
casserole on to a plate for the
toddler. Remove any bay leaf and
cut up any large pieces of beef. Add
potato and cabbage.

**12** Garnish the adults' casserole
with fresh herbs and serve
with potatoes and cabbage. Test the
temperature of the children's food.

# Osso Bucco Pork with Rice

3 pork spare rib chops, about 500g/
  1¼lb

15ml/1 tbsp olive oil

1 onion, chopped

1 large carrot, chopped

2 celery sticks, thinly sliced

2 garlic cloves, crushed

400g/14oz can tomatoes

few sprigs fresh thyme or 1.5ml/
  ¼ tsp dried

grated rind and juice of ½ lemon

150g/5oz/⅔ cup long grain rice

pinch of turmeric

115g/4oz green beans

knob (pat) of butter

20ml/4 tbsp freshly grated Parmesan
  cheese

salt and freshly ground black pepper

1 or 2 sprigs parsley

1 Preheat the oven to 180°C/
  350°F/Gas 4. Rinse the chops
under cold water and pat dry.

2 Heat the oil in a large frying pan,
  add the pork, brown on both
sides and transfer to a casserole dish.

3 Add the onion, carrot and celery
  to the frying pan and fry for
3 minutes, until lightly browned.

4 Add half the garlic, the
  tomatoes, thyme and lemon
juice and bring to the boil, stirring.
Pour the mixture over the pork,
cover and cook in the oven for 1½
hours, or until tender.

5 Half fill two small pans with water
  and bring to the boil. Add
115g/4oz/½ cup rice to one with a
pinch of turmeric and salt, add the
remaining rice to the second pan.
Return to the boil, and simmer.

6 Trim the beans and steam above
  the larger pan of rice for 8
minutes, or until the rice is tender.

7 Drain both pans of rice, return
  the yellow rice to the pan and
add the butter, Parmesan cheese and a
little pepper. Mix together well and
keep warm.

8 Dice one chop, discarding any
  bone if necessary. Spoon a little
of the white rice on to a plate for the
toddler and add half of the diced
chop. Add a few vegetables and a
spoonful of the sauce. Process the
other half of chop, some vegetables,
rice and sauce to the desired
consistency and turn into a small
bowl for the baby.

9 Spoon the yellow rice on to the
  adults' plates and add a pork
chop to each. Season the sauce to
taste and then spoon the sauce and
vegetables over the meat, discarding
the thyme sprigs if used. Finely chop
the parsley and sprinkle over the
pork with the lemon rind and the
remaining crushed garlic.

10 Serve the adults' and
   toddler's portions with green
beans. Test the temperature of the
children's food before serving.

# Pork Stir-fry

250g/9oz pork fillet (tenderloin)

1 courgette (zucchini)

1 carrot

½ green (bell) pepper

½ red (bell) pepper

½ yellow (bell) pepper

200g/7oz packet fresh beansprouts

20ml/4 tsp vegetable oil

25g/1 oz cashew nuts

150ml/¼ pint/⅔ cup chicken stock

30ml/2 tbsp tomato ketchup

10ml/2 tsp cornflour (cornstarch),
    blended with 15ml/1 tbsp cold water

1 garlic clove, crushed

10ml/2 tsp soy sauce

20ml/4 tsp yellow bean paste or
    hoisin sauce

**1** Rinse the pork under cold water, cut away any fat and thinly slice. Halve the courgette lengthways, then thinly slice the carrot, and cut the peppers into strips, discarding the core and the seeds. Place the beansprouts in a sieve (strainer) and rinse well.

**2** Heat 15ml/3 tsp of the oil in a wok or large frying pan, add the cashews and fry for 2 minutes, until browned. Drain and reserve.

**3** Add the sliced pork and stir-fry for 5 minutes, until browned all over and cooked through. Drain and keep warm.

**4** Add the remaining oil and stir-fry the courgette and carrot for 2 minutes. Add the peppers and fry for a further 2 minutes.

**5** Stir in the beansprouts, stock, ketchup and the cornflour mixture, bring to the boil, stirring until the sauce has thickened.

**6** Transfer 1 large spoonful of the vegetables to a bowl and 2–3 large spoonfuls to a plate for the children and set aside. Add the garlic and soy sauce to the pan and cook for 1 minute.

**7** Chop or process four slices of pork with the baby's reserved vegetables to the desired consistency and turn into a baby bowl. Arrange six slices of pork on the toddler's plate with the reserved vegetables. Spoon the vegetables in the wok on to two adult serving plates.

**8** Return the remaining pork to the wok with the nuts and yellow bean paste or hoisin sauce and cook for 1 minute. Spoon on to the adults' plates and serve immediately. Test the temperature of the children's food before serving.

# Sausage Casserole

450g/1lb large sausages

15ml/1 tbsp vegetable oil

1 onion, chopped

225g/8oz carrots, chopped

400g/14oz can mixed beans in water, drained

15ml/1 tbsp plain (all-purpose) flour

450ml/¾ pint/1⅞ cup beef stock

15ml/1 tbsp Worcestershire sauce

15ml/3 tsp tomato purée (paste)

15ml/3 tsp soft brown sugar

10ml/2 tsp Dijon mustard

1 bay leaf

1 dried chilli, chopped

3 medium baking potatoes

salt and freshly ground black pepper

butter and sprigs of fresh parsley, to serve

1 Preheat the oven to 180°C/ 350°F/Gas 4. Prick and separate the sausages.

2 Heat the oil in a frying pan, add the sausages and cook over a high heat until evenly browned but not cooked through. Drain and transfer to a plate.

3 Add the chopped onion and carrots to the pan and fry until lightly browned. Add the drained beans and flour, stir well and then spoon one-third of the mixture into a small casserole. Stir in 150ml/ ¼ pint/⅔ cup stock, 5ml/1 tsp tomato purée and 5ml/1 tsp sugar.

4 Add the Worcestershire sauce, remaining beef stock, tomato purée and sugar to the pan, together with the mustard, bay leaf and chopped chilli. Season and bring to the boil, then pour the mixture into a large casserole.

5 Add two sausages to the small casserole and the rest to the larger dish. Cover both and cook in the oven for 1½ hours.

6 Scrub and prick the potatoes and cook on a shelf above the casserole for 1½ hours, until tender.

7 Spoon two-thirds of the child's casserole on to a plate for the toddler. Slice the sausages and give her two-thirds. Halve one of the baked potatoes, add a knob (pat) of butter and place on the toddler's plate.

8 Scoop the potato from the other half and mash or process with the remaining child's beans to the desired consistency for the baby. Spoon into a dish and serve the remaining sausage slices as finger food.

9 Spoon the adults' casserole on to plates, halve the other potatoes, add butter and garnish with parsley. Test the temperature of the children's food.

# PERFECT POULTRY

Whatever the age of the diner, chicken and turkey are always popular. Available in a range of cuts and prices, there's something to suit all budgets and tastes, from a tasty salad to Pan-fried Turkey with Coriander, Tandoori-style Chicken or Chicken Wrappers with pesto, ham and cheese.

## Chicken and Thyme Casserole

| |
|---|
| 6 chicken thighs |
| 15ml/1 tbsp olive oil |
| 1 onion, chopped |
| 30ml/2 tbsp plain (all-purpose) flour |
| 300ml/½ pint/1¼ cups chicken stock |
| few sprigs fresh thyme or 1.5 ml/ ¼ tsp dried |
| *To Serve* |
| 350g/12oz new potatoes |
| 1 large carrot |
| 115g/4oz/¾ cup frozen peas |
| 5ml/1 tsp Dijon mustard |
| grated rind and juice of ½ orange |
| 60ml/4 tbsp fromage frais or natural (plain) yogurt |
| salt and freshly ground black pepper |
| fresh thyme or parsley, to garnish |

1 Preheat the oven to 180°C/ 350°F/Gas 4. Rinse the chicken under cold water and pat dry.

2 Heat the oil in a large frying pan, add the chicken and brown on both sides, then transfer to a casserole.

3 Add the onion and fry, stirring until lightly browned. Stir in the flour, then add the stock and thyme and bring to the boil, stirring.

4 Pour over the chicken, cover and cook in the oven for 1 hour, or until tender.

5 Meanwhile, scrub the potatoes and cut any large ones in half. Cut the carrot into matchsticks.

6 Cook the potatoes in boiling water 15 minutes before the chicken is ready and cook the carrots and peas in a separate pan of boiling water for 5 minutes. Drain.

7 Take one chicken thigh out of the casserole, remove the skin and cut the meat away from the bone. Place in a food processor or blender with some of the vegetables and gravy and chop or process to the desired consistency. Turn into a baby bowl.

8 Take a second chicken thigh out of the casserole for the toddler, remove the skin and bone and slice if necessary. Arrange on a plate with some of the vegetables and gravy. Test the temperature of the children's food before serving.

9 Arrange two chicken thighs on warmed serving plates for the adults. Stir the mustard, orange rind and juice, fromage frais or yogurt, and seasoning into the hot sauce and then spoon over the chicken. Serve at once, with the vegetables, garnished with a sprig of thyme or parsley.

# Tandoori-style Chicken

6 chicken thighs

150g/5oz natural (plain) yogurt

6.5ml/1¼ tsp paprika

5ml/1 tsp hot curry paste

5ml/1 tsp coriander seeds, roughly
  crushed

2.5ml/½ tsp cumin seeds, roughly
  crushed

2.5ml/½ tsp turmeric

pinch of dried mixed herbs

5ml/2 tsp vegetable oil

*To Serve*

350g/12oz new potatoes

3 celery sticks

10cm/4in piece cucumber

15ml/1 tbsp olive oil

5ml/1 tsp white wine vinegar

5ml/1 tsp mint

salt and freshly ground black pepper

few sprigs of watercress, knob (pat) of
  butter and cherry tomatoes, to
  serve

1 Cut away the skin from the
chicken thighs and slash the
meat two or three times with a small
knife. Rinse under cold water and
pat dry.

2 Place four thighs in a shallow
dish, the other two on a plate.
Place the yogurt, 5ml/1 tsp of the
paprika, the curry paste, both seeds
and almost all the turmeric into a
small bowl and mix together. Spoon
over the four chicken thighs.

3 Sprinkle the remaining paprika
and the mixed herbs over the
other chicken thighs and sprinkle the
remaining pinch of turmeric over one
thigh. Cover both dishes loosely with
clear film (plastic wrap) and chill in
the refrigerator for 2–3 hours.

4 Preheat the oven to 200°C/
400°F/Gas 6. Arrange the
chicken thighs on a roasting rack set
over a small roasting pan and drizzle
oil over the herbed chicken. Pour a
little boiling water into the base of the
pan and cook for 45–50 minutes, until
the juices run clear when the chicken
is pierced with a skewer.

5 Meanwhile, scrub the potatoes
and halve any large ones. Cook
in a pan of boiling water for 15
minutes, until tender.

6 Cut one celery stick and a small
piece of cucumber into
matchsticks. Chop or shred the
remaining celery and cucumber.

7 Blend together the oil, vinegar,
mint and seasoning in a bowl and
add the chopped or shredded celery,
cucumber and watercress, tossing well
to coat.

8 Drain the potatoes and toss in a
little butter. Divide the potatoes
among the adults' plates, toddler's
dish and the baby bowl. Cut the
chicken off the bone for the toddler
and arrange on a plate with half of
the celery and cucumber sticks.

9 Cut the remaining chicken thigh
into tiny pieces for the baby,
discarding the bone, and allow to
cool. Add to the bowl with the
cooled potatoes and vegetable sticks
and allow the baby to feed herself.
Add a few halved tomatoes to each
portion. Test the temperature of the
children's food before serving.

10 For the adults, arrange the
chicken thighs on warmed
serving plates with the potatoes.
Serve with the piquant salad.

# Chicken Wrappers

| |
|---|
| 3 boneless, skinless chicken breasts |
| 5ml/1 tsp pesto |
| 40g/1½oz thinly sliced ham |
| 50g/2oz Cheddar or mild cheese |
| 350g/12oz new potatoes |
| 175g/6oz green beans |
| 15g/½oz/1 tbsp butter |
| 10ml/2 tsp olive oil |
| 1 tomato |
| 6 stoned (pitted) black olives |
| 10ml/2 tsp plain (all-purpose) flour |
| 150ml/¼ pint/⅔ cup chicken stock |
| 15ml/1 tbsp crème fraîche or sour cream (optional) |

**1** Rinse the chicken under cold water and pat dry. Put one chicken breast between two pieces of clear film (plastic wrap) and bat out with a rolling pin. Repeat with the other two chicken breasts.

**2** Spread pesto over two of the chicken breasts and divide the ham among all three. Cut the cheese into three thick slices, then add one to each piece of chicken. Roll up so that the cheese is completely enclosed, then secure with string.

**3** Scrub the potatoes, halve any large ones and cook in a pan of boiling water for 15 minutes, until tender. Trim the beans and cook in a separate pan of boiling water for 10 minutes.

**4** Meanwhile, heat the butter and oil in a large frying pan, add the chicken and cook for about 10 minutes, turning several times, until well browned and cooked through.

**5** Lift the chicken out of the pan, keeping the pieces spread with pesto warm, and leaving the other one to cool slightly.

**6** Cut the tomato into wedges and halve the olives. Stir in the flour and cook for 1 minute. Gradually stir in the stock and bring to the boil, stirring until thickened. Add the tomato and olives.

**7** Snip the string off the chicken and slice the children's chicken breast thinly. Arrange four chicken slices on a child's plate with a couple of spoonfuls of sauce and a few potatoes and green beans. (Don't offer olives unless the child is a very adventurous eater.)

**8** Chop or process the remaining cut chicken with 30ml/2 tbsp of the sauce, one or two potatoes and three green beans to the desired consistency. Test the temperature of the children's food before serving.

**9** Arrange the remaining chicken on plates. Add the crème fraîche or sour cream to the pan, if using, and heat gently. Spoon over the chicken and serve with vegetables.

**TIP**
Depending on the age of the baby, you may prefer to omit the sauce and serve the meal as finger food, cutting it into more manageable pieces first.

# Pan-fried Turkey with Coriander

3 turkey breast steaks

1 onion

1 red (bell) pepper, cored and seeded

15ml/1 tbsp vegetable oil

5ml/1 tsp plain (all-purpose) flour

150ml/¼ pint/⅔ cup chicken stock

30ml/2 tbsp frozen corn

150g/5oz/⅔ cup long grain white rice

1 garlic clove

1 dried chilli

50g/2oz creamed coconut or
200ml/7fl oz/1 cup coconut cream

30ml/2 tbsp chopped fresh coriander
(cilantro)

fresh coriander sprigs, to garnish

fresh lime wedges, to serve

1 Rinse the turkey steaks under cold water, and pat dry. Chop one of the steaks, finely chop one quarter of the onion and dice one quarter of the red pepper. Heat 5ml/ 1 tsp of the oil in a small frying pan and fry the diced turkey and chopped onion until lightly browned all over.

2 Stir in the flour, add the stock, corn and chopped pepper, then bring to the boil, cover and simmer for 10 minutes.

3 Cook the long grain rice in boiling water for 8–10 minutes, or until just tender. Drain.

4 Meanwhile, process or finely chop the remaining pieces of onion and red pepper with the garlic and chilli, including the seeds if you like hot food.

5 Put the coconut into a bowl, pour on 200 ml/7fl oz/1 cup boiling water and stir until it has completely dissolved.

6 Heat the remaining oil in a large frying pan. Brown the turkey breasts on one side, turn over and add the pepper paste. Fry for 5 minutes, until the second side of the turkey has also browned.

7 Pour the coconut milk over the turkey and cook for 2–3 minutes, stirring until the sauce has thickened slightly. Sprinkle with the chopped fresh coriander.

8 Chop or process one-third of the children's portion with 30ml/ 2 tbsp of the rice until the desired consistency is reached. Spoon into a baby bowl.

9 Spoon the child's portion on to a child's plate and serve with a little rice. Test the temperature of the children's food before serving.

10 Spoon the rest of the rice on to warmed serving plates for the adults, and add the turkey and sauce. Garnish with coriander sprigs and serve with lime wedges.

# Chicken Salad

3 chicken breasts, boned and skinned

½ onion, chopped

1 carrot, chopped

150ml/¼ pint/⅔ cup chicken stock

few fresh herbs or a pinch of dried
  mixed herbs

30ml/2 tbsp butter or margarine

15ml/1 tbsp plain (all-purpose) flour

30ml/2 tbsp frozen corn, defrosted

3 slices bread

2 celery sticks

1 green eating apple

1 red eating apple

mixed green salad leaves, to serve

*For the Dressing*

45ml/3 tbsp natural (plain) yogurt

45ml/3 tbsp mayonnaise

5ml/1 tsp ground coriander

salt and freshly ground black pepper

**1** Rinse the chicken breasts under cold water and place in a pan with the chopped onion and carrot, stock and herbs. Cover and cook for 15 minutes, or until the chicken is cooked through.

**2** Cut one chicken breast into small dice, cutting the other two into larger pieces.

**3** Strain the stock into a jug (cup), finely chop the carrot and remove and discard the onion and herbs.

**4** Preheat the oven to 190°C/ 375°F/Gas 5. Melt 15ml/1 tbsp of the butter or margarine in a small pan, stir in the flour. Gradually stir in the strained stock and bring to the boil, stirring continuously, until the sauce is thick and smooth. Add the finely diced chicken, carrot and corn.

**5** Cut the bread into three 7.5cm/ 3in squares, cutting the trimmings into tiny shapes, using cutters. Spread both sides of the squares and one side of the tiny bread shapes with the remaining butter or margarine. Press the squares into sections of a patty tin (muffin pan).

**6** Bake the small shapes in the oven for 5 minutes and the squares for 10 minutes, until crisp and golden brown all over.

**7** Rinse and thinly slice the celery, and quarter, core and chop half of each of the apples.

**8** To make the salad dressing, blend the yogurt, mayonnaise, ground coriander and salt and pepper in a bowl. Add the thickly diced chicken and the celery, pepper and apples, and mix together.

**9** Tear the salad leaves into pieces and arrange on the adults' serving plates. Spoon the chicken salad over the salad leaves.

**10** Chop or process half of the child's chicken mixture to the desired consistency for the baby and spoon into a dish with the tiny bread shapes. Reheat the remaining mixture if necessary, spoon into the bread cases and arrange on a plate for the toddler. Slice the two apple halves, cutting the peel away from a few slices and add to the children's dishes. Check the temperature before serving to the children.

# FISH DINNERS

Q UICK TO MAKE FOR EVERYDAY MEALS OR A SPECIAL OCCASION – HERE ARE SOME FISH RECIPES
FOR ANY DAY OF THE WEEK. CHOOSE FROM FRESH, FROZEN OR CANNED FISH FOR ADDED
CONVENIENCE. ENCOURAGE THE CHILDREN TO TRY HOME-MADE FISH CAKES, WITH A TASTY SAUCE FOR
THE ADULTS, EYE-CATCHING FISH VOL-AU-VENTS OR COLOURFUL SALMON AND COD KEBABS.

## Paella

400g/14oz cod fillet

115g/4oz fish cocktail or a mixture of
  prawns (shrimp), mussels and squid

15ml/1 tbsp olive oil

1 onion, chopped

1 garlic clove, crushed

150g/5oz/²⁄₃ cup long grain white
  rice

pinch of saffron or turmeric

few sprigs of fresh thyme or a pinch
  of dried thyme

225g/8oz can tomatoes

½ red (bell) pepper, cored, seeded and
  chopped

½ green (bell) pepper, cored, seeded
  and chopped

50g/2oz frozen peas

30ml/2 tbsp fresh chopped parsley

salt and freshly ground black pepper

1 Remove any skin from the cod
and place the fish cocktail in a
sieve (strainer) and rinse well with
cold water.

2 Heat the oil in a frying pan, add
the onion and fry until lightly
browned, stirring occasionally. Add
the garlic and 115g/4oz/½ cup of the
rice and cook for 1 minute.

3 Add the saffron or turmeric,
thyme, 2 of the canned
tomatoes, 350ml/12fl oz/1½ cups
water, and salt and pepper. Bring to
the boil and cook for 5 minutes.

4 Put the remaining rice and
canned tomatoes in a small pan
with 90ml/3fl oz/⅓ cup water.
Cover the pan and cook for about
5 minutes.

5 Add 15ml/1 tbsp of the mixed
peppers and 15ml/1 tbsp of the
frozen peas to the small pan, adding
all the remaining vegetables to the
large pan. Place 115g/4oz of the fish
in a metal sieve (strainer), cutting in
half if necessary. Place above a small
pan of boiling water, cover and steam
for 5 minutes. Add the remaining fish
to the paella in the large pan, cover the
pan and cook for 5 minutes.

6 Add the fish cocktail to the
paella, cover the pan and cook
for a further 3 minutes.

7 Stir the chopped parsley into the
paella and spoon on to two
warmed serving plates for the adults.
Spoon half of the tomato rice
mixture and half the fish on to a plate
for the child and process the
remaining fish and rice to the desired
consistency for the baby. Spoon into a
dish and check both children's meals
for bones. Test the temperature of
the children's food before serving.

# Fish Cakes

| |
|---|
| 450g/1lb potatoes, cut into pieces |
| 450g/1lb cod fillet |
| 75g/3oz prepared spinach leaves |
| 75ml/5 tbsp full-fat (whole) milk |
| 25g/1oz/2 tbsp butter |
| 1 egg |
| 50g/2oz/1 cup fresh breadcrumbs |
| 25g/1oz drained sun-dried tomatoes |
| 25g/1oz drained stuffed olives |
| 115g/4oz Greek (US strained plain) yogurt |
| 3 tomatoes, cut into wedges |
| ½ small onion, thinly sliced |
| 15ml/1 tbsp frozen peas, cooked |
| vegetable oil, for frying |
| salt and pepper |
| lemon and tomato wedges, sliced onion and green salad, to serve |

**1** Half fill a large pan or steamer base with water, add the potatoes and bring to the boil. Place the cod in a steamer top or in a colander above the pan. Cover and cook for 8–10 minutes, or until the fish flakes easily when pressed.

**2** Take the fish out of the steamer and place on a plate. Add the spinach to the steamer, cook for 3 minutes, until just wilted, and transfer to a dish. Test the potatoes, cook for 1–2 minutes more if necessary, then drain and mash with 30ml/2 tbsp of the milk and the butter.

**3** Peel away the skin from the fish, and break into small flakes, carefully removing any bones. Chop the spinach and add to the potato with the fish.

**4** For the baby, spoon 45ml/3 tbsp of the mixture into a bowl and mash with another 30ml/2 tbsp of milk. Add a little salt and pepper, if liked, to the remaining fish mixture.

**5** For the older child, shape three tablespoons of mixture into three small rounds with floured hands. For the adults, shape the remaining mixture into four cakes.

**TIP**
Make sure you remove all bones from the fish.

**6** Beat the egg and the remaining milk on a plate. Place the breadcrumbs on a second plate and dip both the toddler and the adult fish cakes first into the egg and then into the crumb mixture.

**7** Chop the sun-dried tomatoes and stuffed olives and stir into the yogurt with a little salt and pepper. Spoon into a small dish.

**8** Heat some oil in a frying pan and fry the small cakes for 2–3 minutes on each side until browned. Drain well and arrange on a child's plate. Add tomato wedges for tails and peas for eyes.

**9** Fry the adult fish cakes, in more oil if necessary, for 3–4 minutes on each side, until browned and heated through. Drain and serve with the dip, lemon and tomato wedges, thinly sliced onion and a green salad. Reheat the baby portion if necessary, but test the temperature of the children's food before serving.

# Fish Vol-au-Vents

250g/9oz puff pastry, thawed if frozen

a little flour

beaten egg, to glaze

350g/12oz cod fillet

200ml/7fl oz/⅓ cup milk

½ leek

30ml/2 tbsp margarine

30ml/2 tbsp plain (all-purpose) flour

50g/2oz fresh prawns (shrimp)

salt and pepper

broccoli, young carrots and mangetouts (snow peas), to serve

**1** Preheat the oven to 220°C/ 425°F/Gas 7. Roll out the pastry on a lightly floured surface to make a rectangle 23 × 15cm/9 × 6in. Cut into three 7cm/3in wide strips.

**2** Cut two fish shapes from one strip. Knock up edges with a knife and cut an oval shape just in from the edge and almost through to the bottom of the pastry. Place the fish shape on a wet baking tray.

**TIP**
You may find it easier to cut a fish shape out of paper and then use this as a template on the pastry.

**3** Neaten the edges of the remaining pastry strips, then cut smaller rectangles 1cm/½in in from the edge of both and remove.

**4** Roll out the smaller rectangles to the same size as the pastry frames. Brush the edges with a little egg and place the frames on top.

**5** Transfer to the baking sheet. Knock up the edges of both rectangles with a small knife and flute between finger and thumb. Repeat the whole process with the third strip of pastry.

**6** Stamp out tiny fish shapes from the pastry trimmings, re-rolling if necessary, and place on the baking sheet. Brush the top of the vol-au-vents with beaten egg and cook for 10 minutes. Remove the small fish and cook the larger vol-au-vents for a further 5 minutes, until they are well risen and golden brown.

**7** Meanwhile make the filling. Cut the fish in two and put in a pan with the milk. Halve the leek lengthways, wash thoroughly, then slice and add to the pan.

**8** Cover and simmer for 6–8 minutes, or until the fish flakes easily when pressed with a knife. Lift out of the pan, peel away the skin and then break into pieces, removing and discarding any bones.

**9** Strain the milk, reserving the leeks. Melt the margarine, stir in the flour and then gradually add in the milk and bring to the boil, stirring until thick and smooth.

**10** Stir the fish into the sauce. Scoop out the centres of the fish-shaped vol-au-vents and fill with a little mixture. Spoon 30ml/2 tbsp of fish mixture into a baby bowl.

**11** Add a prawn to each fish-shaped vol-au-vent and stir the rest into the pan with the leeks and a little seasoning. Heat gently and spoon into the two large pastry cases (pie shells). Transfer to plates and serve with steamed vegetables.

**12** Chop the baby portion with some vegetables, and serve this with some tiny pastry fishes, if wished, in a small bowl. Check the temperature of the children's food before serving.

# Salmon and Cod Kebabs

200g/7oz salmon steak

275g/10oz cod fillet

15ml/3 tsp lemon juice

10ml/2 tsp olive oil

2.5ml/½ tsp Dijon mustard

350g/12oz new potatoes

200g/7oz frozen peas

50g/2oz/4 tbsp butter

15–30ml/1–2 tbsp milk

3 tomatoes, chopped, seeds discarded

¼ round (butterhead) lettuce, finely shredded

salt and freshly ground black pepper

*For the Mustard Sauce*

1 sprig fresh dill

20ml/4 tsp mayonnaise

5ml/1 tsp Dijon mustard

5ml/1 tsp lemon juice

2.5ml/½ tsp soft dark brown sugar

1 Rinse the fish under cold water and pat dry. Cut the salmon steak in half, cutting around the central bone. Cut away the skin and then cut into chunky cubes, making sure you remove any bones. Remove the skin from the cod and cut into similar sized pieces.

2 Cut a few pieces of fish into smaller pieces and thread on to five cocktail sticks (toothpicks). Thread the remaining fish pieces on to long wooden skewers.

3 Mix together the lemon juice, oil, Dijon mustard and a little salt and pepper to taste in a small bowl and set aside.

4 Finely chop the dill and place in a bowl with the other sauce ingredients and mix. Set aside.

5 Scrub the potatoes, halve any large ones and then cook in lightly salted water for 15 minutes, or until tender. Place the peas and half of the butter in a frying pan, cover and cook very gently for 5 minutes.

6 Preheat the grill (broiler), place the kebabs on a baking sheet and brush the larger kebabs with the lemon, oil and mustard mixture. Grill (broil) for 5 minutes, until the fish is cooked, turning once.

7 Remove the fish from two cocktail sticks and mix in a small bowl with a few new potatoes and 15ml/1 tbsp of the peas. Chop or process with a little milk until the desired consistency is reached, then transfer to a baby bowl.

8 Arrange the toddler's kebabs on a small serving plate with a few potatoes, 30ml/2 tbsp peas and a small amount of chopped tomato. Remove the cocktail sticks from the kebabs before serving.

9 Add the tomatoes to the remaining peas and cook for 2 minutes, then stir in the shredded lettuce and cook for 1 minute. Spoon on to serving plates for the adults, add the kebabs and potatoes, and serve.

**CAUTION**

For younger toddlers, it would be safer to remove the cocktail sticks before serving.

# Tuna Florentine

50g/2oz pasta shapes

175g/6oz fresh spinach leaves

50g/2oz frozen mixed vegetables

200g/7oz can tuna in brine

2 eggs

buttered toast and grilled (broiled)
tomatoes, to serve

*For the Sauce*

25g/1oz/2 tbsp margarine

45ml/3 tbsp plain (all-purpose) flour

300ml/½ pint/1¼ cups milk

50g/2 oz/½ cup grated Cheddar or
mild cheese

1 Cook the pasta in boiling water
for 10 minutes. Meanwhile, tear
off any spinach stalks, wash the
leaves in plenty of cold water and
place in a steamer or colander.

2 Stir the frozen vegetables into
the pasta as it is cooking, and
then place the spinach in the steamer
over the top. Cover and cook for the
last 3 minutes, or until the spinach
has just wilted.

**TIP**
Frozen vegetables are usually
more nutritious than fresh
vegetables, as they are frozen at
their peak of perfection – they're
a great time-saver too.

3 Drain the pasta and vegetables
through a sieve (strainer). Chop
one quarter of the spinach and add to
the pasta and vegetables, dividing the
remainder between two shallow
300ml/½ pint/1¼ cup ovenproof
dishes for the adults.

4 Drain the tuna and divide among
the dishes and sieve (strain).

5 Refill the pasta pan with water,
bring to the boil, then break the
eggs into the water and gently
simmer until the egg whites are set.
Remove the eggs with a slotted
spoon, trim the whites and shake off
all the water. Arrange the eggs on
top of the tuna for the adults.

6 To make the sauce, melt the
margarine in a small pan, stir in
the flour, then gradually add the milk
and bring to the boil, stirring until
thick and smooth.

7 Stir the cheese into the sauce,
reserving a little for the topping.
Spoon the sauce over the adults'
portions until the eggs are covered.
Stir the children's pasta, vegetables
and tuna into the remaining sauce
and mix together.

8 Spoon the pasta on to a plate for
the toddler and chop or process
the remainder for the baby, adding a
little extra milk, if necessary, to make
the desired consistency. Spoon into a
dish. Test the temperature of the
children's food before serving.

9 Preheat the grill (broiler),
sprinkle the adults' portions with
the reserved cheese and grill for
4–5 minutes, until browned. Serve
with buttered toast and grilled
(broiled) tomatoes.

# VEGETABLE FEASTS

MORE AND MORE OF US ARE OPTING TO EAT LESS MEAT FOR EITHER HEALTH OR BUDGETARY REASONS. EATING LESS MEAT DOESN'T MEAN LOSING OUT ON FLAVOUR – FAR FROM IT! CHOOSE FROM MEALS SUCH AS PENNE WITH TOMATO SAUCE, CHEESE AND VEGETABLE CRUMBLE OR SLOW-COOKED, SPICED VEGETABLE TAGINE.

## Cheese on Toast

2 thick slices bread

2 thin slices bread

butter or margarine, for spreading

5ml/1 tsp Marmite (optional)

2 thin slices ham

1 garlic clove, halved

15ml/1 tbsp olive oil

200g/7oz Cheddar or mild cheese

1 tomato

6 stoned (pitted) black olives

15ml/1 tbsp chopped fresh basil

a few red onion slices

cucumber sticks and green salad, to serve (optional)

2 Drizzle the oil over the thick slices of toast, then rub with the cut surface of the garlic.

3 Thinly slice the cheese and place over all of the pieces of toast.

1 Toast all the bread and spread the thin slices with butter or margarine. Spread one slice with Marmite, if using, and top this with ham.

4 Slice the tomato and halve the olives. Arrange on the thick toast for the adults, season with pepper and add basil and onion.

5 Grill until the cheese is bubbly. Cut the plain cheese on toast into tiny squares, discarding crusts. Arrange on a small plate for the baby and allow to cool. Cut the Marmite and/or ham-topped toast into triangles and arrange on a plate. Add cucumber sticks to the toddler's portion and test the temperature before serving.

6 Slice the adults' toast and arrange on plates, with a green salad if liked, and serve.

# Penne with Tomato Sauce

150g/5oz penne or small pasta quills

1 onion

2 celery sticks

1 red (bell) pepper

15ml/1 tbsp olive oil

1 garlic clove, crushed

400g/14oz can tomatoes

2.5ml/½ tsp caster (superfine) sugar

8 stoned (pitted) black olives

10ml/2 tsp pesto

1.5ml/¼ tsp dried chilli seeds
   (optional)

50g/2oz/½ cup grated Cheddar or
   mild cheese

salt and freshly ground black pepper

10ml/2 tsp freshly grated Parmesan
   cheese, to serve

green salad, to serve (optional)

1 Cook the pasta in salted boiling water for about 10–12 minutes, until just tender.

2 Meanwhile, chop the onion and the celery. Cut the pepper in half, then scoop out the core and seeds and dice the pepper finely.

3 Heat the oil in a second pan, add the vegetables and garlic and fry for 5 minutes, stirring until lightly browned.

4 Add the tomatoes and sugar and cook for 5 minutes, stirring occasionally, until the tomatoes are broken up and pulpy.

5 Drain the pasta, return to the pan and stir in the tomato sauce.

6 Spoon 45–60ml/3–4 tbsp of the mixture into a bowl or processor and chop or process to the desired consistency for the baby. Spoon 75–90ml/5–6 tbsp of the mixture into a bowl for the toddler.

7 Quarter the olives and stir into the remaining pasta with the pesto, chilli seeds if using, and a little salt and pepper. Spoon into dishes.

8 Sprinkle the grated cheese over all the dishes, and serve the adults' portions with the Parmesan cheese, and a green salad if wished. Test the temperature of the children's food before serving.

# Courgette Gougère

50g/2oz/4 tbsp butter

65g/2½oz plain (all-purpose) flour

2 eggs

2.5ml/½ tsp Dijon mustard

115g/4oz Cheddar or mild cheese

salt and pepper

*For the Filling*

15ml/1 tbsp olive oil

350g/12oz courgettes (zucchini), sliced

1 small onion, chopped

115g/4oz button (white) mushrooms, sliced

225g/8oz tomatoes, skinned and chopped

1 garlic clove, crushed

20ml/4 tsp chopped fresh basil

1 Preheat the oven to 220°C/425°F/ Gas 7 and grease a large baking sheet. Place the butter in a medium pan with 150ml/¼ pint/⅔ cup water. Heat gently until the butter has melted, then bring to the boil.

2 Remove the pan from the heat and quickly add the flour, stir well, then return to the heat and cook for 1–2 minutes, stirring constantly until the mixture forms a smooth ball. Leave to cool for 10 minutes.

3 Beat the eggs, mustard and a little salt and pepper together. Cut 25g/1oz of the cheese into small cubes and grate the rest.

4 Add 50g/2oz of the grated cheese to the dough and then gradually beat in the eggs to make a smooth, glossy paste.

5 Spoon the mixture into a large piping (pastry) bag fitted with a medium plain nozzle. Pipe whirls close together on the baking sheet to make an 18cm/7in circular shape.

6 Pipe the remaining mixture into small balls for the baby and into the older child's initials.

7 Sprinkle the top with the remaining grated cheese.

8 Bake for 15–18 minutes for the small shapes and 25 for the ring, until well risen and browned.

9 Heat the oil in a frying pan, add the courgettes and onion, and fry until lightly browned. Add the mushrooms, fry for a further 2 minutes and then add the tomatoes. Cover and simmer for 5 minutes, until the vegetables are cooked.

10 Spoon a little mixture into the baby's bowl or into a food processor, and chop or process to the desired consistency. Serve with a few cheese balls and a little diced cheese.

11 Spoon a little on to a plate for the toddler, add an initial and the remaining diced cheese. Test the temperature of the children's food before serving.

12 Transfer the cheese ring to a serving plate and split in half horizontally. Stir the garlic, basil and a little extra seasoning into the courgette mixture and heat through. Spoon over the bottom half of the cheese ring and add the top half. Serve the gougère immediately.

**TIP**

Beat the gougère mixture, cheese and eggs together in a food processor, if preferred.

# Cheese Vegetable Crumble

| |
|---|
| 1 onion |
| 225g/8oz carrot |
| 175g/6oz swede (rutabaga) |
| 175g/6oz parsnip |
| 15ml/1 tbsp olive oil |
| 220g/7½oz can red kidney beans |
| 10ml/2 tsp paprika |
| 5ml/1 tsp ground cumin |
| 15ml/1 tbsp plain (all-purpose) flour |
| 300ml/½ pint/1¼ cups vegetable stock |
| 225g/8oz broccoli, to serve |
| *For the Topping* |
| 115g/4oz Cheddar or mild cheese |
| 50g/2oz wholemeal (whole-wheat) flour |
| 50g/2oz plain (all-purpose) flour |
| 50g/2oz margarine |
| 30ml/2 tbsp sesame seeds |
| 25g/1oz blanched almonds |
| salt and freshly ground black pepper |

**1** Preheat the oven to 190°C/ 375°F/Gas 5. Peel and roughly chop the onion. Then peel and cut the carrot, swede and parsnip into small cubes. Heat the oil in a large pan and fry the vegetables for 5 minutes, stirring until lightly browned.

**2** Drain the kidney beans and add to the pan with the spices and flour. Stir well, add the stock, then cover and simmer for 10 minutes.

**3** Meanwhile, make the topping. Cut a few squares of cheese for the baby and grate the rest. Put the two flours in a bowl, add the margarine and rub in with your fingertips until the mixture resembles fine breadcrumbs. Stir in the grated cheese and sesame seeds.

**4** Spoon a little of the vegetable mixture into a 300ml/½ pint/ 1¼ cup ovenproof dish for the toddler. Spoon the remaining mixture into a 900ml/1½ pint/ 3¾ cup ovenproof pie dish for the adults, leaving a little vegetable mixture in the pan for the baby. Season the adults' portion with a little salt and pepper.

### VARIATION
**Lentil and Herb Crumble**
Substitute canned lentils for the red kidney beans. Instead of the paprika and cumin, use 30ml/2 tbsp chopped, fresh mixed herbs. Add more fibre and nuttiness by replacing the plain (all-purpose) flour with rolled oats.

**5** Spoon 45ml/3 tbsp of crumble over the older child's portion. Roughly chop the almonds, add to the remaining crumble with a little salt and pepper and spoon over the large dish. Bake in the oven for 20 minutes for the small dish, and 30 minutes for the large dish, until golden brown on top.

**6** Add 90ml/3fl oz/⅓ cup water to the baby's portion, cover and cook for 10 minutes, stirring occasionally, until the vegetables are very tender. Mash or process to the desired consistency and spoon into a bowl.

**7** Cut the broccoli into florets and cook for 5 minutes, or until tender; drain. Spoon the toddler's portion out of the dish and on to a small plate. Serve the broccoli to all members of the family, allowing the baby to pick up and eat the broccoli and cubed cheese as finger food. Check the temperature before serving to the children.

**Note:** Never give whole nuts to children under five, as they may choke.

# Vegetable Tagine

| |
|---|
| 1 onion |
| 225g/8oz carrots |
| 225g/8oz swede (rutabaga) |
| 75g/3oz prunes |
| 20ml/4 tsp olive oil |
| 425g/15oz can chickpeas |
| 2.5ml/½ tsp turmeric |
| 10ml/2 tsp plain (all-purpose) flour, plus extra for dusting |
| 2 garlic cloves, finely chopped |
| 450ml/¾ pint/1⅞ cups chicken stock |
| 15ml/1 tbsp tomato purée (paste) |
| 2cm/¾in piece fresh root ginger |
| 2.5ml/½ tsp ground cinnamon |
| 3 cloves |
| 115g/4oz couscous |
| 8 green beans |
| 2 frozen peas |
| piece of tomato |
| knob (pat) of butter or margarine |
| salt and freshly ground black pepper |
| fresh coriander (cilantro), to garnish |

1 Peel and chop the onion, and peel and dice the carrots and swede. Cut the prunes into chunky pieces, discarding the stones (pits).

2 Heat 15ml/3 tsp of the olive oil in a large pan, add the onion and fry until lightly browned. Stir in the carrots and swede and fry for 3 minutes, stirring.

3 Drain the chickpeas and stir into the pan with the turmeric, flour and garlic. Add 300ml/½ pint/1¼ cup of the stock, the tomato purée, and the prunes. Bring to the boil, cover and simmer for 20 minutes, stirring occasionally.

4 Place three heaped spoonfuls of mixture in a bowl or food processor, draining off most of the liquid. Mash or process and then form the mixture into a burger with floured hands.

5 Chop or process two heaped spoonfuls of mixture and sauce to the desired consistency for the baby and spoon into a bowl.

6 Finely chop the root ginger and stir into the remaining vegetable mixture with the cinnamon, cloves, remaining stock and seasoning.

7 Place the couscous in a sieve (strainer), rinse with boiling water and fluff up the grains with a fork. Place the sieve above the vegetables, cover and steam for 5 minutes.

8 Fry the veggie burger in the remaining oil until browned on both sides. Trim and cook the beans and peas for 5 minutes. Drain and arrange on a plate like an octopus, with a piece of tomato for a mouth and peas for eyes.

9 Stir the butter or margarine into the couscous and fluff up the grains with a fork. Spoon on to warmed serving plates for adults, add the vegetable mixture and garnish with a sprig of coriander. Check the temperature of the children's food before serving.

# Stilton and Leek Tart

175g/6oz/1½ cups plain (all-purpose) flour

75g/3oz/6 tbsp butter

1 carrot

2 slices ham

10cm/4in piece of cucumber

mixed green salad leaves, to serve

*For the Filling*

25g/1oz/2 tbsp butter

115g/4oz trimmed leek, thinly sliced

75g/3oz Stilton (blue) cheese, diced

3 eggs

175ml/6fl oz/¾ cup milk

40g/1½oz Cheddar or mild cheese, grated

pinch of paprika

salt and pepper

**1** Put the flour in a bowl with a pinch of salt. Cut the butter into pieces and rub into the flour with your fingertips until the mixture resembles fine breadcrumbs.

**2** Mix to a smooth dough with 30–35ml/6–7 tsp water, knead lightly and roll out thinly on a floured surface. Use to line an 18cm/7in flan dish, trimming round the edge and reserving the trimmings.

**3** Re-roll the trimmings and then cut out six 7.5cm/3in circles, using a fluted cookie cutter. Press the pastry circles into sections of a patty tin (muffin pan) and chill all of the tarts.

**4** Preheat the oven to 190°C/375°F/Gas 5. For the filling, melt the butter in a small frying pan and fry the leek for 4–5 minutes, until soft but not brown, stirring frequently. Turn into a bowl, stir in the diced Stilton, and then spread over the base of the large tart.

**5** Beat the eggs and milk together in a small bowl and season with salt and pepper.

**6** Divide the grated Cheddar among the small tartlet shells and pour some of the egg mixture over. Pour the remaining egg mixture over the leek and Stilton tart and sprinkle with paprika.

**7** Cook the small tartlets for 15 minutes and the large tart for 30–35 minutes, until well risen and browned. Leave to cool.

**8** Peel and coarsely grate the carrot. Cut the ham into triangles for "sails". Cut the ham trimmings into small strips for the baby. Cut the cucumber into matchsticks.

**9** Place a spoonful of carrot, some cucumber, a small tart and some ham trimmings in the baby dish. Spread the remaining carrot on to a plate for the older child, place the tarts on top and secure the ham "sails" with cocktail sticks (toothpicks) Serve any remaining tarts the next day. Cut the large tart into wedges and serve with a mixed leaf salad.

# JUST DESSERTS

NO ONE CAN RESIST A DESSERT, ALTHOUGH LOOKING AFTER A YOUNG FAMILY MAY MEAN IT'S MORE OF A WEEKEND TREAT THAN AN EVERYDAY OCCURRENCE. SPOIL THE FAMILY WITH A SELECTION OF THESE TASTY HOT AND COLD TREATS, FROM FRUITY EVE'S PUDDING AND PLUM CRUMBLE TO CHOCOLATE AND ORANGE TRIFLE OR STRAWBERRY PAVLOVA – ALL GUARANTEED TO GET THEM CLAMOURING FOR SECONDS.

## Bread and Butter Pudding

3 dried apricots

45ml/3 tbsp sultanas (golden raisins)

30ml/2 tbsp sherry

7 slices white bread, crusts removed

25g/1oz/½ tbsp butter, softened

30ml/2 tbsp caster (superfine) sugar

pinch of ground cinnamon

4 eggs

300ml/½ pint/1¼ cups milk

few drops of vanilla essence (extract)

pouring cream, to serve

1 Chop two dried apricots and place in a small bowl with 30ml/ 2 tbsp of the sultanas and the sherry. Set aside for about 2 hours. Chop the remaining apricot and mix with the remaining sultanas.

2 Preheat the oven to 190°C/ 375°F/Gas 5. Spread the bread with butter and cut one slice into very small triangles. Layer in a 150ml/¼ pint/⅔ cup pie dish with plain apricots and sultanas and 5ml/ 1 tsp of the sugar.

3 Cut the remaining bread into larger triangles and layer in a 900ml/1½ pint/3¾ cup pie dish with the sherried fruits and all but 5ml/ 1 tsp of the remaining sugar, sprinkling the top with cinnamon. Put the last 5ml/1 tsp sugar in a small ramekin dish.

4 Beat the eggs, milk and vanilla together and pour into the ramekin and two pie dishes.

5 Stand the ramekin dish in a large ovenproof dish and half fill with hot water. Cook the small pie dish and the ramekin for 25–30 minutes, until the custard has just set, and the larger pudding for 35 minutes, until the bread has browned. Serve the adult portions with cream, if liked.

# Eve's Pudding

500g/1¼lb cooking apples

50g/2oz/¼ cup caster (superfine) sugar

50g/2oz frozen or canned
blackberries

*For the Topping*

50g/2oz/4 tbsp butter or margarine

50g/2oz/¼ cup caster (superfine) sugar

50g/2oz/⅓ cup self-raising
(self-rising) flour

1 egg

½ lemon, rind only

15ml/1 tbsp lemon juice

icing (confectioners') sugar, for
dusting

custard, to serve

1 Preheat the oven to 180°C/350°F/
Gas 4. Peel and slice the cooking
apples, discarding the core, and then
place in a pan with the caster sugar
and 15ml/1 tbsp water. Cover and
cook gently for 5 minutes, until
the apple slices are almost tender
but still whole.

2 Half fill a 150ml/¼ pint/⅔ cup
ovenproof ramekin with apple
for the toddler and mash 30ml/2 tbsp
of apple for the baby in a small bowl.

3 Put the remaining apple slices
into a 600ml/1 pint/2½ cup
ovenproof dish. Sprinkle the
blackberries over the apple slices.

4 To make the topping, place the
butter or margarine, sugar, flour
and egg in a bowl and beat until
smooth. Spoon a little of the
pudding mixture over the toddler's
ramekin so that the mixture is
almost to the top of the dish.

5 Half fill three petits fours cases
with the pudding mixture.

6 Grate the lemon rind and stir
with the juice into the remaining
mixture. Spoon over the large dish,
levelling the surface.

7 Put the small cakes, toddler and
adult dishes on a baking sheet and
bake in the oven for 8–10 minutes for
the small cakes, 20 minutes for the
ramekin and 30 minutes for the larger
dish, until they are well risen and
golden brown.

8 Dust the toddler's and adults'
portions with icing sugar and
leave to cool slightly before serving
with the custard. Warm the baby's
portion if liked, and test the
temperature before serving, with the
cakes taken out of their paper cases.

**TIP**
If you can't get blackberries, then
use raspberries instead. There's no
need to defrost before using, as
they will soon thaw when added
to the hot apple.

# Orange and Strawberry Shortcakes

75g/3oz/6 tbsp plain (all-purpose) flour

50g/2oz/4 tbsp butter

25g/1oz/2 tbsp caster (superfine) sugar

grated rind of ½ orange

extra sugar, for sprinkling

*For the Filling*

175g/6oz Greek (US strained plain) yogurt

15ml/1 tbsp icing (confectioners') sugar

250g/9oz strawberries

5ml/1 tsp Cointreau (optional)

2 sprigs of fresh mint, to decorate

**1** Preheat the oven to 180°C/350°F/ Gas 4. Place the flour in a bowl, cut the butter into pieces, and rub into the flour with your fingertips until the mixture resembles fine breadcrumbs.

**2** Stir in the sugar and orange rind and mix to a dough.

**3** Knead the dough lightly, then roll out on a floured surface to 5mm/¼in thickness. Stamp out four 9cm/3½in flower shapes or fluted rounds with a cookie cutter, and 12 small car, train or other fun shapes with novelty cutters, re-rolling the dough as necessary.

**4** Place the shapes on a baking sheet, prick with a fork and sprinkle with a little extra sugar. Bake in the oven for 10–12 minutes, until pale golden, then leave to cool on the baking sheet.

**5** For the filling, blend the yogurt with the sugar and wash and hull the strawberries. Pat dry. Reserve eight of the strawberries and process or liquidize the rest. Press through a sieve (strainer) and discard the seeds.

**6** For the adults, put 45ml/3 tbsp of the yogurt in a bowl and stir in the Cointreau, if using. Slice four strawberries and halve two, place on a plate and cover.

**7** For the toddler, slice two of the strawberries and arrange in a ring on a small plate. Spoon 30ml/ 2tbsp of yogurt into the centre of the ring and serve with three of the small biscuit (cookie) shapes.

**8** For the baby, stir 15ml/1 tbsp of the strawberry purée into the remaining natural yogurt and spoon into a small dish. Serve with one or two of the small biscuit shapes.

**9** To complete the adults' portions, spoon purée over two plates to cover completely.

**10** Spoon the reserved yogurt over two biscuits, add the sliced strawberries and top with the other two biscuits. Arrange on plates and decorate with halved strawberries and tiny sprigs of mint.

**TIP**
If you find shortbread difficult to roll out, then chill for 20 minutes. Knead lightly and roll out on a surface dusted with flour, dusting the rolling pin too.

# Exotic Fruit Brûlée

oil, for greasing

30ml/2 tbsp demerara (raw) sugar

1 ripe mango

1 kiwi fruit

1 passion fruit

30ml/2 tbsp icing (confectioners') sugar

350g/12oz Greek (US strained plain)
  yogurt

4 Peel the kiwi fruit, cut in half lengthways and then slice thinly. Reserve four half slices for decoration and divide the remaining fruit among the dishes, finely chopping the fruit for the baby and toddler. Cut the passion fruit in half and, using a teaspoon, scoop out and place the seeds in the adults' dishes.

6 Spoon the remaining yogurt into the other two ramekins, level the surface with a spoon and chill all of them until required.

1 Line a baking sheet with foil, then with a pencil draw round the tops of two 250ml/8fl oz/1 cup ramekin dishes and one 150ml/¼ pint/⅔ cup ramekin dish. Lightly brush with oil. Sprinkle the sugar inside each marked circle in an even layer.

2 Grill the sugar discs for 2–3 minutes, or until the sugar has melted and caramelized. Leave the discs to cool on the baking sheet.

3 Slice the mango on either side of the central stone (pit) and then cut six thin slices for decoration, cutting away the skin. Cut the rest of the mango flesh from the stone, removing the skin, and finely chop one quarter, dividing between the baby bowl and small ramekin. Roughly chop the remainder and divide between the larger ramekins.

5 Stir the icing sugar into the yogurt and mix 15ml/1 tbsp into the baby's portion. Spoon 30ml/2 tbsp yogurt over the toddler's dish and level the surface with a spoon.

7 When ready to serve, place the larger ramekins on two plates with the reserved mango and kiwi slices arranged around the sides. Peel the sugar discs off the foil and set on top of the adult and toddler portions. Serve the brulées immediately.

## TIP

Traditionally, the sugar topping on a brulée is made by sprinkling demerara sugar over the top of the dessert and then grilling (broiling), or by making a caramel syrup and then pouring it over the dessert. Making the topping on oiled foil is by far the easiest and most foolproof way. Add the cooled sugar discs at the very last minute so that they stay crisp and you get that wonderful mix of crunchy sugar, velvety yogurt and refreshing fruit.

# Plum Crumble

450g/1lb ripe red plums

25g/1oz/2 tbsp caster (superfine) sugar

*For the Topping*

115g/4oz/1 cup plain (all-purpose) flour

50g/2oz/4 tbsp butter, cut into pieces

25g/1oz/2 tbsp caster (superfine) sugar

10ml/2 tsp chocolate dots

75g/3oz marzipan

30ml/2 tbsp rolled oats

30ml/2 tbsp flaked (sliced) almonds

custard, to serve

1 Preheat the oven to 190°C/ 375°F/Gas 5. Wash the plums, cut into quarters and remove the stones (pits). Place in a pan with the sugar and 30ml/2 tbsp water, cover and simmer for 10 minutes.

2 Drain and spoon six plum quarters on to a chopping board and chop finely. Spoon the plums into a small baby dish with a little juice from the pan.

3 Drain and roughly chop six more of the plum quarters and place in a 150ml/¼ pint/⅔ cup ovenproof ramekin dish with a little of the juice from the pan.

4 Spoon the remaining plums into a 750ml/1¼ pint/3⅔ cup ovenproof dish for the adults.

5 Make the topping. Place the flour in a bowl, rub in the butter and then stir in the sugar.

6 Mix 45ml/3 tbsp of the crumble mixture with the chocolate dots, then spoon over the ramekin.

7 Coarsely grate the marzipan and stir into the remaining crumble with the oats and almonds. Spoon over the adults' portion.

8 Place the toddler and adult portions on a baking sheet and cook for 20–25 minutes, until golden brown. Leave to cool slightly before serving. Warm the baby's portion if liked and check the temperature of the children's food before serving. Serve with custard.

**TIP**

Ovens can vary in temperature: with fan-assisted ovens you may need to cover the adults' dish with foil halfway through cooking to prevent overbrowning.

Vary the fruits: cooking apples, peaches and pears also work well. If the plums are very sharp, you may need to add a little extra sugar.

# Chocolate and Orange Trifle

½ chocolate Swiss roll (jelly roll)

3 clementines or satsumas

20ml/4 tsp sherry

50g/2oz dark (bittersweet) chocolate

300ml/½ pint/1¼ cups ready-made custard

90ml/6 tbsp double (heavy) cream

chocolate buttons or M & M's

1 Slice the Swiss roll, halve one slice and put on a plate for the baby. Put a second slice into a ramekin dish for the older child and arrange the remaining slices in two dessert bowls for the adults.

2 Peel one clementine, separate into segments and put a few on the baby plate. Chop the rest and add to the ramekin.

3 Peel the remaining clementines, roughly chop and add to the adults' bowls, sprinkling a little sherry over each.

4 Break the chocolate into pieces and melt in a bowl over a pan of hot water. Stir the melted chocolate into the custard.

5 Spoon 30ml/2 tbsp of the custard into a small bowl for the baby and arrange on the plate with the Swiss roll and fruit. Spoon a little more custard into the ramekin and then add the rest to the adult dishes, smoothing the surface.

6 Whip the cream until it just holds its shape. Add a spoonful to the ramekin dish and two or three spoonfuls each to the adults' dishes, decorating each dish with sweets (candies). Chill until required.

**TIPS**

Chocolate may be melted in the microwave in a microwave-safe bowl for 2 minutes on Full Power (100%), stirring thoroughly halfway through cooking.

Some shops sell ready-made chocolate custard. Buy this if it's available and you're short of time.

Vary the fruits depending on what is in season, Sliced strawberries and orange, or sliced banana and fresh or canned cherries also work well.

# Apple Strudel

450g/1lb cooking apples

50g/2oz dried apricots

45ml/3 tbsp sultanas (golden raisins)

30ml/2 tbsp soft light brown sugar

30ml/2 tbsp ground almonds

5ml/1 tsp ground cinnamon

25g/1oz/2 tbsp butter

150g/5oz/3 sheets filo pastry,
  defrosted if frozen

icing (confectioners') sugar, to dust

pouring (half-and-half) cream, to serve

1 Preheat the oven to 200°C/
400°F/Gas 6. Peel, core and chop
the apples and place 150g/5oz in a
pan. Chop three apricots and
add to the pan with 15ml/1 tbsp
sultanas, 15ml/1 tbsp sugar and
15ml/1 tbsp water. Cover and
simmer for 5 minutes.

2 Chop the remaining apricots
and place in a bowl with the
remaining apples, sultanas, sugar,
ground almonds and cinnamon.
Mix together well.

3 Melt the butter in a small
pan, or microwave in a microwave-
proof bowl for 30 seconds on Full
Power (100%).

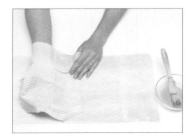

4 Carefully open out the pastry.
Place one sheet on the work
surface, brush with butter, then cover
with a second sheet of pastry and
brush with more butter.

5 Spoon the uncooked apple
mixture in a thick band along
the centre of the pastry.

6 Fold the two short sides up and
over the filling and brush with
butter. Fold the long sides up and
over the filling, opening out the
pastry and folding the pastry for an
attractive finish. Place on a baking
sheet and brush with a little butter.

7 Brush a little of the butter over
half of the third pastry sheet, then
fold the unbrushed half over the top
to make a square. Brush again and
cut into three equal strips.

8 Put a spoonful of apple at the
base of each strip, then fold the
bottom right-hand corner up and
over the filling, to the left side of the
strip, to make a triangle.

9 Continue folding the pastry to
make a triangular pasty. Repeat
with the other strips.

10 Transfer to a baking sheet
and brush with the remaining
butter. Bake for 10 minutes, and the
adults' strudel for 15 minutes, until
golden and crisp. Dust with icing
sugar and cool slightly.

11 Spoon the remaining cooked
apple mixture into a baby
dish. Mash the fruit if necessary.
Transfer the toddler's portion to a
plate. Slice the strudel thickly and
serve with cream.

### TIP
Filo pastry is usually sold frozen
in 275g/10oz packets or larger.
Defrost the whole pack, take out
as much pastry as you need, then
re-wrap the rest and return to
the freezer.

# Strawberry Pavlova

2 egg whites

115g/4oz caster (superfine) sugar

2.5ml/½ tsp cornflour (cornstarch)

2.5ml/½ tsp wine vinegar

*For the Topping*

150ml/¼ pint/⅔ cup double (heavy)
  cream

250g/9oz strawberries

2 chocolate dots

green jelly sweet (candy) or little
  pieces of angelica

1 Preheat the oven to 150°C/300°F/
Gas 2 and line a baking sheet with
baking parchment.

2 Whisk the egg whites until stiff
and then gradually whisk in the
sugar, 5ml/1 tsp at a time. Continue
whisking until smooth and glossy.

3 Blend the cornflour and vinegar
and fold into the egg whites.

4 Spoon the mixture into a large
piping (pastry) bag fitted with a
medium-size plain nozzle. Pipe six
small dots for the baby and a snail for
the older child with a shell about
6cm/2½in in diameter.

5 Pipe the remaining mixture into
two 10cm/4in swirly circles and
cook in the oven for 20–25 minutes,
or until firm. Lift the meringues off
the paper and leave to cool.

**TIP**

For perfect meringues, whisk the
egg whites in a dry grease-free
bowl. Remove any trace of yolk
with a piece of shell and whisk
until the peaks are stiff but still
moist-looking. Add sugar gradually
and continue whisking until very
thick. Meringues may be made
1–2 days in advance. Cover with
baking parchment and decorate
just before serving.

6 Whip the cream until softly
peaking and spoon over the two
large meringues and the snail,
reserving about 15ml/1 tbsp for
the baby.

7 Rinse, hull and slice the
strawberries and arrange a few
in rings over the snail. Place the snail
on a plate and add chocolate eyes and
a slice from a green jelly sweet, or a
little angelica, for the mouth.

8 Add some strawberries to the
adult meringues, then chop or
mash a few extra slices and stir them
into the reserved cream for the baby.
Spoon into a small dish and serve
with tiny meringues.

# Poached Pears

3 ripe pears

450ml/¾ pint/1⅞ cup apple juice

5ml/1 tsp powdered gelatine

few drops of green food colouring

½ small orange, rind only

½ small lemon, rind only

10ml/2 tsp chopped glacé (candied) ginger

5ml/1 tsp clear honey

5ml/1 tsp cornflour (cornstarch)

1 red liquorice bootlace

2 small currants (raisins)

1 large raisin

½ glacé (candied) cherry

1 Peel the pears, leaving the stalks in place. Cut a small circle out of the base of two pears and tunnel out the cores with a small knife.

2 Halve the remaining pear, discard the stalk, scoop out the core and then put them all in a pan with the apple juice. Bring to the boil, cover and simmer for 5 minutes, turning the pears once.

3 Lift out the pear halves and reserve, cooking the whole pears for a further 5 minutes, or until tender. Remove with a slotted spoon and place on a serving dish, reserving the cooking liquor. Finely chop one pear half and put into a small dish for the baby. Reserve the other half pear for the toddler.

4 Pour half of the reserved apple juice into a bowl, place over a pan of simmering water, add the gelatine and stir until completely dissolved. Transfer to a measuring jug (cup) and pour half over the chopped pear and chill.

5 Stir a little green colouring into the remaining gelatine mixture, pour into a shallow dish or a plate with a rim for the toddler, and chill.

6 Cut away the rind from the orange and lemon, and cut into thin strips. Add to the remaining apple juice with the ginger and honey, and simmer over a gentle heat for 5 minutes, until the rinds are soft.

7 Blend the cornflour with a little water to make a smooth paste, stir into the pan, then bring the mixture to the boil and cook, stirring until thickened. Pour over the whole pears and leave to cool.

8 Place the toddler's pear, cut side down, on the green jelly (gelatine). To make a mouse, add a piece of red liquorice for a tail and two pieces for whiskers. Make two small cuts for eyes and tuck a currant into each slit. Add a large raisin for the nose. Halve the cherry and use for ears. Serve slightly chilled, with cream for the adults, if liked.

# Peach Frangipane Tart

175g/6oz/1½ cups plain (all-purpose) flour

75g/3oz/6 tbsp butter

*For the Filling*

50g/2oz/4 tbsp butter

50g/2oz/¼ cup caster (superfine) sugar

1 egg

few drops of almond essence (extract)

50g/2oz/⅔ cup ground almonds

30ml/2 tbsp apricot jam

15ml/1 tbsp chopped glacéed (candied) peel

400g/14oz can peach slices

15ml/1 tbsp flaked (sliced) almonds

15ml/1 tbsp fromage frais or natural (plain) yogurt

icing (confectioners') sugar, for dusting

crème fraîche or natural (plain) yogurt, to serve

1 Place the flour in a bowl, cut the butter into small pieces and rub into the flour with your fingertips until the mixture resembles fine breadcrumbs.

2 Stir in 30–35ml/6–7 tsp water and mix to a smooth dough. Knead lightly on a floured surface and roll out thinly.

3 Lift the pastry over a rolling pin and use to line an 18cm/7in flan dish, pressing down against the sides of the dish. Trim the top.

4 Re-roll the trimmings and cut out twelve 5cm/2in circles with a fluted cookie cutter, pressing into sections of a patty tin (muffin pan). Chill the pastry for 15 minutes.

5 Preheat the oven to 190°C/375°F/Gas 5. Line the large flan dish with baking parchment and fill with baking beans. Cook for 10 minutes, then remove the baking beans and paper and cook the shell for a further 5 minutes.

6 Meanwhile, make the filling: cream together the butter and sugar in a bowl until light and fluffy. Beat the eggs and almond essence together, then gradually beat into the creamed sugar. Stir in the ground almonds and set aside.

7 Divide the jam among the small and large tarts, spread it into a thin layer in the large tart and sprinkle with glacéed peel. Spoon all of the almond mixture over the top and level the surface.

8 Drain the peaches and set aside three slices for the baby. Cut three slices into chunky pieces and divide among six of the small tarts, leaving six with just jam.

9 Arrange the remaining peaches over the top of the large tart and sprinkle with flaked almonds.

10 Cook the small tarts for 10 minutes and the large tart for 25 minutes, until the filling is set and browned. Dust the large tart with icing sugar and leave to cool slightly.

11 Purée the reserved peaches for the baby in a processor or liquidizer. Mix with fromage frais or yogurt and spoon into a small dish. Serve with two plain jam tarts.

12 Arrange a few fruity jam tarts on a plate for the toddler. Cut the large tart into wedges and serve with crème fraîche or natural yogurt for the adults. Test the temperature of the children's tarts before serving.

# Honey and Summer Fruit Mousse

10ml/2 tsp powdered gelatine

500g/1¼lb bag frozen summer fruits, defrosted

20ml/4 tsp caster (superfine) sugar

500g/1¼lb tub fromage frais or Greek (US strained plain) yogurt

150ml/¼ pint/⅔ cup whipping cream

25ml/5 tsp clear honey

1 Put 30ml/2 tbsp cold water in a cup and sprinkle the gelatine over, making sure that all grains of gelatine have been absorbed. Soak for 5 minutes, then heat in a pan of simmering water until the gelatine dissolves and the liquid is clear. Cool slightly.

2 For the baby, process or liquidize 50g/2oz of fruit to a purée and stir in 5ml/1 tsp sugar. Mix 45ml/3 tbsp fromage frais or yogurt with 5ml/1 tsp sugar in a separate bowl.

3 Put alternate spoonfuls of fromage frais or yogurt and purée into a small dish for the baby. Swirl the mixtures together with a teaspoon. Chill until required.

4 For the toddler, process 50g/2oz fruit with 5ml/1 tsp sugar. Mix 60ml/4 tbsp fromage frais or yogurt with 5ml/1 tsp sugar, then stir in 10ml/2 tsp fruit purée.

5 Stir 5ml/1 tsp gelatine into the fruit purée and 5ml/1 tsp into the fromage frais or yogurt mixture. Spoon the fruit mixture into the base of a clear plastic beaker or glass and chill until set.

6 For the adults, whip the cream until softly peaking. Fold in the remaining fromage frais or yogurt and honey and add the remaining gelatine. Pour into two 250ml/8fl oz/ 1 cup moulds. Chill until set.

7 Spoon the remaining fromage frais or yogurt mixture over the set fruit layer in the serving glass for the toddler and chill until set.

8 To serve, dip one of the dishes for the adults in hot water, count to 15, then loosen the edges with your fingertips, invert on to a large plate and, holding mould and plate together, jerk to release the mousse and remove the mould. Repeat with the other mould. Spoon the remaining fruits and some juice around the desserts and serve.

**TIP**

If you have a small novelty mould, you may prefer to set the toddler's portion in this rather than a glass or plastic container.

Make sure the gelatine isn't too hot before adding to fromage frais or yogurt or it may curdle.

# Nutritional Information

The nutritional analysis below is for the whole recipe

**p28 Vegetable Purées** Energy 75Kcal/310kJ; Protein 2.6g; Carbohydrate 10.6g, of which sugars 10.1g; Fat 2.6g, of which saturates 1.6g; Cholesterol 8mg; Calcium 96mg; Fibre 2.4g; Sodium 51mg.

**p29 Fruit Purées** Energy 33Kcal/142kJ; Protein 0.7g; Carbohydrate 6.6g, of which sugars 6.6g; Fat 0.7g, of which saturates 0.4g; Cholesterol 2mg; Calcium 20mg; Fibre 1.1g; Sodium 8mg.

**p34 Autumn Harvest** Energy 420Kcal/1760kJ; Protein 15.4g; Carbohydrate 61.2g, of which sugars 35.7g; Fat 14g, of which saturates 8g; Cholesterol 42mg; Calcium 498mg; Fibre 11.4g; Sodium 199mg.

**p35 Mixed Vegetable Platter** Energy 412Kcal/1727kJ; Protein 19.3g; Carbohydrate 55.3g, of which sugars 28.5g; Fat 13.7g, of which saturates 8g; Cholesterol 42mg; Calcium 482mg; Fibre 8.6g; Sodium 190mg.

**p36 Carrot, Lentil and Coriander Purée** Energy 602Kcal/2531kJ; Protein 26.9g; Carbohydrate 97.5g, of which sugars 42.9g; Fat 13.9g, of which saturates 8.2g; Cholesterol 42mg; Calcium 478mg; Fibre 12.6g; Sodium 254mg.

**p37 Red Pepper Risotto** Energy 419Kcal/1744kJ; Protein 16g; Carbohydrate 60g, of which sugars 19.8g; Fat 12.6g, of which saturates 7.7g; Cholesterol 42mg; Calcium 409mg; Fibre 2.4g; Sodium 163mg.

**p38 Parsnip and Broccoli Mix** Energy 380Kcal/1590kJ; Protein 19g; Carbohydrate 43.7g, of which sugars 28g; Fat 15.2g, of which saturates 8.2g; Cholesterol 42mg; Calcium 511mg; Fibre 13.3g; Sodium 161mg.

**p39 Turkey Stew with Carrots and Corn** Energy 415Kcal/1756kJ; Protein 46.5g; Carbohydrate 49.2g, of which sugars 17.3g; Fat 4.9g, of which saturates 1.9g; Cholesterol 89mg; Calcium 96mg; Fibre 6.6g; Sodium 180mg.

**p40 Chicken and Parsnip Purée** Energy 544Kcal/2287kJ; Protein 43.8g; Carbohydrate 57.3g, of which sugars 33.5g; Fat 16.8g, of which saturates 8.6g; Cholesterol 123mg;

Calcium 503mg; Fibre 16.1g; Sodium 233mg.

**p41 Cock-a-Leekie Casserole** Energy 523Kcal/2204kJ; Protein 43g; Carbohydrate 59.2g, of which sugars 18.2g; Fat 14g, of which saturates 8.2g; Cholesterol 123mg; Calcium 388mg; Fibre 3.9g; Sodium 229mg.

**p42 Trout and Courgette Savoury** Energy 561Kcal/2352kJ; Protein 41.6g; Carbohydrate 59.8g, of which sugars 18.9g; Fat 18.5g, of which saturates 8.6g; Cholesterol 119mg; Calcium 409mg; Fibre 4.3g; Sodium 214mg.

**p43 Fisherman's Pie** Energy 556Kcal/2338kJ; Protein 34.8g; Carbohydrate 76.2g, of which sugars 19g; Fat 14.2g, of which saturates 8.1g; Cholesterol 83mg; Calcium 389mg; Fibre 5.1g; Sodium 222mg.

**p44 Apple Ambrosia** Energy 308Kcal/1285kJ; Protein 11.8g; Carbohydrate 38.8g, of which sugars 19.5g; Fat 12.1g, of which saturates 7.5g; Cholesterol 42mg; Calcium 362mg; Fibre 1.1g; Sodium 130mg.

**p45 Fruit Salad Purée** Energy 142Kcal/604kJ; Protein 2.8g; Carbohydrate 33.8g, of which sugars 33.8g; Fat 0.4g, of which saturates 0g; Cholesterol 0mg; Calcium 35mg; Fibre 6.6g; Sodium 8mg.

**p48 Sheperd's Pie** Energy 487Kcal/2045kJ; Protein 29.4g; Carbohydrate 50.1g, of which sugars 15.2g; Fat 20.1g, of which saturates 8.4g; Cholesterol 69mg; Calcium 54mg; Fibre 5.3g; Sodium 379mg.

**p49 Braised Beef and Carrots** Energy 466Kcal/1959kJ; Protein 43.2g; Carbohydrate 50.7g, of which sugars 22.3g; Fat 11.3g, of which saturates 4.6g; Cholesterol 110mg; Calcium 91mg; Fibre 8g; Sodium 189mg.

**p50 Lamb Hotpot** Energy 365Kcal/1533kJ; Protein 26.8g; Carbohydrate 34.8g, of which sugars 16.7g; Fat 14.2g, of which saturates 6.3g; Cholesterol 87mg; Calcium 118mg; Fibre 7.2g; Sodium 159mg.

**p51 Lamb and Lentil Savoury** Energy 332Kcal/1397kJ; Protein 29.7g; Carbohydrate 24.4g, of which sugars 10.6g; Fat 13.6g, of which saturates 6g; Cholesterol 87mg; Calcium 97mg; Fibre 3.9g; Sodium 388mg.

**p52 Country Pork and Runner Beans** Energy 279Kcal/1174kJ; Protein 28.7g; Carbohydrate 30g, of which sugars 11.7g; Fat 5.7g, of which saturates 1.9g; Cholesterol 73mg; Calcium 71mg; Fibre 5.6g; Sodium 122mg.

**p53 Pork and Apple Savoury** Energy 410Kcal/1730kJ; Protein 42.5g; Carbohydrate 44.3g, of which sugars 16.9g; Fat 8.2g, of which saturates 2.6g; Cholesterol 110mg; Calcium 132mg; Fibre 6.4g; Sodium 170mg.

**p54 Nursery Kedgeree** Energy 625Kcal/2604kJ; Protein 39.2g; Carbohydrate 58.5g, of which sugars 16.3g; Fat 25.9g, of which saturates 12.1g; Cholesterol 494mg; Calcium 483mg; Fibre 1.2g; Sodium 223mg.

**p55 Mediterranean Vegetables** Energy 284Kcal/1202kJ; Protein 12.7g; Carbohydrate 54.5g, of which sugars 25.3g; Fat 3.1g, of which saturates 0.7g; Cholesterol 0mg; Calcium 89mg; Fibre 8.3g; Sodium 362mg.

**p56 Pasta with Sauce** Energy 608Kcal/2537kJ; Protein 30.8g; Carbohydrate 49.2g, of which sugars 27.6g; Fat 32g, of which saturates 20g; Cholesterol 98mg; Calcium 840mg; Fibre 6.4g; Sodium 545mg.

**p57 Apple and Orange Fool** Energy 219Kcal/924kJ; Protein 5.5g; Carbohydrate 37.6g, of which sugars 23.8g; Fat 6.1g, of which saturates 3.8g; Cholesterol 21mg; Calcium 188mg; Fibre 2.1g; Sodium 117mg.

**p58 Orchard Fruit Dessert** Energy 352Kcal/1492kJ; Protein 6.9g; Carbohydrate 71g, of which sugars 57.2g; Fat 6.3g, of which saturates 3.8g; Cholesterol 21mg; Calcium 233mg; Fibre 6.9g; Sodium 122mg.

**p59 Peach Melba Dessert** Energy 153Kcal/650kJ; Protein 7g; Carbohydrate 30.8g, of which sugars 30.8g; Fat 1.3g, of which saturates 0.6g; Cholesterol 2mg; Calcium 238mg; Fibre 1.7g; Sodium 98mg.

**p68 Lamb Couscous** Energy 631Kcal/2643kJ; Protein 40.6g; Carbohydrate 67g, of which sugars 39.3g; Fat 24.1g, of which saturates 9.6g; Cholesterol 133mg; Calcium 160mg; Fibre 6.6g; Sodium 227mg.

**p69 Paprika Pork** Energy 533Kcal/2248kJ; Protein 50.1g; Carbohydrate 60.2g, of which sugars 17.8g; Fat

11.9g, of which saturates 3.2g; Cholesterol 110mg; Calcium 127mg; Fibre 10.7g; Sodium 659mg.

**p70 Chicken and Celery Supper** Energy 331Kcal/1387kJ; Protein 39.5g; Carbohydrate 24.6g, of which sugars 22.1g; Fat 8.9g, of which saturates 2g; Cholesterol 184mg; Calcium 118mg; Fibre 7.3g; Sodium 285mg.

**p71 Cauliflower and Broccoli with Cheese** Energy 750Kcal/3127kJ; Protein 45.9g; Carbohydrate 50.2g, of which sugars 22.9g; Fat 39.9g, of which saturates 24.7g; Cholesterol 115mg; Calcium 1054mg; Fibre 9.4g; Sodium 720mg.

**p72 Cheese Tagliatelle with Broccoli and Ham** Energy 668Kcal/2797kJ; Protein 42.9g; Carbohydrate 53.2g, of which sugars 17.4g; Fat 31.6g, of which saturates 19.3g; Cholesterol 120mg; Calcium 804mg; Fibre 4.4g; Sodium 1101mg.

**p73 Baby Dhal** Energy 305Kcal/1291kJ; Protein 18.1g; Carbohydrate 56.9g, of which sugars 16.6g; Fat 2g, of which saturates 0.4g; Cholesterol 0mg; Calcium 116mg; Fibre 8.8g; Sodium 59mg.

**p74 Fish and Cheese Pie** Energy 620Kcal/2595kJ; Protein 42.9g; Carbohydrate 49.2g, of which sugars 15.4g; Fat 27.9g, of which saturates 17.5g; Cholesterol 125mg; Calcium 701mg; Fibre 3.9g; Sodium 551mg.

**p75 Fish Creole** Energy 283Kcal/1185kJ; Protein 21.1g; Carbohydrate 46.4g, of which sugars 6.3g; Fat 1.2g, of which saturates 0.1g; Cholesterol 41mg; Calcium 43mg; Fibre 1.4g; Sodium 249mg.

**p76 Chocolate Pots** Energy 98Kcal/405kJ; Protein 5.8g; Carbohydrate 5.6g, of which sugars 5.5g; Fat 5.9g, of which saturates 2.8g; Cholesterol 106mg; Calcium 105mg; Fibre 0.1g; Sodium 77mg.

**p77 Vanilla Custards** Energy 94Kcal/392kJ; Protein 5.6g; Carbohydrate 5.5g, of which sugars 5.5g; Fat 5.7g, of which saturates 2.7g; Cholesterol 106mg; Calcium 104mg; Fibre 0g; Sodium 68mg.

**p78 Marmite Bread Sticks** Energy 15Kcal/63kJ; Protein 0.5g; Carbohydrate 2.4g, of which sugars 0.1g; Fat 0.4g, of which saturates 0.1g; Cholesterol 0mg; Calcium 4mg; Fibre 0.1g; Sodium 23mg.

**p79 Bread Fingers with Egg**
Energy 14Kcal/58kJ; Protein 0.7g;
Carbohydrate 1.8g, of which sugars
0.2g; Fat 0.5g, of which saturates
0.1g; Cholesterol 12mg; Calcium
8mg; Fibre 0.1g; Sodium 23mg.

**p80 Cheese Straws** Energy
41Kcal/172kJ; Protein 1.2g;
Carbohydrate 3.3g, of which sugars
0.1g; Fat 2.6g, of which saturates
1.6g; Cholesterol 11mg; Calcium
27mg; Fibre 0.1g; Sodium 32mg.

**p82 Mini Cup Cakes** Energy
31Kcal/130kJ; Protein 0.4g;
Carbohydrate 3.5g, of which sugars
2.1g; Fat 1.8g, of which saturates
0.1g; Cholesterol 7mg; Calcium
9mg; Fibre 0.1g; Sodium 25mg.

**p83 Shortbread Shapes** Energy
28Kcal/117kJ; Protein 0.3g;
Carbohydrate 3.2g, of which sugars
0.9g; Fat 1.7g, of which saturates 1g;
Cholesterol 4mg; Calcium 4mg;
Fibre 0.1g; Sodium 12mg.

**p92 Sticky Chicken** Energy
109Kcal/458kJ; Protein 14.7g;
Carbohydrate 1.2g, of which sugars
1.1g; Fat 5.1g, of which saturates
1.4g; Cholesterol 77mg; Calcium
9mg; Fibre 0g; Sodium 222mg.

**p94 Coriander Chicken
Casserole** Energy 157Kcal/658kJ;
Protein 21.8g; Carbohydrate 7.6g,
of which sugars 4.8g; Fat 4.6g, of
which saturates 1g; Cholesterol
105mg; Calcium 38mg; Fibre 1.6g;
Sodium 101mg.

**p94 Chicken and Cheese Parcels**
Energy 252Kcal/1050kJ; Protein
27.6g; Carbohydrate 0.2g, of which
sugars 0.2g; Fat 15.1g, of which
saturates 6.5g; Cholesterol 87mg;
Calcium 190mg; Fibre 0g;
Sodium 436mg.

**p96 Peppered Beef Casserole**
Energy 229Kcal/958kJ; Protein 18g;
Carbohydrate 26.5g, of which sugars
8.2g; Fat 6.3g, of which saturates
2.3g; Cholesterol 33mg; Calcium
43mg; Fibre 3.3g; Sodium 251mg.

**p 97 Lamb Stew** Energy 152Kcal/
635kJ; Protein 12.3g; Carbohydrate
7.5g, of which sugars 5g; Fat 8.4g, of
which saturates 3.3g; Cholesterol
44mg; Calcium 29mg; Fibre 2.2g;
Sodium 59mg.

**p98 Mexican Beef** Energy
171Kcal/715kJ; Protein 9.5g;
Carbohydrate 11.8g, of which sugars
2.9g; Fat 9.8g, of which saturates

3.9g; Cholesterol 23mg; Calcium
83mg; Fibre 1.7g; Sodium 275mg.

**p98 Lamb and Celery Casserole**
Energy 142Kcal/596kJ; Protein 12.6g;
Carbohydrate 8.4g, of which sugars
3.8g; Fat 6.8g, of which saturates
3.1g; Cholesterol 44mg; Calcium
33mg; Fibre 1.5g; Sodium 67mg.

**p100 Shepherd's Pie** Energy
388Kcal/1617kJ; Protein 21.7g;
Carbohydrate 28.7g, of which sugars
11.9g; Fat 21.5g, of which saturates
10.3g; Cholesterol 69mg; Calcium
69mg; Fibre 4.5g; Sodium 382mg.

**p101 Tuna Fish Cakes** Energy
263Kcal/1104kJ; Protein 16.6g;
Carbohydrate 19.4g, of which sugars
4.9g; Fat 13.9g, of which saturates
1.7g; Cholesterol 81mg; Calcium
80mg; Fibre 3.3g; Sodium 183mg.

**p102 Fish and Cheese Pies**
Energy 300Kcal/1258kJ; Protein
19.3g; Carbohydrate 25.5g, of which
sugars 6.5g; Fat 13.9g, of which
saturates 7.8g; Cholesterol 59mg;
Calcium 228mg; Fibre 1.6g; Sodium
246mg.

**p103 Surprise Fish Parcels**
Energy 89Kcal/376kJ; Protein 17.9g;
Carbohydrate 2.5g, of which sugars
2.4g; Fat 0.9g, of which saturates
0.2g; Cholesterol 32mg; Calcium
36mg; Fibre 1g; Sodium 670mg.

**p104 Cowboy Sausages and
Beans** Energy 225Kcal/944kJ;
Protein 9.8g; Carbohydrate 22.7g, of
which sugars 8.4g; Fat 11.4g, of
which saturates 4.1g; Cholesterol
15mg; Calcium 89mg; Fibre 5.4g;
Sodium 702mg.

**p104 Mini Toad in the Hole**
Energy 282Kcal/1183kJ; Protein
11.5g; Carbohydrate 28.3g, of which
sugars 2.9g; Fat 14.6g, of which
saturates 4.8g; Cholesterol 119mg;
Calcium 131mg; Fibre 1.3g;
Sodium 372mg.

**p106 Pork Hotpot** Energy
230Kcal/967kJ; Protein 21.4g;
Carbohydrate 24.7g, of which sugars
7.4g; Fat 5.7g, of which saturates
1.6g; Cholesterol 55mg; Calcium
32mg; Fibre 2.5g; Sodium 134mg.

**p107 Pork and Lentil Casserole**
Energy 369Kcal/1531kJ; Protein
17.7g; Carbohydrate 12.8g, of which
sugars 5.2g; Fat 27.8g, of which
saturates 9.9g; Cholesterol 63mg;
Calcium 31mg; Fibre 2.1g;
Sodium 65mg.

**p108 Sticky Ribs and Apple Slaw**
Energy 454Kcal/1896kJ; Protein 23g;
Carbohydrate 25.2g, of which sugars
16.4g; Fat 29.8g, of which saturates
8g; Cholesterol 86mg; Calcium
44mg; Fibre 2.1g; Sodium 357mg.

**p109 Mini Cheese and Ham
Tarts** Energy 100Kcal/419kJ;
Protein 3.2g; Carbohydrate 9.6g,
of which sugars 1.3g; Fat 5.6g, of
which saturates 1.2g; Cholesterol
21mg; Calcium 59mg; Fibre 0.4g;
Sodium 101mg.

**p110 Pick-up Sticks** Energy
54Kcal/223kJ; Protein 1.7g;
Carbohydrate 7.7g, of which sugars
6.9g; Fat 2g, of which saturates 0.3g;
Cholesterol 0mg; Calcium 29mg;
Fibre 2.3g; Sodium 318mg.

**p112 Spinach Pancakes with Ham
and Cheese** Energy 265Kcal/
1111kJ; Protein 11.7g; Carbohydrate
22g, of which sugars 5.5g; Fat 15g,
of which saturates 5g; Cholesterol
89mg; Calcium 250mg; Fibre 1.2g;
Sodium 325mg.

**p113 Cauliflower and Broccoli
with Cheese** Energy 264Kcal/
1101kJ; Protein 14.6g; Carbohydrate
11.9g, of which sugars 5.9g; Fat
17.6g, of which saturates 6.1g;
Cholesterol 119mg; Calcium 293mg;
Fibre 2.1g; Sodium 281mg.

**p114 Potato Boats** Energy
257Kcal/1073kJ; Protein 10.9g;
Carbohydrate 24.7g, of which sugars
7.4g; Fat 13.4g, of which saturates
6.4g; Cholesterol 39mg; Calcium
165mg; Fibre 2.9g; Sodium 573mg.

**p115 Fat Cats** Energy 553Kcal/
2308kJ; Protein 13.5g; Carbohydrate
46.6g, of which sugars 4.7g; Fat
36.8g, of which saturates 3.9g;
Cholesterol 18mg; Calcium 258mg;
Fibre 0.9g; Sodium 514mg.

**p116 Potato, Carrot and
Courgette Rosti** Energy 37Kcal/
155kJ; Protein 0.7g; Carbohydrate
5.2g, of which sugars 1g; Fat 1.6g,
of which saturates 0.2g; Cholesterol
0mg; Calcium 5mg; Fibre 0.5g;
Sodium 5mg.

**p116 Veggie Burgers** Energy
118Kcal/495kJ; Protein 4.1g;
Carbohydrate 13.3g, of which sugars
2g; Fat 5.8g, of which saturates 1.7g;
Cholesterol 54mg; Calcium 68mg;
Fibre 1.4g; Sodium 54mg.

**p118 Vegetable Lasagne** Energy
296Kcal/1243kJ; Protein 11.7g;

Carbohydrate 30.7g, of which sugars
8.6g; Fat 14.5g, of which saturates
8g; Cholesterol 33mg; Calcium
243mg; Fibre 2.9g; Sodium 210mg.

**p119 Aubergine Bolognaise**
Energy 184Kcal/781kJ; Protein 8.2g;
Carbohydrate 36.6g, of which sugars
9.6g; Fat 1.5g, of which saturates
0.4g; Cholesterol 0mg; Calcium
39mg; Fibre 4.9g; Sodium 58mg.

**p120 Speedy Chicken Pie** Energy
244Kcal/1015kJ; Protein 14.9g;
Carbohydrate 7.5g, of which sugars
1.6g; Fat 17.2g, of which saturates
4.6g; Cholesterol 54mg; Calcium
68mg; Fibre 0.7g; Sodium 241mg.

**p122 Skinny Dippers** Energy
444Kcal/1870kJ; Protein 33.4g;
Carbohydrate 45.9g, of which sugars
10g; Fat 15.1g, of which saturates
8.2g; Cholesterol 99mg; Calcium
160mg; Fibre 3g; Sodium 771mg.

**p123 Sweet and Sour Chicken**
Energy 338Kcal/1409kJ; Protein
19.3g; Carbohydrate 29g, of which
sugars 6.5g; Fat 16.3g, of which
saturates 4.1g; Cholesterol 170mg;
Calcium 53mg; Fibre 0.9g;
Sodium 351mg.

**p124 Ham and Tomato Scramble**
Energy 192Kcal/808kJ; Protein
15.7g; Carbohydrate 16.7g, of which
sugars 4g; Fat 7.6g, of which saturates
2.1g; Cholesterol 211mg; Calcium
74mg; Fibre 1.2g; Sodium 638mg.

**p124 Ham Salad Clown** Energy
94Kcal/391kJ; Protein 8.5g;
Carbohydrate 2.2g, of which sugars
2.2g; Fat 5.5g, of which saturates
3.2g; Cholesterol 46mg; Calcium
99mg; Fibre 0.2g; Sodium 398mg.

**p126 Spanish Omelette** Energy
130Kcal/546kJ; Protein 9.3g;
Carbohydrate 9.9g, of which sugars
1.8g; Fat 6.4g, of which saturates
1.7g; Cholesterol 110mg; Calcium
22mg; Fibre 1.2g; Sodium 349mg.

**p127 Pasta with Ham Sauce** Energy 434Kcal/1814kJ; Protein 20g; Carbohydrate 37g, of which sugars 5.6g; Fat 23.6g, of which saturates 6.7g; Cholesterol 43mg; Calcium 310mg; Fibre 2.4g; Sodium 635mg.

**p128 Quickie Kebabs** Energy 59Kcal/248kJ; Protein 5.2g; Carbohydrate 3g, of which sugars 2.9g; Fat 3g, of which saturates 0.6g; Cholesterol 15mg; Calcium 6mg; Fibre 0.6g; Sodium 358mg.

**p128 Sausage Wrappers** Energy 272Kcal/1136kJ; Protein 20.4g; Carbohydrate 7.8g, of which sugars 2.8g; Fat 18g, of which saturates 5.7g; Cholesterol 137mg; Calcium 24mg; Fibre 0.8g; Sodium 1342mg.

**p130 Corned Beef Hash** Energy 222Kcal/931kJ; Protein 16.9g; Carbohydrate 18.1g, of which sugars 5g; Fat 9.6g, of which saturates 3.7g; Cholesterol 48mg; Calcium 34mg; Fibre 1.5g; Sodium 628mg.

**p131 Cannibal Necklaces** Energy 240Kcal/1003kJ; Protein 14.1g; Carbohydrate 19.5g, of which sugars 5.2g; Fat 12.2g, of which saturates 4.8g; Cholesterol 36mg; Calcium 231mg; Fibre 2.3g; Sodium 383mg.

**p132 Beef Burgers** Energy 305Kcal/ 1282kJ; Protein 16.3g; Carbohydrate 34.1g, of which sugars 4g; Fat 12.5g, of which saturates 5.1g; Cholesterol 35mg; Calcium 53mg; Fibre 2.5g; Sodium 222mg.

**p133 Four Fast Fishes** Energy 268Kcal/1124kJ; Protein 16.4g; Carbohydrate 27.1g, of which sugars 3.8g; Fat 11.2g, of which saturates 1.6g; Cholesterol 48mg; Calcium 99mg; Fibre 2.3g; Sodium 306mg.

**p134 Tuna Risotto** Energy 190Kcal/798kJ; Protein 15.8g; Carbohydrate 26.6g, of which sugars 3.7g; Fat 2.4g, of which saturates 0.4g; Cholesterol 26mg; Calcium 22mg; Fibre 1.7g; Sodium 243mg.

**p134 Fish Finger Log Cabins** Energy 99Kcal/414kJ; Protein 6.4g; Carbohydrate 9.3g, of which sugars 2.3g; Fat 4.3g, of which saturates 1.3g; Cholesterol 15mg; Calcium 81mg; Fibre 1.1g; Sodium 172mg.

**p136 Shape Sorters** Energy 300Kcal/1250kJ; Protein 12.2g; Carbohydrate 16.2g, of which sugars 2.6g; Fat 20.6g, of which saturates 7.4g; Cholesterol 24mg; Calcium 223mg; Fibre 1.5g; Sodium 416mg.

**p136 Happy Families** Energy 251Kcal/1051kJ; Protein 13.4g; Carbohydrate 22.2g, of which sugars 4.6g; Fat 12.7g, of which saturates 4.6g; Cholesterol 40mg; Calcium 229mg; Fibre 1.1g; Sodium 942mg.

**p138 French Toast Butterflies** Energy 243Kcal/1018kJ; Protein 17.2g; Carbohydrate 17g, of which sugars 3.9g; Fat 12g, of which saturates 5.2g; Cholesterol 127mg; Calcium 216mg; Fibre 2.4g; Sodium 615mg.

**p139 Tuna Flowers** Energy 384Kcal/1607kJ; Protein 17.4g; Carbohydrate 31.8g, of which sugars 4.3g; Fat 21.3g, of which saturates 11.6g; Cholesterol 63mg; Calcium 251mg; Fibre 2g; Sodium 600mg.

**p140 Noughts and Crosses** Energy 379Kcal/1578kJ; Protein 20.5g; Carbohydrate 15.4g, of which sugars 2.6g; Fat 25.4g, of which saturates 14.7g; Cholesterol 68mg; Calcium 462mg; Fibre 1.1g; Sodium 827mg.

**p140 Cheese Strips on Toast** Energy 273Kcal/1137kJ; Protein 15g; Carbohydrate 13.5g, of which sugars 0.9g; Fat 16.9g, of which saturates 10.9g; Cholesterol 49mg; Calcium 400mg; Fibre 0.5g; Sodium 503mg.

**p142 Speedy Sausage Rolls** Energy 91Kcal/378kJ; Protein 2.3g; Carbohydrate 7.1g, of which sugars 0.5g; Fat 6.1g, of which saturates 2.7g; Cholesterol 11mg; Calcium 19mg; Fibre 0.2g; Sodium 171mg.

**p143 Pizza Clock** Energy 204Kcal/856kJ; Protein 10g; Carbohydrate 23.2g, of which sugars 9.3g; Fat 8.1g, of which saturates 4.3g; Cholesterol 25mg; Calcium 173mg; Fibre 2.2g; Sodium 547mg.

**p144 Spotted Sandwiches** Energy 275Kcal/1151kJ; Protein 8.1g; Carbohydrate 28.2g, of which sugars 3.8g; Fat 15.3g, of which saturates 2.7g; Cholesterol 106mg; Calcium 107mg; Fibre 2.1g; Sodium 382mg.

**p144 Sandwich Snails** Energy 188Kcal/783kJ; Protein 6.6g; Carbohydrate 11.6g, of which sugars 2.9g; Fat 12.9g, of which saturates 4.6g; Cholesterol 24mg; Calcium 124mg; Fibre 0.8g; Sodium 345mg.

**p146 Fruit Fondue** Energy 197Kcal/833kJ; Protein 3.8g; Carbohydrate 33.7g, of which sugars 30.2g; Fat 5.4g, of which saturates 2.4g; Cholesterol 4mg; Calcium 107mg; Fibre 1.5g; Sodium 44mg.

**p148 Strawberry Ice Cream** Energy 2026Kcal/8391kJ; Protein 19.9g; Carbohydrate 101.4g, of which sugars 86.5g; Fat 169.2g, of which saturates 100.2g; Cholesterol 420mg; Calcium 606mg; Fibre 5.4g; Sodium 267mg.

**p149 Raspberry Sorbet** Energy 1055Kcal/4518kJ; Protein 10.6g; Carbohydrate 266.2g, of which sugars 266.2g; Fat 2g, of which saturates 0.7g; Cholesterol 0mg; Calcium 288mg; Fibre 16.9g; Sodium 34mg.

**p150 Yogurt Lollies** Energy 41Kcal/ 172kJ; Protein 1.9g; Carbohydrate 7.3g, of which sugars 7.3g; Fat 0.6g, of which saturates 0.4g; Cholesterol 2mg; Calcium 68mg; Fibre 0g; Sodium 27mg.

**p150 Jolly Jellies** Energy 195Kcal/824kJ; Protein 4.9g; Carbohydrate 39.2g, of which sugars 38.9g; Fat 3.2g, of which saturates 2g; Cholesterol 9mg; Calcium 55mg; Fibre 0.3g; Sodium 26mg.

**p152 Pancakes** Energy 285Kcal/1194kJ; Protein 8.1g; Carbohydrate 33.3g, of which sugars 19.9g; Fat 14.2g, of which saturates 6.1g; Cholesterol 66mg; Calcium 163mg; Fibre 1.5g; Sodium 78mg.

**p153 Traffic Light Sundaes** Energy 224Kcal/940kJ; Protein 4.3g; Carbohydrate 36.7g, of which sugars 36.6g; Fat 7.7g, of which saturates 4.5g; Cholesterol 0mg; Calcium 73mg; Fibre 0.5g; Sodium 41mg.

**p154 Cheat's Trifle** Energy 175Kcal/741kJ; Protein 4.7g; Carbohydrate 32.5g, of which sugars 26.2g; Fat 3.1g, of which saturates 0.3g; Cholesterol 2mg; Calcium 115mg; Fibre 0.9g; Sodium 73mg.

**p154 Baked Bananas** Energy 184Kcal/770kJ; Protein 2.9g; Carbohydrate 27g, of which sugars 25.1g; Fat 7.8g, of which saturates 4.6g; Cholesterol 0mg; Calcium 55mg; Fibre 0.9g; Sodium 31mg.

**p156 Orange and Apple Rockies** Energy 87Kcal/366kJ; Protein 1.3g; Carbohydrate 11.6g, of which sugars 4.5g; Fat 4.3g, of which saturates 0.9g; Cholesterol 8mg; Calcium 19mg; Fibre 0.5g; Sodium 42mg.

**p158 Date Crunch** Energy 120Kcal/503kJ; Protein 1.3g; Carbohydrate 15.3g, of which sugars 10.1g; Fat 6.4g, of which saturates 3.6g; Cholesterol 12mg; Calcium 27mg; Fibre 0.4g; Sodium 85mg.

**p159 Chocolate Dominoes** Energy 335Kcal/1400kJ; Protein 2.9g; Carbohydrate 38.8g, of which sugars 31.3g; Fat 19.8g, of which saturates 6.4g; Cholesterol 59mg; Calcium 41mg; Fibre 0.7g; Sodium 199mg.

**p160 Marshmallow Krispie Cakes** Energy 56Kcal/235kJ; Protein 0.7g; Carbohydrate 9g, of which sugars 4.4g; Fat 2.2g, of which saturates 1.1g; Cholesterol 3mg; Calcium 39mg; Fibre 0g; Sodium 28mg.

**p160 Mini-muffins** Energy 67Kcal/281kJ; Protein 1.4g; Carbohydrate 11.1g, of which sugars 4.8g; Fat 2.2g, of which saturates 1.2g; Cholesterol 13mg; Calcium 25mg; Fibre 0.4g; Sodium 19mg.

**p162 Cup Cake Faces** Energy 328Kcal/1374kJ; Protein 3.2g; Carbohydrate 42.5g, of which sugars 33.1g; Fat 17.3g, of which saturates 5.4g; Cholesterol 43mg; Calcium 53mg; Fibre 0.6g; Sodium 127mg.

**p163 Gingerbread People** Energy 94Kcal/395kJ; Protein 1.2g; Carbohydrate 16.5g, of which sugars 9.3g; Fat 3g, of which saturates 0.7g; Cholesterol 0mg; Calcium 19mg; Fibre 0.4g; Sodium 23mg.

**p164 Bread Animals** Energy 147Kcal/624kJ; Protein 4.7g; Carbohydrate 28.5g, of which sugars 1.8g; Fat 2.4g, of which saturates 0.4g; Cholesterol 13mg; Calcium 55mg; Fibre 1.4g; Sodium 139mg.

**p166 Cheese Shapes** Energy 184Kcal/769kJ; Protein 5.2g; Carbohydrate 18.2g, of which saturates 0.4g; Fat 10.4g, of which saturates 2g; Cholesterol 33mg; Calcium 100mg; Fibre 0.4g; Sodium 127mg.

**p169 Marmite and Cheese Whirls** Energy 76Kcal/318kJ; Protein 2.1g; Carbohydrate 5.8g, of which sugars 0.2g; Fat 5.2g, of which saturates 0.8g; Cholesterol 15mg; Calcium 34mg; Fibre 0g; Sodium 82mg.

**p174 Mediterranean Lamb** Energy 1547Kcal/6457kJ; Protein 103.4g; Carbohydrate 63.3g, of which sugars 43g; Fat 99.8g, of which saturates 42.2g; Cholesterol 333mg; Calcium 281mg; Fibre 0.8g; Sodium 951mg.

**p176 Lamb Hotpot** Energy 1217Kcal/5100kJ; Protein 85.2g; Carbohydrate 90.6g, of which sugars 34.3g; Fat 59.6g, of which saturates 27.4g; Cholesterol 298mg; Calcium 256mg; Fibre 19.5g; Sodium 484mg.

**p178 Beef Korma** Energy 1034Kcal/4318kJ; Protein 78.6g; Carbohydrate 48.5g, of which sugars 28.9g; Fat 59.7g, of which saturates 25.2g; Cholesterol 210mg; Calcium 222mg; Fibre 9g; Sodium 542mg.

**p180 Bobotie with Baked Potatoes and Broccoli** Energy 2005Kcal/8426kJ; Protein 126.5g; Carbohydrate 213.8g, of which sugars 70.5g; Fat 77.7g, of which saturates 30.4g; Cholesterol 598mg; Calcium 593mg; Fibre 30.8g; Sodium 1611mg.

**p182 Moussaka** Energy 1805Kcal/7551kJ; Protein 98.9g; Carbohydrate 121.8g, of which sugars 37.6g; Fat 106.1g, of which saturates 46.8g; Cholesterol 360mg; Calcium 684mg; Fibre 15g; Sodium 903mg.

**p184 Chilli Con Carne** Energy 2113Kcal/8830kJ; Protein 125.5g; Carbohydrate 155.4g, of which sugars 46.9g; Fat 114g, of which saturates 44.6g; Cholesterol 297mg; Calcium 387mg; Fibre 29.1g; Sodium 1374mg.

**p186 Beef Bourguignon with Creamed Potatoes** Energy 1690Kcal/7073kJ; Protein 121.4g; Carbohydrate 118.8g, of which sugars 26.2g; Fat 77.2g, of which saturates 32.7g; Cholesterol 318mg; Calcium 303mg; Fibre 12.3g; Sodium 797mg.

**p188 Osso Bucco Pork with Rice** Energy 2089Kcal/8726kJ; Protein 187.1g; Carbohydrate 149g, of which sugars 26.4g; Fat 82.3g, of which saturates 30.5g; Cholesterol 591mg; Calcium 449mg; Fibre 10.4g; Sodium 797mg.

**p190 Pork Stir Fry** Energy 807Kcal/3377kJ; Protein 73.5g; Carbohydrate 58.8g, of which sugars 40.8g; Fat 32.2g, of which saturates 9g; Cholesterol 158mg; Calcium 163mg; Fibre 12.3g; Sodium 1458mg.

**p192 Sausage Casserole** Energy 2486Kcal/10416kJ; Protein 85.3g; Carbohydrate 272.4g, of which sugars 68.3g; Fat 124.7g, of which saturates 47.6g; Cholesterol 180mg; Calcium 641mg; Fibre 40.2g; Sodium 5366mg.

**p194 Chicken and Thyme Casserole** Energy 1320Kcal/5552kJ; Protein 147.1g; Carbohydrate 107.9g, of which sugars 20.9g; Fat 36.2g, of which saturates 10.5g; Cholesterol 635mg; Calcium 235mg; Fibre 13.1g; Sodium 629mg.

**p196 Tandoori-style Chicken** Energy 1209Kcal/5080kJ; Protein 116.5g; Carbohydrate 68.6g, of which sugars 16.8g; Fat 54.1g, of which saturates 13g; Cholesterol 522mg; Calcium 401mg; Fibre 4.5g; Sodium 377mg.

**p198 Chicken Wrappers** Energy 1472Kcal/6187kJ; Protein 175g; Carbohydrate 72.7g, of which sugars 11.7g; Fat 54.3g, of which saturates 24.2g; Cholesterol 527mg; Calcium 512mg; Fibre 8.8g; Sodium 1451mg.

**p200 Pan-fried Turkey with Coriander** Energy 1568Kcal/6566kJ; Protein 122.9g; Carbohydrate 151g, of which sugars 20.5g; Fat 52.5g, of which saturates 33g; Cholesterol 222mg; Calcium 92mg; Fibre 4.2g; Sodium 375mg.

**p202 Chicken Salad** Energy 1058Kcal/4461kJ; Protein 119.4g; Carbohydrate 76.6g, of which sugars 22.4g; Fat 32.7g, of which saturates 17.6g; Cholesterol 379mg; Calcium 224mg; Fibre 7.3g; Sodium 995mg.

**p204 Paella** Energy 1212Kcal/5080kJ; Protein 112.9g; Carbohydrate 149.1g, of which sugars 22.9g; Fat 17.9g, of which saturates 2.6g; Cholesterol 408mg; Calcium 271mg; Fibre 9.7g; Sodium 498mg.

**p206 Fish Cakes** Energy 1349Kcal/5672kJ; Protein 110.3g; Carbohydrate 137.4g, of which sugars 30.6g; Fat 43.2g, of which saturates 21.9g; Cholesterol 287mg; Calcium 595mg; Fibre 13.2g; Sodium 2315mg.

**p208 Fishy Vol-au-Vents** Energy 1690Kcal/7071kJ; Protein 98.5g; Carbohydrate 128.3g, of which sugars 15.5g; Fat 93g, of which saturates 18.3g; Cholesterol 334mg; Calcium 527mg; Fibre 3.1g; Sodium 1351mg.

**p210 Salmon and Cod Kebabs** Energy 1636Kcal/6823kJ; Protein 114g; Carbohydrate 94.6g, of which sugars 24.7g; Fat 91.6g, of which saturates 34.7g; Cholesterol 349mg; Calcium 195mg; Fibre 16.4g; Sodium 724mg.

**p212 Tuna Florentine** Energy 2325Kcal/9709kJ; Protein 164.5g; Carbohydrate 95.1g, of which sugars 20.8g; Fat 139.5g, of which saturates 72.3g; Cholesterol 791mg; Calcium 3035mg; Fibre 8.9g; Sodium 3526mg.

**p214 Cheese on Toast** Energy 1456Kcal/6064kJ; Protein 72g; Carbohydrate 56.1g, of which sugars

3.7g; Fat 102.1g, of which saturates 56.8g; Cholesterol 266mg; Calcium 1644mg; Fibre 3.1g; Sodium 4100mg.

**p216 Penne with Tomato Sauce** Energy 1027Kcal/4327kJ; Protein 38.8g; Carbohydrate 144.3g, of which sugars 36.2g; Fat 35.4g, of which saturates 15.5g; Cholesterol 58mg; Calcium 565mg; Fibre 12.7g; Sodium 519mg.

**p218 Courgette Gougère** Energy 1456Kcal/6051kJ; Protein 58.8g; Carbohydrate 69.4g, of which sugars 17.9g; Fat 104.4g, of which saturates 56.5g; Cholesterol 599mg; Calcium 1132mg; Fibre 9.5g; Sodium 1308mg.

**p220 Cheese Vegetable Crumble** Energy 2051Kcal/8546kJ; Protein 79.8g; Carbohydrate 146.4g, of which sugars 53g; Fat 128.7g, of which saturates 31.5g; Cholesterol 112mg; Calcium 1678mg; Fibre 46.4g; Sodium 2221mg.

**p222 Vegetable Tagine** Energy 1141Kcal/4800kJ; Protein 44.4g; Carbohydrate 190.4g, of which sugars 61.5g; Fat 27.5g, of which saturates 3.3g; Cholesterol 0mg; Calcium 444mg; Fibre 33.7g; Sodium 1071mg.

**p224 Stilton and Leek Tart** Energy 2221Kcal/9261kJ; Protein 81.2g; Carbohydrate 154.7g, of which sugars 20.1g; Fat 145.1g, of which saturates 85.6g; Cholesterol 933mg; Calcium 1148mg; Fibre 9.8g; Sodium 2398mg.

**p226 Bread and Butter Pudding** Energy 1528Kcal/6452kJ; Protein 57.5g; Carbohydrate 214.2g, of which sugars 126g; Fat 52.3g, of which saturates 22.4g; Cholesterol 832mg; Calcium 821mg; Fibre 11.3g; Sodium 1573mg.

**p228 Eve's Pudding** Energy 1198Kcal/5049kJ; Protein 13.7g; Carbohydrate 190.7g, of which sugars 152.6g; Fat 47.9g, of which saturates 27.7g; Cholesterol 297mg; Calcium 201mg; Fibre 11.1g; Sodium 392mg.

**p230 Orange and Strawberry Shortcakes** Energy 1054Kcal/4407kJ; Protein 20.7g; Carbohydrate 118.9g, of which sugars 61.7g; Fat 60.2g, of which saturates 35.3g; Cholesterol 107mg; Calcium 438mg; Fibre 5.1g; Sodium 447mg.

**p232 Exotic Fruit Brûlée** Energy 700Kcal/2940kJ; Protein 24.7g; Carbohydrate 82.4g, of which sugars 81.8g; Fat 36.4g, of which saturates

18.4g; Cholesterol 0mg; Calcium 584mg; Fibre 5.5g; Sodium 259mg.

**p234 Plum Crumble** Energy 1644Kcal/6930kJ; Protein 28g; Carbohydrate 256.1g, of which sugars 145.8g; Fat 63.7g, of which saturates 23.2g; Cholesterol 85mg; Calcium 391mg; Fibre 16.4g; Sodium 287mg.

**p236 Chocolate and Orange Trifle** Energy 1385Kcal/5790kJ; Protein 16.7g; Carbohydrate 139.1g, of which sugars 115.9g; Fat 80.5g, of which saturates 43.7g; Cholesterol 197mg; Calcium 441mg; Fibre 3.5g; Sodium 418mg.

**p238 Apple Strudel** Energy 1189Kcal/5023kJ; Protein 20.6g; Carbohydrate 200.8g, of which sugars 123.8g; Fat 39.5g, of which saturates 14.6g; Cholesterol 53mg; Calcium 316mg; Fibre 16.6g; Sodium 185mg.

**p240 Strawberry Pavlova** Energy 1288Kcal/5375kJ; Protein 10.7g; Carbohydrate 137.7g, of which sugars 137.7g; Fat 80.8g, of which saturates 50.1g; Cholesterol 206mg; Calcium 178mg; Fibre 2.8g; Sodium 177mg.

**p242 Poached Pears** Energy 374Kcal/1597kJ; Protein 1.8g; Carbohydrate 95.7g, of which sugars 95.7g; Fat 0.9g, of which saturates 0g; Cholesterol 0mg; Calcium 81mg; Fibre 9.9g; Sodium 23mg.

**p244 Peach Frangipane Tart** Energy 2481Kcal/10368kJ; Protein 40.9g; Carbohydrate 262.6g, of which sugars 127.4g; Fat 148.2g, of which saturates 70.7g; Cholesterol 458mg; Calcium 534mg; Fibre 14.2g; Sodium 954mg.

**p246 Honey and Summer Fruit Mousse** Energy 1350Kcal/5603kJ; Protein 37.6g; Carbohydrate 76.9g, of which sugars 75.4g; Fat 101g, of which saturates 65.5g; Cholesterol 201mg; Calcium 728mg; Fibre 5.5g; Sodium 249mg.

# GLOSSARY OF PREGNANCY TERMS

**ABORTION**
The spontaneous or induced delivery of the fetus before the 28th week.

**ABRUPTIO PLACENTAE**
Part of the placenta peels away from the wall of the uterus in late pregnancy and often results in bleeding.

**ALPHA-FETOPROTEIN (AFP)**
A protein produced by the fetus which enters the mother's bloodstream. A very high level can indicate neural tube defects of the fetus such as Down's syndrome or spina bifida, but it can also mean that the woman is carrying more than one child.

**AMNIOCENTESIS**
A small amount of amniotic fluid is taken from the uterus through a needle inserted through the woman's abdomen and tested for chromosomal disorders such as Down's syndrome.

**AMNIOTIC FLUID**
The fluid surrounding the fetus in the uterus.

**AMNIOTIC SAC**
The bag of membranes which is filled with amniotic fluid in which the fetus floats during pregnancy.

**ANAEMIA**
A condition where the level of red corpuscles in the blood is abnormally low, which is treated with iron supplements.

**ANALGESICS**
Painkilling drugs which do not cause unconsciousness. Those most commonly used during labour are Entonox (a mixture of nitrous oxide and oxygen, known as "gas and air"), pethidine and meptid.

**ANTE-NATAL**
Before birth.

**APGAR SCORE**
A simple test to assess the baby's condition after birth.

**BEARING DOWN**
The pushing movement made by the uterus during the second stage of labour.

**BIRTH CANAL**
See Vagina.

**BLASTOCYST**
The early stage of the developing embryo when it becomes a cluster of cells.

**BRAXTON HICKS CONTRACTIONS**
Contractions of the uterus which occur throughout pregnancy, but may not be felt until the last month or so. They feel like a painless, but sometimes uncomfortable, hardening across the stomach.

**BREECH PRESENTATION**
The position of a baby when he is bottom down rather than head down in the uterus.

**CAESARIAN SECTION**
Delivery of the baby through a cut in the abdomen and uterine walls.

**CERVIX**
The neck of the uterus or womb which is sealed with a plug of mucus during pregnancy. During labour, muscular contractions open up the cervix until it is about 10cm/4in wide so that the baby can pass through it into the vagina.

**CHLOASMA**
Slight discoloration of the skin, usually on the face, which occurs during pregnancy and disappears within weeks of the birth.

**CHORIONIC VILLUS SAMPLING**
A screening test for genetic handicap which can be done as early as 11 weeks. Cells are taken from the tissue that surrounds the fetus and are then analysed.

**COLOSTRUM**
A fluid that the breasts produce during pregnancy and immediately after the birth. It is full of nutrients and contains antibodies which will protect the baby from some infections.

**CONCEPTION**
The fertilization of the egg by the sperm and its implantation in the wall of the uterus.

**CONGENITAL ABNORMALITIES**
An abnormality or deformity that exists from birth. It is caused by a damaged gene or the effect of some diseases during pregnancy.

**CONTRACTIONS**
Regular tightening of the muscles of the uterus as they work to dilate the cervix and push the baby down the birth canal.

**CROWNING**
The moment when the crown of the baby's head appears in the vagina.

**DILATION**
The gradual opening of the cervix during labour.

**DOPPLER**
A method of using ultrasound vibrations to listen to the fetal heart.

**ECTOPIC PREGNANCY**
A pregnancy which develops outside the uterus, usually in the Fallopian tube.

**EDD**
Estimated date of delivery.

**ELECTIVE INDUCTION**
Induction done for convenience rather than for medical reasons.

**ELECTRONIC FETAL MONITORING**
The continuous monitoring of the fetal heart.

**EMBRYO**
The developing organism in pregnancy from about the 10th day after fertilization until the 12th week of pregnancy when it becomes known as a fetus.

**ENGAGED**
The baby's head is engaged when it drops down deep in the pelvic cavity so that the widest part is through the mother's pelvic brim. Another term for this is "lightening". Most babies are born head first and will have engaged before labour begins.

**ENGORGEMENT**
The breasts become congested with milk if long periods are left between feeds which results in painful engorgement.

**ENTONOX**
Gas and oxygen, a short-term analgesic, which can be inhaled during labour.

**EPIDURAL**
An anaesthetic which is injected into the fluid surrounding the spinal cord at the base of the spine to relieve pain but leave the mother fully conscious.

**EPISIOTOMY**
A small cut made in the perineum to enlarge the vagina if there is a risk of tearing when the baby's head is about to be born.

**FALLOPIAN TUBES**
Two narrow tubes about 10cm/4in long which lead from the ovaries to the uterus.

**FETUS**
The developing baby from the end of the embryonic stage at about the 12th week of pregnancy, until the date of delivery.

**FH**
Fetal heart.

**FMF**
Fetal movement felt.

**FOLIC ACID**
A form of vitamin B which is important for the healthy development of the embryo. A daily supplement of 0.4mg should be taken before becoming pregnant and then until the 12th week of pregnancy.

**FONTANELLES**
The soft spots between the unjoined sections of the skull of the baby.

**FORCEPS**
An instrument sometimes used to assist the baby out of the birth canal.

**FOREMILK**
The first breast milk the baby gets when he begins to suck which satisfies his thirst before the hind milk comes through.

**FUNDUS**
The top of the uterus.

**GAS AND AIR**
See Entonox.

**GENETIC COUNSELLING**
Advice on the detection and risk of
recurrence of inherited disorders.

**GESTATION**
The length of time between conception and
delivery (usually around 40 weeks).

**GP UNIT**
A special unit, usually in a hospital, where a
pregnant woman gives birth under the care
of her GP and midwife.

**HAEMOGLOBIN (HB)**
The pigment that gives blood its red colour
and contains iron and stores oxygen.

**HAEMORRHAGE**
Excessive bleeding.

**HAEMORRHOIDS (PILES)**
A form of varicose veins around the anus.

**HINDMILK**
The calorie-rich breast milk that follows the
foremilk during feed.

**HORMONE**
A chemical produced by the body to
stimulate organs within the body, particularly
those to do with growth and reproduction.

**HUMAN CHORIONIC GONADOTROPHIN
(HCG)**
A hormone produced early in pregnancy by
the developing placenta. Its presence in the
urine is used to confirm pregnancy.

**IMPLANTATION**
The embedding of the fertilized egg in the
wall of the uterus.

**INCOMPETENT CERVIX**
A weakened cervix that is unable to hold the
fetus in the uterus for the full nine months.
Sometimes a cause of late miscarriage or
premature birth.

**INDUCTION**
The process of artificially starting off labour.

**INTRAVENOUS DRIP**
The infusion of fluids directly into the
bloodstream through a fine tube into a vein.

**JAUNDICE**
Neonatal jaundice often occurs in newborn
babies because of the inability of the liver to
successfully break down an excess of red
blood cells.

**LABOUR**
The process of childbirth.

**LANUGO**
A very fine covering of hair which appears
all over the fetus during late pregnancy.

**LIE**
The position of the fetus in the uterus.

**LIGHTENING**
See Engaged.

**LINEA NIGRA**
A line of dark pigmentation which appears
down the centre of the abdomen on some
women during pregnancy.

**LOCHIA**
Post-natal vaginal discharge.

**MECONIUM**
The green matter passed from the baby's
bowels during the first days after birth.
Meconium in the amniotic fluid before
delivery is usually a sign of fetal distress.

**MISCARRIAGE**
The loss of a baby before 24 weeks gestation.

**MONITOR**
Machine or instrument to measure the
baby's heartbeat and breathing.

**MOULDING**
The shaping of the bones of the baby's skull
as it passes through the birth canal.

**MUCUS**
A sticky secretion.

**NAD**
A medical term often used on medical records
meaning "nothing abnormal detected".

**NEURAL TUBE DEFECT**
Development defect of the brain and/or
spinal cord.

**OBSTETRICIAN**
Medical specialist in pregnancy and childbirth.

**OEDEMA**
Swelling caused by fluid retention.

**OVARY**
Female organ responsible for production of
sex hormones and eggs (ova).

**OVULATION**
The production of a ripe egg by the ovary,
usually on a monthly basis.

**PALPATION**
Manual examination of the uterus through
the wall of the abdomen.

**PELVIC FLOOR**
The muscles which support the bladder and
the uterus.

**PERINATAL**
Period from before delivery until seven days
after the birth.

**PERINEUM**
The area between the opening of the vagina
and the anus.

**PETHIDINE**
A drug given during labour for pain relief
and relaxation.

**PLACENTA**
Also known as "afterbirth", this is the fetus's
life-support system which is attached to one
side of the wall of the uterus and to the baby
by means of the umbilical cord. All the
fetus's nourishment passes from the mother
through the placenta while the fetus's waste
products pass out through it.

**PREMATURE OR PRETERM**
A baby born before the 37th week.

**PRESENTATION**
The position of the fetus in the uterus before
and during the delivery.

**PRIMIGRAVIDA**
A woman who is having her first baby.

**PROSTAGLANDIN**
A hormone which stimulates the onset of
labour contractions.

**QUICKENING**
The first movements of the fetus in the
uterus.

**ROOTING**
The baby's instinctive searching for the
mother's nipple.

**RUBELLA (GERMAN MEASLES)**
A virus which can be dangerous if caught
during the first three months of pregnancy.

**SCAN**
A way of screening the fetus in the uterus by
bouncing high-frequency sound waves off it
which build up a picture.

**SHARED CARE**
Ante-natal care shared between a GP and a
hospital consultant.

**SHOW**
A vaginal discharge of blood-stained mucus
that occurs before or during labour.

**STILLBIRTH**
The delivery of a baby who has already died
in the uterus after 28 weeks of pregnancy.

**STRETCH MARKS**
Silvery lines that may appear where the skin
has been stretched during pregnancy.

**TERM**
The end of pregnancy - around 40 weeks
from the date of conception.

**TERMINATION**
An artificially induced abortion before the
end of 28th week of pregnancy.

**TOXOPLASMOSIS**
A parasitic disease spread by cat faeces that
can cause blindness in a baby.

**TRIMESTER**
Pregnancy is divided into three trimesters,
each making up one third of pregnancy.

**UMBILICAL CORD**
The cord connecting the fetus to the placenta.

**UTERUS (WOMB)**
The hollow muscular organ in which the
fertile egg becomes embedded.

**VACUUM EXTRACTOR (VENTOUSE)**
An instrument sometimes used to pull the
baby out of the vagina.

**VAGINA**
The birth canal through which the baby
makes its way from the uterus.

# USEFUL ADDRESSES

*There is no need to feel alone during pregnancy or in the months after the birth.*
*The organizations mentioned below are happy to offer help and support to anyone who contacts them.*
*Remember to enclose an SAE when writing to them.*

### ANTE-NATAL AND BIRTH

**Active Birth Centre**
25 Bickerton Road, London N19 5JT
Tel: 020 7281 6760
www.activebirthcentre.com

**Association for Improvements in the Maternity Services (AIMS)**
Tel: 0870 765 1433
www.aims.org.uk

**Baby Lifeline**
Empathy Enterprise Building, Bramston Crescent, Tile Hill Lane, Tile Hill Coventry CV4 9SW
Tel: 024 7642 2135
www.babylifeline.org.uk

**Tommy's Campaign**
1 Kennington Road, London SE1 7RR
Tel: 08707 70 70 70
www.tommys-campaign.org

**Birthchoice UK**
www.birthchoiceuk.com

**National Childbirth Trust (NCT)**
Alexandra House, Oldham Terrace, Acton, London W3 6NH
Tel: 0870 444 8707
www.nctpregnancyandbabycare.com

**Stillbirth and Neonatal Death Society (SANDS)**
28 Portland Place, London W1N 4DE
Helpline: 020 7436 5881
www.uk-sands.org

**Wellbeing**
27 Sussex Place, London NW1 4SP
Tel: 020 7772 6400
www.wellbeing.org.uk

**Foundation for the Study of Infant Death (SIDS)**
Artillery House, 11-19 Artillery Row, London SW1P 1RT
Helpline: 0870 7870554
www.sids.org.uk

**The Miscarriage Association**
c/o Clayton Hospital, Northgate, Wakefield, West Yorks WF1 3JS
Tel: 01924 200799
www.miscarriageassociation.org.uk

**Independent Midwives Association**
1 The Great Quarry, Guildford, Surrey GU1 3XN
Tel: 01483 821104
www.independentmidwives.org.uk

### FAMILY LINKS

**Gingerbread**
16-17 Clerkenwell Road, London EC1R 0AN
Helpline: 0800 0184318
www.gingerbread.org.uk

**Parentline Plus**
520 Highgate Studios, 53-79 Highgate Road, London NW5 1TL
Helpline: 0808 800 2222

**National Childminding Association**
8 Masons Hill, Bromley, Kent BR2 9EY
Helpline: 0800 169 4486
www.ncma.org.uk

**National Council for One Parent Families**
255 Kentish Town Road, London NW5 2LX
Tel: 0800 0185026
www.oneparentfamily.org.uk

**Families Need Fathers**
134 Curtain Road, London EC2A 3AR
Helpline: 08707 607 496
www.fnf.org.uk

### SPECIAL NEEDS

**The Birth Defects Foundation**
Martindale, Hawks Green, Cannock, Staffs WS11 2XN
www.birthdefects.co.uk

**Galactosaemia Support Group**
31 Cotysmore Road, Sutton Coldfield B75 6BJ
Tel: 0121 378 5143
www.galactosaemia.org

**Down's Syndrome Association**
155 Mitcham Road, London SW17 9PG
Tel: 020 8682 4001
www.downs-syndrome.org.uk

**Cerebral Palsy Helpline**
PO Box 833, Milton Keynes, Bucks MK12 5NY
Helpline: 0808 800 3333
www.scope.org.uk

**ASBAH** (Association for Spina Bifida and Hydrocephalus)
ASBAH House, 42 Park Road, Peterborough PE1 2UQ
Tel: 01733 555988
www.asbah.org

**Climb** (The National Information and Advice Centre for Metabolic Diseases)
The Quadrangle, Crewe Hall, Crewe CW1 6UR
Tel: 01270 250221
www.climb.org.uk

**Cystic Fibrosis Research Trust**
11 London Road, Bromley, BR1 1BY
Tel: 020 8464 7211
www.cftrust.org.uk

**Diabetes UK**
Macleod House, 10 Parkway, London
NW1 7AA
Tel: 020 7424 1000
www.diabetes.org.uk

**British Epilepsy Association**
New Anstey House, Gateway Drive,
Yeardon, Leeds LS19 7XY
Helpline: 0808 800 5050
www.epilepsy.org.uk

**Mencap** (Royal Society for Mentally
Handicapped Children and Adults)
123 Golden Lane, London EC1Y 0RT
Tel: 020 7454 0454
www.mencap.org.uk

**National Asthma Campaign**
Providence House, Providence Place,
London N1 0NT
Helpline: 0845 701 0203
www.asthma.org.uk

**National Eczema Society**
Hill House, Highgate Hill, London
N19 5NA
Tel: 020 7281 3553
www.eczema.org

**Royal National Institute for the
Blind (RNIB)**
224 Great Portland Street, London
W1N 6AA
Helpline: 0845 766 9999
www.rnib.org.uk

**National Autistic Society**
393 City Road, London EC1V 1NG
Tel: 020 7833 2299
www.nas.org.uk

**National Meningitis Trust**
Fern House, Bath Road, Stroud, Glos
GL5 3TJ
Helpline: 0845 6000 800
www.meningitis-trust.org.uk

**SENSE** (National Deaf-Blind & Rubella
Association)
11-13 Clifton Terrace,
London N4 3SR.
Tel: 020 7272 7774
www.sense.org.uk

**Sickle Cell Society**
54 Station Road, Harlesden,
London NW10 4UA
Helpline: 0800 001 5660
www.sicklecellsociety.org

FAMILY WELFARE

**TAMBA (Twins & Multiple Births
Association)**
2 The Willows, Gardner Road,
Guildford,
Surrey GU1 4PG
Helpline: 0870 770 3305
www.tamba.org.uk

**Association for Post-natal Illness**
145 Dawes Road, Fulham,
London SW6 7EB
Helpline: 020 7386 0868
www.apni.org

**BLISS** (Baby Life Support Systems)
2nd Floor, Camelford House,
87-89 Albert Embankment,
London SE1 7TP
Helpline: 0500 618140
www.bliss.org.uk

**CRY-SIS**
164 Gordon Hill, Enfield,
Middlesex EN2 0QT
Helpline: 08451 228 669
www.cry-sis.org.uk

**La Leche League**
LLL Books, 160 Bleinheim Street,
Hull HE5 3PN
Helpline: 0845 120 2918
www.laleche.org.uk

**Pre-school Learning Alliance**
69 Kings Cross Road, London
WC1X 9LL
Tel: 020 7833 0991
www. pre-school.org.uk

**Association of Breastfeeding
Mothers**
PO Box 207, Bridgewater,
Somerset TA6 7YT
Tel: 0870 401 7711
www.abm.me.uk

**Action for Sick Children**
No 3, Abbey Business Centre,
Keats Lane,
Earl Shilton,
Leicestershire LE9 7DQ
Tel: 01455 845 600
www.actionforsickchildren.org

**Contact-a-family**
170 Tottenham Court Road,
London W1T 7NR
Helpline: 0808 808 3555
www.cafamily.org.uk

**Cruse** (Bereavement care)
Cruse House, 126 Sheen Road,
Richmond, Surrey TW9 1UR
Helpline: 0870 167 1677
www.crusebereavementcare.org.uk

**Family Planning Association**
2-12 Pentonville Road,
London N1 9FP
Helpline: 0845 310 1334
www.fpa.org.uk

**Family Welfare Association**
501-505 Kingsland Road,
London E8 4AU
Tel: 020 7254 6251
www.fwa.org.uk

**National Society for the Prevention
of Cruelty to Children (NSPCC)**
National Centre,
42 Curtain Road,
London EC2A 3NH
Freephone: 0800 800 5000
www.nspcc.org.uk

**The Baby Products Association
(BPA)**
FREEPOST ANG 5097,
Vicarage Road, Pitstone,
Beds LU7 9ZZ
Helpline: 01296 660990

# INDEX

Page numbers in *italic* refer to the illustrations.

## A

abbreviations and terms, 27
abdomen, after delivery, 92
abdominal pain, 78
abortion, 500
abruptio placentae, 65, 500
accidents, first aid, 162-7
aches and pains, 78
active birth, 58, *58*, 59, 60-1, *61*
acupuncture, 51, 83
air travel, 66, 156
alcohol, 12
allergies, 108, 116-17, 142, 260
alpha fetoprotein (AFP), 24, 500
amniocentesis, 24, *24*, 74, 500
amniotic fluid, 31, 86, 500
amniotic sac, 15, 500
anaemia, 49, 62, 64, 500
anaesthetics, 82, *83*
analgesics, 500
ante-natal, 500
ante-natal care, 18-19, 22-5, 74
ante-natal classes, 58-9, 72, *73*
Apgar score, 98, 172-3, 500
apples:
    apple and orange fool, 305
    apple ambrosia, 292
    apple strudel, 486
    chicken salad, 450
    Eve's pudding, 476
    fruit fondue, 394
    fruit salad purée, 293
    orange and apple rockies, 404
    pork and apple savoury, 301
    purée, 277
    sticky ribs and apple slaw, 356
apricots:
    apricot and chocolate chip ice cream, 396
    bread and butter pudding, 474
    mini-muffins, 408
areola, 106
aromatherapy, 51, *51*, 83
artificial rupture of the membranes (ARM), 82
asthma, 56
    family history of, 260
aubergines:
    aubergine bolognese, 367
    moussaka, 430
    vegetable lasagne, 366
autumn harvest, 282

## B

babbling, 235-6
baby carriers, 156, *156*, 177
baby feeding itself, 310
baby walkers, *245*, *248*, *250*
backache, 28, *51*, 66, *67*
baked beans:
    bobotie with baked potatoes and broccoli, 428
    cowboy sausages and beans, 352
    Mediterranean lamb, 422
    Mexican mince, 346
    paprika pork, 317
balanced diet, 338
bananas:
    baked bananas, 402
    bananarama, 307
    fruit fondue, 394
    orange and banana muffins, 408
    pancakes, 400
bandages, 165
batch cooking, 269
bathing babies, 101, 130, *130-3*
bathrooms, safety, 160
batter:
    mini toad-in-the-hole, 352
bean sprouts:
    pick-up sticks, 358
    pork stir fry, 438
bearing down, 500
bedtime tips, 135
beef:
    beef burgers, 380
    beef Bourguignon with creamed potatoes, 434
    beef korma, 426
    bobotie with baked potatoes and broccoli, 428
    braised beef and carrots, 297
    cannibal necklaces, 379
    chilli con carne, 432
    Mexican mince, 346
    peppered beef casserole, 344
    shepherd's pie, 296, 348
bending in pregnancy, 66, *67*
bibs, 310, 311
birth *see* labour
birth canal *see* vagina
birthplans, 62, *62*
biscuits:
    date crunch, 406
bites and stings, 165
blackberries:
    Eve's pudding, 476

blankets, 55
blastocysts, 500
bleeding:
    in early pregnancy, 20
    in late pregnancy, 78
    nosebleeds, 167
    placental problems, 64-5
blood pressure, 20, *20*, 21, 22, 74
blood tests, 23, *23*, 24
bobotie with baked potatoes and broccoli, 428
bonding, 232
bones, broken, 165
books, 203, *249*, 251
bottle-feeding, 57, 92, 108-11, *108-11*, 220
bottles, weaning from, 261
bouncing cradles, *161*, 248
braised beef and carrots, 297
bras:
    during pregnancy, 40, 46, *46*, 60, 68
    nursing bras, 56, 68, 107
Braxton Hicks contractions, 34, 68-9, 84, 500
bread:
    bread and butter pudding, 474
    bread animals, 412
    bread fingers with egg, 327
    cheese on toast, 462
    cheese strips on toast, 388
    French toast butterflies, 386
    happy families, 386
    Marmite bread sticks, 326
    noughts and crosses, 388
    sandwich snails, 392
    shape sorters, 384
    speedy sausage rolls, 390
    spotted sandwiches, 392
    tuna flowers, 387
breakfast, importance of, 338
breast-feeding, 56-7, *56*, 57, 92, 104-7
breast pads, 107, *107*
breast pumps, 106, *107*
breasts:
    baby's, 101
    bras, 40, 46, *46*, 56, 68, 107
    colostrum, 46, 62, 92, 105
    during pregnancy, 56
    engorged, 107
    toning, *45*
breathing, resuscitation, 162-4
breathing techniques, 59
breathlessness, 68, 80
breech birth, 84, *84*
breech presentation, 500

broccoli:
  bobotie with baked potatoes and
    broccoli, 428
  cauliflower and broccoli with cheese, 319,
    361
  fat cats, 363
  French toasts butterflies, 386
  mixed vegetable platter, 283
  parsnip and broccoli mix, 286
  tagliatelle and cheese with broccoli and
    ham, 320
  veggie burgers, 364
bruises, 165
Brussels sprouts:
  pasta with sauce, 304
  veggie burgers, 364
buggies, 54-5, 54-5
burns, 164-5

C
cabbage:
  baby dahl, 321
  fish and cheese pie, 350
  fish finger log cabins, 384
  mixed vegetable platter, 283
  sticky ribs and apple slaw, 356
Caesarean birth, 61, 89, 500
cakes:
  alphabet cakes, 410
  chocolate chip muffins, 408
  chocolate dominoes, 407
  cup cake faces, 410
  gingerbread people, 411
  marshmallow krispie cakes, 408
  mini cup cakes, 330
  mini-muffins, 408
  orange and apple rockies, 404
  orange and banana muffins, 408
  traffic light cakes, 407
cannibal necklaces, 379
car seats, 55, 55, 156
car travel, 66, 66, 156
carrots:
  autumn harvest, 282
  baby dahl, 321
  braised beef and carrots, 297
  carrot, lentil and coriander purée, 284
  mixed vegetable platter, 283
  pick-up sticks, 358
  potato, carrot and courgette rösti, 364
  turkey stew with carrots and
    corn, 287
  vegetable lasagne, 366
  vegetable tagine, 470
  veggie burgers, 364
casseroles and stews:
  chicken and thyme casserole, 442
  cock-a-leekie casserole, 289

coriander chicken casserole, 342
  lamb and celery casserole, 346
  lamb stew, 345
  peppered beef casserole, 344
  pork and lentil casserole, 355
  sausage casserole, 440
  turkey stew with carrots and
    corn, 287
cauliflower:
  baby dahl, 321
  cauliflower and broccoli with cheese, 319,
    361
celery:
  chicken and celery supper, 318
  fish Creole, 323
  lamb and celery casserole, 346
  lamb and lentil savoury, 299
  osso bucco pork with rice, 436
  pick-up sticks, 358
  speedy chicken pie, 368
cervical smear test, 92
cervix, 500
  dilation, 70, 86, 88
cheat's trifle, 402
cheese:
  cauliflower and broccoli with cheese, 319,
    361
  cheese on toast, 462
  cheese shapes, 416
  cheese straws, 328
  cheese strips on toast, 388
  cheese vegetable crumble, 468
  chicken and cheese parcels, 342
  chicken wrappers, 446
  courgette gougère, 466
  fish and cheese pies, 322, 350
  fat cats, 363
  French toast butterflies, 386
  ham salad clown, 372
  happy families, 384
  Marmite and cheese whirls, 415
  Mexican beef, 348
  mini cheese and ham tarts, 357
  noughts and crosses, 388
  pizza clocks, 390
  potato boats, 362
  sandwich snails, 392
  pasta with ham sauce, 375
  pasta with sauce, 304
  spinach pancakes with ham and cheese,
    360
  shape sorters, 384
  skinny dippers, 370
  speedy chicken pie, 368
  Stilton and leek tart, 472
  tagliatelle and cheese with broccoli and
    ham, 320
  tuna flowers, 387
  vegetable lasagne, 366
chest compression, 164

chickpeas:
  vegetable tagine, 470
chicken:
  chicken and celery supper, 318
  chicken and cheese parcels, 342
  chicken and parsnip purée, 288
  chicken and thyme casserole, 442
  chicken salad, 450
  chicken wrappers, 446
  cock-a-leekie casserole, 289
  coriander chicken casserole, 342
  skinny dippers, 370
  speedy chicken pie, 368
  sticky chicken, 340
  sweet and sour chicken, 371
  tandoori-style chicken, 444
chickenpox, 149, 149
children, and new babies, 73
chilli con carne, 432
chips:
  skinny dippers, 370
  Spanish omelette, 374
chloasma, 500
chocolate:
  apricot and chocolate chip ice
    cream, 396
  chocolate and orange trifle, 484
  chocolate chip muffins, 408
  chocolate dominoes, 407
  chocolate pots, 324
  date crunch, 406
  fruit fondue, 394
choking, 114, 165-6, 166, 311
cholestasis, 48
chorionic villus sampling (CVS), 24-5, 500
chromosome disorders, 25, 74
cleaning teeth, 140-1, 141, 222
clothes:
  baby's, 54-5, 54, 124, 125-9
  during pregnancy, 40, 40-1
coconut:
  beef korma, 426
  pan fried turkey with coriander, 448
cod:
  fish and cheese pie, 322
  fish cakes, 454
  fish Creole, 323
  fish vol-au-vents, 456
  fisherman's pie, 291
  four fast fishes, 381
  nursery kedgeree, 300
  paella, 452
  salmon and cod kebabs, 458
colds, 145
colic, 138, 138, 154, 178-9
colostrum, 46, 62, 92, 105, 500
complications, during birth, 84-5
conception, 14-15, 14-15, 500
congenital abnormalities, 500
constipation, 28, 146

contraception, 12, 92
contractions, 500
  Braxton Hicks, 34, 68-9, 84
  breathing techniques, 59
  first stage of labour, 86, 87
  positions for labour, 70
  sexual intercourse and, 34, 35
convulsions, 142
cordocentesis, 25
coriander:
  carrot, lentil and coriander purée, 284
  coriander chicken casserole, 342
  pan fried turkey with coriander, 448
corn:
  aubergine bolognese, 367
  fisherman's pie, 291
  four fast fishes, 381
  sandwich snails, 392
  tuna fish cakes, 349
  turkey stew with carrots and
    corn, 287
corned beef hash, 378
cortisone, 80
cot death, 134, 161
cots, 55, 161
coughs, 145
country pork and runner beans, 300
courgettes:
  courgette gougère, 466
  Mediterranean vegetables, 301
  moussaka, 430
  potato, carrot and courgette
    rösti, 364
  trout and courgette savoury, 286
  vegetable lasagne, 366
couscous:
  lamb couscous, 316
  peppered beef casserole, 344
  vegetable tagine, 470
cowboy sausages and beans, 352
cow's milk, 261
cradle cap, 102-3
cramp, 28
cravings, 46
crawling, 198, 206-7, 207, 218, 242, 243,
  244, 244
croup, 166
crowning, 500
crying, 100-1, 136-7, 138, 172, 178-80,
238, 240
curl-ups, 94
curry:
  beef korma, 426
  bobotie with baked potatoes and
    broccoli, 428
  tandoori-style chicken, 444
custard:
  apple and orange fool, 305
  cheat's trifle, 402

chocolate and orange trifle, 484
fruit fondue, 394
orchard fruit dessert, 306
strawberry ice cream, 396
vanilla custards, 325
cuts and grazes, 164
cystic fibrosis, 24

D

dates:
  date crunch, 406
deafness, 229
dental care, 141
depression, post-natal, 95
developmental checks, 180-1, 181,
  203-4
diarrhoea, 146
diet:
  after delivery, 94
  during pregnancy, 30-1, 30-1, 36, 37
  preparation for pregnancy, 13
  see also feeding
dilation, 500
diphtheria, 142-3
discharges, vaginal, 29, 92, 171
discipline, 212
discomfort during pregnancy, 28-9, 68-9,
  78-9
diseases, 147-9
  immunization, 142-3
disposable nappies, 118, 121, 123, 123
doctors, 18, 32-3, 92
Domino scheme, 19
Doppler, 500
Down's syndrome, 24, 74
dreams, 72
dressing babies, 124, 125-9
drinks, 116, 117, 220, 265
drowning, 166-7

E

ears:
  hearing, 228-9
  infections, 146
eating together, 338, 420-3
ectopic pregnancy, 20-1, 500
eczema, 56
  family history of, 260
EDD, 500
egg (ovum), fertilization, 14, 14-15
eggs, 116
  bread fingers with egg, 327
  chocolate pots, 324
  courgette gougère, 466
  French toast butterflies, 386
  ham and tomato scramble, 372

nursery kedgeree, 302
Spanish omelette, 374
spotted sandwiches, 392
tuna Florentine, 460
vanilla custards, 325
elective induction, 500
electric shock, 167
electronic fetal monitoring, 85, 85, 500
embryo, 14, 500
emotions, in late pregnancy, 72-3
employment, during pregnancy, 36-7
engagement, baby's head, 80, 500
engorged breasts, 107, 500
Entonox, 82, 500
epidural anaesthetic, 61, 82, 83, 500
episiotomy, 61, 85, 88, 89, 500
equipment:
  baby's, 54-5
  bathing, 130
  bottle-feeding, 108
  introducing solids, 113
  nappy-changing, 119
  safety, 160
estimated date of delivery (EDD), 17, 17, 86
Eve's pudding, 476
exercise:
  during pregnancy, 44, 44-5, 69
  post-natal exercises, 92, 92-5, 95-6
  preparing for pregnancy, 13, 13
exotic fruit brulée, 480
expressing milk, 56-7, 106
eyes, 100-1
  sight, 174-5, 177, 224-7, 224-7
  squint, 196, 204, 227

F

fainting, 28, 60
Fallopian tubes, 14, 20-1, 500
fat cats, 363
fats, 341
  in diet, 116
feeding:
  bottle-feeding, 57, 92, 108-11, 108-11,
    220
  breast-feeding, 56-7, 56, 57, 92, 104-7
  self-feeding, 113, 114, 200-1, 201, 208,
    220
  weaning on to solids, 112-17, 112-17,
  186-9, 189, 220
feeding cup, 261
feeding schedule, 263
feet:
  baby's footwear, 124
  exercises, 45, 95
fertilization, 14, 14-15
fetus, 500
  abnormalities, 24-5, 74

distress, 74
engagement of head, 80
kick charts, 69, 69
monitoring, 60, 74-5, 85, 85
movements, 48, 49
fever, 144
fever strips, 144, 145
FH, 500
filo pastry, apple strudel, 486
finger foods, 113, 114, 201, 208, 220, 312
first aid, 162-7
first aid kit, 163
first tastes, 269
fish finger log cabins, 382
fisherman's pie, 291
fluid retention, 20, 23, 42, 48-9, 49
fluoride toothpaste, 140, 141
FMF, 500
folic acid, 13, 30, 500
fontanelles, 99-100, 500
food allergy, 116-17
food cravings, 46
food fads, 335
food hygiene, 267
food preparation, 266
forceps delivery, 84, 500
                                        foremilk, 500
formula milk, 57, 108, 111
fractures, 165
freezing, 278
fromage frais:
    honey and summer fruit mousse, 494
    jolly jellies, 398
fruit, 341
    drinks, 265
    exotic fruit brulée, 480
    fruit fondue, 394
    fruit salad purée, 293
    honey and summer fruit mousse, 494
    purées, 112, 114, 277
    summer fruit sorbet, 397
    see also apples; bananas
fundus, 500
furniture, nursery, 53
fussy eaters, 313, 336-9

G

games, 208-9, 247, 247, 251
gardens, safety, 161
gas and air, 82, 82
gates, safety, 158, 159
general practitioners (GPs), 32-3
genetic counselling, 25, 25, 501
genitals, baby's, 98, 101, 170-1, 203

German measles (rubella), 12-13, 23, 92, 142-3, 147-8
gestation, 501
ginger:
    gingerbread people, 411
glue ear, 56
goat's milk, 261
GP units, 501
green beans:
    chicken wrappers, 446
    country pork and runner beans, 300
    noughts and crosses, 388
    pasta with sauce, 304
    pick-up sticks, 358
    tuna fish cakes, 349
gums, bleeding, 24, 28, 40
Guthrie Test, 172, 173

H

haemoglobin (Hb), 501
Haemophilus influenzae type b, 142-3
haemorrhage, 501
haemorrhoids, 28-9, 501
hair:
    after pregnancy, 96-7
    baby's, 100, 170
    during pregnancy, 42, 42
ham:
    chicken and cheese parcels, 342
    chicken wrappers, 446
    French toast butterflies, 386
    ham and tomato scramble, 372
    ham salad clown, 372
    happy families, 384
    mini cheese and ham tarts, 357
    pasta with ham sauce, 375
    pizza clocks, 390
    potato boats, 362
    quickie kebabs, 376
    sausage wrappers, 376
    Spanish omelette, 374
    Stilton and leek tart, 472
    tagliatelle and cheese with broccoli and ham, 320
hands, dexterity, 199-200, 200-1, 206, 218
head, engagement, 80
health hazards, 36-7
health visitors, 32, 33, 204
hearing, 228-9
hearing tests, 204, 228-9
heartburn, 46, 48, 48
height, mother's, 22-3
hiccups, 171-2
high blood pressure, 20
high-chairs, 55, 194-5
    choosing, 272

convertible, 272
country-type, 273
elevator, 272
folding, 273
portable, 273
three-in-one, 272
high-tech birth, 61
hindmilk, 501
hoki:
    fish and cheese pies, 350
    four fast fishes, 381
holding babies, 98, 100
home birth, 18-19, 89
home-made foods, 315
honey and summer fruit mousse, 494
hormones, 501
    during pregnancy, 26-7
    induction of labour, 82
    menstrual cycle, 14
    pregnancy tests, 16
hospitals:
    final preparations, 76-7
    hospital birth, 19, 19, 60, 60
    parentcraft classes, 58
human chorionic gonadotrophin (HCG), 26, 501
hygiene:
    bottle-feeding, 57
    newborn babies, 101-2
hypnosis, 83

I

ice cream:
    apricot and chocolate chip ice cream, 396
    baked bananas, 402
    strawberry ice cream, 396
    strawberry ripple ice cream, 396
    traffic light sundaes, 401
illnesses, 144-9
immunization:
    babies, 142-3, 143, 180, 185, 189
    mothers, 12-13, 66, 92
implantation, 501
incompetent cervix, 501
induction of labour, 35, 61, 82, 501
infant carriers, 161
infectious diseases, 147-9
injections, pain relief, 82
insect bites and stings, 165
insomnia, 48, 48
intensive care baby unit (ICBU), 80-1
internal examination, 23, 79, 92
intravenous drip, 501
IQ (intelligence quotient), 196
iron, in diet, 62, 64
itching, 48

## J

jaundice, *147*, 501
jelly:
  jolly jellies, 398
  traffic light sundaes, 401

## K

kebabs:
  quickie kebabs, 376
  salmon and cod kebabs, 458
kedgeree:
  nursery kedgeree, 302
kick charts, 69, *69*
kidney beans:
  cheese vegetable crumble, 468
  chilli con carne, 432
  peppered beef casserole, 344
kidney infections, 64, 66
kitchens, safety, 160, *160*
kiwi fruit:
  exotic fruit brûlée, 480
  traffic light sundaes, 401

## L

labour, 501
  birthplans, 62, *62*
  choices in, 60-1
  complications, 84-5
  induction, 35, 61, 82
  older mothers, 74-5
  pain relief, 82-3, *83*
  positions, 70-1, *70-1*
  signs of, 86
  stages of, 87-8
lactose intolerance, 108
lamb:
  lamb and celery casserole, 346
  lamb and lentil savoury, 299
  lamb couscous, 316
  lamb hotpot, 298, 424
  lamb stew, 345
  Mediterranean lamb, 422
  moussaka, 430
lanugo, 39, 80, 170, 501
learning with toys, 150-1, *150-3*
leeks:
  aubergine bolognese, 367
  cock-a-leekie casserole, 285
  fish vol-au-vents, 456
  fish and cheese pie, 322
  lamb hotpot, 298
  pick-up sticks, 358
  potato boats, 361
  Stilton and leek tart, 472
leg slide exercise, *94*

lentils:
  aubergine bolognese, 367
  baby dahl, 321
  carrot, lentil and coriander purée, 284
  lamb and lentil savoury, 299
  pork and lentil casserole, 355
lie, 501
"lightening", 80
*Linea nigra*, 38, 501
liquidizers, 266
listeria, 36
living rooms, safety, 158-60
lochia, 92, 501

## M

mangoes:
  exotic fruit brulée, 480
manufactured foods, 317
Marmite:
  Marmite and cheese whirls, 415
  Marmite bread sticks, 326
marshmallow krispie cakes, 408
"mask of pregnancy", 42
massage:
  babies, *101*, 154, *154-5*
  during pregnancy, 51, *51*, 83, 96
mastitis, 107
maternity record cards, 27
maternity rights and benefits, 40
mattresses, cot, 55, 134
measles, 142-3, 148, *148*
meconium, 121, 501
medicines, 12, 144, *146*
Mediterranean lamb, 422
meningitis, 142-3
menstrual cycle, 14
meptid, 82
Mexican beef, 346
microwave:
  fruit purées, 277
  reheating, use for, 270
  sterilizing in, 269
  vegetables, preparing, 270
microwave ovens, 114
midwives, 18, 19, 32, 88
milia, 175
milk:
  bottle-feeding, 57, 108-10, *111*
  breast-feeding, 56, 104-5
  cow's milk, 117, 220
milk feeds, weaning from, 260, 261
milk teeth, 139
minerals, tooth formation, 139-41
mini cheese and ham tarts, 357
mini toad-in-the-hole, 352
miscarriage, 20, 21, 501
mixed vegetable platter, 283
mobility, 242-4, *242-5*

monitoring, fetal, *60*, 74-5, 85, *85*, 501
morning sickness, 17, 18
Moses baskets, *53*, 55
moulding, baby's head, 501
mousse:
  honey and summer fruit mousse, 494
moussaka, 430
mouth-to-mouth resuscitation, 162-4
mucus, 501
muffins:
  chocolate chip muffins, 408
  mini-muffins, 408
  orange and banana muffins, 408
mumps, 142-3, 148, *148*
mushrooms:
  beef burgers, 380
  Mediterranean vegetables, 301
  potato boats, 362
  quickie kebabs, 376
  shepherd's pie, 294
mussels, paella, 452

## N

NAD, 501
nails:
  baby's, 100, *101*, 103
  mother's, 46, *46*, 97
nappies, *103*, 118-23, *118-23*
nappy buckets, 130
nappy rash, 123
National Childbirth Trust (NCT), 59
natural birth, 60, *61*, 82
nausea, 17, 18, 78-9
navel, 99
nectarines:
  fruit salad purée, 293
nesting instinct, 81
nettle rash, 175-6
neural tube defects, 13, 501
newborn babies, 170-3
  bottle-feeding, 108-11, *108-11*
  breast-feeding, 104-7, *104-7*
  care of, 98-103
nipple shields, 107, *107*
nipples:
  breast-feeding, 106
  cracked, 107
  during pregnancy, 46, 56, *57*
nitrous oxide, 82, *82*
nosebleeds, 167
nursery:
  preparation, 52-3, *52-3*
  safety, 160-1
nursery kedgeree, 300
nursery rhymes, 210-12, *246*

nursing bras, 56, 68, 107
nutrition, 13
nuts, 116

# O

obstetricians, *32*, 33, 501
oedema, 20, 23, 42, 48-9, *49*, 501
older mothers, 74-5
oranges:
    apple and orange fool, 305
    chocolate and orange trifle, 484
    fruit fondue, 394
    orange and apple rockies, 404
    orange and banana muffins, 408
    orange and strawberry shortcake, 478
    pancakes, 400
    traffic light sundaes, 401
orchard fruit dessert, 306
orgasm, 34
osso bucco pork with rice, 436
ovaries, 14, *14*, 53, 501
ovulation, 14, 501
oxygen, during labour, 59

# P

paella, 452
pain, in late pregnancy, 78
pain relief, 61, 82-3, *83*
palpation, 23, 501
pan fried turkey with coriander, 448
pancakes, 400
    spinach pancakes with ham and cheese,
      360
paprika pork, 317
parentcraft classes, 58-9, 72
parsnips:
    autumn harvest, 282
    cheese vegetable crumble, 468
    chicken and parsnip purée, 288
    parsnip and broccoli mix, 286
partners:
    during birth, 62-3, *63*
    emotions, 72
passion fruit:
    exotic fruit brulée, 482
pasta:
    aubergine bolognese, 367
    beef korma, 426
    Mediterranean vegetables, 303
    pasta with ham sauce, 375
    pasta with sauce, 304
    penne with tomato sauce, 464
    tagliatelle and cheese with broccoli and
      ham, 320
    vegetable lasagne, 366
pastry:
    cheese shapes, 414

fat cats, 363
fish vol-au-vents, 456
    Marmite and cheese whirls, 415
    mini cheese and ham tarts, 357
    peach frangipane tart, 492
    Stilton and leek tart, 472
peaches:
    fruit salad purée, 293
    peach and melon blush, 293
    peach frangipane tart, 492
    peach melba dessert, 307
peanut butter:
    shape sorters, 384
    sticky chicken, 340
pears:
    fruit salad purée, 293
    orchard fruit dessert, 306
    poached pears, 490
    purée, 277
peas:
    fisherman's pie, 291
    four fast fishes, 381
    French toast butterflies, 386
    nursery kedgeree, 300
    paella, 452
    salmon and cod kebabs, 458
    shepherd's pie, 348
    tuna fish cakes, 349
pediatricians, 33, *33*
pelvic floor, 501
pelvis:
    during labour, 70-1
    exercises, *45*, *92*, 96
    size of, 23, 79, 84
peppers:
    aubergine bolognese, 367
    Mediterranean lamb, 422
    Mediterranean vegetables, 303
    Mexican beef, 346
    paella, 452
    peppered beef casserole, 344
    pick-up sticks, 358
    pork stir-fry, 440
    quickie kebabs, 376
    red pepper risotto, 285
    sandwich snails, 392
perinatal, 501
perineum, 501
    episiotomy, 61, 85, 88, 89
    soreness, 94
pessaries, induction of labour, 82
pethidine, 82, 501
phenylketonuria, *172*, 173
pick-up sticks, 358
picking up babies, 98, *100*
piles, 28-9
pizza:
    pizza clocks, 390
    shape sorters, 384
placenta, 501

delivery of, 81, 89
development of, 14-15
placenta praevia, 64
    placental insufficiency, 65
play, 150-1, *150-3*, 246-51,
    *246-51*
plums:
    jolly jellies, 398
    orchard fruit dessert, 306
    plum crumble, 482
poisoning, 167
polio, 142-3, *147*
pork:
    country pork and runner beans, 300
    osso bucco pork with rice, 436
    paprika pork, 317
    pork and apple savoury, 301
    pork and lentil casserole, 355
    pork hot-pot, 354
    pork stir-fry, 438
    sticky ribs and apple slaw, 356
port wine stains, 175
positions for labour, 70-1, *70-1*
possetting, 111
post-natal care, 92-7
post-natal depression (PND), 95
potatoes:
    autumn harvest, 282
    baby dahl, 321
    bobotie with baked potatoes and
      broccoli, 428
    braised beef and carrots, 295
    cauliflower and broccoli with cheese, 319
    chilli con carne, 432
    cock-a-leekie casserole, 289
    fish and cheese pies, 322, 350
    fisherman's pie, 291
    lamb hotpot, 298, 424
    lamb stew, 345
    mixed vegetable platter, 283
    moussaka, 430
    paprika pork, 317
    pork and apple savoury, 301
    pork hot-pot, 354
    potato, carrot and courgette rösti,
      364
    potato boats, 362
    salmon and cod kebabs, 458
    shepherd's pie, 296, 348
    trout and courgette savoury, 290
    tuna fish cakes, 349
    turkey stew with carrots and
      corn, 287
    veggie burgers, 364
prams, 54-5, *54*, 176-7
prawns:
    fishy vol-au-vents, 456
    paella, 452
pre-eclampsia, 20
pregnancy tests, 16, *17*

premature babies, 75, 80-1, 501
preparation for pregnancy, 12-13
presentation, 501
primigravida, 501
prostaglandins, 35, 82, 501
purées, *112*

## Q

quickening, 501

## R

raspberries:
  fruit salad purée, 293
  peach melba dessert, 307
  raspberry sorbet, 397
  strawberry ripple ice cream, 396
reading to babies, 203
recovery position, 164
reflexes, 171, *171*, *172*, 174
reflexology, 83
reheating baby food, 270
relaxation, 50-1, 96
reproductive system:
  female, *14*
  male, *15*
rest, 42, *64-5*, 96
resuscitation, 162-4
rhesus factor, 24
ribs, during pregnancy, 50
rice:
  apple ambrosia, 292
  baby, 262, 274
  fish Creole, 323
  nursery kedgeree, 302
  paella, 452
  pan fried turkey with coriander, 448
  red pepper risotto, 285
  sweet and sour chicken, 371
  tuna risotto, 382
rooting, 501
rubella (German measles), 12-13, 23, 92,
  142-3, 147-8, 501

## S

safety, 158-61, *158-61*
safety gates, 158, *159*
salad, chicken, 450
salmon and cod kebabs, 458
salt, 116
sanitary towels, 92
sausages:
  cowboy sausages and beans, 352
  mini toad-in-the-hole, 354
  noughts and crosses, 388

quickie kebabs, 376
sandwich snails, 392
sausage casserole, 440
sausage log cabins, 382
sausage wrappers, 376
speedy sausage rolls, 390
scalds, 164-5
scans, ultrasound, 38, *38*, 64, *74-5*,
  501
sciatica, 59
seat belts, 66, *66*
separation anxiety, 202
sex of child, 15
sexual intercourse, 21, 34-5
shared care, 501
sheep's milk, 261
shepherd's pie, 296, 348
shock, 167
shoes, 124, *129*, 215
shortbread shapes, 331
show, 86, 501
shyness, 222
skin care, 42, *42-3*, 46, 97
skinny dippers, 370
skull, fontanelles, 99-100
sleep, 48, 96, 134-5, *134-5*, 177,
  185
slings, *157*, 177
smacking, 212
smell, sense of, 230
smiling, 183, 238-40
smoked haddock:
  surprise fish parcels, 351
smoking, 12, 161
snacks, 341
sneezing, 172
social behaviour, 238-41
solid foods:
  equipment for feeding, 264
  feeding schedule, 263
  introduction to, 112-17, *112-17*, 186-9,
    *189*, 258, 262, 263
  weaning to, 260, 261
sorbets:
  raspberry sorbet, 397
  summer fruit sorbet, 397
Spanish omelette, 374
special care baby units (SCBUs), 80-1,
  *80*, 173, *173*
sperm, 14, *15*
spices, 116
spina bifida, 13, 24, 74
spinach:
  beef korma, 426
  fish cakes, 454
  spinach pancakes with ham and cheese,
    360
  tuna Florentine, 460
spoon, eating from, 262, 263
squatting:

during labour, 70-1, *71*
  exercises, *45*, *59*
squid:
  paella, 452
squint, 196, 204, 227
stairs, safety, 158, *158*, *159*
standing up, *209-11*, *216*, *243*, 244,
  *245*
sterilization, bottle-feeding
  equipment, *110*
sterilizing equipment, 267
  in microwave, 269
  solution sterilizer, 268
  steam sterilizer, 268
sticky chicken, 340
sticky ribs and apple slaw, 356
stillbirth, 501
Stilton and leek tart, 472
stitches, 92, 94
stork marks, 175
strains and sprains, 165
strawberries:
  cheat's trifle, 402
  fruit salad purée, 293
  orange and strawberry shortcake, 478
  purée, 278
  strawberry ice cream, 396
  strawberry Pavlova, 488
  strawberry ripple ice cream, 396
  traffic light sundaes, 401
strawberry marks, 175
stretch marks, 40, 46, *47*, 501
stretching exercises, *59*
stretchsuits, 124
Sudden Infant Death Syndrome (SIDS), 134
sugar, 116
surprise fish parcels, 351
swede:
  autumn harvest, 282
  cheese vegetable crumble, 468
sweet and sour chicken, 371
swimming, *69*
syntocinon, 82

## T

table manners, 420
talcum powder, *131*
talking, 196, *200*, 201, 207-8, 214-15, 220,
  228, 234-6
tampons, 92
tandoori-style chicken, 444
taste, sense of, 231
Taylor exercises, *45*
tears, baby's, 100-1
teats, bottle-feeding, 110-11
teeth, baby's, 139-41, *139-41*, 220-2
teething, *139*, 146, 191-3, *193*, 222
temperature, taking, 144, *145*